TABLE OF THE SIX TRIGONOMETRIC

A°	Radians	Sin A	Cos A	Tan A	Ctn A	Sec A	C		
0	.0000	.0000	1.0000	1.0000	.....	1.000	.....	1.5708	90
1	.0175	.0175	.9998	.0175	57.29	1.000	57.30	1.5533	89
2	.0349	.0349	.9994	.0349	28.64	1.001	28.65	1.5359	88
3	.0524	.0523	.9986	.0524	19.08	1.001	19.11	1.5184	87
4	.0698	.0698	.9976	.0699	14.30	1.002	14.34	1.5010	86
5	.0873	.0872	.9962	.0875	11.43	1.004	11.47	1.4835	85
6	.1047	.1045	.9945	.1051	9.514	1.006	9.567	1.4661	84
7	.1222	.1219	.9925	.1228	8.144	1.008	8.206	1.4486	83
8	.1396	.1392	.9903	.1405	7.115	1.010	7.185	1.4312	82
9	.1571	.1564	.9877	.1584	6.314	1.012	6.392	1.4137	81
10	.1745	.1736	.9848	.1763	5.671	1.015	5.759	1.3963	80
11	.1920	.1908	.9816	.1944	5.145	1.019	5.241	1.3788	79
12	.2094	.2079	.9781	.2126	4.705	1.022	4.810	1.3614	78
13	.2269	.2250	.9744	.2309	4.331	1.026	4.445	1.3439	77
14	.2443	.2419	.9703	.2493	4.011	1.031	4.134	1.3265	76
15	.2618	.2588	.9659	.2679	3.732	1.035	3.864	1.3090	75
16	.2793	.2756	.9613	.2867	3.487	1.040	3.628	1.2915	74
17	.2967	.2924	.9563	.3057	3.271	1.046	3.420	1.2741	73
18	.3142	.3090	.9511	.3249	3.078	1.051	3.236	1.2566	72
19	.3316	.3256	.9455	.3443	2.904	1.058	3.072	1.2392	71
20	.3491	.3420	.9397	.3640	2.747	1.064	2.924	1.2217	70
21	.3665	.3584	.9336	.3839	2.605	1.071	2.790	1.2043	69
22	.3840	.3746	.9272	.4040	2.475	1.079	2.669	1.1868	68
23	.4014	.3907	.9205	.4245	2.356	1.086	2.559	1.1694	67
24	.4189	.4067	.9135	.4452	2.246	1.095	2.459	1.1519	66
25	.4363	.4226	.9063	.4663	2.145	1.103	2.366	1.1345	65
26	.4538	.4384	.8988	.4877	2.050	1.113	2.281	1.1170	64
27	.4712	.4540	.8910	.5095	1.963	1.122	2.203	1.0996	63
28	.4887	.4695	.8829	.5315	1.881	1.133	2.130	1.0821	62
29	.5061	.4848	.8746	.5543	1.804	1.143	2.063	1.0647	61
30	.5236	.5000	.8660	.5774	1.732	1.155	2.000	1.0472	60
31	.5411	.5150	.8572	.6009	1.664	1.167	1.942	1.0297	59
32	.5585	.5299	.8480	.6249	1.600	1.179	1.887	1.0123	58
33	.5760	.5446	.8387	.6494	1.540	1.192	1.836	.9948	57
34	.5934	.5592	.8290	.6745	1.483	1.206	1.788	.9774	56
35	.6109	.5736	.8192	.7002	1.428	1.221	1.743	.9599	55
36	.6283	.5878	.8090	.7265	1.376	1.236	1.701	.9425	54
37	.6458	.6018	.7986	.7536	1.327	1.252	1.662	.9250	53
38	.6632	.6157	.7880	.7813	1.280	1.269	1.624	.9076	52
39	.6807	.6293	.7771	.8098	1.235	1.287	1.589	.8901	51
40	.6981	.6428	.7660	.8391	1.192	1.305	1.556	.8727	50
41	.7156	.6561	.7547	.8693	1.150	1.325	1.524	.8552	49
42	.7330	.6691	.7431	.9004	1.111	1.346	1.494	.8378	48
43	.7505	.6820	.7314	.9325	1.072	1.367	1.466	.8203	47
44	.7679	.6947	.7193	.9657	1.036	1.390	1.440	.8029	46
45	.7854	.7071	.7071	1.000	1.000	1.414	1.414	.7854	45
A°	Radians	Cos A	Sin A	Ctn A	Tan A	Csc A	Sec A	Radians	A°

ARITHMETIC

IN A LIBERAL EDUCATION

ARITHMETIC

IN A LIBERAL EDUCATION

DEWEY C. DUNCAN

Professor Emeritus of Mathematics
Formerly Chairman, Department of Mathematics
East Los Angeles College

McGRAW-HILL BOOK COMPANY

New York   San Francisco   St. Louis   Toronto   London   Sydney

ARITHMETIC IN A LIBERAL EDUCATION

Printed in the United States of America.

Library of Congress catalog card number: 69-16253

1234567890 MAMM 754321069

18203

☙ *Somewhat later he was asked privately about the meaning of the story. "You who are teachers," he replied, "should have caught the gist of it as applying to the varied behavior of school children, more particularly those in elementary arithmetic:*

☙ *"First, the seed falling on the bypaths are those unlucky fellows who have been diverted by misguided counsellors whose so-called aptitude tests have branded them as of low I.Q., and hence incapable of learning mathematics.*

☙ *"Secondly, the seed in the shallow soil represents those students who are delighted to begin the study and easily master the first stages, say, learning to count up to ten; but, when they realize that some small effort is required to progress along to subsequent operations, are unwilling to make the necessary effort to succeed, and soon become dropouts.*

☙ *"Thirdly, the seed among the weeds are the competent and willing students who become bogged down by too many extracurricular activities and deterring off-campus obligations, and have no time to work out the daily assignments of the course, and soon become hopelessly lost and fail utterly.*

☙ *"Finally, the seed in good ground are the energetic, serious, and enterprising students, who regularly and thoroughly execute all assigned work, and master the course completely. Their investment of time and effort yields the most gratifying returns of competence and satisfaction far beyond their highest expectations."*

—Adapted from *Mark, Chapter 4*

❧PREFACE

The constant search for ever better ways to teach arithmetic has evoked varied pedagogical cults and styles; meanwhile veritable ghettos of arithmetical poverty persist. The cults range from the dictatorial "this is the way it is, and this is the way you must do it, or so much the worse for you" to the conformable "this is what the book says; don't ask me 'why?' The system must be right and proper, or it wouldn't be here." Then there's the postulational "it's simply a matter of some undefined terms and several unprovable propositions, from which the entire mathematics may be evolved to be of service in solving the multifarious problems of mankind." This latter cult is aided and abetted by the set-theorist who is confident that his peculiar symbolism and vocabulary are adequate to deliver arithmetic from its difficulties.

De gustibus non est disputandum (one must not argue about tastes). The author of this text prefers a psychologico-traditional stance which grafts upon the learner's meager intuitional experience the tender shoots of primitive arithmetic, then nourishes them into the luxuriance of complete exfoliation. The person who can orally count several pieces of candy, some coins, or a few apples has already mastered the first important step of arithmetic; if not, he can quite quickly and easily learn to count. The unspoiled logical mind instantly notes the absurdity of the creed that is enunciated by Bertrand Russell as "mathematics is the science in which we don't know what we are talking about, nor whether what we say is true," which is both Law and Gospel to the postulationists. The inquiring mind wonders how such a creed can appeal to its devotees, as assuredly it is formulated in sounds (words) that must themselves be devoid of meaning.

From oral counting, it is an easy step to the formulation of symbols that express in writing these counting numbers; then, by strategic combinations of these written symbols, to exhibit an endless array of such counting numbers, *the system of natural numbers of arithmetic.* The three direct operations upon natural numbers arise from the operation of counting; thus addition is repeated countings, multiplication is repeated additions, and involution is repeated multiplications. For economy in time and effort one commits to memory the sums and products of all pairs of the simplest (one-digit) natural numbers. The reversal of the three direct operations upon natural numbers evolves the inverse operations, namely, subtraction, division, and evolution and indexing. The direct operations upon natural numbers, stemming from the primitive operation of counting, must always yield a natural number as the required sum, product, or power; however, the inverse operations upon natural numbers do not invariably yield a unique natural number for the required difference, quotient, root, or logarithm. Hence the system of natural numbers is enlarged by the creation and introduction of zero, negative integers, fractions, and irrational surds. Then, expanding the definitions of the direct and inverse operations to apply to these new kinds of numbers, one is led to the comprehensive system of complex numbers. The unexpected and astonishing surprises that spring up along the road leading to the complete exploitation of the number system cannot fail to increase the interest and admiration of students of all ages, particularly when they realize that they can master the use of the number system in an enormous range of applications within the brief space of one school semester. Moreover, the use of checks frees him from the uncertainty about the accuracy of his results.

Concisely stated, the purpose of this text is to realize the objectives that were promulgated over a half century ago by Professor Felix Klein, as currently applied to the teaching of arithmetic:

1. An understanding development of the number system of mathematics, from the simple intuitive counting numbers to the all-embracing system of complex numbers

2. Perfect accuracy in the use of all numbers, facilitated by the use of appropriate checks for correctness of results; precise knowledge of the validity of calculated results made upon inaccurate data

3. Solid understanding of the application of arithmetic to a wide variety of problems arising in life situations

4. Introduction to the charms of arithmetical recreations

May this text serve to further these timely ends.

DEWEY C. DUNCAN

NOTE TO THE INSTRUCTOR

Die ganze Zahl schuf der liebe Gott,
Alles übrige ist Menschenwerke.
(The integer the gracious God designed,
All else was made by man's inventive mind.)

—Leopold Kronecker.

The fundamental undefinables in this text are the counting numbers and the operation of counting. The counting numbers are also known as the natural numbers. These opening wedges into arithmetic generally become familiar to children in their preschool days. Then, step by step, one develops the consequent direct operations of addition, multiplication, and involution, and their inverses, subtraction, division, evolution, and indexing. The new necessary varieties of number are created and adapted: the system of integers, the system of rational numbers, the system of real numbers, and finally, the all-embracing system of complex numbers. Although the human mind has an unfathomable potential of insight and development, one must not be too forcible or too solicitous in providing assistance.

Just watch the moth's persistent toil
To leave his prison and be free.
Don't try to help him out—you'll spoil
His tender limbs, and then he'll be
A mutilated counterfoil.

The double aim of arithmetic is to provide the learner with the tools of arithmetic and skill in using them and to develop self-discipline and confidence in our universal heritage of innate arithmetical capacity. This text has been prepared to assist in the realization of this double aim; it is a revision of the author's *Arithmetic in General Education*, now out of print, which has yielded gratifying returns to countless earnest students. For admission into the course, as well as for remaining in the class, three prerequisites were set forth: The ability to read and understand simple English, a genuine desire to master the subject, sufficient time to read the materials of each lesson and solve the accompanying problems. As a reflection of the current term "new mathematics," tireless effort has been expended to provide:

1. Clarity in the development of all arithmetical concepts, beginning from "scratch," coupled with an appreciative understanding of the scope and purpose of arithmetic in the solutions of a wide range of problems that occur in life situations, science, industry, commerce, etc.

2. Perfection in all numerical computations, assisted by simple tests to detect the presence of errors, and in the use of approximate data, circumspection to diagnose the validity of the results. For example, if the measured length and width of a rectangle are 62.7 and 41.3 inches, with a possible margin of error not to exceed 0.05 inches, the computed area of $2{,}589.5 \pm 5.2$ square inches more truly expresses the area with margin of uncertainty than does the simple product, 2,589.51 square inches.

3. Various topics in mathematical culture and recreations of absorbing interest, supplied in notes at the close of each lesson and in the Supplement.

To acquire intellectual independence and to develop arithmetical confidence and skill, the student must expend a minimum of 2 hours in concentrated effort upon the materials of each assignment, beginning with the first assignment. As an incentive toward these goals, a 15-minute quiz at the end of each class meeting will prove invaluable. The earnest student will approve of such a regimen; the indolent student will conform or withdraw to areas of less challenge and fewer compensations.

The introductory sections of Lessons 1 through 15, exclusive of all notes and the supplement, may serve adequately for a refresher course. For a bona fide course in college arithmetic the 17 lessons in toto, with optional selections from the supplement, would be sufficient. The entire text and manual should be mastered by prospective teachers. The manual may assist persons working independently through the text, particularly students earning college credit without attending class at institutions that admit this practice.

Every teacher fully understands how easy it is to present materials that may be understood, and contrariwise how extremely difficult it is to provide materials that cannot be misunderstood. The author will be happy to respond to queries from users of this text that may be occasioned by his failure to measure up in this latter premise.

☙NOTE TO THE STUDENT

You will know the truth,
And the truth will make you free.

—John 8: 32.

Many students find arithmetic quite distasteful; few would choose it as their favorite subject.   This status of "the third R" is occasioned by such reasons as

1. Failure to understand its basic aims and concepts

2. A feeling of lack of necessary mental endowment to learn the subject, perhaps fostered by school counselors because of low I.Q. scores in arithmetic

3. A discouraging tendency to commit arithmetical errors resulting from failure to learn the simple sums and products of one-digit whole numbers

4. Certain currently fashionable programs of introducing mathematical studies under the name of "the new math," which may confuse rather than enlighten

NOW—regardless of your past experience in arithmetic, however frustrating and disappointing it has been, or of any notion you may hold as to an innate incapacity to learn mathematics—one brief semester of earnest effort through this text, starting from "scratch," can prove astonishingly rewarding and liberating. The author himself failed his seventh grade arithmetic with a final examination score of 14 percent, but his wise mother persuaded him to work patiently through *Ray's Modern Practical Arithmetic* (1908) during the ensuing summer vacation.   This he did with amazing success, discovering, incidentally, the very narrow margin between knowing and not knowing; that is, between frustration and satisfaction, which is so very easily bridged by a small amount of personal determination and persistence.   Since that critical summer he found all subsequent courses in mathematics equally challenging and conquerable, and has taught all levels of mathematics from a one-room rural school to the university graduate school.

This text has been written for students of all ages who sense their weakness in arithmetic, but who wish to gain a successful working mastery of the subject. Their assurance for complete success in the undertaking rests upon three necessary and sufficient conditions, namely, (1) an ability to read and understand simple English words and sentences, (2) a sincere desire to understand arithmetic and to be able to use it effectively, and (3) available time and energy to expend a minimum of two hours on each assignment, beginning with the first assignment and continuing to the end of the course.

Unlike other school subjects, arithmetic may be completely mastered in one school semester by any normal, mentally mature person, so that the successful student will then be able to solve any problem that anybody else can solve by the procedures of arithmetic.   The first basic operation of arithmetic, *counting*, or reciting the names of the natural numbers as far as ten, or somewhat further, is generally mastered by children in their preschool days.   The remaining direct operations are

1. *Addition*, or repeated counting

2. *Multiplication*, or repeated addition

3. *Involution*, or repeated multiplication

Simple devices called *algorithms* are devised to perform these operations with a minimum of labor.   Checks are also made available to certify the correctness of the results, or to warn of the presence of errors.

These three direct operations upon natural numbers always yield only one correct resulting natural number.   The reversal of these direct operations yields the four *inverse* operations, namely

1. *Subtraction*, the inverse of addition

2. *Division*, the inverse of multiplication

3. *Evolution* (root-extraction), one inverse of involution

4. *Indexing* (obtaining logarithms), the other inverse of involution

Unlike the direct operations upon natural numbers, these inverse operations upon natural numbers may or may not yield results that are natural numbers. To make the inverse operations upon natural numbers possible in every instance, new kinds of numbers are required; these new kinds of numbers, the zero, negative integers, fractions, irrational surds, and transcendental numbers, are invented and introduced into the system of available working numbers of arithmetic. Finally, the extension of the operations, both direct and inverse, upon these new kinds of numbers leads to the all-embracing, comprehensive system of complex numbers that suffices for all subsequent courses of mathematics in professional and scientific curricula. This text develops this all-inclusive system of complex numbers.

Extensive lists of pure and applied problems are provided within and supplementary to each of the 17 lessons. The purely numerical problems present the opportunity to develop patience, persistence, skill, and confidence; the applied, or "word," problems provide a wide range of information while developing incisive diagnostic skills. Perspicuity in solving these applied problems is sharpened by recognizing and surmounting the three ever-present obstacles:

1. Gaining a clear understanding of the circumstances of the problem; i.e., noting particularly the numerical information that is given as known data, and what information the solution of the problem is intended to yield

2. Determining precisely what mathematical operations are to be used to yield the required information from the given data

3. Performing without error the required mathematical operations; i.e., applying checks for the presence of errors in the calculated results

The topics in the Supplement are provided for the adventurous and inquisitive mind that finds excitement and joy in exploring fields off the beaten path. The curious student may even surprise his classmates and instructor by the discovery of new arithmetical items hitherto unknown.

Finally, it should be noted that there is a significant difference between students in their quickness of grasping new ideas, just as there is a physical difference in size, strength, and speed between individual persons. However, these individual mental differences have been greatly exaggerated by educational theorists. If 20 normal lads, not especially trained for running, were to participate in a 100-yard dash, all 20 lads would finish within a range of not more than 5 or 6 seconds. The two vital facts are: Every lad who desires to finish the race does finish it; the actual difference in time between the fastest and the slowest runner is not very great. Similarly, in the impending arithmetical race you must feel confident that you will finish the course satisfactorily, and that the range of success between the fastest learner and the slowest learner will not be very great.

Within a few brief months may every one who enters this course share the apostle's exultation,

> *I have made the great effort—I have finished the course!*
> *Henceforth I will enjoy the victor's crown of satisfaction.*

—II Timothy 4: 7–8.

❧TABLE OF CONTENTS

Preface   *vii*

Note to the instructor   *ix*

Note to the student   *xi*

LESSON 1 ∞ NATURAL NUMBERS, THEIR NAMES AND SYMBOLS IN THE DECIMAL SYSTEM ∞ COUNTING   2

   1.1   The natural numbers, also known as
the counting numbers   3

   1.2   The first basic operation upon natural
numbers is called counting   3

   1.3   Appropriate names and symbols for natural
numbers in correct order   4

   1.4   Symbolism for the successor of any natural number   4

   1.5   Naming the natural numbers following 20 as far as 99   5

   1.6   Naming the natural numbers from 100 to 999 inclusive   5

   1.7   Names of natural numbers that are greater than 999   6

   ∞   PROBLEMS   6

xv

1.8   Recapitulation   7

1.9   Natural numbers used as cardinal and as ordinal numbers   7

∽   PROBLEMS [CONCLUDED]   8

*Note 1   Uniqueness of the cardinal number
          of a set of objects*   10

*Note 2   The decimal nomenclature for large
          numbers is not unique*   12

*Note 3   Symbolism of natural numbers in systems
          other than the decimal system*   12

LESSON 2 ∽ ADDITION OF NATURAL NUMBERS ∽
THE OPERATION OF REPEATED COUNTING   14

2.1   Two uses of a natural number in the normal
      array of natural numbers   15

2.2   Addition of two natural numbers   15

2.3   Commutative law of addition of two natural numbers   16

2.4   Addition of three natural numbers.
      Associative law of addition   16

2.5   Addition of more than three natural numbers   17

2.6   Simplified method of adding large natural numbers   17

∽   PROBLEMS   20

2.7   Observations on the solution of problems of arithmetic   21

∽   PROBLEMS [CONCLUDED]   21

Note 1   The first infinite cardinal number, aleph-zero   24

Note 2   A meterstick slide rule for addition of natural numbers   25

xvi

Note 3   *Certain unicursal problems*
         that are solved by counting   29

∞   SUPPLEMENTARY PROBLEMS   32

LESSON 3 ∞ MULTIPLICATION AND INVOLUTION
OF THE NATURAL NUMBERS   38

3.1   Multiplication of two natural numbers   39

3.2   Commutative law of multiplication
      of two natural numbers   39

3.3   Multiplication of three natural numbers.
      Associative law of multiplication of natural numbers   40

3.4   The distributive law of multiplication and addition
      of natural numbers: $a \times (b + c) = a \times b + a \times c$ 42

3.5   Multiplications involving more than
      three natural numbers   43

3.6   The use of zero as a factor in multiplication   44

3.7   Multiples of a natural number   44

3.8   Short multiplication—multiplication of a natural
      number by a single-digit natural number   45

3.9   Long multiplication—multiplication of a natural number by a
      natural number consisting of more than a single digit   46

3.10 Recapitulation of the five laws of addition and multiplication   47

3.11 Priority of multiplications over additions   48

3.12 Involution of the natural numbers   48

3.13 The use of zero in involution   49

3.14 Involution is not commutative   49

∞   PROBLEMS   49

3.15 Measurement of rectangular areas   51

∽ PROBLEMS [CONTINUED]   51

3.16 Measurement of rectangular volumes   52

∽ PROBLEMS [CONCLUDED]   53

Note 1 Condensed multiplication of natural numbers ending in 5   54

Note 2 Commutative multiplication curios   57

∽ SUPPLEMENTARY PROBLEMS   59

LESSON 4 ∽ FOUR FUNDAMENTAL OPERATIONS UPON NATURAL NUMBERS ∽ SUBTRACTION ∽ SYSTEM OF INTEGERS 64

4.1 Résumé of the four direct operations
upon the natural numbers   65

4.2 The four fundamental inverse operations
upon natural numbers   66

4.3 Possible and impossible inverse operations
upon natural numbers   67

4.4 New types of numbers required to perform all inverse
operations upon any natural numbers whatever   68

4.5 New definitions of direct and inverse operations upon
these new kinds of numbers must be formulated   69

4.6 Inverse operation of subtraction that
is possible with natural numbers   69

4.7 Two alternative procedures for performing
subtraction of large natural numbers   72

∽ PROBLEMS   74

4.8 Inverse operation of subtraction that is
impossible with natural numbers   75

4.9   The two different uses of the positive
and negative signs, $+$ and $-$ 76

4.10   Extending basic properties of natural numbers
to the enlarged system of integers   77

4.11   Addition of integers   77

4.12   Subtraction of integers   79

4.13   Recapitulation of addition and subtraction of integers   80

4.14   Algebraic multiplication   81

4.15   Algebraic involution of integers   81

ↀ   PROBLEMS [CONTINUED]   81

4.16   Certain commonly used scales involving negative numbers   83

ↀ   PROBLEMS [CONCLUDED]   85

Note 1   *The logical validity of the rules
of operations upon integers*   86

Note 2   *Introduction of integers as pairs
of natural numbers*   89

ↀ   SUPPLEMENTARY PROBLEMS   90

LESSON 5 ↀ DIVISION OF NATURAL NUMBERS ↀ FRACTIONS ↀ SYSTEM OF RATIONAL NUMBERS   98

5.1   Division as the inverse operation of multiplication   99

5.2   Simple methods of performing division
of natural numbers   99

5.3   Division of integers; three exceptional situations   102

5.4   Division is not associative.
Rule of procedure   102

扳 PROBLEMS 103

5.5 Basic definitions and relationships
     pertaining to fractions   105

5.6 Location of positions for proper fractions
     on the number line   106

5.7 The fundamental property of fractions   108

5.8 The complete system of rational numbers
     as portrayed on the number line   109

扳 PROBLEMS [CONTINUED] 110

5.9 Equality and inequality of two fractions.
     Appropriate symbolism   110

扳 PROBLEMS [CONCLUDED] 111

Note 1   The system of rational numbers
         is not discrete, but is dense   112

Note 2   The cardinal number of the set
         of rational numbers is aleph-zero   112

Note 3   The fractions as pairs of integers   115

扳 SUPPLEMENTARY PROBLEMS 116

LESSON 6 扳 CONCLUSION OF THE BASIC OPERATIONS UPON FRACTIONS 扳 PRIME FACTOR FORMS

                                                          122

6.1 Résumé of common fractions   123

6.2 Addition and subtraction of common fractions   124

6.3 Common multiples of two or more numbers   125

6.4 The prime factor form of a natural number   125

6.5 Reduction of a natural number from its standard
     form to its prime factor form   126

6.6 Tests for divisibility of a natural number
     by prime divisors   127

6.7 The fundamental theorem of arithmetic   128

6.8 Determination of the lowest common multiple
     by prime factor forms   129

6.9 Multiplication and division of natural numbers
     in prime factor forms   129

6.10 The laws of exponents for natural numbers   130

∾   PROBLEMS   130

6.11 Multiplication and division of fractions
     by natural numbers   131

6.12 Multiplication and division of fractions
     by fractions   131

6.13 Hints for simplifying basic operations
     upon fractions   132

6.14 Euclid's algorithm   133

∾   PROBLEMS [CONCLUDED]   134

Note 1   Some operational features of the number line   139

Note 2   Euclid's algorithm   142

*Note 3   A geometrical justification of the rule
of multiplication of fractions, namely,
that a/b · c/d = ac/bd wherein a, b, c, d
are natural numbers*   144

∾   SUPPLEMENTARY PROBLEMS   144

LESSON 7 ∾ RÉSUMÉ OF THE COMPLETE SYSTEM OF RATIONAL NUMBERS

LESSON 7 ∾ RÉSUMÉ OF THE COMPLETE SYSTEM
OF RATIONAL NUMBERS   150

7.1 Generalization of common fractions   151

∾   PROBLEMS   153

7.2   Algebraic multiplication and division of fractions   154

∽   PROBLEMS [CONCLUDED]   155

7.3   Recapitulation.   Retrospect and prospect   157

Note 1   The set of all fractions equivalent
to a given fraction is denumerable   162

Note 2   The set consisting of all fractions, proper,
improper, positive, negative, equivalent,
nonequivalent, is denumerable   163

Note 3   The set of unequal fractions lying between
two unequal fractions is denumerable   164

∽   SUPPLEMENTARY PROBLEMS   166

LESSON 8 ∽ REVIEW OF THE COMPLETE SYSTEM OF RATIONAL NUMBERS AND OPERATIONS UPON THEM 178

8.1   The three direct arithmetical operations
upon natural numbers   179

∽   PROBLEM   179

8.2   Direct operations versus inverse operations
upon the natural numbers   180

∽   PROBLEMS [CONTINUED]   181

8.3   Enlargement of the system of natural numbers
to include all rational numbers   181

8.4   Scope of exponents enlarged to include all integers   182

8.5   The complete number system of analysis   182

∽   PROBLEMS [CONTINUED]   183

8.6   Order of performing the seven fundamental
operations of arithmetic   184

∽   PROBLEMS [CONTINUED]   184

8.7　Graphical representation of the system
of rational numbers 184

❧　PROBLEMS [CONCLUDED] 186

*Note 1　A suggestion pertaining to an extensive
long division* 187

Note 2　The Roman system of writing natural numbers 187

*Note 3　Conversion of natural numbers from
one base to another base* 189

❧　SUPPLEMENTARY PROBLEMS 191

LESSON 9 ❧ EQUIVALENCE OF COMMON AND DECIMAL FRACTIONS ❧ PROPERTIES OF DECIMAL FRACTIONS

198

9.1　Some advantages of decimal fractions
over common fractions 199

9.2　Definition and symbolism of decimal fractions 199

9.3　Converting a decimal fraction to its equivalent
common fractional form 200

9.4　Converting a common fraction to its equivalent
decimal fractional form 200

❧　PROBLEMS 201

9.5　Converting a common fraction to its equivalent
decimal fractional form by division 202

❧　PROBLEMS [CONTINUED] 203

9.6　Converting a mixed decimal fraction to its
equivalent common fractional form 203

❧　PROBLEMS [CONTINUED] 203

9.7　Conversion of common fractions to mixed
decimal fractions 204

☙   PROBLEMS [CONTINUED]   206

9.8   Repeating decimal fractions, also called
      periodic or circulating decimal fractions   206

☙   PROBLEMS [CONTINUED]   207

9.9   Delayed periodic decimal fractions   208

9.10 Two remarkable properties of the period of
      a decimal fraction whose equivalent
      common fraction, in its lowest terms,
      contains in its denominator only one prime
      factor p that is different from 2 or 5   210

☙   PROBLEMS [CONTINUED]   210

9.11 Three appropriate methods of reading
      decimal fractions   211

☙   PROBLEMS [CONCLUDED]   212

Note 1   Scientific notation   213

Note 2   Some mysteries cleared by rational
         operations upon numbers   214

Note 3   Terminating and repeating (periodic) forms
         for fractions using a base different from ten 216

☙   SUPPLEMENTARY PROBLEMS   219

LESSON 10 ☙ THE FOUR RATIONAL OPERATIONS
WITH DECIMAL FRACTIONS   224

10.1 The decimal point assigns positional values
      as positive and negative powers of ten   225

10.2 Addition and subtraction of decimal fractions   225

10.3 Multiplication and division of decimal fractions 226

∾   PROBLEMS   228

10.4   The reduction of repeating (periodic) decimal fractions
to their equivalent common fractional forms   229

∾   PROBLEMS [CONTINUED]   230

10.5   Rational numbers versus irrational numbers   231

10.6   Four very important formulas involving π that pertain to
circles and spheres   231

∾   PROBLEMS [CONCLUDED]   232

*Note 1   The operation of partitioning applied
to natural numbers*   233

*Note 2   Partitioning a proper fraction
into two or more fractions*   235

Note 3   Lists of periods of repeating decimal fractions   238

∾   SUPPLEMENTARY PROBLEMS   240

LESSON 11 ∾ EVOLUTION—THE INVERSE OPERATION OF INVOLUTION

244

11.1   Definitions and symbolism pertaining to evolution   245

∾   PROBLEMS   246

11.2   Involution does not yield unique results   246

11.3   One kind of irrational number: the surd numbers   247

11.4   The six basic operations, addition,
subtraction, multiplication, division, involution,
and evolution, performed upon surd numbers   248

∾   PROBLEMS [CONTINUED]   251

11.5   Using decimal approximations for surds   251

꧁   PROBLEMS [CONTINUED]   252

11.6   Obtaining the square root of a natural number   252

꧁   PROBLEMS [CONTINUED]   259

11.7   The Pythagorean relationship   260

꧁   PROBLEMS [CONTINUED]   260

11.8   Obtaining the cube root of a natural number   261

꧁   PROBLEMS [CONTINUED]   270

11.9   Obtaining higher roots of natural numbers than square
       and cube roots   271

꧁   PROBLEMS [CONCLUDED]   272

Note 1   The use of the binomial theorem for obtaining
         rational approximations for surds   273

Note 2   Algebraic numbers versus transcendental numbers   274

Note 3   Positions for the irrational numbers on
         the number line.   The cardinal number
         of the set of irrational numbers, aleph-sub-one, $\aleph_1$. 278

꧁   SUPPLEMENTARY PROBLEMS   282

LESSON 12 ꧁ TESTS FOR CORRECTNESS OF RESULTS ꧁ CASTING NINES AND ELEVENS ꧁ CONGRUENT NUMBERS   288

12.1   Checking the results of arithmetical operations   289

12.2   Simple checks by casting out nines and elevens   291

꧁   PROBLEMS   293

12.3   Congruent numbers   294

12.4 Products and differences of congruent numbers 295

12.5 Validity of the checks by casting nines and elevens 296

12.6 Cube roots of perfect cubes less than 1,000,000
determined by inspection 297

∾ PROBLEMS [CONCLUDED] 297

Note 1 *Equivalence of the two definitions
of congruent numbers* 298

Note 2 *Validity of the test of divisibility by seven* 299

Note 3 *Divisibility tests for any prime number* 299

Note 4 *"Right-end" long division* 300

∾ SUPPLEMENTARY PROBLEMS 300

LESSON 13 ∾ PERCENT RELATIONSHIPS ∾ BASE, RATE, PERCENTAGE ∾ AMBIGUITIES

304

13.1 Meaning of percent and its fractional equivalences 305

∾ PROBLEMS 306

13.2 Percentage situations simplified by
base-rate-percentage relationships 307

∾ PROBLEMS [CONCLUDED] 309

Note 1 *Percent versus percentage* 312

Note 2 *Percentage may exceed base—rate may
exceed 100 percent* 312

Note 3 *Ambiguity in percentage relationships* 313

Note 4 *Ambiguity not present if rate exceeds 100 percent* 313

∾ SUPPLEMENTARY PROBLEMS 314

LESSON 14 ∾ SIGNIFICANT DIGITS ∾ SIGNIFICANCE COMPUTATIONS

320

14.1   Exact numbers versus approximate numbers   321

14.2   Significant digits   321

14.3   Reliability of calculations that are based upon data of known inaccuracy   322

14.4   Significance computation—multiplication   323

∾   PROBLEMS   327

14.5   Significance computation—division and evolution   328

∾   PROBLEMS [CONCLUDED]   329

Note 1   *A pretaste of trigonometry*   330

Note 2   *The three Pythagorean trigonometric identities*   332

Note 3   *The meaning of the names of the six trigonometric functions*   332

∾   SUPPLEMENTARY PROBLEMS   333

LESSON 15 ∾ MENSURATION ∾ EXACT AND APPROXIMATE EQUIVALENCES OF VARIOUS UNITS OF MEASURE

336

15.1   The use of various units to provide measurements   337

15.2   Various systems of measurement   337

15.3   Some important relationships of measurement with their mnemonic formulas   339

∾   PROBLEMS   342

15.4   Heron's formula for the area of a triangle   343

15.5   Primitive Heronic triangles   344

15.6   Rational features of Heronic triangles   344

ᗡᑎ   PROBLEMS [CONCLUDED]   345

Note 1   The determination of geometrical figures   347

Note 2   Standard symbolism and formulas
         pertaining to the triangle   348

Note 3   Solution of triangle by use of trigonometry   349

ᗡᑎ   SUPPLEMENTARY PROBLEMS   350

LESSON 16 ᗡᑎ THE USE OF LOGARITHMS
AND THE SLIDE RULE IN ARITHMETIC   352

16.1   The use of logarithms greatly simplifies
       arithmetical operations.   Laws of exponents   353

ᗡᑎ   PROBLEMS   354

16.2   Logarithms with the base number two   354

16.3   Laws of logarithms   355

16.4   Common logarithms   357

ᗡᑎ   PROBLEMS [CONTINUED]   358

16.5   Tables of common logarithms—mantissa and
       characteristic of a common logarithm   358

ᗡᑎ   PROBLEMS [CONTINUED]   360

16.6   Improving accuracy in logarithmic computation—
       larger tables and interpolation   360

16.7   Interpolation to obtain mantissa   361

16.8 Interpolation for one additional digit
       in an antilogarithm   361

꜊ PROBLEMS [CONCLUDED]   362

16.9 Construction of a slide rule.
       Its use in computations   363

Note 1 Subdividing the degree, the common
         unit-of-angle measure   365

Note 2 The radian—a very useful unit-of-angle measure   365

Note 3 Applications of radian measurement   366

꜊ SUPPLEMENTARY PROBLEMS   367

LESSON 17 ꜊ THE IMAGINARY AND COMPLEX NUMBERS

                                                                  372

17.1 Imaginary numbers.   Recapitulation
       of the real numbers   373

17.2 The four rational operations upon
       imaginary numbers   373

17.3 Complex numbers.   The four rational
       operations upon complex numbers   374

17.4 Comprehensive character of complex numbers   374

17.5 Graphical representation of the imaginary numbers   375

17.6 Graphical representation of complex numbers   376

17.7 Geometrical location of the rational complex
       numbers in the complex plane   377

17.8 Positions for irrational complex numbers
       that may be located geometrically   379

꜊ PROBLEMS   380

Note 1   The denumerable set of infinite, or transfinite,
         cardinal numbers, $\aleph_0, \aleph_1, \aleph_2, \aleph_3, \aleph_4, \ldots$ 381

Note 2   The sum of an infinite (unending) series
         of numbers; the number e   383

Note 3   Résumé of the development of the system
         of natural numbers of primitive arithmetic
         into the complete number system and basic
         operations of modern analysis   387

∽   SUPPLEMENTARY PROBLEMS   390

SUPPLEMENT ∽ SPECIAL TOPICS   394

S.1   A subtraction-addition curio   395

S.2   A long-division curio   396

S.3   Obtaining mentally the kth powers of
      the natural numbers from 1 to n^k 398

S.4   Standard magic squares of order three   401

S.5   Nonstandard magic squares of order three   403

S.6   Standard magic squares of order four   406

S.7   Pandiagonal magic squares of order five   409

S.8   A second fundamental property of fractions   412

S.9   The dyadic or binary system of representing
      natural numbers   413

S.10 Identifying the secret number   415

S.11 The Russian peasant's method of multiplying
      natural numbers   416

S.12 The game of Nim   418

S.13 The sieve of Eratosthenes   420

S.14 Factor tables   422

S.15 Euler's formula for prime numbers   423

S.16 Pythagorean numbers   424

S.17 Generalized Pythagorean numbers   427

S.18 Perfect numbers   428

S.19 The Fibonacci (natural) numbers   430

S.20 The fundamental theorem of arithmetic   435

S.21 Some curious consequences of the fundamental
      theorem of arithmetic   439

S.22 Cyclical integers   442

S.23 The period of the decimal fractional form
      for $1/p$, for p as prime   444

S.24 The concept of infinity   450

S.25 The seven indeterminates   451

Answers   *455*
Index   *487*

ARITHMETIC

IN A LIBERAL EDUCATION

LESSON I ❧ NATURAL NUMBERS, THEIR NAMES AND SYMBOLS IN THE DECIMAL SYSTEM ❧ COUNTING

"Why," said the Dodo, *"the best way to explain it is to do it."*

—Lewis Carroll, *Alice in Wonderland, III.*

1·1 ∿ THE NATURAL NUMBERS, ALSO KNOWN AS THE COUNTING NUMBERS

The natural numbers provide answers to the questions "How many?" and "Which particular one?" in any designated collection of objects or individuals. Such collections are usually referred to as *sets, groups, aggregates, assemblages,* etc. The system of natural numbers must be plentiful enough to supply answers to the foregoing two questions for any proposed set. The natural numbers themselves are described, or *postulated,* as follows:

1. There is a definite *beginning* or *smallest* or *first* natural number, which is designated, or named, as *one*.

2. Every natural number has an *immediate successor,* or next larger natural number; therefore there is no last, or largest, natural number.

3. Every natural number, except *one,* has an *immediate predecessor,* or next smaller natural number.

The *decimal system* uses the familiar digit symbols 1, 2, 3, 4, 5, 6, 7, 8, 9, 0, alone or in combination, to represent all the natural numbers. Such written expressions are often called *numerals*. In this text the symbols and names are used interchangeably for the natural numbers they represent.

1·2 ∿ THE FIRST BASIC OPERATION UPON NATURAL NUMBERS IS CALLED COUNTING

Counting is the act of setting forth in their correct order any complete set of natural numbers, beginning with *one*. This act of counting may be done orally, mentally, or by writing down the numbers using their digit symbols. The last, or largest, natural number so used is called the *result of the counting*.

3

1·3 ∼ Appropriate names and symbols for natural numbers in correct order

The *first*, or smallest, natural number is *one*, written as 1.
The *second* natural number, or successor of one, is *two*, written as 2.
The *third* natural number, or successor of two, is *three*, written as 3.
The *fourth* natural number, or successor of three, is *four*, written as 4.
The *fifth* natural number, or successor of four, is *five*, written as 5.
The *sixth* natural number, or successor of five, is *six*, written as 6.
The *seventh* natural number, or successor of six, is *seven*, written as 7.
The *eighth* natural number, or successor of seven, is *eight*, written as 8.
The *ninth* natural number, or successor of eight, is *nine*, written as 9.
The *tenth* natural number, or successor of nine, is *ten*, written as 10.

The names and symbols for the natural numbers that follow in order immediately after ten are *eleven* or 11, *twelve* or 12, *thirteen* or 13, *fourteen* or 14, *fifteen* or 15, *sixteen* or 16, *seventeen* or 17, *eighteen* or 18, *nineteen* or 19, *twenty* or 20.

One observes that the symbols for these natural numbers following *ten* are formed by replacing the 0 in 10, successively, by 1, 2, 3, 4, 5, 6, 7, 8, 9, and that the symbol for the number following 19 is formed by replacing the 1 in 19 by 2 and the 9 in 19 by 0, thereby forming 20. In this way one obtains the key for representing by the digit symbols all larger natural numbers, namely,

1. The right end digit symbols are replaced in succession throughout the ordered cycle 1, 2, 3, 4, 5, 6, 7, 8, 9, 0.

2. When the cycle is completed by 0, the other part of the number symbolism is replaced by its successor, which has already appeared in the list of symbols for the natural numbers.

Steps (1) and (2) are alternately applied, repeatedly, as often as desired. The successor of 29 is 30; the successor of 39 is 40; the successor of 99 is 100, formed by replacing the right end 9 by 0 and the left end 9 by 10. Likewise, the successor of 100 is 101; the successor of 109 is 110; the successor of 999 is 1000.

1·4 ∼ Symbolism for the successor of any natural number

Simple rules for writing the symbols for the successor of any natural number whatever appear as follows:

1. If the final (right end) digit is 0, 1, 2, 3, 4, 5, 6, 7, or 8, this final digit is replaced by the next larger digit, namely, 1, 2, 3, 4, 5, 6, 7, 8, 9. No other change is made. Thus the successor of 3572 is 3573; the successor of 10040700 is 10040701.

2. If the final digit is 9, and the digit preceding this 9 is not 9, the final digit 9 is replaced by 0, and the preceding digit is replaced by the next larger digit in the cycle 0, 1, 2, 3, 4, 5, 6, 7, 8, 9.   Thus the successor of 459 is 460; the successor of 5859 is 5860; the successor of 1002009 is 1002010.

3. If the right portion of the natural number consists of a *succession of nines*, these nines are all replaced by a corresponding *succession of zeros* (0s), and the digit preceding the succession of 9s is replaced by the next larger digit in the cycle of digits 0, 1, 2, 3, 4, 5, 6, 7, 8, 9.   Thus the successor of 799 is 800; the successor of 72399999 is 72400000.

4. If the natural number consists entirely of 9s, each 9 is replaced by a 0, and a 1 is then placed before the succession of 0s.   Thus the successor of 99 is 100; the successor of 9999 is 10000.

1·5 ∽ Naming the natural numbers following 20 as far as 99

The symbolic representation of the natural numbers from 20 to 99, inclusive, consists of two digits, and are named or read as follows: The first, or left end digit, 2, 3, 4, 5, 6, 7, 8, or 9, is pronounced respectively as "twenty, thirty, forty, fifty, sixty, seventy, eighty, or ninety"; then the right end digit is pronounced, if it is not 0, for the *zero is not pronounced*.   Thus 53 is read as "fifty-three," 98 is read as "ninety-eight," 70 is read simply as "seventy."   One notes the use of the hyphen in writing the names of these numbers that do not have 0 for the right end digit.   The right end position in these numbers is called the units place; the left end position is called the tens place.   Numbers from 1 to 9 inclusive are called one-digit or single-digit numbers; numbers from 10 to 99 inclusive are called two-digit numbers.

1·6 ∽ Naming the natural numbers from 100 to 999 inclusive

The left end digit of these three-digit numbers is pronounced, then followed by the name "hundred"; then the remaining part of the number is pronounced, as was previously indicated for two-digit natural numbers.   Thus 463 is read as "four hundred sixty-three," 802 is read as "eight hundred two," 700 is read as "seven hundred."   One observes again that the zeros are not pronounced in reading a number that contains them.   The left end position of a three-digit natural number is called the hundreds place, the middle position is called the tens place, and the right end position is called the units place.

1·7   ∾   NAMES OF NATURAL NUMBERS THAT ARE GREATER THAN 999

These larger natural numbers, consisting of more than three digits, are pronounced (i.e., named or read) in accordance with the following three procedures:

1. Mark off by commas the successive groups of three digits *beginning at the right end*. The digits remaining at the extreme left end of the number may comprise a one-digit, a two-digit, or a three-digit natural number. Exhibitions of such markings are:

    5,851,440   or   89,542,600,360   or   320,146,000

2. The names of the successive positions to the *left* of the successive commas, as listed *from the right*, are respectively *thousand, million, billion, trillion, quadrillion, quintillion, sextillion, septillion, octillion, nonillion, decillion, undecillion,* and so on, as suggested by the corresponding successive Latin number names.

3. The complete number is then pronounced by reading each individual three-digit number that is marked off by the commas *beginning from the left end* and then pronouncing the appropriate Latin number name. However, the digits marked off at the extreme left end of the given large natural number may comprise a single-digit or a two-digit number. Accordingly, the three large natural numbers exhibited in (1) are read as follows:

5,851,440	Five million, eight hundred fifty-one thousand, four hundred forty
89,542,600,369	Eighty-nine billion, five hundred forty-two million, six hundred thousand, three hundred sixty-nine
320,146,000	Three hundred twenty million, one hundred forty-six thousand

One observes that the commas are retained in the written names of large natural numbers, unless the three-digit number between successive commas consists of zeros only, for again the zeros are not pronounced.

∾ PROBLEMS ∾

1.1.   Write the immediate successor and the immediate predecessor of the natural numbers:

a.	47	*d.*	271	*g.*	10,000	*j.*	9,009
b.	60	*e.*	3,000	*h.*	12,345		
c.	89	*f.*	65,099	*i.*	67,890		

The *predecessor* of a given number is obtained by reversing the rules for obtaining its successor.

1.2. Mark off properly with commas, then write out the names of the natural numbers:

   a. 52180   *c.* 1020030004000005

   b. 322875436107   *d.* 7853800742

1.3. Express with digit symbols the natural numbers: (*a*) thirty-six billion, one hundred thirty-seven million, sixty-four thousand, three hundred five; (*b*) fifty-six million, eight hundred ninety-three; (*c*) one million, two hundred thousand, three; (*d*) one hundred eighty-six thousand, two hundred thirty; (*e*) five hundred eighty-six trillion.

1.4. Beginning with the smallest, arrange the natural numbers in order of size in a vertical column so that the units positions are under one another: 1,020,300, 7,000, 23, 98,738, 976, 230,499, 31,416.

1.5. Arrange in a vertical column in order of size, beginning at the top with the smallest natural number: 4,623, 6,429, 6,247, 2,641, 2,460, 4,265.

1·8 ∾ Recapitulation

The foregoing sections provide all necessary rules for performing with the decimal symbols the first basic operation upon the natural numbers, known as *counting*. These rules indicate how one may write down in their correct order the symbols for all natural numbers from one to any specified natural number. The accompanying system of names is adequate for all natural numbers that occur in the applications to life situations, science, industry, finance, etc.

1·9 ∾ Natural numbers used as cardinal and as ordinal numbers

The cardinal number of a set of objects is obtained by counting them, as follows: One assigns to each individual object of the set a natural number, beginning with the natural number *one*, and continues with the natural numbers in their correct serial order until each object of the set has a natural number assigned to it. The last, or largest, natural number so used is called the *cardinal number* of the set of objects. The cardinal number of the set supplies the answer to the question, "How many objects are there in the set?" The specific natural number that is assigned to any particular object of the set is called the *ordinal number* of that particular object. Thus, the ordinal number supplies the answer to the question, "Which particular object of the set is this object?"

The distinction between cardinal number and ordinal number is exhibited in the following illustration. One may count the Presidents of the United States in the *order of their service* from Washington to Lincoln, inclusive, by assigning correctly the natural numbers, thus:

1	Washington	5	Monroe	9	Harrison	13	Fillmore
2	Adams	6	J. Q. Adams	10	Tyler	14	Pierce
3	Jefferson	7	Jackson	11	Polk	15	Buchanan
4	Madison	8	Van Buren	12	Taylor	16	Lincoln

The last, or largest, natural number used in this counting is 16; therefore, the cardinal number of this set of persons is 16. These natural numbers from 1 to 16 inclusive also represent individually the ordinal number of the President to whom it is assigned, and are generally pronounced as first, second, third, fourth, fifth, sixth, seventh, eighth, ninth, tenth, eleventh, twelfth, thirteenth, fourteenth, fifteenth, and sixteenth, respectively. Here Polk is the eleventh (11th) President, Lincoln the sixteenth (16th), and Washington the first (1st) President in order of service.

Arranged alphabetically, this set of Presidents would have the *same cardinal number*, but each President would, in general, have a *different ordinal number*. Counting them *alphabetically*, one has

1	Adams	5	Harrison	9	Madison	13	Taylor
2	Adams, J. Q.	6	Jackson	10	Monroe	14	Tyler
3	Buchanan	7	Jefferson	11	Pierce	15	Van Buren
4	Fillmore	8	Lincoln	12	Polk	16	Washington

In this alphabetical arrangement Washington is the sixteenth (16th) in the list; therefore his ordinal number here is 16. In this list the ordinal number of Lincoln is eight, or eighth, as the natural number 8 is assigned to him in this arrangement. The ordinal number of any particular object or person in a set depends upon the scheme of assigning the natural numbers to the objects or persons in the set. These 16 names may be listed in very many different ways, actually 19,428,304,896,000 ways altogether; in each such listing its cardinal number will be 16. The fact that the cardinal number of a set does not depend upon the arrangement of the items of the set is proved in the first note at the end of this lesson (Note 1).

໙ PROBLEMS [concluded] ໙

1.6. What is the cardinal number of the following sets of objects?

a. The letters in the English alphabet

b. In the American Flag: (i) the stars, (ii) the stripes, (iii) the red stripes

c. The set of known planets in the solar system (refer to Problem 2.19) *d.* The set consisting of the different arrangements that three children can take in a row of three chairs

1.7. What is the ordinal number of the specified item in each of the indicated sets?

a. Alaska, in order of admission as a state in the United States

b. President Polk as listed in (i) alphabetical order of the first 16 presidents; (ii) order of service

c. The earth in the set of planets in order of increasing distance from the sun

d. The month of the year and the day of the month celebrated in this country as (i) Independence Day, (ii) Armistice Day, (iii) New Year's Day, (iv) Columbus Day

1.8. In the series of consecutive natural numbers from 1 to 99, inclusive:

a. How many times does the digit 9 occur?

b. How many times does the digit 0 occur?

c. How many digits occur altogether?   (How often do digits occur?)

1.9. *a.* How many single-digit natural numbers are there?

b. How many two-digit natural numbers are there?

c. How many three-digit natural numbers are there?

d. How many ten-digit natural numbers are there? (A ten-digit natural number contains exactly ten digits, such as 6,997,501,002.)

1.10. *a.* Write in a vertical column seven consecutive natural numbers if (i) the smallest number is 90,998; (ii) the largest number is 10,204.

b. Write in a vertical column in order of size, beginning with the smallest, all *even* natural numbers in Problem 1.10*a*. An *even* natural number has an even digit in its units place; the even digits are 0, 2, 4, 6, and 8.

c. Write in a vertical column in order of size, beginning with the largest, all odd natural numbers in Problem 1.10*a*. An *odd* natural number has an odd digit in its units place; the odd digits are 1, 3, 5, 7, and 9.

1.11. Draw a triangular configuration of dots by placing one dot in the top row, two dots in the second row, three dots in the third row, and so on. How many dots are there in the (*a*) first row? (*b*) first two rows? (*c*) first three rows? (*d*) first four rows? The correct answers to these questions are called *triangular numbers*. (*e*) Make a list of the first 10 triangular numbers.

1.12. Draw a configuration of dots by placing one dot in the first row, three dots in the second row, five dots in the third row, and so on, making each successive row contain the consecutive odd number of dots.   How many dots are there in the (*a*) first row?   (*b*) first two rows?   (*c*) first three rows?   (*d*) first four rows?   The correct answers to these questions are consecutive *square numbers*.   (*e*) Make a list of the first 10 square numbers by counting the appropriate dots.   (*f*) Why are these numbers called *square numbers?*

1.13.   Draw configurations of dots by placing one more dot in each row than the number of rows, such as (*a*) one row containing two dots, (*b*) two rows containing three dots in each row, (*c*) three rows containing four dots in each row.   The correct number of dots in each such configuration is called an *oblong number*.   (*d*) By counting the dots in appropriate configurations obtain the first 10 oblong numbers.   Note that the number of dots in any oblong configuration is equal to the same number of dots in two equal triangular configurations of Problem 1.11, and that two consecutive triangulars equal a square number.

1.14.   In the configuration of Problem 1.12, how many dots are in the (*a*) first row?   (*b*) the next two (2d and 3d) rows?   (*c*) the next three rows (4th, 5th, and 6th)?   The correct answers to these questions are the first three *cube numbers*.   (*d*) By appropriate counting of dots obtain the first five cube numbers.

1.15.   A farmer wishes to set out ten trees in five rows, so that each row contains exactly four trees.   How did he do this?   *Hint:* Place five trees at equal intervals along the circumference of a circle, then draw lines from each of these five trees to the other four trees.   The places where these lines cross one another should be the positions of the other five trees.   How many other rows of trees are there in this arrangement that contain just two trees in each row?

*N*ote 1 ∽ *Uniqueness of the cardinal number of a set of objects.*

In this lesson the cardinal number of a set of objects has been defined as the *last natural number* used in counting the objects of the set if, during the counting operation:

No object is removed from the set.

No other object is introduced into the set.

No error is made in counting the objects of the set.

The ensuing argument is designed to prove that the same cardinal number attaches to any given set of objects, regardless of the order of counting the objects of the set.

Let the set of objects be counted by attaching to the individual objects *red* tags marked with the appropriate natural numbers.   The last red tag so used indicates by its natural number the cardinal number of the set, according to this special counting.

Next, let this same set of objects be counted again in some other order, or arrangement, by attaching to the individual objects *blue* tags marked with appropriate natural numbers. The last blue tag indicates by its natural number the cardinal number of the set according to the blue counting. It must now be shown that the last, or largest, natural number on the red tags is the same as the last, or largest, natural number on the blue tags. This is demonstrated as follows:

1. Each object of the set now carries a red tag and a blue tag, each tag marked with its appropriate natural number.

2. Observe the object that carries the *red* 1; if this same object carries also the *blue* 1, the blue tag is not disturbed. But if the blue tag carries some other natural number than 1, this blue tag is interchanged with the blue tag on that other object that does have the blue tag marked with 1, so that each object still carries a red and a blue tag, and now one object carries both the red 1 and the blue 1.

3. Next observe the object that carries the *red* 2; if this same object carries also the *blue* 2, the blue tag is not disturbed. But if the blue tag carries some other natural number than 2, this blue tag is interchanged with the blue tag on that other object that does have the blue tag marked with 2, so that each object still carries a red and a blue tag, and now one object carries both the red 2 and the blue 2.

4. Apply this same procedure to the other objects in the serial order of the red numbering, bringing next the blue tag carrying 3 to the object that carries the red 3 by an interchange of blue tags, if necessary, and so on, until finally each object is made to carry a red and a blue tag that are marked with the *same* natural number. Thus, the largest red number is the same as the largest blue number; i.e., the cardinal number of the set is the same natural number regardless of differing orders of counting the individual objects of the set.

Otherwise stated, every collection of objects or persons always has a special characteristic called its cardinal number. The uniqueness of the cardinal number of a set has led to the definition of cardinal number by means of this property, to wit: "The cardinal number of a group of things is that property of the group which remains unchanged if we rearrange the things within the group, or replace them one by one by other things"; or again, "it is that property of a group which is independent of the *character* of the things themselves and of their *arrangement* within the group."[1]

---

[1] H. B. Fine, "A College Algebra," p. 2, Ginn and Company, Boston, 1904.

N*ote 2 ⚬⚬ The decimal nomenclature for large numbers is not unique.*

Certain other countries, notably England, employ a different method of pointing off with commas and of reading the decimal expressions for large natural numbers. There the practice is to mark off the digits into groups of *six* digits instead of *three*, counting from the right end of the natural number. Then each set of *six* digits is read as a six-digit natural number by the previously indicated scheme of reading a six-digit natural number; the distinguishing names, *million, billion, trillion,* etc., are pronounced before the individual commas. For example, in the United States the national debt as of November 1, 1965, which was $320,886,558,984, is read "three hundred twenty billion, eight hundred eighty-six million, five hundred fifty-eight thousand, nine hundred eighty-four." The Englishman would mark off this number as 320886,558984 and pronounce it as "three hundred twenty thousand eight hundred eighty-six *million,* five hundred fifty-eight thousand nine hundred eighty-four." Our reading of this national debt would mean to an Englishman $320,000886,558984, or nearly a thousand times as large as it really is. Referring to the answer to Problem 3.19, one may reconcile the two statements: "There are nearly six billion miles in a light year," states Queen Elizabeth. "There are nearly six trillion miles in a light year " states President Johnson.

N*ote 3 ⚬⚬ Symbolism of natural numbers in systems other than the decimal system.*

The familiar *decimal* system employs *ten* digit symbols: 1, 2, 3, 4, 5, 6, 7, 8, 9, and 0 (*decem* is a Latin word meaning *ten*). Systems employing more or less than ten digits are quite useful in certain special situations. In each such system the set of the fundamental cycle of digits is used in the same general way that the ten fundamental digits are used in the decimal system. The number of distinct digit symbols used in any system denotes the *base* of that system. The base of our familiar decimal system is *ten,* as this system employs ten different digit symbols; the base of the binary, or dyadic, system is *two,* as this system employs only two digit symbols, namely, the 1 and the 0. The first twenty natural numbers are written in the binary system as follows: 1, 10, 11, 100, 101, 110, 111, 1000, 1001, 1010, 1011, 1100, 1101, 1110, 1111, 10000, 100001, 10010, 10011, 10100.

The *septimal* system, of base *seven,* employs the seven digit symbols 1, 2, 3, 4, 5, 6, and 0. The first twenty natural numbers are written in the septimal system as follows: 1, 2, 3, 4, 5, 6, 10, 11, 12, 13, 14, 15, 16, 20, 21, 22, 23, 24, 25, 26.

The system of base *thirteen* requires the use of thirteen digit symbols. Here one may use the letters *a, b, c,* as digit symbols, in order to have the thirteen digit symbols 1, 2, 3, 4, 5, 6, 7, 8, 9, *a, b, c,* 0. The first twenty natural numbers in the system of base thirteen appear as follows: 1, 2, 3, 4, 5, 6, 7, 8, 9, *a, b, c,* 10, 11, 12, 13, 14, 15, 16, 17.

Various situations that advantageously use the natural numbers as written to a base different from *ten* occur in the supplementary sections of this text (S.9). As examples, the Russian peasant's method of multiplying and the Game of Nim are clarified in terms of binary numbers. Simple methods of converting the form of a natural number from one base to another base are presented in Note 3 of Lesson 8.

Examples of the same natural number when written to the bases ten, seven, two, and thirteen appear as follows:

Ten	*Seven*	*Two*	*Thirteen*
100	202	1100100	79
1,000	2626	1111101000	5bc
1,492	4231	10111010100	8aa
1,776	5115	11011110000	a68
1,970	5513	11110110010	b87
2,048	5654	100000000000	c17
1,000,000	11333311	11110100001001000000	290221

It is to be noted that the larger the base, the fewer the digits required to express a natural number. Thus the digital expression of one million requires seven digits in the decimal system, eight digits in the septimal system, and twenty digits in the binary system.

LESSON 2 ❧ ADDITION OF NATURAL NUMBERS ❧ THE OPERATION OF REPEATED COUNTING

For the person who is to be taught,
For him who is to gain knowledge,
It is rule upon rule, and rule upon rule,
Line after line, and line after line,
A little bit here, and a little bit there.

—Isaiah 28: 9a, 10.

2·1 ❧ Two uses of a natural number in the normal array of natural numbers

The normal array of natural numbers is their exhibition in decimal form, in a horizontal line in increasing order from left to right, namely,

1 2 3 4 5 6 7 8 9 10 11 12 13 14 15 . . .

The series of dots on the right end of the line indicates that the series of numbers is unending toward the right.   In this normal array each natural number has two uses:

Each natural number is the *cardinal number* of the set of natural numbers from 1 to itself, inclusive, and indicates *how many* natural numbers occur in the line from 1 to that particular natural number, inclusive.

Each natural number is the *ordinal number* of itself in the normal array of natural numbers, thus indicating its proper position in the array of natural numbers.

To illustrate, the natural number *seven* indicates that there are *seven* natural numbers in the set 1, 2, 3, 4, 5, 6, 7; and that seven is the *seventh* (7th) natural number in the normal array of natural numbers

1 2 3 4 5 6 7 8 9 10 11 . . .

2·2 ❧ Addition of two natural numbers

Definitions.   If the letters a and b represent two different natural numbers, or the same natural number, then the *sum* of a and b, represented symbolically as $a + b$, is the last number encountered if a natural numbers and b natural numbers are successively counted off in the normal array of natural numbers, starting with 1.   This operation of successive counting is called *addition*.   The natural numbers a and b are called *addends* in the *operation of addition*.

15

For example, to compute the sum of 7 and 5, expressed symbolically as $7 + 5 = ?$, one counts off seven natural numbers, starting with 1, or one selects the 7 directly in the normal array of the natural numbers; then one counts off five more natural numbers. The last number so used in the countings is the required sum of 7 and 5. These two successive countings are indicated by the numbers with asterisks (*), as follows:

```
1   2   3   4   5   6   7   8   9   10   11   12   13   14   15   16   . . .
1 * 2 * 3 * 4 * 5 * 6 * 7 * 1 * 2 *  3 *  4 *  5 *
```

The last, or largest, number used in these countings, 12, is the required sum of 7 and 5. Thus, $7 + 5 = 12$.

2·3 ∾ COMMUTATIVE LAW OF ADDITION OF TWO NATURAL NUMBERS

The foregoing discussion shows that the cardinal number of the set of numbers marked with asterisks, which is 12, represents the sum of the natural numbers, $7 + 5$. Thus, the cardinal number of the set consisting of 1 * 2 * 3 * 4 * 5 * 6 * 7 * 1 * 2 * 3 * 4 * 5 * is also the cardinal number of the set 1 * 2 * 3 * 4 * 5 * 1 * 2 * 3 * 4 * 5 * 6 * 7 *, by Note 1 in Lesson 1, or by actual counting. Moreover, these last numbers marked with asterisks would be used in adding the same two numbers, 7 and 5, in reverse order: $5 + 7 = 12$. Likewise, $7 + 5 = 5 + 7$. And, quite generally, for any natural numbers a and b, it is true that $a + b = b + a$, for, by Note 1 in Lesson 1, the cardinal number of the set of asterisked numbers 1 * 2 * $\cdots$ a * 1 * 2 * $\cdots$ b * must be the same as the cardinal number of the set 1 * 2 * $\cdots$ b * 1 * 2 * $\cdots$ a *, as these two sets contain the very same members in different arrangements.

The fact that any two natural numbers, a and b, have the same sum, whether computed as $a + b$ or as $b + a$, is called *eommutative law of addition of natural numbers*, $a + b = b + a$.

2·4 ∾ ADDITION OF THREE NATURAL NUMBERS.
ASSOCIATIVE LAW OF ADDITION

To add *three* natural numbers, a, b, and c, one may add c to the sum of a and b, which is indicated symbolically as $(a + b) + c$. Or one may add the sum of b and c to a, which is indicated symbolically as $a + (b + c)$. For example, to add the three natural numbers 5, 7, 3, one may proceed as $(5 + 7) + 3 = 12 + 3 = 15$; or one may proceed as $5 + (7 + 3) = 5 + 10 = 15$. The validity of the commutative law of addition for the natural numbers follows from these two facts:

The sum of the natural numbers a, b, and c is the cardinal number of the set of natural numbers

$$1, 2, \ldots, a \qquad 1, 2, \ldots, b \qquad 1, 2, \ldots, c$$

The cardinal number of a set remains the same for any separate groupings of the elements within the set, such as

$$(1, 2, \ldots, a, 1, 2, \ldots, b), 1, 2, \ldots, c$$
and
$$1, 2, \ldots, a (1, 2, \ldots, b, 1, 2, \ldots, c)$$

The commutative law of addition, $a + b = b + a$, and the associative law of addition, $(a + b) + c = a + (b + c)$, have been proved to be true if a, b, c represent any natural numbers whatever and if the operation of addition, denoted by the symbol $+$, is defined as repeated countings of sets of natural numbers beginning with 1 and continuing to the natural number so specified by a, b, or c. For other interpretations of the letters a, b, c and the symbol $+$ these two laws are not necessarily true, as will be noted subsequently in this text.

2·5 ∞ ADDITION OF MORE THAN THREE NATURAL NUMBERS

To add more than three natural numbers, one replaces the sum of any two or three of them by their sum, repeatedly, until the final single sum is obtained. To add the numbers 5, 8, 3, 7, and 2 one may proceed in order as follows:

$$5 + 8 = 13 \qquad 13 + 3 = 16 \qquad 16 + 7 = 23 \qquad 23 + 2 = 25$$

Or one may select convenient pairs for individual additions, thus:

$$3 + 7 = 10 \qquad 8 + 2 = 10 \qquad \text{then} \qquad 10 + 10 + 5 = 25$$

The sum of these numbers, 5, 8, 3, 7, and 2 is merely the cardinal number of the set of natural numbers

$$1, 2, 3, 4, 5 \qquad 1, 2, 3, 4, 5, 6, 7, 8 \qquad 1, 2, 3 \qquad 1, 2, 3, 4, 5, 6, 7 \qquad 1, 2$$

which is the same number, regardless of any rearrangements of the several smaller groups of natural numbers within the entire set of these 25 natural numbers.

2·6 ∞ SIMPLIFIED METHOD OF ADDING LARGE NATURAL NUMBERS

The addition of large natural numbers would become extremely tedious by the operation of repeated additions. Hence, the operation of addition is greatly simplified by the following five considerations:

1. A new natural number, called *zero*, and represented by the symbol 0, is introduced and defined by the properties:

$$0 + a = a \qquad a + 0 = a \qquad 0 + 0 = 0$$

in which *a* represents any natural number.

2. The 55 sums of the pairs of single-digit natural numbers *must be memorized immediately*. This will make unnecessary any additions by the process of repeated countings. The thoughtful student will recognize simple relationships to recall these 55 sums. (He may also recover them by counting on his fingers.)

$0 + 0 = 0$	$1 + 5 = 6$	$3 + 4 = 7$	$5 + 7 = 12$
$0 + 1 = 1$	$1 + 6 = 7$	$3 + 5 = 8$	$5 + 8 = 13$
$0 + 2 = 2$	$1 + 7 = 8$	$3 + 6 = 9$	$5 + 9 = 14$
$0 + 3 = 3$	$1 + 8 = 9$	$3 + 7 = 10$	$6 + 6 = 12$
$0 + 4 = 4$	$1 + 9 = 10$	$3 + 8 = 11$	$6 + 7 = 13$
$0 + 5 = 5$	$2 + 2 = 4$	$3 + 9 = 12$	$6 + 8 = 14$
$0 + 6 = 6$	$2 + 3 = 5$	$4 + 4 = 8$	$6 + 9 = 15$
$0 + 7 = 7$	$2 + 4 = 6$	$4 + 5 = 9$	$7 + 7 = 14$
$0 + 8 = 8$	$2 + 5 = 7$	$4 + 6 = 10$	$7 + 8 = 15$
$0 + 9 = 9$	$2 + 6 = 8$	$4 + 7 = 11$	$7 + 9 = 16$
$1 + 1 = 2$	$2 + 7 = 9$	$4 + 8 = 12$	$8 + 8 = 16$
$1 + 2 = 3$	$2 + 8 = 10$	$4 + 9 = 13$	$8 + 9 = 17$
$1 + 3 = 4$	$2 + 9 = 11$	$5 + 5 = 10$	$9 + 9 = 18$
$1 + 4 = 5$	$3 + 3 = 6$	$5 + 6 = 11$	

3. The *positional property* of the individual digits in the decimal expression of a natural number must be understood. Note that $1 + 1 + 1 + 1 + 1 + 1 + 1 + 1 + 1 + 1 = 10$; hence the 1 in the tens position of 10 represents *ten* 1s. Again, since $10 + 10 = 20$, $10 + 10 + 10 = 30$, $10 + 10 + 10 + 10 = 40$, $10 + 10 + 10 + 10 + 10 = 50$, . . . , it is clear that the digit symbol in the tens position in 10, 20, 30, 40, and 50, respectively, represents the *number of tens* whose sum is equal to the corresponding two-digit number. Similarly, for the hundreds, 100, 200, 300, . . . , the digit in the hundreds position denotes the *number of hundreds* whose sum is equal to the corresponding three-digit number; that is, $200 = 100 + 100$, $300 = 100 + 100 + 100$, ... Quite generally, an expression for a natural number consisting of a single nonzero digit followed by a series of zeros, such as 400,000, is equal to the sum of as many numbers represented by 1 followed by the same number of zeros, and taken as many times as the original nonzero digit in the given number. Thus, $400{,}000 = 100{,}000 + 100{,}000 + 100{,}000 + 100{,}000$.

4. Any natural number expressed by more than a single digit is equal to the sum of the numbers that the individual digits represent. Thus, 7,538 = 7,000 + 500 + 30 + 8. If the symbol for zero occurs in the expression of the large natural number, it is ignored, as it denotes a complete absence of units in the position that it occupies. Thus, 50,003,490 = 50,000,000 + 3,000 + 400 + 90.

5. The addition of two or more natural numbers, consisting of one or more digits, is accomplished by expressing each natural number as the sum of its positional unit elements, as described in (4), listing the same unit elements under one another. One then adds these numbers of units separately in their appropriate columns, repeating these procedures whenever necessary, with the results already so obtained, until one obtains an indicated sum of nine or fewer units in each positional unit. To illustrate, let the sum of 576, 29, 8,683, and 548 be required. Each step in the solution must be completely understood before continuing to the next step.

$$
\begin{array}{rl}
576 = & 500 + 70 + 6 \\
29 = & 20 + 9 \\
8{,}683 = 8{,}000 + & 600 + 80 + 3 \\
548 = & 500 + 40 + 8 \\
\hline
\end{array}
$$

One may note that one needs to know the sum of two single-digit natural numbers, as listed in (2) above, to perform the entire addition. Thus, 6 + 9 = 15 = 10 + 5; then 5 + 3 = 8, 8 + 8 = 16 = 10 + 6. The 6 is the required units digit in the completed sum of the original large numbers. Adding the two tens that arose in the sum of the units digits to the second column of tens, one must add 20, 70, 20, 80, and 40. Here the number of tens is obtained thus: 2 + 7 = 9, 9 + 2 = 11 = 10 + 1; 1 + 8 = 9, 9 + 4 = 13 = 10 + 3. There are three 10s in the required sum. Combining the two 10s here arising, one has 10 + 10 = 20 tens, or 200, which must next be added to the list of hundreds, namely, 200 + 500 + 600 + 500. Adding these numbers of hundreds, one has 2 + 5 = 7; 7 + 6 = 13 = 10 + 3; 3 + 5 = 8. Thus there are 8 hundreds in the required sum. The 10 hundreds here arising represent 1,000, which must be added to the list of thousands, namely, 1,000 + 8,000 = 9,000. Accordingly, the final complete required sum is 9,000 + 800 + 30 + 6, or 9,836.

That this procedure does, indeed, yield the correct unique sum is evident from earlier discussions that the sum of two or more natural numbers does not depend upon the order of the individual numbers to be used in the addition operation.

Instead of recasting the several given large natural numbers into their positional digital components, the digits of the given numbers may be immediately added quite conveniently, if they are listed vertically in such a way that the units digits are under one another in the same vertical column.   Again using the same number:

```
  576
   29
 8683
  548
```
```
   26   The sum of the digits in the units position.
   21   The sum of the digits in the tens position.
   16   The sum of the digits in the hundreds position.
    8   The sum of the digits in the thousands position.
 9836   Each digit of this final sum is the sum of the digits in the same column.
```

This procedure may be further condensed by writing only the right end digit of the sum of digits in any column directly under that particular column, while the other digits of such a sum are placed in the adjoining column to the left. These *carryovers* are indicated by daggers.   Using the same example:

```
†1 †2 †2
    5  7 6
       2 9
 8  6  8 3
    5  4 8
 9  8  3 6
```

Finally, the carryover *need not be written*, as shown with the asterisk, but may immediately be added to the numbers of the next column of digits.

P ROBLEMS

2.1. Obtain the sum of:

a.   The ten smallest natural numbers that contain the digit 9

b.   The nine ensuing natural numbers that contain the digit 9

c.   All natural numbers less than 100 that contain the digit 9

2.2. Obtain the sum of the ten natural numbers that occur in Problem 1.1.

2.3. Obtain the sum of the four natural numbers that occur in Problem 1.2.

2.4. Obtain the sum of the five natural numbers that occur in Problem 1.3.

2.5. Calculate the sum of the seven natural numbers that occur in Problem 1.4.

2.6. Obtain the sum of the six natural numbers that occur in Problem 1.5.

2.7. Obtain the sum of the answers to Problems 2.2 to 2.6, inclusive.

2.8. Obtain the sum of 10 consecutive even natural numbers, the smallest of which is 19,988.

2.9. Obtain the sum of 12 consecutive odd natural numbers, the largest of which is 10,011.

2·7 ⤳ OBSERVATIONS ON THE SOLUTION OF PROBLEMS OF ARITHMETIC

To make arithmetic a useful and efficient tool, *one must solve a variety of problems.* Reading and understanding the text is necessary, but not sufficient. By solving problems one detects and remedies his own hidden deficiencies, expands his powers of observation and insight, develops habits of persistency and accuracy, and acquires self-confidence and intellectual independence.

In undertaking to solve a given problem one must attempt to: (1) grasp completely all directions or prescribed instructions; (2) understand completely the situation described by the statements of the problem; and (3) understand clearly just what information the solution should yield. Should any feature of the problem still appear vague, one must seek the requisite information to clarify it *before attempting to solve the problem.*

The preceding nine problems require careful countings and various additions of natural numbers. The ensuing problems of this lesson also require the operation of addition of natural numbers, which are, indeed, cardinal numbers of various sets of objects, persons, or units of measurements.

In the ensuing lessons one will encounter other operations upon the natural numbers than the operation of addition and still other kinds of numbers than the natural numbers. These other operations and other kinds of numbers will provide the means of solving ever more complicated kinds of problems. In the solution of all such problems it will be discovered that all necessary pertinent operations must be performed upon *numbers.* The student must perform all such operations with extreme care to avoid making errors which will lead to an incorrect result. Lesson 13 will supply simple tests to detect the presence of errors in the result of every arithmetical operation upon numbers.

⤳ PROBLEMS [CONCLUDED] ⤳

2.10. The length of a rectangular field is 762 feet greater than its width. How many feet of fencing are needed to enclose it completely? The field is 1,997 feet wide.

2.11. John has twelve books. Mary has seven more than John. Frank has six more than Mary and John together. William has three more books than Frank. (*a*) How many books has William? (*b*) How many books have all four persons together?

2.12. In 1940 the population of Los Angeles, Calif., exceeded the combined populations of San Francisco, Calif., Boston, Mass., and Evansville, Ind., by 1,863. The populations of San Francisco, Boston, and Evansville were, respectively, 634,536, 770,536, and 97,062.

    a. Compute the population of Los Angeles in 1940.

    b. Compute the combined population of these four cities in 1940.

    c. Solve parts (*a*) and (*b*) after replacing respectively, the five numbers in the problem by 1960, 899,959, 740,316, 697,197, and 141,543.

2.13. A clerk received in 1937 an annual salary of $1,475. In each subsequent year his annual salary was increased by $135 over that of the preceding year. Compute the total amount of salary he received in the six consecutive years beginning with his salary of 1939.

2.14. A serious college student enrolls in mathematics, Spanish, English, history, and physical education. These classes meet, respectively, 5, 5, 3, 2, and 2 hours each week. All classes, excepting physical education, require 2 hours of study before each meeting of 1 hour. He spends daily 2 hours in transportation and 1 hour for lunch. How many hours does his college require of him during a regular week?

2.15. A certain algebra class contains 19 women students and 25 men students. When all students are seated, there are six unoccupied student chairs in the classroom. How many student chairs does the classroom contain?

2.16. There are 22 letters in the Hebrew alphabet, two more in the Greek alphabet, and two more letters in the English alphabet than in the Greek alphabet. How many letters occur altogether in these three alphabets?

2.17. The original 13 states of the United States comprised an area of 982,135 square miles. In the ensuing years it has acquired an additional area of 2,846,260 square miles. What is the present total area of the United States of America?

2.18. The national debt of the United States in 1930 was $16,185,309,831. During the next decade (10 years) it increased by $26,782,221,207. From 1940 to 1946 it increased by $226,454,586,135. During the ensuing two decades it increased by $52,737,213,740 (February 15, 1966). In the ensuing single year it has continued to increase by $7,882,427,796. Compute the national debt as of February 15, 1967.

2.19. In 1930 the known planets of the solar system, with their corresponding number of satellites, were tabulated as follows: Mercury 0, Venus 0,

Earth 1, Mars 2, Jupiter 9, Saturn 9, Uranus 4, and Neptune 1. By February 1967 another planet, Pluto, had been discovered with no detected satellites, and astronomers had discovered three additional satellites of Jupiter, one additional satellite of each of the planets Saturn, Uranus, and Neptune. Compute the total number of planets and satellites that were known to exist in the solar system as of this latter date.

2.20. Dairyman *R* has 35 more cows than dairyman *S*. Dairyman *T* has 8 more than dairyman *R*. How many cows have these three dairymen altogether if dairyman *S* has 193 cows?

2.21. Two technicians, *A* and *B*, were employed on January 1, 1960, with salary inducements as follows: *A* is to receive a beginning monthly salary of $350, with monthly increases of $10, for each subsequent month; *B* is to receive a beginning monthly salary of $400, with annual increases of $1,400 for each subsequent year. Calculate their annual salaries for each of their first 3 years under these salary schedules.

2.22. Add these numbers horizontally and vertically, placing the sums on the appropriate lines. Then add separately the set of vertical sums and the set of horizontal sums, noting that these two resulting sums must be the same. To add horizontally one may underline each individual digit as it is used, thus facilitating the correct choice of subsequent digits to be added from one horizontal number to the next horizontal number.

$$
\begin{array}{rrrrrl}
4{,}567 + & 8{,}093 + & 7{,}911 + & 3{,}147 + & 4{,}444 & = \underline{\hphantom{0000}} \\
1{,}001 + & 573 + & 35 + & 199 + & 1{,}492 & = \underline{\hphantom{0000}} \\
68 + & 23 + & 1{,}776 + & 7 + & 36 & = \underline{\hphantom{0000}} \\
\underline{512} + & \underline{100} + & \underline{800} + & \underline{8{,}273} + & \underline{1} & = \underline{\hphantom{0000}} \\
+ & + & + & + & & = \underline{\hphantom{0000}}
\end{array}
$$

2.23. Alfred the Great died in 901 A.D. The signing of the Magna Charta occurred 314 years later, and 506 years before the outbreak of the American Revolutionary War. In what year did the American Revolutionary War begin?

2.24. At the Battle of Waterloo, in June 1815, the estimated loss of the English was 12,000, of the French 40,000, of the Prussians 38,000, of the Belgians 8,000, and of the Bavarians 3,500. What was the total estimated loss of life in this single battle?

2.25. A merchant began business with $7,000 cash, goods worth $4,875, bank stock worth $5,600, and other stocks worth $12,875. In his first year he made a net profit of $3,500. What was his worth at the end of the year?

*N*ote 1 ∽ *The first infinite
cardinal number, aleph-zero.*

If two sets of objects have the same cardinal number, the individual objects of
the two sets can be paired off in a one-to-one correspondence.   For example,
three coins, a penny, a nickel, and a dime, may be paired off with three children,
A, *B*, and *C*, by assigning one coin to each child, such as the penny to *A*, the
nickel to *B*, and the dime to *C*.   Actually, this pairing off of coins with children
can be done in *six* different ways, as here indicated, letting *P*, *N*, and *D* denote
respectively the penny, nickel, and dime.

	1	2	3	4	5	6
A	*P*	*P*	*N*	*N*	*D*	*D*
B	*N*	*D*	*P*	*D*	*P*	*N*
C	*D*	*N*	*D*	*P*	*N*	*P*

Each such pairing is called a *one-to-one correspondence* between the members of
the two sets.   Conversely, if the members of two sets can be paired off in a
one-to-one correspondence, the two sets have the *same cardinal number*.   The set
that consists of all of the natural numbers is called an *infinite* set.   The cardinal
number of this special set is represented by the first letter of the Hebrew alphabet,
with subscript zero, $\aleph_0$, and is read as "aleph-zero."   Accordingly, any set of
objects that can be paired off with the set of natural numbers must also have
this same infinite cardinal number aleph-zero.

For example, the set consisting of those natural numbers that are multiples of
100, namely, 100, 200, 300, 400, . . . has the cardinal number $\aleph_0$, since the
100 may be paired with 1, the 200 may be paired with 2, the 300 may be paired
with the 3, and so on, so that each multiple may be paired with a natural number, and conversely, each natural number would be paired with a multiple of 100.

Now a *subset* of a given set of elements consists of some, or all, of the elements of
the given set.   A *proper subset* of a given set consists of some *but not all* of the elements of a given set.   Thus, the multiples of 100 comprise a proper subset of
the set of natural numbers.   An infinite set may also be defined as a set that
may be paired off in a one-to-one correspondence with a proper subset of itself.
In such cases the set and its subset must have the same infinite cardinal number.
The set of natural numbers whose decimal representations consist only of the
digit 9, namely,

9   99   999   9,999   99,999   999,999   9,999,999 . . .

is a proper subset of the entire set of natural numbers.   It is to be noted that this subset may be paired in a one-to-one correspondence with the set of natural numbers, by assigning 9 to 1, 99 to 2, 999 to 3, . . . , assigning a number consisting of k nines to the natural number k.   Accordingly, the set of all natural numbers and this particular subset can be paired off in a one-to-one correspondence, and must have the same infinite cardinal number, namely, aleph-zero.

Two sets are said to be *equivalent sets* if their elements can be paired off in a one-to-one correspondence and, consequently, have the same cardinal number. Infinite sets having the cardinal number $\aleph_0$, aleph-zero, are also called *denumerable sets*.   In subsequent lessons one will encounter sets that have ever larger cardinal numbers than $\aleph_0$, namely, $\aleph_1$, $\aleph_2$, $\aleph_3$, . . . , read, respectively as "aleph-zero," "aleph-one," "aleph-two," "aleph-three."   These so-called infinite cardinal numbers are not natural numbers; sets having an infinite cardinal number are called *infinite sets;* sets having natural numbers for their cardinal numbers are called *finite sets*.   Moreover, the set consisting of $\aleph_0$, $\aleph_1$, $\aleph_2$, . . . , is denumerable.

Finally, the set A is said to have a larger cardinal number than set B, if every possible attempt to set up a one-to-one correspondence between the elements of A with the elements of B leaves elements of A unmatched with elements of B, while every element of B has an element of A assigned to it.

*N*ote 2 ⤳ *A meterstick slide rule for addition of natural numbers.*

The conventional meterstick is slightly longer than a yardstick.   The graduation markings on the meterstick are made in accordance with the metric system of length units:

  10 millimeters = 1 centimeter
  10 centimeters = 1 decimeter = 100 millimeters
  10 decimeters = 1 meter = 100 centimeters = 1,000 millimeters

Now let each tiny millimeter graduation mark represent a natural number from 1 to 1,000; the left end, or lower end, represents zero, and the right end, or upper end, represents 1,000.   The decimeter markings 10, 20, 30, 40, 50, 60, 70, 80, 90 denote the number of *centimeters* from the left end of the meterstick. Between the consecutive decimeter markings the centimeters are marked with the numbers 1, 2, 3, 4, 5, 6, 7, 8, 9.   The tiny millimeter markings are not identified by written numbers; however, the fifth millimeter marking within each centimeter is slightly longer than the other millimeter markings.

The natural numbers from 1 to 1,000 are identified with these graduation markings:

1. The decimeter markings represent multiples of 100.   Thus, the 10 represents 100, the 20 represents 200, the 30 represents 300, . . . , the 90 represents 900, the right end of the meterstick represents 1,000.

2. The centimeter markings represent multiples of 10. Beginning at the left end of the meterstick, the 1 represents 10, the 2 represents 20, the 3 represents 30, . . . , the 9 represents 90. The first decimeter marking represents 100. The 1 following (to the right of) this decimeter marking 10 represents 110. In general, any centimeter marking between two consecutive decimeter markings represents the multiple of 10 to be added to the multiple of 100 that the decimeter marking on its left represents. Thus the 7 between decimeter markings 30 and 40 represents 70 + 300, or 370.

3. The natural number that any tiny millimeter marking represents is obtained by adding the number of millimeter markings from the centimeter marking immediately on the left side of it to the millimeter marking in question.

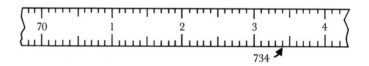

FIGURE 2.1

Thus, the natural number 734 is represented by the fourth millimeter marking to the right of the centimeter marking representing 730, as illustrated in the sketch of that portion of the meterstick (Figure 2.1).

Wrap two parallel metersticks securely with Scotch tape, permitting the third meterstick to slide easily between them. The sticky surface of the tape extending between the two outer metersticks must be covered with pieces of scotch tape to permit easy movement of the middle meterstick between the two outer metersticks thus held rigidly by the tape. The zero ends of the three metersticks should be at the left ends of all three metersticks. For convenience let the two fixed metersticks be designated as A scales, the middle meterstick as B scale. The right ends of the three scales represent 1,000.

By use of the meterstick slide rule one may obtain the sum of two or more natural numbers of any size whatever. Care in manipulating the instrument will always yield the correct sum of the given addends. Note carefully the several situations that occur:

1. To add two natural numbers, *P* and *Q*, each of which is less than 1,000, and whose sum is also less than 1,000: Slide the B scale (the middle meterstick) so that its *left* end, representing 0, touches the graduation marking on the A scale that represents the natural number *P*. Now the millimeter marking on the B scale that represents the natural number *Q* touches the

marking on the A scale that represents the sum $P + Q$ (Figure 2.2). The repeated counting of appropriate natural numbers, which comprises the operation of addition of natural numbers, is thus done mechanically by the numbered markings on the metersticks. One should perform and check the additions: (*a*) $135 + 472 = ?$ (*b*) $531 + 397 = ?$ (*c*) $368 + 477 = ?$ (*d*) $444 + 387 = ?$ (*e*) $673 + 327 = ?$

2.   To add two natural numbers, P and Q, each of which is less than 1,000, but whose sum is greater than 1,000: Slide the B scale (the middle meterstick) so that its *right* end, representing 1,000, touches the graduation marking on the A scale that represents the natural number P. Now the millimeter

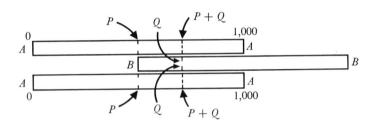

FIGURE 2.2

marking on the B scale that represents the natural number Q touches the marking on the A scale, which increased by 1,000, represents the required sum, $P + Q$. Figure 2.3 exhibits the validity of this procedure in which the A scales represent the natural numbers from 1,000 to 2,000 on the two outer metersticks. The A scales are *imagined* to extend toward the left from 1,000 down to 0, as shown by the dotted portions. One should now perform and check the additions: (*a*) $523 + 765 = ?$ (*b*) $666 + 999 = ?$ (*c*) $875 + 758 = ?$ (*d*) $380 + 803 = ?$ (*e*) $682 + 801 = ?$

3.   To add more than two natural numbers, each of which is less than 1,000, one merely adds each ensuing natural number to the sum already obtained by the methods of (1) and (2), noting that whenever it is necessary to place the right end of the B scale at the marking of the A scale that represents the first addend, or any ensuing sum, one must mentally add 1,000 to the next ensuing sum. One should perform meterstick additions and check the following: (*a*) $235 + 411 + 137 = ?$ (*b*) $563 + 312 + 735 = ?$ (*c*) $115 + 238 + 322 + 430 = ?$ (*d*) $357 + 783 + 541 + 402 = ?$ (*e*) $682 + 691 + 952 + 712 + 123 = ?$

4. Slide rule addition of two or more numbers, some or all of which are larger than 1,000, is presented in the single example:

$$
\begin{array}{r}
14,456,631 \\
8,588,308 \\
487,972,857 \\
\hline
\end{array}
$$

The addition is accomplished by adding the individual three-digit natural numbers that are under one another and separated by the commas, as follows: $631 + 308 = 939$; $939 + 857 = 1,796$. Thus 7, 9, and 6 are the three right end digits of the required sum. Adding mentally the carryover 1 to 456, one proceeds thus: $457 + 588 = 1,045$, $045 + 972 = 1,017$.

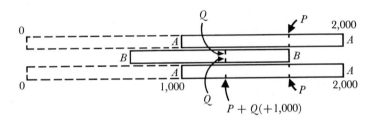

FIGURE 2.3

Thus 0, 1, and 7 are the next three digits of the required sum. Adding the two carryovers of 1 mentally to 14, one adds $16 + 8 = 24$, $24 + 487 = 511$, which are the next and final digits of the required sum, yielding the entire required sum, 511,017,796, by meterstick addition. One should perform meterstick additions and check the following:

143,705	307,471,554	444,323,700
87,811	9,748,777,987	753,864,681
781,038	8,465,111,523	999,888,555
543,651	75,532,698	567,432,231

Besides exhibiting the fundamental principles of mechanical adding machines, the meterstick slide rule provides the proper orientation for the understanding of the conventional slide rule to be presented in Lesson 16.

N*ote 3 ⚭ Certain unicursal problems*
   that are solved by counting.

A *unicursal* problem requires the drawing of one continuous line, without gaps or retracings, to meet certain prescribed conditions.

The Königsberg problem is perhaps the most famous problem of this kind. The city of Königsberg occupies both sides of the river Pregel, an island in the river, and the area between two branches of the river. Seven bridges connect the four regions of the city, marked *A*, *B*, *C*, and *D* (Figure 2.4). The problem is to show how to cross each of the seven bridges only once in journeying about the city. One may begin his journey in any one of the four sections of the city. By examining various sketches of arbitrary regions having one, two, three, or

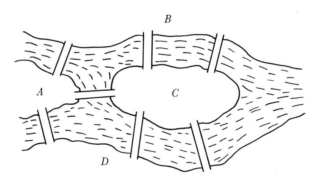

FIGURE 2.4

four, etc., entrances and exits, such as bridges, one may convince himself of the following two situations:

To use only once each an *even* number of entrances and exits, the traveler must *begin and end* his journey in that special region, or he must *begin and end* his journey outside that special region.

To use only once each an *odd* number of entrances and exits, the traveler must *begin* his journey *in that special* region and then must *end* his journey *outside that special region*, or, vice versa, he must *begin* his journey *outside* that special region and *end* his journey *inside* that special region. Concisely stated, one end of his journey must be inside an area that has an *odd* number of exits and entrances.

Now the traveler in the Königsberg problem has an *odd* number of bridges as exits or entrances of each of the *four* regions *A*, *B*, *C*, and *D*. Therefore, one end of his journey about the city must be in each of these four regions. But his journey has only *two* ends, the start and the finish. As these two ends cannot be in *four* different regions, the Königsberg problem is clearly unsolvable.

Another well-tried problem is to draw a continuous line through each of the

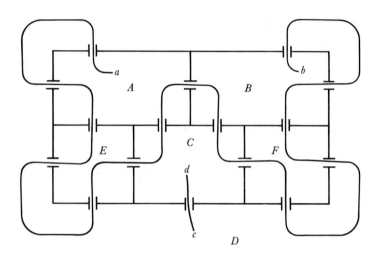

FIGURE 2.5

sixteen openings or "doors" in Figure 2.5. As each of the regions marked *A, B, C, D* has an *odd* number of entrances and exits this problem also cannot be solved. As one end of the line must lie in *four* regions, and as a single line has only *two* ends, two lines are required to use all 16 entrances. The ends of the two lines are marked as *a, b, c,* and *d* respectively.

It is interesting to observe that the problem exhibited in Figure 2.5 becomes solvable if the diagram is drawn upon the torus; i.e., a surface like an inflated innertube, as displayed in Figure 2.6. Here the regions *C* and *D* become a *single* region having 12 exits and entrances. The line in Figure 2.5 that separates regions *C* and *D* ceases to be an effective barrier in Figure 2.6, as a path may lead from *C* to *D* by passing through the opening of the torus.

Incidentally, all unicursal problems like those presented in Figures 2.4 and 2.5, whether solvable or not by one continuous path, always contain an *even* number of *odd* regions. (An *odd* region has an odd number of entrances and exits, such as regions *A, B, C,* and *D*, in Figures 2.4 and 2.5; regions *E* and *F* are *even* regions, as they contain an *even* number of entrances and exits.) Accordingly, such unicursal problems can be solved if they contain only two odd regions, since the beginning and end of the path must lie in odd regions. Moreover, if the figure contains $2k$ odd regions, then k separate paths must be drawn in order to use all exits and entrances of the entire figure.

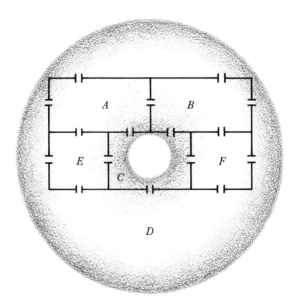

FIGURE 2.6

One should test the accuracy of the foregoing discussion by investigating the solvability of the following unicursal problems:

1. A square (two even regions, no odd regions)

2. A square and its two diagonals (one even region, four odd regions)

3. A square surmounted by a triangle

4. A square with its two diagonals, surmounted by a triangle

5. A circle and three chords that divide the interior of the circle into seven regions (arcs of the circle are here regarded as boundaries of seven of the eight regions)

6. The five lines that join the five pairs of five noncollinear points (six odd regions, one even region)

Another favorite type of unicursal problem is to draw a prescribed figure without raising the pencil or repeating, or crossing, a line portion already drawn. Here an end of the drawn line, or a place where an odd number of lines meet, is called an *odd point*. Such figures must have an even number of such odd points. One may demonstrate that this kind of unicursal problem is solvable if there are only two odd points; furthermore, k separate lines are required to draw completely a prescribed figure having $2k$ odd points. One may now show that the figures indicated in 1, 3, 4, and 6 are solvable, while 2 and 5 are insolvable. One may also solve both types of the unicursal problem consisting of two or more concentric circles and a line cutting all circles and passing through their common center. The semicircular arcs represent a single portion of boundary of each of the areas for unicursal problems of the earlier type.

◌◦ SUPPLEMENTARY PROBLEMS ◦◌

. . . *"And yet so sensible were the Romans of the imperfection of valor without skill and practice, that, in their language, the name of an army was borrowed from the word which signified exercise. Military exercises were the important and unremitted object of their discipline. The recruits and young soldiers were constantly trained both in the morning and in the evening, nor was age or knowledge allowed to excuse the veterans from the daily repetition of what they had completely learned. . . ."*

—Edward Gibbon, *Decline and Fall of the Roman Empire*, *I*, 10.

S2.1. Express the following numbers in digit symbols:
- *a.* Seventy-nine
- *b.* Three hundred fifty
- *c.* Nine hundred twenty-five
- *d.* Sixty-two thousand, two hundred seventy-one
- *e.* Two hundred five thousand, ninety-five
- *f.* Seventy-eight million, six hundred nineteen
- *g.* Nineteen billion, two hundred seventy-six thousand
- *h.* Thirty-nine billion, two hundred forty-three million, four hundred
- *i.* Fifteen trillion, sixteen million, seventeen thousand, eighteen
- *j.* Six quadrillion, three hundred twenty-one million, four hundred eight

S2.2. Express the following numbers in words:

a.	8	*h.*	466577911	*o.*	5764338900776431
b.	37	*i.*	6668888331	*p.*	10910819089767523
c.	492	*j.*	97531024680	*q.*	678954327689000913
d.	8641	*k.*	411399288366	*r.*	9787526870011102319
e.	74820	*l.*	1300450067005	*s.*	7563429870055466789 1
f.	465768	*m.*	86675364489041	*t.*	60283948576599888876 2
g.	7060385	*n.*	446009704115008	*u.*	300004000050000700009 9

S2.3. Add the following sets of natural numbers:
  a. Twenty-five, eighty-nine, thirty-one, and seven
  b. Forty-one, ninety-nine, thirty-five, forty-eight, and seventeen
  c. Fifty-three, fifty-one, forty-nine, forty-seven, and forty-five
  d. Eleven, twenty-three, thirty-five, eighty-seven, and twelve

S2.4. By appropriate successive additions extend the following lists of natural numbers until the indicated final number is reached.   Such lists are called *arithmetical progressions*.

  a. 6, 8, 10, 12, . . . , 30   *e.* 5, 11, 17, 23, . . . , 95
  b. 8, 11, 14, 17, . . . , 71   *f.* 7, 15, 23, 31, . . . , 87
  c. 7, 11, 15, 19, . . . , 87   *g.* 6, 13, 20, 27, . . . , 90
  d. 8, 13, 18, 23, . . . , 73

S2.5. Obtain the sum of the first numbers in each of the lists in Problem S2.4.

S2.6. Obtain the sum of the third numbers in each of the lists in Problem S2.4.

S2.7. Obtain the sum of the last numbers in the arithmetical progressions in Problem S2.4.

S2.8. Obtain the sum of all even natural numbers that occur in the seven arithmetical progressions of Problem S2.4.

S2.9. Which of the seven arithmetical progressions listed in Problem S2.4 consist of (*a*) even numbers only?   (*b*) odd numbers only?

S2.10. Obtain the sum of all even natural numbers that lie between 21 and 33.

S2.11. Obtain the sum of all odd natural numbers between 18 and 26.

S2.12. Obtain the sum of all two-digit natural numbers if the digits are 0, 1, or 2.

S2.13. Obtain the sums of the indicated sets of single-digit natural numbers:

a.	*b.*	*c.*	*d.*	*e.*	*f.*
6	4	5	7	1	5
2	7	8	9	8	7
7	6	5	4	3	2
9	8	7	6	5	4
8	2	3	4	5	6
1	1	2	3	4	5

S2.14. Obtain the sums of the following sets of two-digit natural numbers:

a.	*b.*	*c.*	*d.*	*e.*	*f.*
36	71	13	35	31	72
41	54	27	67	14	28
76	99	47	82	55	83
65	48	89	19	52	71

S2.15. Obtain the sums of the following sets of three-digit natural numbers:

a.	*b.*	*c.*	*d.*	*e.*
214	251	678	731	137
342	453	564	675	786
612	714	816	918	110
359	460	571	682	793
135	791	264	468	961

S2.16. Obtain the sums of the following sets of four-digit natural numbers:

	a.	*b.*	*c.*	*d.*	*e.*
	3,701	8,519	1,234	5,309	1,414
	6,299	2,863	5,678	1,767	3,590
	4,557	4,863	7,904	2,554	6,564
	6,108	5,991	6,981	4,447	8,552
	7,995	9,740	8,808	7,326	9,882

S2.17. Obtain the sums of the following sets of five-digit natural numbers:

	a.	*b.*	*c.*	*d.*	*e.*
	47,972	58,231	50,119	24,375	54,321
	84,437	82,997	43,589	11,392	66,907
	13,579	24,680	97,421	86,431	31,416
	27,181	51,246	65,537	45,001	64,729
	16,256	25,625	36,215	49,343	99,268

S2.18. Compute the sum of the six sums obtained in Problem S2.13.

S2.19. Compute the sum of the six sums obtained in Problem S2.14.

S2.20. Compute the sum of the five sums obtained in Problem S2.15.

S2.21. Compute the sum of the five sums obtained in Problem S2.16.

S2.22. Compute the sum of the five sums obtained in Problem S2.17.

S2.23. Add horizontally and vertically, placing the sums to the right and under the appropriate rows and columns of numbers. Then add these two sets of sums; these two final sums must be the same natural number.

a.
$$4 + 7 + 8 + 3 + 2 + 1 =$$
$$3 + 5 + 7 + 9 + 2 + 4 =$$
$$5 + 8 + 3 + 4 + 5 + 6 =$$
$$9 + 7 + 8 + 6 + 7 + 9 =$$
$$8 + 6 + 4 + 9 + 2 + 1 =$$
$$9 + 7 + 5 + 6 + 9 + 6 =$$
$$+ \quad + \quad + \quad + \quad + \quad =$$

b.
$$35 + 47 + 82 + 97 + 12 + 83 =$$
$$84 + 36 + 48 + 83 + 98 + 13 =$$
$$23 + 85 + 37 + 49 + 84 + 99 =$$
$$14 + 24 + 86 + 38 + 50 + 85 =$$
$$71 + 25 + 15 + 87 + 39 + 88 =$$
$$91 + 72 + 26 + 16 + 88 + 40 =$$
$$+ \quad + \quad + \quad + \quad + \quad =$$

c.
$$4,562 + 6,901 + 4,326 + 8,223 =$$
$$3,987 + 5,673 + 7,002 + 5,437 =$$
$$9,334 + 4,098 + 6,784 + 8,132 =$$
$$9,243 + 5,445 + 5,199 + 7,895 =$$
$$8,740 + 7,883 + 6,647 + 7,097 =$$
$$3,114 + 3,225 + 4,552 + 6,303 =$$
$$+ \quad + \quad + \quad =$$

S2.24. Obtain the sums of the following sets of natural numbers:

    a.   3, 5, 12, 37, 429, 409, 4,239, and 56,792

    b.   34, 46, 407, 512, 729, 4,872, and 4,921

    c.   357, 472, 599, 45,900, 47,125, and 312

    d.   43,107, 16, 2,300, 129, 5,280, and 101,337

    e.   34, 43,221, 15, 23, 8, 17, and 65,537

S2.25. Continue the following series of natural numbers making each ensuing number the sum of the two preceding numbers, until 20 of these so-called *Fibonacci numbers* are obtained:

    1, 1, 2, 3, 5, 8, 13, 21, 34, . . .

S2.26. Obtain the list of Fibonacci numbers as far as the fortieth Fibonacci number.

S2.27. Obtain the following sums of Fibonacci numbers, beginning with the first Fibonacci number, 1, until you recognize how the sum may be obtained without the operation of addition:

    $1 + 1 = ?$

    $1 + 1 + 2 = ?$

    $1 + 1 + 2 + 3 = ?$

    $1 + 1 + 2 + 3 + 5 = ?$

    . . . .

S2.28. Obtain the sums of alternate Fibonacci numbers, beginning with the first 1, until you recognize how the sum may be obtained immediately without the operation of addition:

    $1 + 2 = ?$

    $1 + 2 + 5 = ?$

    $1 + 2 + 5 + 13 = ?$

    $1 + 2 + 5 + 13 + 34 = ?$

    . . . .

S2.29. Obtain the sums of alternate Fibonacci numbers, beginning with the second 1, until you recognize how the sum may be obtained immediately without the operation of addition:

    $1 + 3 = ?$

    $1 + 3 + 8 = ?$

    $1 + 3 + 8 + 21 = ?$

    $1 + 3 + 8 + 21 + 55 = ?$

S2.30. Obtain with very little computation the sum of the 20 numbers required in Problem S2.25.

S2.31. Obtain very easily the sum of the 40 numbers required in Problem S2.26.

S2.32. Louise has 12 books, Thelma has 5 more than Louise, Edna has 7 more than Louise and Thelma have together. Helen has 6 more than Thelma. How many books have the four girls altogether?

S2.33. Chester read 16 library books during the school year while Beecher read 7 more than Chester. Roy read 2 more than Chester and Beecher together. How many books did all three lads read during the school year?

S2.34. Compute the total number of (*a*) electoral votes and (*b*) popular votes that were recorded for the three presidential candidates in the United States in

1960, if these items were tabulated as follows:

CANDIDATE	ELECTORAL VOTES	POPULAR VOTES
John F. Kennedy	303	34,221,349
Richard M. Nixon	219	34,108,647
Harry F. Byrd	15	440,298

S2.35. In a certain class of college arithmetic, 17 students received grade A, 23 received grade B, and the remainder, 9, received grade C. Students whose accumulating scores fell below grade C during the semester were required to withdraw from the class. How many students finished the course?

S2.36. In three lists of problems in a certain text, containing respectively 25, 40, and 40 problems, Elmer correctly solved 11 on Monday, 17 on Tuesday, 21 on Wednesday, 25 on Thursday, and 31 on Friday. (*a*) How many problems did Elmer solve during that week? (*b*) How many problems were in the three lists altogether?

S2.37. A certain lobbyist had to make three special trips from Washington D.C. to the following cities, and return to Washington D.C. How many miles did he fly in making these three round trips, if the distances from Washington are listed as follows:

New York, 203 miles   Honolulu, 4,839 miles   Chicago, 598 miles

S2.38. A world traveler flies around the world in the following stages:
a. From New York to London, England   3,472 miles
b. From London to Tokyo, Japan   5,955 miles
c. From Tokyo to Honolulu, Hawaii   3,860 miles
d. From Honolulu to New York   4,969 miles
Compute the total distance this traveler flew in the trip around the world.

S2.39. The student enrollment of the four national academies in 1966–67 was listed as follows:

U.S. Military Academy, West Point, N.Y.	3,302
U.S. Naval Academy, Annapolis, Md.	4,000
U.S. Air Academy, Colorado Springs, Colo.	3,150
U.S. Coast Guard Academy, New London, Conn.	760

Compute the total enrollment.

S2.40. From the following data compute the total population of Europe and Asia in 1965 and as forecast for the year 2000:

	1965	2000
Europe (excluding U.S.S.R.)	440,000,000	526,000,000
Asia (excluding U.S.S.R.)	1,828,000,000	3,458,000,000
U.S.S.R.	231,000,000	353,000,000

S2.41. The area of Maine is 33,040 square miles, of New Hampshire 9,305 square miles, of Vermont 9,565 square miles, of Massachusetts 8,315 square miles, of Rhode Island 1,250 square miles, and of Connecticut 4,990. Calculate the total area of New England.

S2.42. A contractor paid $6,000 for a lot, $300 for grading, $13,250 for building materials, $1,200 for stonework, $2,500 for brickwork, $1,400 for carpenterwork, and $1,500 for painting. What was the entire cost of his investment?

S2.43. A house has two parlors each requiring 32 square yards of carpeting, four bedrooms each requiring 21 square yards, a dining room requiring 24 square yards, a reception room requiring 27 square yards, and a study requiring 18 square yards. How many square yards of carpeting are required altogether?

S2.44. Each of five natural numbers is equal to the sum of the three preceding numbers. Calculate their sum, if the first three numbers are 34,699, 67,109, and 12,347.

S2.45. Dick asked his little brother Larry to write three natural numbers in a column. Dick wrote two more numbers in the column, then immediately wrote the exact sum of all five numbers. After three such attempts Larry discovered Dick's trick. Check the additions and discover, if you can, Dick's trick:

46,902	42,673	86,741
57,411	43,715	72,407
97,832	22,334	75,623
53,098	57,327	27,593
42,589	77,666	24,377
297,832	243,715	286,741

S2.46. The first four *odd* numbered months and the last three *even* numbered months of each year have 31 days each. All other months, except February, have 30 days each. In an ordinary year February has 28 days, but in a leap year February has 29 days. Calculate the number of days in (*a*) an ordinary year, (*b*) a leap year.

S2.47. The precise instant of time when one season ends and the next one begins occurs when the center of the sun appears to be farthest north, farthest south, or to cross the celestial equator from south to north or from north to south. The exact time of these occurrences, day and hour, depends upon the local time of the observer. Assuming that the seasons began at midnight on the indicated dates (12 P.M.), at a particular location, calculate the lengths of the four seasons there in an ordinary year and in a leap year.

Spring	March 21	Autumn	September 23
Summer	June 22	Winter	December 22

Note. To simplify the foregoing Problem S2.47, the seasons were assumed to begin at midnight. However, in the year 1967, using Eastern Standard Time, the seasons began as follows, to the nearest minute of time:

Spring	March 21, 12:37 P.M.	Autumn	September 23, 10:38 P.M.
Summer	June 22, 7:23 A.M.	Winter	December 22, 6:17 P.M.

The more precise length of a tropical year (year of one cycle of the four seasons) is very slightly more than 365 days, 5 hours, 48 minutes, and 46 seconds, or slightly less than $365\frac{1}{4}$ days. The leap year of 366 days every fourth year makes the yearly average too long by nearly 11 minutes and 14 seconds. This inaccuracy in the length of year accumulates to approximately 75 hours, or slightly more than 3 days, in 400 years. In 1582 the Gregorian calendar was introduced, on the authority of Pope Gregory XIII, and has since been adopted in Western Europe and America. This calendar discards three days in 400 years by making the century years 1700, 1800, 1900, 2000, . . . , ordinary years instead of leap years, unless these numbers are divisible by 400. Accordingly, 1900 was not a leap year, although 1896 and 1904 were leap years. Even with this correction an error still persists in the Gregorian calendar which will amount to one day in nearly 3,000 years. Quite likely the calendar will be modified to diminish even this small error during the ensuing 3,000 years.

LESSON 3 ❧ MULTIPLICATION AND INVOLUTION OF THE NATURAL NUMBERS

As I was going to Saint Ives,
I met a man with seven wives.
Every wife had seven sacks,
Every sack had seven cats,
Every cat had seven kits.
Kits, cats, sacks, and wives,
How many were there going to Saint Ives?

—Nursery rhyme

3·1 ∾ Multiplication of two natural numbers

Definitions. If the letters a and b represent two different natural numbers, or the same natural number, then the *product* of a and b, expressed symbolically as $a \times b$, is the natural number that is obtained by adding the natural number a, as an addend, b times. The natural number a, which is repeatedly used as an addend, is called the *multiplicand*. The number b, which indicates the number of times a is used as an addend, is called the *multiplier*. The natural number so obtained as the result of the operation is called the *product*. The natural numbers a and b are also referred to as *factors*, or "makers" of the product.

For example, 7×3, which may be read as "seven multiplied by three," or "seven times three," means $7 + 7 + 7$ or 21, whence $7 \times 3 = 21$. Now 3×7, when read as "three multiplied by 7," means $3 + 3 + 3 + 3 + 3 + 3 + 3$, which also equals 21. Thus, $3 \times 7 = 7 \times 3$, indicating that in this example the roles of multiplicand and multiplier may be interchanged without affecting the product. If a and b represent any natural numbers whatever, then $a \times b$ and $b \times a$ yield the same product, as is proved in the next section.

3·2 ∾ Commutative law of multiplication of two natural numbers

The important arithmetical fact that $a \times b = b \times a$, if a and b represent any arbitrary natural numbers, is called the *commutative law of multiplication of natural numbers*. Its validity is established as follows.

1 2 3 4 5 · · · a Let a and b represent any two natural numbers.
1 2 3 4 5 · · · a Now set forth b successive rows of the natural
1 2 3 4 5 · · · a numbers from 1 to a, inclusive. The dots indicate
· · · · · · · · · · · · · symbolically the numbers and rows of numbers
1 2 3 4 5 · · · a that would be written to exhibit the complete

array of numbers. There are b distinct lines, each line containing a natural numbers from 1 to a, inclusive. The total *number* of natural numbers in this complete array, namely, the a natural numbers from 1 to a taken b times, represents the result of the operation $a \times b$, interpreted as "a multiplied by b" or "b times a."

Next, let this entire array of numbers be turned clockwise through an angle of 90°; this movement of the array would not introduce any more natural numbers, nor lose any of the numbers from the original array. The entire array now must appear as shown. The array now exhibits a distinct lines of natural numbers, each line having b repetitions of the same natural number in it, namely, b 1s in the top line, b 2s in the second line, b 3s in the third line, etc. The total *number* of natural numbers in this array, namely, the b repeated natural numbers in each of the a rows, represents the result of the operation $b \times a$, interpreted as "b multiplied by a," or "a times b." Since the actual number of natural numbers appearing in each of these two arrays is the same, it must be true that $a \times b = b \times a$.

```
1  1  1  1  1  · · ·  1
2  2  2  2  2  · · ·  2
3  3  3  3  3  · · ·  3
4  4  4  4  4  · · ·  4
5  5  5  5  5  · · ·  5
·  ·  ·  ·  ·  ·  ·  ·  ·  ·  ·  ·
a  a  a  a  a  · · ·  a
```

3·3 ∞ MULTIPLICATION OF THREE NATURAL NUMBERS.
ASSOCIATIVE LAW OF MULTIPLICATION OF NATURAL NUMBERS

To obtain the product of three natural numbers, such as $7 \times 5 \times 3$, one may multiply the product of 7 and 5 by 3, which is indicated symbolically as $(7 \times 5) \times 3$. Thus $7 \times 5 = 35$, then $35 \times 3 = 105$. Or, one may multiply 7 by the product of 5 and 3, which is indicated symbolically as $7 \times (5 \times 3)$. Thus $5 \times 3 = 15$, then $7 \times 15 = 105$. The fact that both procedures yield the same product of the three natural numbers is called the *commutative law of multiplication of natural numbers*. The validity of this law for *any three natural numbers whatever*, a, b, and c, may be established as follows.

The product $a \times b \times c$ may be exhibited by the *number* of cubical blocks that are stacked into a rectangular pile having a blocks in its length, b blocks in its width, and c blocks in its height, wherein a, b, and c represent any three natural numbers whatever. In Figure 3.1 the top layer of blocks consists of b rows of blocks with a blocks in each row; therefore, the top layer contains exactly $a \times b$ blocks. Every layer contains the same number of blocks as this top layer, as the sets of blocks in two contiguous layers of blocks may be paired off in a one-to-one correspondence, for each block of the upper layer may be matched with the block in the lower layer that supports it, and each block of the lower layer is matched with the block of the upper layer that rests upon it.

Since each layer contains also $a \times b$ blocks, and there are c such layers in the entire pile of blocks, the pile must consist of $(a \times b) \times c$ blocks.

One can also regard the rectangular pile of blocks as consisting of vertical slices, as slices of a loaf of bread. The first slice at one end of the rectangular pile of blocks consists of c rows of blocks, one above another, each row containing exactly b blocks. This first slice must then contain $b \times c$ blocks. Each slice must contain the same number of blocks as this first slice, as the sets of blocks in

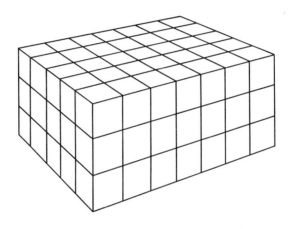

FIGURE 3.1

two contiguous slices may be paired off in a one-to-one correspondence, for each block in one slice may be matched with the other slice that adjoins it. Since each slice also contains $b \times c$ blocks, and there are a slices in the entire pile of blocks, the pile must contain $a \times (b \times c)$ blocks.

As the rectangular pile contains the same number of blocks, regardless of how they may be counted, the two products must be equal, $(a \times b) \times c = a \times (b \times c)$, thus establishing the validity of the associative law of multiplication of natural numbers.

The equality of the product of the three natural numbers a, b, and c, in all six possible orders of multiplication, namely,

$$a \times b \times c \qquad b \times a \times c \qquad c \times a \times b$$
$$a \times c \times b \qquad b \times c \times a \qquad c \times b \times a$$

may be established by using the commutative and associative laws of multiplication, as follows:

$$a \times b \times c = a \times (b \times c) = a \times (c \times b) = a \times c \times b$$
$$a \times b \times c = (a \times b) \times c = (b \times a) \times c = b \times a \times c$$
$$a \times b \times c = a \times (b \times c) = (b \times c) \times a = b \times c \times a$$
$$a \times b \times c = (a \times b) \times c = c \times (a \times b) = c \times a \times b$$
$$a \times b \times c = a \times (b \times c) = (b \times c) \times a = (c \times b) \times a = c \times b \times a$$

3·4 ∾ THE DISTRIBUTIVE LAW OF MULTIPLICATION AND ADDITION OF NATURAL NUMBERS: $a \times (b + c) = a \times b + a \times c$

The distributive law of multiplication and addition is quite useful in simplifying the operation of multiplication of large natural numbers. The validity of this law is established as follows.

Let a, b, and c represent any three natural numbers whatever. Now consider two rectangular arrays of dots, the first array containing b dots in each row, the second array containing c dots in each row, and both arrays containing a rows of dots. Thus:

b DOTS IN LENGTH c DOTS IN LENGTH

a DOTS IN WIDTH

The total number of dots in the two arrays is equal to the sum of the number of dots in each array, namely, $a \times b + a \times c$.

Now let these two rectangular arrays of dots be moved together to form a single larger rectangular array. The length of this new array will contain $b + c$ dots, the width of the array will remain the same as the width of the two original arrays, containing c rows of dots.

$b + c$ DOTS IN LENGTH

a DOTS IN WIDTH

As no new dots were introduced by the shift of the two original arrays of dots, the number of dots in this latter array, $a \times (b \times c)$, must be equal to the number of dots in the two original arrays, namely, $a \times b + a \times c$. Therefore, the distributive law $a \times (b + c) = a \times b + a \times c$ must be valid for all possible natural numbers.

3·5 ∾ Multiplications involving more than three natural numbers

Definitions. The product of *four* natural numbers, such as $4 \times 2 \times 7 \times 3$, is equal to the product of the product of the first three of the natural numbers (by Section 3.3) and the fourth natural number. Thus, $4 \times 2 \times 7 \times 3 = (4 \times 2 \times 7) \times 3 = 56 \times 3 = 168$.

The product of *five* natural numbers, such as $4 \times 2 \times 7 \times 3 \times 6$, is equal to the product of the product of the first four of the natural numbers (by the previous definition) and the fifth natural number. Thus, $4 \times 2 \times 7 \times 3 \times 6 = (4 \times 2 \times 7 \times 3) \times 6 = 168 \times 6 = 1,008$.

Quite generally, the product of *any number of arbitrary natural numbers*, represented symbolically as $a \times b \times c \times d \times \cdots \times p \times q$, is equal to the product of the product of all but the last of these natural numbers, namely, $a \times b \times c \times d \times \cdots \times p$ and the last one of these natural numbers, q.

By repeated use of the commutative and associative laws of multiplication of natural numbers, it can be proved that the product of any specified set of natural numbers is the same natural number for all possible arrangements of the given natural numbers and for all possible associations of two or more of the given natural numbers. Examples are: $4 \times 2 \times 7 \times 3 = (7 \times 4) \times (2 \times 3) = 28 \times 6 = 168$; $4 \times 2 \times 7 \times 3 = (4 \times 3 \times 2) \times 7 = 24 \times 7 = 168$.

The distributive law of multiplication and addition of natural numbers, $a \times (b + c) = a \times b + a \times c$, may be extended to involve *any arbitrary number of natural numbers*, such as

$$a \times (b + c + d + e + f) = a \times b + a \times c + a \times d + a \times e + a \times f$$

The validity of the more comprehensive form of the distributive law may be established by the same kind of reasoning as that used in Section 3.4. One merely provides the appropriate original arrays of dots whose individual lengths correspond to the natural numbers within the pair of parentheses and whose common width corresponds to the natural number preceding the parentheses. The number of dots in the individual rectangular arrays are respectively the corresponding products of the pairs of natural numbers, $a \times b$, $a \times c$, $a \times d$, $a \times e$, and $a \times f$. When these individual rectangular arrays of dots are moved together to form one larger rectangular array, its length must be equal to the sum of the lengths of the individual original arrays, its width must be the same as the common width of the original arrays. Its total number of dots, therefore, must be equal to $a \times (b + c + d + e + f)$. As the number of dots remains unchanged, one must be assured that

$$a \times (b + c + d + e + f) = a \times b + a \times c + a \times d + a \times e + a \times f$$

3·6 ∾ THE USE OF ZERO AS A FACTOR IN MULTIPLICATION

Multiplications that involve the special number zero are established, or agreed upon, by three postulates:

$a \times 0 = 0 \times a = 0$, if a represents *any* natural number
$0 \times 0 = 0$
$0 \times 0 \times 0 \times 0 \cdots 0 = 0$, for any specific number of 0s used as factors

3·7 ∾ MULTIPLES OF A NATURAL NUMBER

Definition. The *multiples* of a given natural number are the products of the natural number by 1, by 2, by 3, by 4, ... To facilitate the operation of multiplication of large natural numbers *one must memorize* the first nine multiples of the single-digit natural numbers as listed in the following table. One observes that the numbers in any horizontal row are the successive multiples of the number at the left end of that particular row, and that the numbers in any vertical column are the successive multiples of the number at the top of that column, and, finally, that each number in the array is the product of the two numbers at the left end of its row and at the top of its column.

1	2	3	4	5	6	7	8	9
2	4	6	8	10	12	14	16	18
3	6	9	12	15	18	21	24	27
4	8	12	16	20	24	28	32	36
5	10	15	20	25	30	35	40	45
6	12	18	24	30	36	42	48	54
7	14	21	28	35	42	49	56	63
8	16	24	32	40	48	56	64	72
9	18	27	36	45	54	63	72	81

The ensuing seven observations should make easy the memorization of this "multiplication table."

1. For the multiples of 2, one has the even natural numbers; i.e., the unit digits are two cycles of the even digits, 2, 4, 6, 8, 0, 2, 4, 6, 8 in their natural order.

2. For the multiples of 8 the unit digits are two cycles of the even digits in *reverse* order, 8, 6, 4, 2, 0, 8, 6, 4, 2.

3. For the multiples of 3 and of 7, the unit digits pass through cycles of all nine digits, not in natural order, but in cycles opposite to each other, 3, 6, 9, 2, 5, 8, 1, 4, 7 and 7, 4, 1, 8, 5, 2, 9, 6, 3, respectively.

4. For the multiples of 4 and of 6, the unit digits pass through two cycles of even digits, not in correct order, but in opposing orders, 4, 8, 2, 6, 0, 4, 8, 2, 6 and 6, 2, 8, 4, 0, 6, 2, 8, 4, respectively.

5. For multiples of 5, the unit digits alternate between 5 and 0.

6. For the multiples of 9, the unit digits are the single-digit natural numbers in reverse order; the sum of the two digits in each multiple is *nine*.

7. The unit digits of the multiples of 1, 3, 7, and 9 pass through entire cycles of *all of the nine digits*. This important feature will be exploited in certain long divisions to be presented in Lesson 5.

Incidentally, the commutative law limits the set of necessary memorizations to only 55 products, from $0 \times 0 = 0$ to $9 \times 9 = 81$.

3·8 ∾ SHORT MULTIPLICATION—MULTIPLICATION OF A NATURAL NUMBER BY A SINGLE-DIGIT NATURAL NUMBER

The multiplication of a natural number of more than a single digit by a single-digit natural number is accomplished by the aid of the *distributive law of multiplication and addition:*

$$a(b + c + d + \cdots) = a \cdot b + a \cdot c + a \cdot d + \cdots$$

A single example, such as $53,176 \times 7$, will clarify the procedure.

$$7 \times 53,176 = 7(5 \times 10,000 + 3 \times 1,000 + 100 + 7 \times 10 + 6)$$
$$= 7 \times 5 \times 10,000 + 7 \times 3 \times 1,000 + 7 \times 100 + 7 \times 7 \times 10 + 7 \times 6$$
$$= 350,000 + 21,000 + 700 + 490 + 42 = 372,232$$

Note on symbolism. The dot, written slightly higher than the period, is frequently used instead of the $\times$ to denote multiplication. Moreover, the *absence* of an operational symbol between literal or parenthetical quantities implies *multiplication*. Thus, ab means $a \times b$; $a(b + c)$ means $a \times (b + c)$.

These several stages in the development of the product may be tabulated conveniently:

```
53176
    7
```
42	The product of 7 × 6
490	The product of 7 × 70
700	The product of 7 × 100
21000	The product of 7 × 3,000
350000	The product of 7 × 50,000
372232	The complete product is the sum of five partial products.

The written work may be somewhat shortened by omitting the 0, 00, 000, and 0000 from the successive partial products, by writing only the single digit that occurs before 0s in the partial products, by writing the other digit of the partial product above the next digit to be used in the multiplicand, and proceeding as explained below in detail:

```
2154
53176
    7
```
2	7 × 6 = 42, place the 4 above 7 in multiplicand
3-	7 × 7 + 4 = 53, place the 5 above 1 in multiplicand
2--	7 × 1 + 5 = 12, place the 1 above 3 in multiplicand
2---	7 × 3 + 1 = 22, place the 2 above 5 in multiplicand
37----	7 × 5 + 2 = 37, place entire 37 in partial product
372232	The required product

It is to be noted that the digits appearing in the partial products are in their correct positions of the complete product; accordingly, these digits may be written immediately in the required complete product, while the appropriate multiplications and involvement of carryovers may all be performed *mentally*.

```
53,176
     7
372,232
```
or 7 × 53,176 = 372,232, in which all necessary intermediate calculations are performed mentally

3·9 ⚬ Long multiplication—multiplication of a natural number by a natural number consisting of more than a single digit

A single example of long multiplication, such as 53,176 × 8,432, will clarify the procedure. Here the distributive law of multiplication and addition performs the multiplication of 53,176 by the individual parts of 8,432:

$$53,176(8 \times 1,000 + 4 \times 100 + 3 \times 10 + 2)$$

or, more particularly,

$$53,176(2 + 3 \times 10 + 4 \times 100 + 8 \times 1,000)$$

or

53176	
8432	
106352	53,176 × 2, obtained by short multiplication
1595280	53,176 × 3 × 10 or 3 × 53,176 × 10
21270400	53,176 × 4 × 100 or 4 × 53,176 × 100
425408000	53,176 × 8 × 1,000 or 8 × 53,176 × 1,000
448380032	The complete product is the sum of the partial products.

The 0s may again be omitted from the partial products; the right end digit of each partial product is placed directly under the digit of the multiplier that produces that particular partial product. The various steps of long multiplication must be performed very carefully to avoid an error which will yield an incorrect product. The product may be tested for correctness by interchanging the roles of multiplicand and multiplier, then performing the long multiplication again. The two products must be alike, although the intermediate partial products may be quite different. Very simple tests for correctness of the product will be provided in Lesson 12. The two appropriate multiplications appear as follows:

53176	8432
8432	53176
106352	50592
159528	59024
212704	8432
425408	25296
448380032	42160
	448380032

3·10 ∽ Recapitulation of the five laws of addition and multiplication

If a, b, and c represent 0 or any natural numbers whatever (1, 2, 3, 4, . . .), the definitions of the operations of addition and multiplication provide proof of the correctness of the following five laws.

For the addition of natural numbers:

The commutative law, $a + b = b + a$
The associative law, $(a + b) + c = a + (b + c)$

For the multiplication of natural numbers:

> *The commutative law, $a \cdot b = b \cdot a$*
> *The associative law, $(a \cdot b)c = a(b \cdot c)$*

For the combined multiplication and addition of natural numbers:

> *The distributive law, $a(b + c) = a \cdot b + a \cdot c$*

It must be noted that the operations of addition and multiplication are not associative, as a single example will demonstrate. To evaluate $2 + 3 \times 7$, regarded as $(2 + 3) \times 7 = 5 \times 7 = 35$, but also regarded as $2 + (3 \times 7) = 2 + 21 = 23$. Hence to evaluate $2 + 3 \times 7$, one must prescribe the required procedure. To avoid ambiguity in such situations, the required procedure is established in the next section.

3·11 ∿ Priority of multiplications over additions

If several operations of additions and multiplications are to be performed in an indicated line of such operations, the *multiplications must be performed first*, before any of the additions, and *then* all additions must be performed upon the resulting products and the other numbers in the line. For example, to evaluate the indicated expression involving additions and multiplications of $3 + 5 \times 5 + 4 + 2 \times 6 \times 7 + 9 + 8$, one must first replace the indicated multiplications, 5×5 and $2 \times 6 \times 7$, by their products, 25 and 84 respectively, in the line of numbers, obtaining $3 + 25 + 4 + 84 + 9 + 8$, which yields the sum 133 as the required final result.

Any departure from this prescribed priority of multiplications must be indicated by *aggregation symbols*, such as pairs of parentheses. The operations occurring within the aggregation symbols must be performed in accordance with the rule of priority of multiplications, as indicated above.

The introduction of parentheses into the foregoing line of operations upon natural numbers alters the problem markedly, as the two alterations demonstrate:

$(3 + 5) \times 5 + 4 + (2 \times 6) \times (7 + 9) + 8 = ?$
$8 \times 5 + 4 + 12 \times 16 + 8 = 40 + 4 + 192 + 8 = 244$

$(3 + 5) \times 5 + (4 + 2 \times 6) \times 7 + 9 + 8 = ?$
$8 \times 5 + (4 + 12) \times 7 + 9 + 8 = 40 + 16 \times 7 + 9 + 8 = 40 + 112 + 9 + 8 = 169$

3·12 ∿ Involution of the natural numbers

Definitions. The operation of obtaining the product of two or more equal numbers is called *involution*. For example, the product of three 7s, or $7 \times 7 \times 7 = 343$, which is represented symbolically as $7^3 = 343$, is called the *third power of seven.* The number that is repeatedly multiplied, as the 7 in this example, is called the *base* of the involution. The number of times the base is used as a factor is called the *exponent,* as the 3 in this example. Quite generally, if *a* and *k* represent any natural numbers whatever, then a^k means $a \cdot a \cdot a \, \cdots$, until the *a* has been used *k* times as a factor. Here *a* is the base, *k* is the exponent, and the result of the operation is called the *k*th *power of the base a.* If the exponent is 2, the result is called the *square* of the base; if the exponent is 3, the result is called the *cube* of the base. Thus 144 is called the square of 12, because $12^2 = 12 \times 12 = 144$; 64 is called the cube of 4, because $4^3 = 4 \times 4 \times 4 = 64$. Incidentally 64 is also the square of 8, since $8^2 = 64$. It so happens that 64 is also the sixth power of 2, as $2^6 = 2 \times 2 \times 2 \times 2 \times 2 \times 2 = 64$.

3·13 ∽ T<small>HE USE OF ZERO IN INVOLUTIONS</small>

If *k* represents any natural number, 1, 2, 3, 4, . . . , then:

$$k^0 = 1 \quad \text{thus} \quad 4^0 = 1 \quad 365^0 = 1 \quad 1{,}000{,}000^0 = 1$$
$$0^k = 0 \quad \text{thus} \quad 0^1 = 0 \quad 0^2 = 0 \quad 0^{2{,}000} = 0$$

0^0 may have any value whatever, and will be excluded from consideration in this course. The expression 0^0 is called an *indeterminate form* and is investigated, along with the six other commonly encountered indeterminate forms, in the Supplement of this text (S.21).

3·14 ∽ I<small>NVOLUTION IS NOT COMMUTATIVE</small>

It is to be noted that if *a* and *b* represent *different* natural numbers, a^b and b^a yield different results. Examples are: $2^3 = 8$ and $3^2 = 9$. Further examples, to be verified, are:

$$3^5 = 243, \; 5^3 = 125 \qquad 5^4 = 625, \; 4^5 = 1{,}024$$
$$2^1 = 2, \; 1^2 = 1 \qquad 10^2 = 100, \; 2^{10} = 1{,}024$$

Incidentally, if no exponent is written over any natural number, the exponent is assumed to be 1. Thus 6 and 6^1 denote the name number 6; 35 and 35^1 denote 35.

∽ P<small>ROBLEMS</small> ∽

3.1. Perform the short multiplications:

    a. 3,456 × 7   *c.* 65,536 × 8   *e.* 12,345,679 × 6

    b. 87,351 × 5   *d.* 12,345,679 × 9   *f.* 12,345,679 × 3

g. What peculiarity do you detect in the digits that occur in the products obtained by multiplying 12,345,679 by 1, by 2, by 4, by 5, by 7, and by 8?

3.2. Perform the long multiplications in two different ways, by use of the commutative law of multiplication:

    a. 37,907 × 217   *b.* 10,103 × 5,783   *c.* 12,345 × 54,321

3.3. Obtain *mentally* the following products:

    a. 32 × 5 × 3 × 2   *d.* 25 × 879 × 4

    b. 756 × 600   *e.* 2 × 7 × 5 × 11 × 25 × 4

    c. 8 × 97 × 125

3.4. Perform the indicated operations:

    a. $8 + 2 \times 7 \times 5 + 12 + 8 \times 7 + 3 = ?$

    b. $2 + 13 \times 5 + 8 \times 6 + 23 + 2 \times 12 \times 5 + 10 \times 4 = ?$

    c. $1 + 19 \times 5 \times 2 + 148 + 16 + 3 \times 5 \times 3 = ?$

3.5. Perform the involutions: (*a*) 13^3, (*b*) 26^2, (*c*) 3^8, (*d*) 8^3, (*e*) 10^{10}, (*f*) 0^5, (*g*) 5^0.

3.6. Obtain the sum of the cubes of all natural numbers from 1 to 9, inclusive.

3.7. Obtain the cube of the sum of all natural numbers from 1 to 9, inclusive.

3.8. List the fourth powers of the natural numbers from 1 to 6, inclusive.

3.9. Perform the indicated additions:

    a. $1 = 1$ *e.* $1 + 3 + 5 + 7 + 9 = ?$

    b. $1 + 3 = ?$ *f.* $1 + 3 + 5 + 7 + 9 + 11 = ?$

    c. $1 + 3 + 5 = ?$ *g.*

    d. $1 + 3 + 5 + 7 = ?$ *h.*

Continue this procedure until you recognize the kind of numbers so obtained. Then write the rule that these relationships seem to imply.

3.10. Perform the indicated additions. Continue the procedures until you recognize the relationship between the two sums in the same line of additions. Then write the rule that these relationships seem to imply.

    a. $1 = 1$ *a′.* $1^3 = 1$

    b. $1 + 2 = 3$ *b′.* $1^3 + 2^3 = 9$

    c. $1 + 2 + 3 = ?$ *c′.* $1^3 + 2^3 + 3^3 = ?$

    d. $1 + 2 + 3 + 4 = ?$ *d′.* $1^3 + 2^3 + 3^3 + 4^3 = ?$

    e. $1 + 2 + 3 + 4 + 5 = ?$ *e′.* $1^3 + 2^3 + 3^3 + 4^3 + 5^3 = ?$

    f. $1 + \cdots$ *f′.* $1^3 + \cdots$

3.11. If a motor car will travel 18 miles on 1 gallon of gasoline, how far will it travel on 438 gallons at this rate? Calculate the cost of this fuel at 32 cents per gallon.

3.12. What is the total cost of the following bill of items?

75 reams of paper @ 89 cents per ream
7 boxes of carbon paper @ 96 cents per box
3 bottles of ink @ 17 cents per bottle
6 pens @ 19 cents each
12 pencils @ 8 cents each

3·15 ~ MEASUREMENT OF RECTANGULAR AREAS

Definitions. A square foot is a unit of area in the form of a square that is 1 foot long and 1 foot wide. Other commonly used units of area are the square inch, 1 inch long and 1 inch wide; the square mile, 1 mile long and 1 mile wide; the square centimeter, 1 centimeter long and 1 centimeter wide. Quite generally, any unit of length whatever will give rise to a corresponding unit of area, in the form of a square having the corresponding unit of length for the length and width of the square. The rule for computing a rectangular area is:

The total number of units of area in a rectangle is equal to the product of the number of corresponding length units in the length and the width of the rectangle.

The number of square inches in a rectangle 6 inches long and 4 inches wide is $6 \times 4 = 24$ square inches (note Figure 15.1). There are 144 square inches in a square foot, as the square foot is 12 inches long and 12 inches wide. Quite generally, if any unit of length contains a smaller units of length, then the corresponding unit of area will contain a^2 corresponding smaller units of area. Thus if 1 foot = 12 inches, then 1 square foot = 12^2, or 144 square inches.

~ PROBLEMS [CONTINUED] ~

3.13. How many square feet of floor are there in a room that is 12 feet wide and 15 feet long? How many square yards does it contain? How many square inches?

3.14. What is the cost of linoleum that would be required to cover completely the floor of a kitchen that is 3 yards wide and 4 yards long? The linoleum costs 37 cents per square foot.

3.15. What would be the cost of paving a highway that is 76 miles long and 32 feet wide, at $3 a square foot? One mile = 5,280 feet.

3.16.   What is the cost of plastering the four walls and ceiling of a room that is 18 feet wide, 24 feet long, and 12 feet high, if the charge of the plastering is 50 cents per square yard, and if no allowance is made for doors and windows? If an allowance were made for the space occupied by doors and windows, how much would this allowance be for four windows, 6 by 9 feet, and for two doors, 9 by 9 feet?

3·16 ∽ MEASUREMENT OF RECTANGULAR VOLUMES

Definitions.   A cubic foot is a unit of volume in the form of a cube that is 1 foot long, 1 foot wide, and 1 foot high. Other commonly used units of volume are the cubic inch, 1 inch long, 1 inch wide, and 1 inch high; the cubic yard, 1 yard long, 1 yard wide, and 1 yard high; the cubic centimeter, 1 centimeter long, 1 centimeter wide, and 1 centimeter high. Quite generally, any unit of length whatever will give rise to a corresponding unit of volume, in the form of a cube having the corresponding unit of length for the length, the width, and the height of the cube. The rule for computing a rectangular volume is:

> *The total number of units of volume in a rectangular object is equal to the product of the number of corresponding length units in the length, the width, and the height of the rectangular object.*

The number of cubic inches in a rectangular object that is 7 inches long, 5 inches wide, and 3 inches high is $7 \times 5 \times 3 = 105$ cubic inches (note Figure 3.1). There are 1,728 cubic inches in a cubic foot, as the cubic foot is 12 inches long, 12 inches wide, and 12 inches high. Quite generally, if any unit of length contains a smaller units of length, then the corresponding unit of volume must contain a^3 corresponding smaller units of volume. If 1 foot = 12 inches, then 1 cubic foot = 12^3, or 1,728 cubic inches.

The relationships between corresponding units of length, area, and volume may be conveniently remembered by mnemonics:

> *Inches times inches equals square inches.*
> *Feet times feet equals square feet.*
> *Yards times yards times yards equals cubic yards.*
> *Feet times square feet equals cubic feet.*
>   . . . .

In fact, one does not multiply feet by feet, or square yards by yards; one does, however, multiply the *number* of specified units by the *number* of specified units to obtain the required *number* of new designated units. The area of the floor of a rectangular room 12 feet long and 10 feet wide is equal to 12 (the *number* of feet in the length) multiplied by 10 (the *number* of feet in the width), which yields 120 square feet (the number of square feet in the area). If the room is 8 feet high, the volume of the room is equal to 120 (the *number* of square feet in the area of the floor) multiplied by 8 (the *number* of feet in the height), which yields 960 cubic feet, the required number of cubic feet in the volume of the room.

✺ PROBLEMS [CONCLUDED] ✺

3.17. How many cubic feet of liquid can be put into a rectangular cistern that is 3 feet long, 2 feet wide, and 45 feet deep? Compute the weight of this liquid if it weighs 62 pounds per cubic foot.

3.18. *a.* How many cubic feet of storage space does a room contain if it is 7 yards long, 5 yards wide, and 3 yards high?

  b. How much would it cost to paint the four walls and ceiling of this room, at 35 cents per square yard for the walls and 45 cents per square yard for the ceiling?

3.19. How far does light travel in 1 year of 365 days, if light travels 186,326 miles in 1 second? This enormous distance is called a *light year*, which is a fundamental unit of distance used in astronomy.

3.20. If a father can give his son 1 cent on Sunday, 2^2 cents on Monday, 3^3 cents on Tuesday, 4^4 cents on Wednesday, and so on at this same increasing rate, how much money would he give him on Saturday of this same week? What would be the total amount for this week of 7 days?

3.21. Suppose that each major league in baseball contains 10 teams, as was the situation in 1968. (*a*) How many games are scheduled for one season in a major league if each team plays every other team nine games at its own home field? (*b*) If one particular player plays in two games with each visiting team in the season, and if his playing attracts 3,000 additional attendance at $2 a seat, compute his additional value to the team during the season.

3.22. Bill mounted eight butterfly specimens on each page of his 40-page album. How many specimens did his filled book contain?

3.23. A certain automobile runs 13 miles on 1 gallon of gasoline. (*a*) How far will it travel on 197 gallons? (*b*) Compute the cost of this gasoline at 31 cents per gallon.

3.24. Mr. Brown reads, on the average, one important book each month, besides various magazines, news publications, etc. How many such important books will he read at this same rate during the ensuing half century? How much would these books cost at an average of $4.75 a volume?

3.25. Compute the sum of the numbers in each horizontal row in the triangular array of numbers, beginning with $3 + 5 = 8$. Continue to extend the array of consecutive odd numbers until you recognize the nature of the sums so obtained. Then write in words the rule that seems to be implied.

$$
\begin{array}{ccccc}
 & & 1 & & \\
 & 3 & & 5 & \\
 7 & & 9 & & 11 \\
13 & & 15 & & 17 & & 19 \\
21 & & 23 & & 25 & & 27 & & 29 \\
\end{array}
$$

. . . .

*N*ote 1 ∾ *Condensed multiplication of natural numbers ending in 5.*

Square a natural number whose unit digit is 5, such as $(10a + 5)^2 = ?$ Some examples are:

$$35 \times 35 = 1{,}225 \qquad 85 \times 85 = 7{,}225$$
$$95 \times 95 = 9{,}025 \qquad 125 \times 125 = 15{,}625$$

Observe that each such product has for its final two digits 25; the other portion of the product is obtained by multiplying the left portion of the original number by 1 more than itself. Thus, the four preceding products end in 25 and have for their other portions respectively:

$$3 \times 4 = 12 \qquad 8 \times 9 = 72$$
$$9 \times 10 = 90 \qquad 12 \times 13 = 156$$

This rule is proved to be valid in all such cases by squaring $10a + 5$, which represents a natural number ending in 5, if a denotes any natural number. An example of performing multiplication by use of the distributive law is

$$(10a + 5)(10a + 5) = (10a + 5)(10a) + (10a + 5) \times 5 =$$
$$100a^2 + 50a + 50a + 25 = 100a^2 + 100a + 25 = 100a(a + 1) + 25$$

which is the symbolic expression for this prescribed procedure of squaring the natural number $10a + 5$.

The following two paragraphs explain how to obtain the product of two *different* natural numbers whose unit digits are 5, that is, $(10a + 5)(10b + 5) = ?$

When the sum $a + b$ is an even number. Some examples are:

$$45 \times 85 = 3{,}825 \qquad 4 + 8 = 12 \qquad \text{(Note that these are } even \text{ numbers)}$$
$$55 \times 95 = 5{,}225 \qquad 5 + 9 = 14$$
$$75 \times 15 = 1{,}125 \qquad 7 + 1 = 8$$
$$35 \times 115 = 4{,}025 \qquad 3 + 11 = 14$$

Observe that all such products end in the digits 25; the other portion of each product is the product of those portions of the two original numbers that precede the unit digit 5, increased by half the sum of these portions. In these four examples,

> Half of $(8 + 4)$ is 6, hence, $4 \times 8 + 6 = 38$
> Half of $(5 + 9)$ is 7, hence, $5 \times 9 + 7 = 52$
> Half of $(7 + 1)$ is 4, hence, $7 \times 1 + 4 = 11$
> Half of $(3 + 11)$ is 7, hence, $3 \times 11 + 7 = 40$

This rule is proved to be valid in all such cases by using the distributive law to perform the multiplication of $(10a + 5) \times (10b + 5)$, if a and b represent any natural numbers and if the sum $a + b$ is an *even* number. Accordingly,

$$
\begin{aligned}
(10a + 5)(10b + 5) &= (10a + 5)(10b) + (10a + 5) \times 5 \\
&= 100ab + 50b + 50a + 25 \\
&= 100ab + 50(a + b) + 25 \\
&= 100ab + \frac{100}{2}(a + b) + 25 \\
&= 100ab + 100\,\frac{(a + b)}{2} + 25 \\
&= 100\left(ab + \frac{a + b}{2}\right) + 25
\end{aligned}
$$

which is the symbolic expression for this prescribed procedure of multiplying $10a + 5$ by $10b + 5$, in which $a + b$ is even.

When the sum $a + b$ is an odd number. Some examples are:

> $45 \times 95 = 4{,}275$, $4 + 9 = 13$, which is odd, and half of $13 = 6\frac{1}{2}$
> $35 \times 85 = 2{,}975$, $3 + 8 = 11$, which is odd, and half of $11 = 5\frac{1}{2}$
> $115 \times 165 = 18{,}975$, $11 + 16 = 27$, which is odd, and half of $27 = 13\frac{1}{2}$
> $105 \times 535 = 56{,}175$, $10 + 53 = 63$, which is odd, and half of $63 = 31\frac{1}{2}$

Observe that all such products end in the digits 75; the other portion of each product is the product of those portions of the two original numbers that precede the unit digit 5, increased by half the sum of these portions, ignoring the $\frac{1}{2}$. Thus, in these four examples:

> $4 \times 9 + 6 = 42$
> $3 \times 8 + 5 = 29$
> $11 \times 16 = 176$, $176 + 13 = 189$
> $10 \times 53 = 530$, $530 + 31 = 561$

This rule is proved to be valid in all such cases by using the distributive law to perform the multiplication of $(10a + 5)(10b + 5)$, if a and b represent any natural numbers, and if the sum $a + b$ is an odd number. Accordingly,

$$(10a + 5)(10b + 5) = 100ab + 50a + 50b + 25$$

$$= 100ab + 100\left(\frac{a+b}{2} - \frac{1}{2} + \frac{1}{2}\right) + 25$$

$$= 100ab + 100\left(\frac{a+b}{2} - \frac{1}{2}\right) + 100 \times \frac{1}{2} + 25$$

$$= 100ab + 100\left(\frac{a+b-1}{2}\right) + 50 + 25$$

$$= 100\left(a + b + \frac{a+b-1}{2}\right) + 75$$

which is the symbolic expression for this prescribed procedure of multiplying $10a + 5$ by $10b + 5$, in which $a + b$ is *odd*.

∾ CHALLENGES

1. Evaluate the following sums of squares:

    a. $15^2 + 25^2$

    b. $15^2 + 25^2 + 35^2$

    c. $15^2 + 25^2 + 35^2 + 45^2$

    d. $15^2 + 25^2 + 35^2 + 45^2 + 55^2$

    e. $15^2 + 25^2 + 35^2 + 45^2 + 55^2 + 65^2$

    Then evaluate the expression

    $$\frac{100n^3 + 300n^2 + 275n}{3}$$

    for $n = 1, 2, 3, 4, 5$. What do these results seem to imply? Evaluate the expression for $n = 10$; verify the result by adding the 10 appropriate squares.

    Compute by this valid formula the sum of 10 consecutive squares of numbers ending in 5, namely $15^2, 25^2, 35^2, \ldots$.

2. Evaluate the following:

    a. 15×15 c. $15 \times 15 + 15 \times 25 + 15 \times 35$

    b. $15 \times 15 + 15 \times 25$ d. $15 \times 15 + 15 \times 25 + 15 \times 35 +$
                                               15×45

    Then evaluate the expression $3 \times 25n(n + 2)$ for $n = 1, 2, 3,$ and 4.

    Evaluate the following:

    e. 25×25 g. $25 \times 25 + 25 \times 35 + 25 \times 45$

    f. $25 \times 25 + 25 \times 35$ h. $25 \times 25 + 25 \times 35 + 25 \times 45 +$
                                               25×55

Then evaluate the expression $5 \times 25n(n + 4)$ for $n = 1, 2, 3,$ and 4.

Evaluate the following:

i. 35×35 *k.* $35 \times 35 + 35 \times 45 + 35 \times 55$

j. $35 \times 35 + 35 \times 45$ *l.* $35 \times 35 + 35 \times 45 + 35 \times 55 +$
$$35 \times 65$$

Then evaluate the expression $7 \times 25n(n + 6)$ for $n = 1, 2, 3,$ and 4.

From the preceding three sets of evaluations can you surmise the following sum?   Use the surmised formula $? \times 25n(n + ?)$.

$$65 \times 65 + 65 \times 75 + 65 \times 85 + 65 \times 95 + 65 \times 105 + 65 \times 115$$

Add these six products to check your surmised result.

Using the appropriate surmised formula compute the sum of the first hundred products in the series of products,

$$95 \times 95 + 95 \times 105 + 95 \times 115 + 95 \times 125 + 95 \times 135 + \cdots$$

If a and n represent any natural numbers whatever, the correctly surmised formula, $a \times 25n(n + a - 1)$, does assuredly yield the correct sum of the n products.

$$(10a + 5)(10a + 5) + (10a + 5)(10\overline{a + 1} + 5) +$$
$$(10a + 5)(10\overline{a + 2} + 5) + (10a + 5)(10\overline{a + 3} + 5) + \cdots$$

The line written above $a + 1, a + 2, a + 3$ serves the same purpose as a pair of parentheses; thus $\overline{a + 1}$ means the same as $(a + 1)$.   This overline, called a *vinculum*, is used to avoid a double set of enclosing parentheses.

$\mathcal{N}$ote 2 ↔ *Commutative multiplication curios.*

Certain very special products remain unchanged if one reverses the order of the digits throughout the two factors.   Examples are:

$$23 \times 96 = 69 \times 32 \qquad 48 \times 63 = 36 \times 84 \qquad 46 \times 32 = 23 \times 64$$

Such expressions are called *palindromic*, as they read the same from right to left as from left to right.   Not all pairs of two-digit numbers have this palindromic feature, as $23 \times 45 = 1,035$, while $54 \times 32 = 1,728$.

Pairs of two-digit palindromic factors may be found as follows.   If $a, b, c,$ and d are single digits, alike or different, then one must have the necessary equality, $(10a + b)(10c + d) = (10d + c)(10b + a)$.   The two indicated multiplications and subsequent simplifications yield $a \cdot c = b \cdot d$, which is the clue for obtaining these special palindromic factors.   Hence, one must obtain two pairs of single-digit numbers that have the same product. Thus 3×8 and 4×6 yield the same product, 24. One pair of factors, such as 3 and 8, may serve as the tens digits, the other pair, the 4 and 6, will serve as the units digits. Accordingly, $34 \times 86 = 68 \times 43$ and $36 \times 84 = 48 \times 63$ are two valid palindromic products, which should be immediately checked for correctness.

⁊ CHALLENGES

1. Obtain the 14 such two-digit multiplication curios. These numbers do not contain the digit zero.

2. Obtain the 45 other two-digit multiplication curios that contain the digit zero, regarding 02 as a two-digit number.

    One may also obtain multiplication curios involving a two-digit and a three-digit natural number, such as $26 \times 341 = 143 \times 62$. If a, b, c, d, and e are single-digit natural numbers, then

    $$(10a + b)(100c + 10d + e) = (100e + 10d + c)(10b + a)$$

    and yields the required clues, namely,

    $$a \cdot c = b \cdot e \qquad a(d - e) = b(d - c) \qquad d = c + e$$

    Any pair of two-digit palindromic factors yields the digits a, b, c, and e. Then, if the sum $c + e$ is a single-digit number, this sum will be d. Since $6 \times 2 = 3 \times 4$, $a = 6$, $c = 2$, $b = 3$, $e = 4$, whence $c + e = 2 + 4 = 6$, yielding $63 \times 264 = 462 \times 36$.

3. Obtain the 17 such palindromic pairs of two-digit and three-digit natural numbers.

    From any pair of two-digit palindromic factors, such as $68 \times 43 = 34 \times 86$, arising from $6 \times 4 = 8 \times 3$, one may obtain a pair of palindromic factors having any desired number of digits whatever. This may be done as follows: Let p and q represent any single-digit numbers that are proportional to the units digit and to the tens digit, respectively, of the two given two-digit palindromic factors. Here one must take for p and q any single-digit numbers proportional to 6 and 3, or to 8 and 4; p,q, may be taken as 2,1 or 4,2 or 6,3 or 8,4 respectively. One may now insert the *same number* of p's and q's between the tens digit and units digit of the original two-digit palindromic factors. Thus, using 2 and 1 five times one obtains

    $$6{,}222{,}228 \times 4{,}111{,}113 = 3{,}111{,}114 \times 8{,}222{,}226$$

    In performing the two long multiplications one observes that the corresponding partial products are also equal to each other.

Now if $a \cdot c = b \cdot d$, $p = k \cdot a$, $q = k \cdot d$, and if a, b, c, d, p, and q are each single-digit numbers, then, using a, b, c, d, p, q as digits, $a\,p\,p\,\cdots\,p\,b \times c\,q\,q\,\cdots\,q\,d = d\,q\,q\,\cdots\,q\,c \times b\,p\,p\,\cdots\,p\,a$, in which the same number of p's and q's are inserted between a and b and between c and d.

The palindromic character of such products appears from the fact that corresponding individual products in each corresponding partial products of the two long multiplications are equal numbers. Thus to demonstrate that $a\,p\,b \cdot c\,q\,d = d\,q\,c \cdot b\,p\,a$ one should replace p by $k \cdot a$ and q by $k \cdot d$, and remember that $a \cdot c = b \cdot d$.

a	$k \cdot a$	b		d	$k \cdot d$	c

$$
\begin{array}{ccc}
a & k \cdot a & b \\
c & k \cdot d & d \\
\hline
d \cdot a & d \cdot k \cdot a\ d \cdot b \\
k \cdot d \cdot a\ k^2 \cdot a \cdot d\ k \cdot d \cdot b \\
c \cdot a\ c \cdot k \cdot a & c \cdot b \\
\hline
\end{array}
\qquad
\begin{array}{ccc}
d & k \cdot d & c \\
b & k \cdot a & a \\
\hline
a \cdot d & a \cdot k \cdot d\ a \cdot c \\
k \cdot a \cdot d\ k^2 \cdot a \cdot d\ k \cdot a \cdot c \\
b \cdot d\ b \cdot k \cdot d & b \cdot c \\
\hline
\end{array}
$$

Since the individual corresponding terms of all partial products are equal numbers, the two complete products must be equal.

4. Repeat the foregoing proof in detail by performing the appropriate two long multiplications of five-digit numbers; i.e., after inserting three p's and three q's instead of the one p and one q as shown above.

∾ SUPPLEMENTARY PROBLEMS ∾

Practice makes perfect.

S3.1. Perform the indicated multiplications, then add the resulting products:
    a. (i) 7×6, (ii) 9×3, (iii) 6×9, (iv) 8×7, (v) 7×4, (vi) 8×9
    b. (i) $2 \times 3 \times 4$, (ii) $2 \times 6 \times 5$, (iii) $5 \times 7 \times 8$, (iv) $4 \times 4 \times 4$, (v) $3 \times 3 \times 3$
    c. (i) 32×5, (ii) 47×4, (iii) 93×6, (iv) 75×8, (v) 89×7, (vi) 77×7
    d. (i) 241×6, (ii) 812×8, (iii) 907×4, (iv) 540×9, (v) 753×5
    e. (i) $3,125 \times 8$, (ii) $5,609 \times 3$, (iii) $9,203 \times 4$, (iv) $4,096 \times 9$

S3.2. Perform the multiplications:

a.	195×3	*h.*	$866,709,113 \times 11$
b.	$3,749 \times 4$	*i.*	$6,096,441,231 \times 12$
c.	$13,657 \times 5$	*j.*	$72,216,803,512 \times 13$
d.	$847,248 \times 6$	*k.*	$149,162,536,496 \times 14$
e.	$8,674,179 \times 7$	*l.*	$4,811,001,212,562 \times 15$
f.	$37,013,523 \times 8$	*m.*	$97,531,864,201,412 \times 16$
g.	$684,887,348 \times 9$	*n.*	$121,133,146,415,107 \times 17$

S3.3. Perform the multiplications in two ways, i.e., use commutative law:

a. 58 × 37	*e.* 512 × 125	*i.* 4,096 × 3,125	*m.* 4,012 × 275
b. 63 × 29	*f.* 256 × 625	*j.* 6,904 × 5,213	*n.* 3,002 × 683
c. 84 × 36	*g.* 375 × 768	*k.* 7,531 × 8,642	*o.* 1,112 × 974
d. 48 × 63	*h.* 357 × 246	*l.* 9,911 × 1,199	*p.* 3,469 × 123

S3.4. Perform the indicated involutions:

a. 3^2	*d.* 6^0
b. 2^3	*e.* 7^4
c. 0^6	*f.* 4^7

S3.5. Multiply three thousand, four hundred twenty-six by five thousand, nine hundred thirty-seven, in two different ways.

S3.6. Obtain the square of fifty-six thousand, thirty.

S3.7. Obtain the fourth power of 45; obtain the sixth power of 15.

S3.8. Compute John's weekly earnings if he worked 8 hours on 5 days and 4 hours on the sixth day.   His hourly rate of pay was 87 cents.

S3.9. What is the value of seven booklets of airmail stamps, if each booklet contains 25 stamps?   Each stamp is worth 10 cents.   What was the value of these booklets in 1967 when airmail stamps cost 8 cents each?

S3.10. Heather bought 19 two-cent stamps, 53 three-cent stamps, and 12 six-cent stamps.   What did she pay for them?

S3.11. Mr. *A*, earning $5,000 in 1960, paid for himself and his wife $416 federal income tax, $15.56 state income tax, $289.64 property tax, $85.07 gasoline tax, and $73.59 sales tax.   Compute the total amount of these taxes for that year.

S3.12. By 1967 Mr. *A* of Problem S3.11 has had his salary doubled.   However, in 1967 he paid $1,458 federal income tax, $69 state income tax, $458.76 property tax, $92.34 gasoline tax, and $112.44 sales tax.   Compute the total of these taxes.

S3.13. William spent 88 cents each day for transportation and 45 cents for lunch on each of 178 school days during a school year.   Compute the total cost of these two items during the school year.

S3.14. During the two semesters of the school year William's scholastic record was as follows:

FALL SEMESTER			SPRING SEMESTER		
Course	*Units*	*Grade*	*Course*	*Units*	*Grade*
Trigonometry	3	A	Calculus	5	A
Grammar	3	C	Literature	3	B
History	3	B	Astronomy	3	A
German	5	A	German	5	B
Gymnasium	1	B	Gymnasium	1	B

a. How many units of credit did William earn during the entire school year?

b. If each unit of credit yields 4 scholarship points for A, 3 scholarship points for B, 2 scholarship points for C, compute William's total points earned during each semester and for the entire school year.

S3.15. If each classroom of a certain community contains an average of 17 pupils, how many pupils could be accommodated in 214 classrooms?

S3.16. If the average salary of all school personnel in a school district was $12,304.27, what would be the annual payroll in this district employing 259 persons?

S3.17. An enterprising community, anticipating a necessary future school building program, deposits into a reserve account $92,960 each year for 20 years. During these 20 years these deposits also earn interest of $1,912,784.45. What is the total accumulated amount at the end of 20 years?

S3.18. On a particular trip from Boston to Los Angeles a jet airliner carried 12 first-class passengers at $167.25 each, 79 coach passengers at $152.25 each, and 19 economy passengers at $54.40 each for just part of this trip. Compute the total amount of these fares.

S3.19. On a certain trip a plane carried 79 pieces of luggage at an average of 57 pounds and 19 pieces at an average of 63 pounds. Calculate the total weight of this luggage.

S3.20. On a vacation trip a family traveled on successive days 312, 59, 107, 26, 105, 455, and 371 miles respectively. If each mile traveled cost an average of 4 cents and if each of the 7 days averaged an additional expenditure of $14.75, calculate the entire cost of the week's vacation.

S3.21. A pyramid is constructed of successive layers of equal cubical blocks of stone. The bottom layer contains 100 blocks in the form of a square with 10 blocks on each side. Each successive higher layer is made of equally sized blocks arranged in the form of a square having one less block in each edge than the layer of blocks immediately below it. If the topmost layer consists of a single block, how many blocks comprise the entire pyramid?

S3.22. The formula $\dfrac{n(n+1)(2n+1)}{6}$ yields the number of blocks required to build a pyramid like the one in Problem S3.21 which has n layers of cubical blocks. Use this formula to compute the total number of blocks in a pyramid having: (*a*) 3 layers, (*b*) 6 layers, (*c*) 10 layers, (*d*) 50 layers.

S3.23. If each block in the bottom layer of the pyramid in Problem S3.21 weighs 650 pounds, each block in the next higher layer 625 pounds, and so on, each block in each successive layer weighing 25 pounds less than the next lower layer, calculate the total weight of the pyramid.

S3.24. If $1 will amount to $5.74 in 30 years at compound interest of 6 percent, compounded annually, how much would $250 amount to at the same rate of increase in 30 years?

S3.25. A person deposits $1 each year for 40 years in a savings account that earns 5 percent compounded annually and thereby accumulates $90.32. How much would he have accumulated under the same terms if he had deposited $75 each year, instead of the $1?

S3.26. Anticipating the purchase of a car for $2,000 in 30 months, Alfred deposits $62.75 monthly in a savings account that earns interest at 5 percent compounded annually. If the total amount of interest earned is $118.40, will Alfred accumulate the necessary purchase price?

S3.27. John purchases a car immediately for $2,000 and obligates himself to make monthly payments of $72.86 for the ensuing 30 months to pay for it. How much of his total payments is interest on his indebtedness? The interest charged is the amount that his total payments exceed the purchase price of $2,000. (Rate charged is 7 percent.)

S3.28. In a distant city Mr. *X* rented an automobile from the Budget Car Loan Company, agreeing to pay $6 a day for its use, $7.50 for complete insurance coverage, 6 cents for each mile he drives the car, and to pay for gasoline to refill the tank upon returning it. Mr. *X* used the car for 6 days while driving it 723 miles, and, upon returning the car he paid the company for refilling the tank with 4 additional gallons of fuel at 35 cents per gallon.

    a. How much did Mr. *X* pay to the Car Loan company upon returning it?

    b. How much did this entire undertaking cost Mr. *X* if he bought also 12 gallons of gasoline at 31 cents per gallon, 14 gallons at 34 cents per gallon, and 13 gallons at 29 cents per gallon?

S3.29. A grass fire burned over an area in the form of a rectangle 8 miles long and 5 miles wide. Calculate the number of acres in this area if 1 square mile contains 640 acres.

S3.30. If there are 5,280 feet in 1 mile, compute the number of square inches in 1 square mile.

S3.31. If four boys can cut a cord of wood in 3 hours, how long would it take one boy to cut four cords of wood at the same rate? How many cubic feet of wood would this be, if one cord is 8 feet long, 4 feet wide, and 4 feet high?

S3.32. How many pages do three dozen books contain, if one book contains 356 pages?

S3.33. How far can an ocean liner travel in 1 week at a speed of 43 miles per hour?

S3.34. How far can a jet plane travel in 7 hours at a speed of 17 miles per minute?

S3.35. What would be the annual expenses of a factory if the average monthly expenses total $407,593.25?

S3.36. How many seconds are there from midnight to 7:53 A.M.?

S3.37. Evaluate the expression $2^k + 1$, if $k = 2^n$ and if n has the values 0, 1, 2, 3, and 4.

S3.38. If 2 pints are equivalent to 1 quart, and 4 quarts equivalent to 1 gallon, how many pints are equivalent to 2,473 gallons?

S3.39. It is generally (inaccurately) stated that 100 bushels contain exactly 215,042 cubic inches. How does this compare with the content of 124 cubic feet? With 125 cubic feet? How does it compare with 930 gallons? With 931 gallons? One gallon contains *exactly* 231 cubic inches.

S3.40. If one hen averages two eggs in 3 days, how many eggs are to be expected at this rate from 100 hens in 30 days?

S3.41. The number of different ways that n persons may seat themselves in n chairs is exactly $n!$ The expression $n!$ means the product of all consecutive numbers from 1 to n. Thus, 2! means 1×2, or 2; $3! = 1 \times 2 \times 3 = 6$. In how many different ways can a class of 15 students seat themselves in a classroom containing 15 fixed chairs?

S3.42. A blacksmith offers to equip a horse with four iron shoes at $4 for each shoe, or to charge 1 cent for the first nail, 2 cents for the second nail, 4 cents for the third nail, and so on, doubling the charge for each successive nail. If each shoe contains six nails, what would be his charges at the two options?

S3.43. Don declares that he can tell Ron his complete product and his multiplier, if Ron tells him the left end digit of the product. Is this possible, if Don restricts the multiplicand to be 142,857 and the multiplier to be any natural number less than 8? (*Hint:* Compute the seven possible products.)

S3.44. In Problem S3.43 Don actually tells Ron the complete product and his multiplier if Ron tells him all digits of the product except the final five right end digits of the product. Now show that under these circumstances Ron may use any multiplier less than 1 million (instead of using only numbers less than 8).

S3.45. Reformulate Problem S3.43 if Don restricts the multiplier to be
(*a*) 0,588,235,294,117,647, (*b*) 076,923.

S3.46. Reformulate Problem S3.44 to employ the numbers given in Problem S3.45.

S3.47. Three rectangular plots of ground are offered for sale purporting to comprise 1 acre each. Identify each as being smaller than, greater than, or exactly equal to 1 acre. One must know that 5,280 feet equal 1 mile and that 640 acres equal 1 square mile. The three plots have lengths and widths as follows: (*a*) 208 feet by 208 feet; (*b*) 220 feet by 198 feet; (*c*) 217 feet by 200 feet.

S3.48. The numbers arising in Problem S3.37, namely, 3, 5, 17, 257, and 65,537, are the only unfactorable (prime) numbers that represent the number of sides of regular polygons that can be constructed by the rules of elementary geometry. Accordingly, the only such polygons so constructible are those that have as number of sides these five numbers and all possible products of these five numbers. Now obtain these $2^5 - 1$ such numbers.

S3.49. In a particular lottery organized to raise money, 1,000 *A* tickets were sold for $1 each, 500 *B* tickets were sold for $5 each, 100 *C* tickets were sold for $10 each, 50 *D* tickets for $25 each, 10 *E* tickets for $50 each, and 2 *F* tickets for $100 each. In the lottery drawing, only one ticket was drawn, which paid 10 times its sales price. If there were no expenses or taxes to be paid, how much did the project yield? There are six possible answers.

S3.50. A promoter inaugurated a dime-chain-letter swindle as follows: He mailed one letter to a prospective victim containing a list of 10 different names by which he received mail at the 10 associated addresses. This letter also contained the instructions:

Send one dime to the person whose name is at the top of this list.
Remove his name from the top of the list and add your own name and address at the bottom of the list.
Send 10 copies of this new list to 10 of your friends with these same instructions, with the assurance that each participant will be richly rewarded with dimes when his name reaches the top of the lists.

Now if all persons receiving such letters comply with the instructions, how much will the promoter receive by the time all of his 10 names have been removed from ensuing lists?

LESSON 4 ❧ FOUR FUNDAMENTAL OPERATIONS UPON NATURAL NUMBERS ❧ SUBTRACTION ❧ SYSTEM OF INTEGERS

. . . On reaching the summit, the long-desired prospect burst upon his view. It was as if a new world were unfolded to him, separated from all hitherto known by this mighty barrier of mountains.

—Washington Irving, *Voyages of the Companions of Columbus, IX.*

4·1 ∿ Résumé of the Four Direct Operations upon the Natural Numbers

The three previous lessons have presented the four fundamental direct operations upon the natural numbers:

Counting, or setting forth the natural numbers in their correct order, beginning with 1, and continuing to any desired natural number as 1, 2, 3, 4, 5, 6, 7, 8, 9, 10, 11, 12, 13, ...

Addition, or repeated counting, symbolically expressed as $a + b = ?$

Multiplication, or repeated addition, symbolically expressed as $a \times b = ?$ or $a \cdot b = ?$ or $a(b) = ?$ or $ab = ?$

Involution, or repeated multiplication, represented symbolically as $a^b = ?$

Counting is possible to any specified natural number since the array of natural numbers is endless (Section 1.1). Moreover, addition, multiplication, and involution can always be performed upon any two natural numbers whatever, a and b, and yield only one correct natural number as the result, which is called respectively the *sum*, the *product*, and the *power*. To facilitate the procedures it was necessary to commit to memory the sums and products of the 55 pairs of single-digit numbers, which are 0, 1, 2, 3, 4, 5, 6, 7, 8, 9. Finally, the conventional algorithms for performing these operations were shown to be universally valid by the use of five proved laws of addition and multiplication of natural numbers:

The commutative law of addition, $a + b = b + a$
The commutative law of multiplication, $ab = ba$
The associative law of addition, $(a + b) + c = a + (b + c)$
The associative law of multiplication, $(ab)c = a(bc)$
The distributive law of multiplication and addition, $a(b + c) = ab + ac$

4·2 ∽ THE FOUR FUNDAMENTAL INVERSE OPERATIONS UPON NATURAL NUMBERS

Each of the previous direct operations of addition, multiplication, and involution involves three natural numbers, a, b, c, in their respective relationships:

$$a + b = c \qquad ab = c \qquad \text{and} \qquad a^b = c$$

These three operations yield a desired resulting natural number c from the originally prescribed natural numbers a and b. Such operations are called *direct* operations.

Contrariwise, if, in one of these three relationships involving the natural numbers a, b, c, one must perform an operation to obtain a from the known natural numbers b and c or b from the known natural numbers a and c, such an operation is called an *inverse operation* of the given direct operation.

The *four* fundamental inverse operations are listed as follows:

Subtraction, the operation of obtaining the unknown number designated by ? in the relationship, or the statement, $a + ? = c$, or in $? + b = c$, in which the indicated letters a, c or b, c represent known specific natural numbers.

The customary symbolic expression for subtraction in these two situations is $c - a = ?$ or $c - b = ?$ respectively. The sign of subtraction, the dash, $-$, is called a *negative sign*, or a *minus* sign. Since addition of natural numbers is commutative, addition has just one inverse operation. The number c, which was called the *sum* in the operation of addition, is now called the *minuend* in the corresponding operation of subtraction; the other known number, the a or the b respectively, is called the *subtrahend*. The result of subtraction is called the *difference*.

Division, the operation of obtaining the unknown number designated by the ? in the relationship, or the statement, $a \times ? = c$, or in $? \times b = c$, in which the indicated letters a, c, or b, c, represent specific known natural numbers.

The customary symbolic expression for division in these two situations is $c \div a = ?$ or $c \div b = ?$ respectively. The sign of division, the dash separating a pair of dots, $\div$, is read as "divided by." Since multiplication of natural numbers is commutative, multiplication has just one inverse operation. The number c, which was called the *product* in the operation of multiplication, is now called the *dividend* in the operation of division; the other known number, the a or the b respectively, is called the *divisor;* the result of division is called the *quotient*.

The direct operation of involution has two inverse operations, since involution is not commutative; that is, a^b and b^a yield different results.

Evolution, the operation of obtaining the unknown number designated by ? in the relationship, or the statement $?^b = c$, in which the letters b and c represent specific natural numbers.

The customary symbolism for evolution in this situation is $\sqrt[b]{c} = ?$ The number c, which was called the bth power in the operation of involution, is now called the *radicand* in the operation of evolution; the number b, formerly called the exponent, is here called the *index;* the missing number represented by ?, formerly called the base of the involution, is now called the bth root of the evolution.

Indexing, or obtaining the logarithm, the operation of obtaining the unknown number designated by ? in the relationship, or the statement, $a^? = c$, in which the letters a and c represent specific natural numbers.

The customary symbolism for indexing in this situation is $\log_a c = ?$ The number a is here called the *base;* the required number ? is called the logarithm of c for the base a; the number c is called the antilogarithm of ? for the base a.

4·3 ∾ Possible and impossible inverse operations upon natural numbers

Every direct operation upon specific natural numbers yields a definite natural number for its sum or product or power. The corresponding inverse operations employing these same specific natural numbers must yield one definite natural number for its difference or quotient or root or index, respectively. If the natural numbers that occur are quite small, these inverse operations may be easily performed mentally by recasting the inverse form of operation into the corresponding direct form of operation.

Here are four examples of possible inverse operations upon natural numbers:

1. $8 - 3 = ?$ is equivalent to $3 + ? = 8$. The addition tables of Section 2.6 require the ? to represent 5, giving $8 - 3 = 5$.

2. $36 \div 4 = ?$ is equivalent to $4 \times ? = 36$. The multiplication tables of Section 3.7 require the ? to represent 9. Accordingly, $36 \div 4 = 9$.

3. $\sqrt[3]{8} = ?$ is equivalent to $?^3 = 8$. A few trials will show that the ? must represent 2. Accordingly, $\sqrt[3]{8} = 2$.

4. $\log_3 81 = ?$ is equivalent to $3^? = 81$. Again, a few simple trials, as $3^2 = 9$, $3^3 = 27$, $3^4 = 81$, show that the ? must represent 4. Accordingly, $\log_3 81 = 4$.

In these four examples of inverse operations the numbers that occur are selected from corresponding direct operations upon natural numbers, respectively,

$$3 + 5 = 8 \qquad 4 \times 9 = 36 \qquad 2^3 = 8 \qquad 3^4 = 81$$

Contrariwise, if the numbers that occur in an indicated inverse operation do not occur also in the corresponding operation upon natural numbers, the indicated operation is impossible upon natural numbers.

Here are four examples of impossible inverse operations upon natural numbers:

1. $4 - 7 = ?$ is equivalent to $7 + ? = 4$. This is clearly an absurd, or impossible, relationship for any natural number whatever, since the sum 4 must be larger than the addend 7.

2. $9 \div 2 = ?$ is equivalent to $2 \times ? = 9$. This relationship again is impossible, since the product of 2 by any natural number whatever must be an *even natural number*, whereas 9 is an *odd natural number*.

3. $\sqrt[3]{7} = ?$ is equivalent to $?^3 = 7$. But $1^3 = 1$, $2^3 = 8$, $3^3 = 27$, and the cubes (third power) of natural numbers larger than 3 are still larger than 27 and therefore can never be equal to 7. Accordingly, $\sqrt[3]{7}$ cannot be equal to any natural number.

4. $\log_4 9 = ?$ is equivalent to $4^? = 9$. But $4^1 = 4$, $4^2 = 16$, and all larger powers of 4 are still larger than 16. Consequently, $\log_4 9$ cannot be equal to any natural number.

4·4 ～ NEW TYPES OF NUMBERS REQUIRED TO PERFORM ALL INVERSE OPERATIONS UPON ANY NATURAL NUMBERS WHATEVER

The four preceding illustrations of the inverse operations that cannot be performed upon natural numbers are examples of the following general situations, if a and b represent natural numbers. That is to say, no natural number whatever can serve as the correct result of these inverse operations:

Subtraction, $a - b = ?$, if a is not larger than b.
Division, $a \div b = ?$, if a is not a multiple of b.
Evolution, $\sqrt[b]{a} = ?$, if a is not the bth power of some natural number.
Indexing, $\log_a b$, if b is not a power of a.

To provide appropriate numbers other than the natural numbers to serve as the convenient correct result in each of these inverse operations upon a and b so specified, respectively, one must invent or devise several new kinds of numbers and introduce them into the system of available numbers. These new numbers then supply at least one correct result for each of these designated operations. The new kinds of numbers that have been devised and introduced into the number system to make possible the inverse operations upon natural numbers are, respectively,

For subtraction: zero and the negative integers

For division: the fractions

For evolution: surd numbers, or radical numbers, one kind of irrational numbers

For indexing: the transcendental numbers, another kind of irrational numbers

4.5 ∾ NEW DEFINITIONS OF DIRECT AND INVERSE OPERATIONS UPON THESE NEW KINDS OF NUMBERS MUST BE FORMULATED

The three direct operations of addition, multiplication, and involution of *natural numbers* have been defined as the results of appropriate countings of natural numbers (Section 4.1). These definitions are not applicable to the new kinds of numbers encountered in the preceding section; therefore, new definitions of the direct operations upon these new numbers must be formulated, and they must be formulated to apply also to natural numbers to retain the same names of addition, multiplication, and involution. A large part of this program is completed in the ensuing lessons of this text and reveals some curious results, namely, that the operation of subtraction is performed by *adding* certain corresponding numbers; division is performed by *multiplying* certain corresponding numbers; evolution and involution are performed by the *same* operation upon corresponding numbers. Furthermore, only the operations of addition (and subtraction) and multiplication (and division) always yield only one correct result; the other direct and inverse operations in general yield more than one correct result, most frequently an endless number of correct results. And most importantly, these newly defined direct and inverse operations (addition, multiplication, involution, and their inverses) when performed upon these newly formulated kinds of numbers always yield kinds of numbers that have already been formulated, so that no further kinds of numbers can ever be conceived as necessary. Differently expressed, the system of numbers so devised is *closed*, which means that any of these designated operations upon any of them always leads to numbers of the same system.

4.6 ∾ INVERSE OPERATION OF SUBTRACTION THAT IS POSSIBLE WITH NATURAL NUMBERS

The operation of subtraction of natural numbers, namely, $a - b = ?$, is expressible as $b + ? = a$ or as $? + b = a$, since, by the commutative law of addition of natural numbers, $b + ? = ? + b$.

To solve $b + ? = a$ one must determine how many consecutive numbers immediately larger than b must be counted off to arrive at a. To illustrate, consider the solution of $8 - 5 = ?$ in the form $5 + ? = 8$. As previously performed, the counting is indicated by numbers with asterisks, *.

$$1 \quad 2 \quad 3 \quad 4 \quad 5 \quad 6 \quad 7 \quad 8 \quad 9 \quad 10 \quad 11 \quad 12 \quad 13 \ldots$$
$$ 1* \; 2* \; 3*$$

Thus there are three consecutive natural numbers immediately following 5 as far as 8, or $5 + 3 = 8$. Therefore, $8 - 5 = 3$.

Considering the alternate form of the problem, $? + b = a$, with these same numbers, $? + 5 = 8$, one must determine the natural number designated by ? such that five consecutive natural numbers immediately following ? arrive at 8. This may be done by counting backward from 8 with the counting numbers indicated with the asterisks.

$$1 \quad 2 \quad 3 \quad 4 \quad 5 \quad 6 \quad 7 \quad 8 \quad 9 \quad 10 \quad 11 \quad 12 \quad 13 \quad 14 \ldots$$
$$ 5* \; 4* \; 3* \; 2* \; 1*$$

That is to show that if five of the largest natural numbers are removed from the set of eight natural numbers 1, 2, 3, 4, 5, 6, 7, 8, the remaining numbers are 1, 2, 3, or *three* numbers remaining. Therefore, again $8 - 5 = 3$. Of these two equivalent ways of solving $8 - 5 = ?$, this latter scheme most readily leads to the formulation of negative integers, which afford solutions to subtractions in which the minuend a is not larger than the subtrahend b.

To illustrate again, compute $12 - 7 = ?$ One must count off seven natural numbers toward the left, beginning with 12; the next uncounted number is the required difference. Otherwise expressed, one must remove the seven largest natural numbers from the set of the twelve smallest natural numbers; the largest of the remaining numbers is the required result. The actual counting is indicated with the asterisked numbers:

$$1 \quad 2 \quad 3 \quad 4 \quad 5 \quad 6 \quad 7 \quad 8 \quad 9 \quad 10 \quad 11 \quad 12 \quad 13 \quad 14 \quad 15 \quad 16 \ldots$$
$$ 7* \; 6* \; 5 \quad 4* \quad 3* \quad 2* \quad 1*$$

Therefore, $12 - 7 = 5$. To have any natural numbers remaining to constitute the required difference, the subtrahend (meaning in Latin "to be removed") must be smaller than the minuend (meaning in Latin "to be made smaller"). The inverse operation of subtraction is possible for natural numbers (i.e., yielding a natural number for result) if, and only if, the subtrahend is smaller than the minuend.

The counting procedure for performing subtraction upon natural numbers would become quite tedious for a large minuend and subtrahend, but this operation is made brief and easy by three considerations:

1. Operations of subtraction involving zero are defined as follows, if a represents any natural number: $a - 0 = a$, $a - a = 0$, $0 - 0 = 0$. These definitions are made to harmonize with the corresponding operations of addition that involve zero (Section 2.6).

2. One must know thoroughly the 100 valid subtractions that involve single-digit subtrahends and differences.   These differences are easily adjusted in mind by recalling the corresponding direct additions that have already been committed to memory (Section 2.6).   Thus $12 - 9 = ?$ should recall $9 + ? = 12$ or $9 + 3 = 12$, whence $12 - 9 = 3$.   Of these 100 subtractions, 19 involve zero:

$0 - 0 = 0$	$5 - 5 = 0$	$1 - 0 = 1$	$6 - 0 = 6$
$1 - 1 = 0$	$6 - 6 = 0$	$2 - 0 = 2$	$7 - 0 = 7$
$2 - 2 = 0$	$7 - 7 = 0$	$3 - 0 = 3$	$8 - 0 = 8$
$3 - 3 = 0$	$8 - 8 = 0$	$4 - 0 = 4$	$9 - 0 = 9$
$4 - 4 = 0$	$9 - 9 = 0$	$5 - 0 = 5$	

The remaining 81 subtractions do not involve zero:

$18 - 9 = 9$	$12 - 9 = 3$	$10 - 4 = 6$	$7 - 5 = 2$
$17 - 9 = 8$	$12 - 8 = 4$	$10 - 3 = 7$	$7 - 4 = 3$
$17 - 8 = 9$	$12 - 7 = 5$	$10 - 2 = 8$	$7 - 3 = 4$
$16 - 9 = 7$	$12 - 6 = 6$	$10 - 1 = 9$	$7 - 2 = 5$
$16 - 8 = 8$	$12 - 5 = 7$	$9 - 8 = 1$	$7 - 1 = 6$
$16 - 7 = 9$	$12 - 4 = 8$	$9 - 7 = 2$	$6 - 5 = 1$
$15 - 9 = 6$	$12 - 3 = 9$	$9 - 6 = 3$	$6 - 4 = 2$
$15 - 8 = 7$	$11 - 9 = 2$	$9 - 5 = 4$	$6 - 3 = 3$
$15 - 7 = 8$	$11 - 8 = 3$	$9 - 4 = 5$	$6 - 2 = 4$
$15 - 6 = 9$	$11 - 7 = 4$	$9 - 3 = 6$	$6 - 1 = 5$
$14 - 9 = 5$	$11 - 6 = 5$	$9 - 2 = 7$	$5 - 4 = 1$
$14 - 8 = 6$	$11 - 5 = 6$	$9 - 1 = 8$	$5 - 3 = 2$
$14 - 7 = 7$	$11 - 4 = 7$	$8 - 7 = 1$	$5 - 2 = 3$
$14 - 6 = 8$	$11 - 3 = 8$	$8 - 6 = 2$	$5 - 1 = 4$
$14 - 5 = 9$	$11 - 2 = 9$	$8 - 5 = 3$	$4 - 3 = 1$
$13 - 9 = 4$	$10 - 9 = 1$	$8 - 4 = 4$	$4 - 2 = 2$
$13 - 8 = 5$	$10 - 8 = 2$	$8 - 3 = 5$	$4 - 1 = 3$
$13 - 7 = 6$	$10 - 7 = 3$	$8 - 2 = 6$	$3 - 2 = 1$
$13 - 6 = 7$	$10 - 6 = 4$	$8 - 1 = 7$	$3 - 1 = 2$
$13 - 5 = 8$	$10 - 5 = 5$	$7 - 6 = 1$	$2 - 1 = 1$
$13 - 4 = 9$			

3. Interpret the indicated subtraction, quite correctly, as the inverse of the addition in which the known minuend represents the sum of the given known subtrahend and the unknown difference.   The digits of the required difference may then be obtained by performing the pertinent subtraction as the inverse of an addition in which the sum and one addend is known and the other addend is unknown.   Two examples should suffice to clarify the procedure.

Subtract 536 from 987.   Place the subtrahend under the minuend as in the algorithm of addition:

897   Minuend (sum)
536   Subtrahend (one addend)
___
???   Difference (the other addend)

The missing digits of the difference may be found by considering the successive additions $? + 6 = 7$, $? + 3 = 9$, $? + 5 = 8$, or the corresponding differences, respectively, $7 - 6 = ?$, $9 - 3 = ?$, $8 - 5 = ?$, which yield the required digits of the difference, 1, 6, and 8, providing the required complete difference 861.

Care must be exercised in performing the individual additions if "carry-overs" occur, as appear in the example $79,628 - 39,258 = ?$

79,628
39,258
___
?? ???

The successive ?s are identified, working from the right, or units position. $? + 8 = 8$, therefore the ? represents 0.

The addition $? + 5 = 2$ is impossible, as 2 is smaller than 5.   There must be a carryover of 1 in the addition $? + 5 = 12$; therefore this ? represents 7, as $7 + 5 = 12$.

The next step, $? + 2 = 6$, must include the carryover from the previous addition, and must be $? + 3 = 6$, uniting the carryover 1 with the subtrahend digit 2.   Hence, the ? in $? + 3 = 6$ must represent 3.

In the next step the ? in $? + 9 = 9$ must represent 0, as $0 + 9 = 9$.

In the last step, the ? in $? + 3 = 7$ must represent 4, as $4 + 3 = 7$.
Accordingly, the entire required difference must be 40,370.

Representing the carryover by a small 1, the work should appear thus:

79,628
39,258
  1
___
40,370

This result may be quickly and easily verified as correct, or checked by noting that the sum of the difference and the subtrahend does equal the minuend; that is, $40,370 + 39,258 = 79,628$.

4·7 ∾ TWO ALTERNATIVE PROCEDURES FOR PERFORMING SUBTRACTION OF LARGE NATURAL NUMBERS

In the scheme of representing large natural numbers the value of 1 in any position, other than the units position, is equivalent to ten 1s in the next position to its right. Thus 1 in the thousands position is equivalent to 10 hundreds. Accordingly, one may subtract the digits of the subtrahend, one by one, from the corresponding digits of the minuend, if the digits of the subtrahend are smaller than or equal to the corresponding digits of the minuend; otherwise the smaller digit of the minuend may be increased by 10 by transferring a 1 from the adjoining position to the left in the minuend, repeating the procedure whenever necessary. The two methods are clarified by the following examples.

The Cancellation Method. The digit of the minuend from which a unit is transferred is cancelled out by / and the next smaller digit is written above it; the 10 introduced into the next position in the numerator to the right is represented by a before the smaller digit, thus increasing its value by 10. The steps of the procedure are described in order and must be completely understood.

```
6  ·2  ·1   9
7   3   2  ·0  ·7  6
2   4   5   6   9   2
─────────────────────
4   8   6   3   8   4
```

The appropriate steps that yield the successive digits of the required difference are now described completely as follows:

1. $6 - 2 = 4$, the units digit of the difference.

2.   *a.* $7 - 9 = ?$ is impossible, as 7 is not larger than 9.
    b. A unit cannot be taken from the next digit which is 0.
    c. A unit is taken from the digit 2 which adjoins the 0; mark the 2 by by *2*; replace 1 above the *2*; transfer the unit to 0, making 10, as indicated by ·0.
    d. Remove a unit from ·0, leaving 9 above the cancelled ·*0*.
    e. Transfer the unit to the 7, making it 17, represented by ·7.
    f. Now $17 - 9 = 8$, the tens digit of the difference.

3. $9 - 6 = 3$, the hundreds digit of the difference.

4. $1 - 5 = ?$ is impossible, as 1 is smaller than 5.
    a. Transfer a unit from 3, leaving 2 written above the *3*, to the 1, making it become 11, as indicated by ·1.
    b. Now $11 - 5 = 6$, the thousands digit of the difference.

5. $2 - 4 = ?$ again is impossible, as 2 is smaller than 4.
    a. Transfer a unit from the 7 to the 2, writing 6 above the cancelled *7*, and making 2 into 12, as indicated by ·2.
    b. Now $12 - 4 = 8$, the ten thousands digit of the difference.

6. $6 - 2 = 4$, the hundred thousands digit of the difference.

The entire required difference is 486,384. Note that this difference is entirely correct, since $486,384 + 254,692 = 732,076$, the original minuend.

The "Borrowing and Repaying Procedure."   The borrowing and repaying method of subtraction is considerably less cumbersome than the previously outlined method of subtraction.   It rests upon the principle that an individual subtraction yields the same difference if a 1 is added to the subtrahend or subtracted from the minuend, before the subtraction is done.   Thus, whenever a minuend digit is smaller than the corresponding subtrahend digit, the minuend digit is increased by 10, and instead of taking for this 10 a unit from the adjoining minuend, a unit is added to ("repaid to") the adjoining subtrahend digit. These borrowings and repayings are indicated by dots as for the example given for the cancellation method.

$$
\begin{array}{cccccc}
7 & \cdot 3 & \cdot 2 & \cdot 0 & \cdot 7 & 6 \\
2 & 4 & 5 & 6 & 9 & 2 \\
\cdot & & \cdot & \cdot & & \\
\hline
4 & 8 & 6 & 3 & 8 & 4
\end{array}
$$

Again the steps yielding the successive digits of the difference are described in detail:

1. $6 - 2 = 4$, the units digit of the difference.

2. $7 - 9 = ?$ is impossible; borrow 1, making $\cdot 7$, repay this 1, making $\underset{.}{6}$, which represents 7.   Now, $17 - 9 = 8$, the tens digit of the difference.

3. $0 - 7 = ?$ is impossible; borrow 1, making $\cdot 0$, repay it, making $\underset{.}{5}$, which represents 6.   Now, $10 - 7 = 3$, the hundreds digit of the difference.

4. $2 - 6 = ?$ is impossible; borrow 1, making $\cdot 2$, repay it, making $\underset{.}{4}$, or 5. Now, $12 - 6 = 6$, the thousands digit of the difference.

5. $3 - 5 = ?$ is impossible; borrow 1, making $\cdot 3$, repay it making $\underset{.}{4}$.   Now $13 - 5 = 8$, the ten thousands digit of the difference.

6. Finally, $7 - 3 = 4$, the hundred thousands digit of the difference, thus completing the required difference, namely, 486,384.

∾ PROBLEMS ∾

4.1.   Perform the following subtractions: (*a*) $17 - 8$, (*b*) $13 - 5$, (*c*) $11 - 7$, (*d*) $15 - 8$, (*e*) $14 - 6$, (*f*) $16 - 7$, (*g*) $12 - 5$.

4.2.   All parts of Problem 4.1 may be checked simultaneously, as follows: (*a*) Add all seven minuends.   (*b*) Add all seven subtrahends.   (*c*) Subtract the sum in (*b*) from the sum in (*a*); this resulting difference must be the same number as that obtained by adding the seven differences of

Problem 4.1.   Is this an absolutely reliable check?   That is, could errors be present that this check would not disclose?

4.3.   Perform the indicated subtractions, and check the results as described in Problem 4.2.   (*a*) 34 − 19, (*b*) 42 − 28, (*c*) 73 − 37, (*d*) 47 − 26, (*e*) 81 − 63.

4.4.   Solve and check the results: (*a*) 325 − 144, (*b*) 543 − 345, (*c*) 1,030 − 729, (*d*) 1,234 − 96.

4.5.   Solve and check the results: (*a*) 1,467,387 − 723,777, (*b*) 857,142 − 142,857, (*c*) 1,000,000 − 1,234.

4.6.   Solve and check the results: (*a*) 5,000,000,000 − 4,567,899,999, (*b*) 5,543,210 − 1,234,567.

4·8 ∾ INVERSE OPERATION OF SUBTRACTION THAT IS IMPOSSIBLE WITH NATURAL NUMBERS

The operation of subtraction of natural number *b* from natural number *a*, indicated symbolically as *a* − *b*, yields the number of natural numbers remaining in the set of natural numbers 1, 2, 3, . . . , *a* after the *b* largest natural numbers have been removed; this may be done by counting off *b* natural numbers from the right, or larger, end of the set.   The number of remaining natural numbers is indicated by the largest natural number remaining, as any natural number is the cardinal number of the set of natural numbers from 1 to that particular natural number.   For the subtraction *a* − *b* to yield a natural number as a result, or difference, *a* must be larger than *b*.

Now the subtraction *a* − *a* = 0 has been established by definition in Section 4.6.   The operation of backward counting is also applicable in such situations if the number 0 is placed before (to the left of) the 1 in the array of natural numbers, as may be illustrated in the subtraction 6 − 6 = 0.   As previously exhibited, the counting numbers represented by the subtrahend are marked with asterisks.

```
0  1  2  3  4  5  6  7  8  9  10  11  . . .
   6* 5* 4* 3* 2* 1*
```

The counting begins with the minuend 6; the next number to the left of the final counting number 6* (subtrahend) is the required difference, namely, 0.

To perform a subtraction *a* − *b* by this backward counting if the natural number *b* is larger than *a*, one must have numbers in the array that extend to the left of the zero, as illustrated by the attempted subtraction 5 − 9 = ?

```
         0  1  2  3  4  5  6  7  8  9  10  11  . . .
9* 8* 7* 6* 5* 4* 3* 2* 1*
```

The required numbers that will extend to the left of the zero are called the *negative integers* and are expressed by the same symbols used for the natural numbers, prefixed by a dash, −, appearing as −1, −2, −3, −4, −5, −6, −7, −8, −9, −10, −11, −12, . . . without end.   Placing these symbols in the array of 0 and the natural numbers, one has a representation of numbers that is unending in both directions, to the left as well as to the right, to wit:

$$. . .\ -12\ -11\ -10\ -9\ -8\ -7\ -6\ -5\ -4\ -3\ -2\ -1\ 0\ 1\ 2\ 3\ 4\ 5\ 6\ 7\ . . .$$

This enlarged system of numbers is called the *complete system of integers*, comprising the negative integers, the zero, and the natural numbers.   The natural numbers are also called *positive integers* and may be prefixed by the plus sign, +, to emphasize this new role.   Thus 8 and +8, read respectively as "eight" and "plus eight," are the same number; the negative integer −12 is read as "minus twelve."

Within the system of integers the operation of subtraction $a - b = ?$ is always possible if a and b represent any *natural numbers* whatever.   Thus $5 - 9 = ?$ is possible (i.e., has a valid solution) even though the natural number 9 is larger than the natural number 5.   The nine numbers to be counted off are indicated by the natural numbers marked with asterisks.   The next integer to the left of the last integer involved in the counting is the required difference.

$$. . .\quad -5\quad -4\quad -3\quad -2\quad -1\quad 0\quad 1\quad 2\quad 3\quad 4\quad 5\quad 6\quad 7\quad 8\quad . . .$$
$$9^*\quad 8^*\quad\ 7^*\ 6^*\ 5^*\ 4^*\ 3^*\ 2^*\ 1^*$$

Accordingly, $5 - 9 = -4$.

4·9 ∽ THE TWO DIFFERENT USES OF THE POSITIVE AND NEGATIVE SIGNS, + AND −

Signs of Operation.   For this purpose the positive sign + is used to denote the operation of addition and should be pronounced as "and."   One reads $7 + 5 = 12$ as "seven *and* five equal twelve," or "the sum of seven and five is twelve."   Likewise, the negative sign − is used to denote the operation of subtraction and should be pronounced as "less."   One reads $8 - 3 = 5$ as "eight *less* three equal five" or as "the difference of eight less three is five."

Signs of Quality.   For this purpose the + sign indicates a positive number, or a number greater than zero, and should be read as "plus."   Thus +7 is pronounced as "plus seven."   However, any positive number may also be written without the positive sign as every number so written is assumed to be positive. As a sign of quality the negative sign − is used to indicate a negative number, or a number less than zero, and should be pronounced as "minus."   Thus −13 must be read as "minus thirteen."   In this use the minus sign must not be omitted from a negative number as its omission would denote a positive number.

To avoid the possibility of confusion of the use of a sign as indicating operation or quality, a negative sign and its number may be enclosed within parentheses. In such indicated operations of addition and subtraction as $(-3) + (-9) = ?$, $7 - (-3) = ?$, the parentheses preserve the distinction. These indicated operations are read as "The sum of minus three and minus nine equals what" and "seven less minus three equals what."

4·10 ∾ EXTENDING BASIC PROPERTIES OF NATURAL NUMBERS TO THE ENLARGED SYSTEM OF INTEGERS

The cardinal and ordinal properties of natural numbers extend to integers by noting that, if a is a positive integer, a is the *cardinal* number of the set of numbers to the right of zero and extending to and including the integer a; as an *ordinal* number a is the ath integer to the *right* of 0. Moreover $-a$ is the ath integer lying to the *left* of 0.

The even integers have as a units digit 0, 2, 4, 6, or 8; odd integers have as a units digit 1, 3, 5, 7, or 9. Within the system of integers:

There is no last or largest number.
There is no first, or smallest number.
Every integer has an immediate successor and an immediate predecessor.

Accordingly, one may select any set of consecutive integers whatever, with any specified integer as the largest or as the smallest integer of the set.

4·11 ∾ ADDITION OF INTEGERS

Let M and N represent any integers whatever. Thus M may represent $+a$ or $-a$, and N may represent $+b$ or $-b$, if a and b denote any natural numbers whatever.

Definition. The *sum* of the integers M and N, indicated by $M + N$, is the bth integer to the *right* of M if N is positive, or the bth integer to the *left* of M if N is *negative*. One notes that if M and N are both positive this definition of addition of integers is precisely the same as the definition of addition of natural numbers. The other three possibilities are exhibited in the following examples (quality plus signs are shown).

EXAMPLES ∾

1. $(-2) + (+7) = ?$ The countings are shown by natural numbers with *.

$\cdots$ -4 -3 -2 -1 0 1 2 3 4 5 6 7 8 $\cdots$
1^* 2^* 3^* 4^* 5^* 6^* 7^* ($+5$ is seventh after -2)

Thus 5 is the seventh integer to the right of -2; hence $(-2) + (+7) = +5$ or 5.

2. $(+8) + (-12) = ?$

$$\cdots \quad -6 \quad -5 \quad -4 \quad -3 \quad -2 \quad -1 \quad 0 \quad 1 \quad 2 \quad 3 \quad 4 \quad 5 \quad 6 \quad 7 \quad 8$$
$$12^* \quad 11^* \quad 10^* \quad 9^* \ 8^* \ 7^* \ 6^* \ 5^* \ 4^* \ 3^* \ 2^* \ 1^*$$

Note that -4 is the twelfth integer before 8.   Hence $(+8) + (-12) = -4$.

3. $(-2) + (-5) = ?$

$$\cdots -9 \ -8 \ -7 \quad -6 \quad -5 \quad -4 \quad -3 \quad -2 \ -1 \ 0 \ 1 \ 2 \ 3 \ 4 \ \cdots$$
$$5^* \quad 4^* \quad 3^* \quad 2^* \quad 1^*$$

Note that -7 is the fifth integer before -2.   Hence $(-2) + (-5) = -7$.

To add three or more integers one adds the next integer to the sum of those already added.   It may be proved that addition of integers so defined obeys the commutative and the associative laws of addition (Section 4.17).   Positive integers must obey these laws as positive integers are the same as natural numbers.   The validity of the commutative law of addition is illustrated in the three following examples.

EXAMPLES ᴄᴡᴏ

1. $(+7) + (-2) = ?$

$$\cdots \quad -2 \quad -1 \quad 0 \quad 1 \quad 2 \quad 3 \quad 4 \quad 5 \quad 6 \quad 7 \quad 8 \quad 9 \quad 10 \quad 11 \quad \cdots$$
$$2^* \quad 1^*$$

The number line shows that $(+7) + (-2) = +5$, as $+5$ is the *second* integer to the left of $+7$.   Therefore $(-2) + (+7) = (+7) + (-2)$.

2. $(-12) + (+8) = ?$

$$\cdots \quad -13 \quad -12 \quad -11 \quad -10 \quad -9 \quad -8 \quad -7 \quad -6 \quad -5 \quad -4 \quad -3 \cdots$$
$$1^* \quad 2^* \quad 3^* \quad 4^* \quad 5^* \quad 6^* \quad 7^* \quad 8^*$$

In this example, $(-12) + (+8) = -4$, as -4 is the eighth integer to the right of -12.   Therefore, $(+8) + (-12) = (-12) + (+8)$.

3. $(-5) + (-2) = ?$

$$\cdots -9 \ -8 \ -7 \quad -6 \quad -5 \ -4 \ -3 \ -2 \ -1 \ 0 \ 1 \ 2 \ 3 \ 4 \ \cdots$$
$$2^* \quad 1^*$$

Here, $(-5) + (-2) = -7$, as -7 is the second integer to the left of -5. Therefore, $(-2) + (-5) = (-5) + (-2)$.

Incidentally, $(+a) + (-a) = (-a) + (+a) = 0$, if a represents any natural number.

The validity of the associative law of addition of integers is illustrated in computing the sum of the integers -7, $+13$, and -2.   That is, one must show   that $[(-7) + (+13)] + (-2) = (-7) + [(+13) + (-2)]$.   Now $[(-7) + (+13)] + (-2) = (+6) + (-2) = +4$, and $(-7) + [(+13) + (-2)] = (-7) + (+11) = +4$.

One may therefore add any set of integers in any order whatever. It is convenient to add the sum of all positive integers to the sum of all negative integers. Thus, to add -7, -11, $+13$, -8, $+25$, and -2, one obtains the sum of the negative integers, $(-7) + (-11) + (-8) + (-2) = -28$; the sum of the positive integers, $(+13) + (+25) = +38$; finally $(-28) + (+38) = +10$, or simply 10.

4·12 ~ SUBTRACTION OF INTEGERS

Again let M and N represent any integers whatever, so that M may represent $+a$ or $-a$, and N may represent $+b$ or $-b$, as a and b represent any natural numbers.

Definition. The *difference* of the integers M and N, indicated by $M - N$, is the bth integer to the *left* of M if N denotes a positive integer, or the bth integer to the *right* of M if N is negative. M is called the minuend, N the subtrahend, and the result is called the difference.

EXAMPLES ~

1. $(+4) - (+7) = ?$

$\cdots \quad -5 \quad -4 \quad -3 \quad -2 \quad -1 \quad 0 \quad 1 \quad 2 \quad 3 \quad 4 \quad 5 \quad 6 \quad 7 \cdots$
$ 7^* \quad 6^* \quad\quad 5^* \, 4^* \, 3^* \, 2^* \, 1^*$

The number line shows that $(+4) - (+7) = -3$, as -3 is the seventh number to the left of $+4$, since $+7$ is *positive*.

2. $(+5) - (-3) = ?$

$\cdots \quad -3 \quad -2 \quad -1 \quad 0 \quad 1 \quad 2 \quad 3 \quad 4 \quad 5 \quad 6 \quad 7 \quad 8 \quad 9 \quad 10 \quad 11 \quad \cdots$
$ 1^* \, 2^* \, 3^*$

In this example $(+5) - (-3) = +8$, as $+8$ is the third number to the right of $+5$, since -3 is *negative*.

3. $(-2) - (+5) = ?$

$\cdots \quad -9 \quad -8 \quad -7 \quad -6 \quad -5 \quad -4 \quad -3 \quad -2 \quad -1 \quad 0 \quad 1 \quad \cdots$
$ 5^* \quad\quad 4^* \quad\quad 3^* \quad\quad 2^* \quad\quad 1^*$

Here, $(-2) - (+5) = -7$, as -7 is the fifth integer to the left of -2, since $+5$ is positive.

4. $(-3) - (-8) = ?$

$\cdots \quad -5 \quad -4 \quad -3 \quad -2 \quad -1 \quad 0 \quad 1 \quad 2 \quad 3 \quad 4 \quad 5 \quad 6 \quad 7 \quad \cdots$
$ 1^* \quad\quad 2^* \, 3^* \, 4^* \, 5^* \, 6^* \, 7^* \, 8^*$

Accordingly, $(-3) - (-8) = +5$, since $+5$ is the eighth integer to the *right* of -3, as -8 is *negative*.

4·13 ~ RECAPITULATION OF ADDITION AND SUBTRACTION OF INTEGERS

Definitions. The *absolute value* of an integer is the numerical value of the natural number that is represented by an integer without its $+$ or $-$ sign. The absolute value of -7 is simply 7; the absolute value of $+12$, or 12, is 12; the absolute value of 0 is 0. Moreover, $+0 = -0 = 0$.

Operations that are performed upon natural numbers are called *arithmetical* operations; operations performed upon integers are called *algebraic* operations. Quite generally, operations that involve only positive numbers (integers and fractions) are called *arithmetical* operations; operations that may or do involve one or more negative numbers (integers or fractions) are called *algebraic* operations.

The rules of algebraic addition (i.e., addition of two integers) may be stated concisely as follows:

If the two integers are of the same sign, that is, both integers are positive or both integers are negative, one adds their absolute values and applies the common sign to their sums.

If the two integers are of opposite sign, that is, one integer is positive, the other integer negative, one subtracts arithmetically the smaller absolute value from the larger absolute value, and applies to the result the sign that was associated with the larger absolute value.

To illustrate:

$$(-4) + (-9) = -(4 + 9) = -13$$
$$(-13) + (+7) = -(13 - 7) = -6$$
$$(+5) + (+12) = +(5 + 12) = +17$$
$$(-17) + (+21) = +(21 - 17) = +4$$

The rule for algebraic subtraction (i.e., subtraction of two integers) may be stated concisely thus:

Algebraic subtraction may be performed correctly by changing the sign of the subtrahend, and then by performing the operation of algebraic addition upon the resulting integers.

The following problems illustrate this rule:

$$(-8) - (-12) = (-8) + (+12) = +4$$
$$(-7) - (+5) = (-7) + (-5) = -12$$
$$(+11) - (-8) = (+11) + (+8) = +19$$
$$(+13) - (+18) = (+13) + (-18) = -5$$
$$43 - 51 = (+43) + (-51) = -(51 - 43) = -8$$
$$0 - 23 = 0 + (-23) = -(23 - 0) = -23$$
$$3,675 - 5,280 = (+3,675) + (-5,280) = -(5,280 - 3,675) = -1,605$$

4·14 ~ ALGEBRAIC MULTIPLICATION

The operation of multiplication as applied to integers is defined by three special rules. The same three names are used for the integers that were used for natural numbers in arithmetical multiplication, namely, multiplicand, multiplier, and product.

The absolute value of the product of two integers is equal to the product of the absolute values of the two integers.

If the multiplicand and multiplier have like signs, that is, if both are positive or both are negative, the sign of the product is positive; contrariwise, if the signs of multiplicand and multiplier are unlike, that is, one sign is positive and the other sign negative, the sign of the product is negative.

If the multiplicand or multiplier is zero, the product is zero.

The following problems illustrate these rules:

$(+7) \times (+9) = +63$ or 63
$(-4) \times (-8) = +32$ or 32 $(-23) \times 0 = 0$
$(+45) \times (-8) = (-360)$ or -360 $(+37) \times 0 = 0$
$(-17) \times (+7) = (-119)$ or -119 $0 \times (-98) = 0$

4·15 ~ ALGEBRAIC INVOLUTION OF INTEGERS

The use of zero and the negative integers as exponents will be presented in Lesson 8. If the exponent is a positive integer, the involution is performed as a repeated multiplication.

$(-4)^3 = (-4)(-4)(-4) = (-64)$ or -64

Making the individual multiplications:

$(-4)(-4) = +16$ then $(+16)(-4) = -64$
$(-3)^4 = (-3)(-3)(-3)(-3) = +81$

Note that an *even* power of a negative integer is positive; an *odd* power of a negative integer is negative.

~ PROBLEMS [CONTINUED] ~

4.7. Perform the indicated subtractions. The first, or upper, number is the minuend in each individual example.

a.　3 − 33

b.　23 − 529

c.　15,673 − 97,007

d.　1,000,000 − 3,579,765

e.　857,142 − 571,428

f.　142,857 − 714,285

g.　$\begin{array}{r} -12 \\ +\ 3 \\ \hline \end{array}$

h.　$\begin{array}{r} -10 \\ -\ 6 \\ \hline \end{array}$

i.　$\begin{array}{r} +6 \\ -2 \\ \hline \end{array}$

j.　$\begin{array}{r} -\ 7 \\ +10 \\ \hline \end{array}$

k.　$\begin{array}{r} -\ 8 \\ -11 \\ \hline \end{array}$

l.　$\begin{array}{r} 0 \\ +6 \\ \hline \end{array}$

m.　$\begin{array}{r} 0 \\ -7 \\ \hline \end{array}$

n.　$\begin{array}{r} -37 \\ -43 \\ \hline \end{array}$

o.　$\begin{array}{r} +43 \\ +37 \\ \hline \end{array}$

p.　$\begin{array}{r} -4 \\ 0 \\ \hline \end{array}$

4.8. Add horizontally and vertically, writing the *sums* of the horizontal rows of integers to the right and the sums of the columns of integers under the respective columns. Then add these two sets of sums, which must yield the same final sum:

$$\begin{array}{ccccccccccc}
- 3 & + & - 6 & + & + 8 & + & - 3 & + & -11 & = & \\
+12 & + & +13 & + & - 2 & + & - 7 & + & -14 & = & \\
-31 & + & +11 & + & - 7 & + & +13 & + & -19 & = & \\
- 1 & + & +10 & + & + 9 & + & - 5 & + & - 2 & = & \\
+20 & + & - 1 & + & -10 & + & + 8 & + & 0 & = & \\
\hline
\end{array}$$

4.9. Multiply the three integers in each of the three rows and columns, placing the products to the right and under the respective rows and columns. Then multiply the two sets of products obtained from the three rows and from the three columns. These two products must be the same integer.

$$\begin{array}{ccccccc}
-4 & \times & +7 & \times & -2 & = & \\
+5 & \times & -6 & \times & +9 & = & \\
-8 & \times & +3 & \times & -1 & = & \\
\hline
\end{array}$$

4.10. Evaluate the indicated expressions. Again, all multiplications must be performed before the additions or subtractions.

a.　$(-2)(-5) + (-6)(+3) + (-7)4 = ?$

b.　$(-8) + (-15)(-3) + 6(-2)(-9) = ?$

c.　$3 + 7 \times 8 + 2 \times 7 \times 11 - 4 + 6 \times 2 + 8 - 2 \times 7 \times 11 = ?$

d.　$(-8) - (+16) + 7 - (-3)(-2) = ?$

e.　$-8 - 16(7) - (13) - (-2) = ?$

f.　$(-6)(-3) + 8(-7) - 6 \times 5 \times (-1) + (-7)(-9) = ?$

g.　$4(-2) + 7(-2) - 12(-2) = ?$

Fortunately, the interpretation of the $+$ and $-$ signs as *signs of operation* upon *natural numbers*, or as *signs of quality* in the operation of algebraic *addition of integers*, must yield the same result, as illustrated in the next two examples:

h. $4 - 2 + 7 - 2 - 12 - 2 = ?$

i.   Add: 4, -2, $+7$, -2, -12, -2

4.11.   Perform the involutions:

   a. $(-2)^5$ *c.* $(-3)^6$ *e.* $(-10)^5$ *g.* $(-7)^3$

   b. $(-5)^2$ *d.* $(-6)^3$ *f.* $(-10)^6$ *h.* $(-3)^7$

4·16 ∾ Certain commonly used scales involving negative numbers

Temperature. Temperatures are designated in various graduated scales on thermometers ("heat measurers") such as the centigrade scale, on which the 0 represents the temperature of the freezing point of water and 100 the boiling point of water under standard conditions. The name centigrade means "hundred-step"; each step, or degree, is identified by the symbol $\circ$, which is written to the right of the specific number. On the centimeter scale the freezing and boiling points of water are 0°C and 100°C, respectively; the temperature of the healthy human body is 37°C; the sun's center about 15,000,000°C, the sun's surface about 6,000°C, the moon's lighted surface ranges from 100°C to -50°C, the dark surface from -50°C to -150°C. Apparently there is no highest possible temperature, just as there is no largest possible natural number; however, there is a lowest possible temperature, which is -273°C, generally referred to as *absolute zero*.

Another familiar temperature scale is the Fahrenheit temperature scale, named after the Prussian scientist Gabriel Daniel Fahrenheit (1686–1736). On this scale the freezing and boiling points of water are, respectively, 32°F and 212°F; the temperature of the healthy human body is slightly above 98°F; the temperature of the moon's surface ranges between around -240°F to $+210$°F.

The readings on the centigrade and Fahrenheit scales, C and F, for the same temperature are related by the formula $5F = 9C + 160$. Thus, five degrees or steps on the centigrade scale are equivalent to nine degrees or steps on the Fahrenheit scale.

Note on symbolism. The signs that denote multiplication, namely, the $\cdot$ and the $\times$, may be omitted, if no possibility of misinterpretation of context can occur by such omission. Thus, $(-2) \times (+7)$ or $(-2) \cdot (+7)$ may appear as $(-2)(+7)$. But 2×3 may not be expressed as 23, for 23 means twenty *and* three, while 2×3 means 6.

To avoid the use of negative temperature readings the Kelvin scale may be used on which absolute zero temperature is represented as zero, while each individual degree step is exactly equivalent to a degree step on the centigrade scale. Thus, $0°K = -273°C$, $273°K = 0°C$. The relationship between readings of the same temperature on these two scales is $K = C + 273$. Incidentally, this latter scale is named in honor of the British scientist Lord Kelvin, né William Thomson (1824–1907).

Height.   The height of a place on the earth is measured in terms of the number of feet above or below sea level.   On this scale the average level of the ocean is called zero elevation; heights above sea level are designated by positive numbers, depths below sea level by negative numbers.   Formerly, the extreme elevations in the United States both occurred in California: the top of Mt. Whitney is 14,495 feet and the floor of Death Valley is −282 feet.   With the admission of Alaska as a state the highest point is now Mt. McKinley, 20,320. The extreme elevations on the surface of the entire world are the top of Mt. Everest between India and China, which is 29,028 feet, and the surface of the Dead Sea between Israel and Jordan, −1,296.   The greatest depth of ocean, −36,198 feet, occurs in the Marianas Trench off the coast of the Philippines.

Latitude and Longitude.   Positions on the surface of the earth are specified by means of latitude and longitude.   Thus the latitude of all positions along the earth's equator is designated as zero latitude; all positions north of the equator have positive latitudes; all positions south of the equator have negative latitudes.   The extreme latitudes are $+90°$ at the North Pole and $-90°$ at the South Pole.   The latitude of Los Angeles, Calif., is $+34°$, the latitude of Buenos Aires, Argentina, is $-34°$.   Lines on the surface of the earth extending from one pole to the other are called meridians, or "mid-day" lines, since it is noon, or mid-day, at the same time along the same meridian.   These meridians are marked off into 180 steps, or degrees, from pole to pole, $1°, 2°, 3°, \ldots,$ $90°$, from the equator to the North Pole, and $-1°, -2°, -3°, \ldots, -90°$, from the equator to the South Pole.   Longitude is measured eastward and westward from the prime meridian, the meridian that passes through the site of the Greenwich Observatory near London, which was established in 1675. Longitudes west of the Greenwich meridian are regarded as positive and are measured as $1°, 2°, \ldots, 180°$, or $1°W, 2°W, \ldots$; longitudes east of the prime meridian are negative, and are expressed as $-1°, -2°, -3°, \ldots,$ $-180°$, or $1°E, 2°E, 3°E, \ldots, 180°E$.   For greater accuracy, 1 degree is subdivided into 60 equal parts, called *minutes* ("small parts"); each minute is subdivided into 60 equal parts called *seconds* (meaning "second subdivisions"). The ancient Babylonians, who appear to have initiated this *sexagesimal* system, continued to subdivide each smaller unit into 60 equal parts, thus making 1 second equal to 60 *thirds*, one third equal to 60 *fourths*, etc.   The symbols for degree, minute, second, third, are, respectively, $°, \prime, \prime\prime, \prime\prime\prime$.   The symbol for the degree, the °, was suggested perhaps by the complete circle originally divided up into 360 equal parts called *degrees.*

$$60'' = 1'$$
$$60' = 1°$$
$$360° = \text{entire circle}$$

Longitude is also measured in time units: hours, minutes, and seconds. Thus westward longitude extends from 0 to +12 hours, eastward longitude extends from 0 to −12 hours. Accordingly 1° is equivalent to 4 minutes of time, 1 hour of time is equivalent to 15°. The longitude of four cities may be written as follows:

San Francisco	+122°25′	or	+8 hr 9 min 40 sec
New York	+ 73°59′		+4 hr 55 min 54 sec
Moscow	− 37°34′		−2 hr 30 min 16 sec
Tokyo	−139°46′		−9 hr 19 min 4 sec

Financial Status. Financial status may be represented in positive or negative numbers, positive numbers denoting assets or resources, negative numbers denoting debts and obligations to be met. Thus if a person owns property worth $45,000, has money on deposit amounting to $23,000 but owes $42,000, his net worth or financial status is the sum of the integers $45,000, $23,000, −$42,000, namely, $26,000. If, however, his debts amounted to $90,000, his financial status would be $45,000 + 23,000 − 90,000 = −22,000$, or a net deficiency of $22,000.

Dates. Historical dates may be expressed with positive or negative integers, with reference to a specific event as marking the zero date. Our present system of using the date of the birth of Jesus of Nazareth as the zero date was introduced over 1,400 years ago by the distinguished mathematician and astronomer Dionysius Exiguus in Rome; dates after the accepted date of the birth of Jesus are reckoned as positive, earlier events are dated as negative. Columbus discovered America in the year +1,492; Socrates was executed in −399. However, instead of using the + and − signs, one generally uses the letters A.D. (anno Domini—from the year of the Lord), and B.C. (before Christ), respectively. Incidentally, although the zero date marks the separation of dates as A.D., or +, and B.C. or −, more recent researches in history indicate that the actual birth of Jesus of Nazareth more probably occurred prior to the zero date.

PROBLEMS [CONCLUDED]

4.12. Calculate the differences between the temperatures of the dark and the light sides of the moon in: (*a*) the centigrade scale, (*b*) the Fahrenheit scale, (*c*) the Kelvin scale.

4.13. The + and − signs, as signs of operation, denote deposits and withdrawals, respectively. They also denote quality signs, the status of the account itself. Indicate the status of the account at the end of each of 10 consecutive business days, if the transactions on each day are the following:

Day 1 +$1,500.00	Day 5 −$435.25	Day 8 +$1,250.00
Day 2 −$255.00	Day 6 +$20.00	Day 9 −$115.40
Day 3 +$165.75	Day 7 −$1,000.00	Day 10 −$159.65
Day 4 +$20.55		

When was this account at a maximum? When at a minimum?

4.14. *a.* Which event occurred later, and by how many years? The founding of Rome in 753 B.C.; the assassination of Julius Caesar in 44 B.C.

    b. Compute the length of the reign of Augustus Caesar who died in 14 A.D. after becoming emperor in 31 B.C.

4.15. An eccentric uncle follows the practice of giving his nephews and nieces birthday checks in dollars, determined as follows: the product of the nephew's (or niece's) height in inches by his (or her) age in years added to the difference obtained by subtracting his (or her) weight in pounds from 140 pounds.

    a. How much does Frank receive this year, if he weighs 160 pounds and is 5 feet, 2 inches tall on his fifteenth birthday?

    b. How much does Nell receive, if she is 3 years older than Frank, is 1 foot, 1 inch shorter, and 50 pounds lighter than Frank?

4.16. How much did the two persons in the preceding problem receive 2 years ago, if Frank grew 4 inches and Nell 1 inch during these years, while Frank gained 20 pounds and Nell lost 5 pounds?

*N*ote 1 ↔ *The logical validity of the*
    rules of operations upon integers.

The correctness of the rules of operation upon integers as presented in this lesson cannot be established by use of the rules of operation upon the natural numbers that were previously established. Now these basic operations, addition, multiplication, and involution, and their inverses, subtraction, division, evolution, and indexing, when performed upon integers, must be so defined as to be equivalent to the same operations upon the natural numbers whenever the integers are all positive, as positive integers are identical with the natural numbers. One must simply assume that the rules of operation upon integers, as presented in this lesson, are universally valid, or one must devise arbitrary machinery by which these rules of operation upon integers may be logically proved to be correct. This latter method of proof is provided in Note 2.

    The validity of the rules of operation upon *integers* may be established by *assuming* a persistent, continuing behavior of certain special results of operations upon *natural numbers*, as the involved series of natural numbers is extended through the zero and the negative integers. The ensuing examples should clarify this procedure.

The rules for adding a positive integer and zero and for adding a positive integer and a negative integer evolve as follows:

$2 + 3 = 5$
$2 + 2 = 4$
$2 + 1 = 3$
$2 + 0 = 2$
$2 + (-1) = 1$
$2 + (-2) = 0$
$2 + (-3) = -1$
$2 + (-4) = -2$
$2 + (-5) = -3$

One observes that the first of these two addends remains unchanged, namely 2, while the second addend, 3, is replaced by the next smaller natural number 2, which in the next line is replaced by the next smaller natural number 1. While these replacements of natural numbers are made, the resulting sums also diminish by 1 in each ensuing line, namely, 5, 4, 3. As natural numbers are the same as positive integers, these natural numbers may be regarded as integers, omitting their positive signs. By continuing to replace the second integer in each ensuing line, and assuming that the sums will also continue to decrease by 1 in each ensuing line, one arrives at the evolvement of the two rules of addition of integers, if one of them is positive.

To establish the rule of addition of two negative integers, one again devises a series of additions, as follows:

$5 + (-3) = 2$
$4 + (-3) = 1$
$3 + (-3) = 0$
$2 + (-3) = -1$
$1 + (-3) = -2$
$0 + (-3) = -3$
$-1 + (-3) = -4$
$-2 + (-3) = -5$

The first three lines are valid from the previous paragraph. Continuing the series of natural numbers as positive integers in the first and third columns, namely, 5, 4, 3, 2, 1, and 2, 1, to 0 and the negative integers, the rule of addition of two negative integers emerges.

The following lines exhibit the emergence of the rules of subtraction of integers. Again, the natural numbers are to be regarded as identical with the positive integers.

$4 - 3 = 1$	$5 - 3 = 2$	$4 - (-3) = 7$
$4 - 2 = 2$	$4 - 3 = 1$	$3 - (-3) = 6$
$4 - 1 = 3$	$3 - 3 = 0$	$2 - (-3) = 5$
$4 - 0 = 4$	$2 - 3 = -1$	$1 - (-3) = 4$
$4 - (-1) = 5$	$1 - 3 = -2$	$0 - (-3) = 3$
$4 - (-2) = 6$	$0 - 3 = -3$	$-1 - (-3) = 2$
$4 - (-3) = 7$	$-1 - 3 = -4$	$-2 - (-3) = 1$
$4 - (-4) = 8$	$-2 - 3 = -5$	$-3 - (-3) = 0$
$4 - (-5) = 9$	$-3 - 3 = -6$	$-4 - (-3) = -1$
$4 - (-6) = 10$	$-4 - 3 = -7$	$-5 - (-3) = -2$

The emergence of the rules of algebraic multiplication may be effected as follows, obtaining first the multiplication of a negative integer by a positive integer, the multiplication of a negative integer by a natural number, and then regarding the multiplication as a repeated *addition* of the negative integer, as demonstrated in this note.

$$(-4) \times 2 = (-4) + (-4) = -8$$
$$(-4) \times 3 = (-4) + (-4) + (-4) = -12$$

Then the other rules of multiplication of integers may be made to emerge as follows:

$4 \times 2 = 8$	$-3 \times 4 = -12$
$3 \times 2 = 6$	$-3 \times 2 = -6$
$2 \times 2 = 4$	$-3 \times 1 = -3$
$1 \times 2 = 2$	$-3 \times 0 = 0$
$0 \times 2 = 0$	$-3 \times (-1) = 3$
$-1 \times 2 = -2$	$-3 \times (-2) = 6$
$-2 \times 2 = -4$	$-3 \times (-3) = 9$
$-3 \times 2 = -6$	$-3 \times (-4) = 12$

Again, the original lines in each development involve the well-established multiplications of natural numbers. Ensuing lines alter by 1 these natural numbers, and the natural numbers of the products are examined as to their ensuing behavior. As the lines are extended, the persistent behaviors of the products cause the rules of multiplication of integers to emerge.

These induction proofs of the rules of operation upon the integers are completed by *assuming* similar behaviors ensuing from any initially selected natural numbers. Under all the assumptions in the preceding discussions one establishes the universal validity of the rules of operation upon the numbers comprising the complete system of integers.

Certain assumptions were made in the foregoing discussions regarding the persistence of behavior of the resulting sums, differences, and products of special natural numbers in their roles as positive integers as these integers are replaced step by step by ensuing integers. Although these assumptions do lead to workable and universally accepted rules of addition, subtraction, and multiplication for all integers, one must realize that such assumptions in other circumstances may lead to absurd results. Samples of such fantastic results are provided in the following three examples:

John's heights on his ninth, tenth, and eleventh birthdays were 48 inches, 50 inches, and 52 inches, respectively. Assuming that he continues to grow 2 inches each year, how tall will he be on his twenty-first and eighty-first birthdays? Answers: 72 inches or 6 feet; 192 inches or 16 feet.

Mr. Nick O'Teen smokes two more cigarettes each ensuing day prior to his demise, or "zero day"; if on the fifth day before this transition day he smoked 79 cigarettes, how many cigarettes did he smoke on the fifth day following his zero day? The extended table appears thus:

5	79	1	87	-3	95	
4	81	0	89	-4	97	
3	83	-1	91	-5	99	cigarettes on the specified day
2	85	-2	93			

The "Big Bang Hypothesis" of one group of astronomers utilizes the fact that the remote galaxies, or "island universes," all appear to be receding from us at velocities that are proportional to their distance. Then working backward in time they compute the instant when they began their journey at the very beginning of time and substance in one tiny atom.

What assumptions are necessary so that these three examples will yield valid (correct) results?

*N*ote 2 ⟿ *Introduction of integers as pairs of natural numbers.*

The method of introducing new kinds of numbers as pairs of numbers already available is logically proper. Thus, the integer is regarded as a pair of natural numbers, the fraction as a pair of integers, and finally the complex number as a pair of real numbers, as will be presented in following lessons.

Definitions. An integer is a pair of natural numbers, symbolically represented as (a,b), in which a and b represent any natural numbers whatever. If a and b are the *same* natural number, as (a,a), the integer is called *zero;* if a is larger than b, the integer is called a *positive* integer; if b is larger than a, the integer (a,b) is called a *negative* integer. Examples of zero: (3,3), (28,28), or (1000,1000). There are as many different ways of expressing the integer zero as there are different natural numbers. Two integers, (a,b) and (c,d), are said to be equal if $a + d = b + c$. Thus, $(9,28) = (2,21)$ because $9 + 21 = 28 + 2 = 30$; $(5,3) = (11,9)$, because $5 + 9 = 3 + 11 = 14$. The same integer may also be expressed in many different ways, using different natural numbers.

The sum, difference, and product of two integers, (a,b) and (c,d), are defined as follows:

$$(a,b) + (c,d) = (a + c, b + d)$$
$$(a,b) - (c,d) = (a + d, b + c)$$
$$(a,b) \times (c,d) = (ac + bd, ad + bc)$$

By use of the foregoing definitions, one may prove that integers also obey the five laws that were previously shown to be valid for natural numbers, namely, the commutative, associative, and distributive laws. To prove the commutative law of addition for integers $(a,b) + (c,d) = (c,d) + (a,b)$, observe that

$$(a,b) + (c,d) = (a + c, b + d)$$
$$(c,d) + (a,b) = (c + a, d + b) = (a + c, b + d)$$

since $c + a = a + c$ and $d + b = b + d$, as a, b, c, d are natural numbers which do obey the commutative law. The student will find satisfaction in proving the other four laws.

One may also prove the rules of operation of integers that were presented in this lesson, namely, that the product of two positive integers is equal to a positive integer, etc. If the absolute value of an integer (a,b) is defined as the arithmetical difference between the two natural numbers a and b, one proves that the product of two negative integers is a positive integer whose absolute value is equal to the product of their absolute values, as follows.

Note that if a, b, h, and k are natural numbers, the two integers $(a, a + h)$ and $(b, b + k)$ are negative and have h and k as their respective absolute values. Then, by definition of product for integers,

$$(a, a + h)(b, b + k) = (ab + ab + ak + ah + bh,\ ab + ak + ab + bh)$$
$$= (hk + bh, bh)$$

which is a positive integer of absolute value hk, which is equal to the product of the absolute values of $(a, a + h)$ and $(b, b + k)$, respectively. The student should find satisfaction in proving all other previously stated rules of operations upon integers.

Finally, to identify the number pairs with the integers as previously defined as numbers representing equally spaced positions on the unending number line on which two consecutive positions were taken as 0 and as 1, positions to the right of 0 as representing the positive integers as identical with the natural numbers, and positions to the left of the 0 as representing the negative integers and symbolized by the natural numbers with the dash — prefixed to them, one states that (a, a) is identical with 0; (a, b) is identical with the positive integer $+(a - b)$, if a is larger than b, or is equal to the negative integer $-(b - a)$, if b is larger than a. As examples:

(3,3) is identical with 0;
$(7,3) = (5,1)$, which are identical with $7 - 3 = 4$
$(2,8) = (1,7)$, which are identical with $-(8 - 2)$, or -6

To assure one of complete understanding of this note, one should perform the indicated operations upon integers as number pairs and identify all number pairs with their more familiar representation as $+a$ and $-a$, in which a is a natural number:

$(3,5) + (6,2) - (6,12) = ?$
$(2,5)(7,3) = ?$ $(8,3)(12,5) = ?$ $(1,6)(4,11) = ?$
$(3,7)^2 = ?$ $(5,2)^5 = ?$ $(5,6)^7 = ?$ $(12,11)^3 = ?$
$(2,6) + (7,2)(8,4) - (5,2)(2,5) + (45,40) - (101,97) - (87,101) = ?$

∾ SUPPLEMENTARY PROBLEMS ∾

*Genius is one per cent inspiration
and ninety-nine per cent perspiration.*

—Thomas A. Edison.

Perform the subtractions in Problems S4.1 to S4.5. Check each individual part of each problem by noting that the sum of the difference and subtrahend must be the minuend.

Then note that the sum of all differences and all the subtrahends must equal the sum of all the minuends of each of the five problems.

S4.1. *a.* $7 - 4$ *e.* $13 - 8$ *h.* $7 - 15$

    b. $12 - 7$ *f.* $5 - 8$ *i.* $8 - 17$

    c. $15 - 9$ *g.* $6 - 13$ *j.* $9 - 14$

    d. $11 - 4$

S4.2. *a.* 28   *e.* 86   *i.* 25   *m.* 6
          19   27   38   19

    b. 79   *f.* 91   *j.* 43   *n.* 0
          35   52   77   21

    c. 41   *g.* 93   *k.* 19   *o.* 44
          29   79   33   49

    d. 73   *h.* 78   *l.* 12   *p.* 56
          47   58   21   72

S4.3. *a.* $+138$ *c.* -750 *e.* -119
         $+318$ -987 $+73$

    b. -362 *d.* $+101$ *f.* -251
         $+400$ -67 -312

S4.4. *a.* 1,253,701   *c.* 34,776,231   *e.* 3,462,923   *g.* 34,785,900
         1,087,456   11,782,421   8,230,421   42,234,200

    b. 5,002,103   *d.* 10,340,101   *f.* 1,002,347   *h.* 23,789,500
         2,365,812   9,562,678   9,234,110   31,345,250

S4.5. *a.* $385 - 975$ *c.* $-642 - 831$ *e.* $-63 - (-91)$ *g.* $57 - 275$

    b. $107 - 86$ *d.* $47 - (-59)$ *f.* $512 - 1{,}024$ *h.* $5{,}280 - 7{,}000$

Obtain the algebraic sum of the four evaluations in each part, (*a*) through (*d*), of Problems S4.6 through S4.10.

S4.6. *a.* $4 + 5 \times 3 + 8$ *c.* $4 + 5 \times (3 + 8)$

    b. $(4 + 5) \times 3 + 8$ *d.* $(4 + 5)(3 + 8)$

S4.7. *a.* $3 - 5 \times 2 + 3 - 5 \times 4$ *c.* $3 - 5(2 + 3 - 5) \times 4$

    b. $3 - 5(2 + 3) - 5 \times 4$ *d.* $(3 - 5) \times 2 + 3 - (5 \times 4)$

S4.8. *a.* $37 + 62 \times 97 + 46$ *c.* $37 + 62(97 + 46)$

    b. $(37 + 62) \times 97 + 46$ *d.* $(37 + 62)(97 + 46)$

S4.9. *a.* $35 - 56 \times 27 + 38 \times 59$ *c.* $35 - (56 \times 27 + 38) \times 59$

    b. $(35 - 56) \times 27 + 38 \times 59$ *d.* $(35 - 56)(27 + 38) \times 59$

S4.10. *a.* $(-2)^3 + (-3)^2 - (-5)(-6) + (-9)(-2)(-5) - (65)$

    b. $(-3)^3 - (-2)^2 + (+5)(-6) - (-7)(-6)(-5) + (75)$

    c. $(-5)^3 + (-6)^2 - (-4)(-3)(-2) + (-1)(-2)(-3)(-4)$

    d. $(2 \times 3 + 3 \times 4 - 4 \times 5) - (5 \times 6 - 7 \times 8 + 9 \times 10)$

S4.11. Perform the algebraic additions:

a. $\quad$ -23	*b.* $\quad$ $+102$	*c.* $\quad$ $-1,238$	*d.* $\quad$ $+23,501,237$
$+55$	$+56$	$+4,557$	$+5,756,625$
$+19$	-372	$-5,000$	$-30,000,000$
-77	$+109$	$+2,734$	$+1,712,338$

S4.12. Perform the algebraic subtractions:

a. $\quad$ -37	*b.* $\quad$ $+76$	*c.* $\quad$ $+125$	*d.* $\quad$ $+142,857$	*e.* $\quad$ $-285,714$
-45	-24	-625	$-428,571$	$-999,999$

S4.13. Which of the following statements are true?

a. $\quad 333^2 + 444^2 = 555^2$ $\qquad$ *d.* $\quad 3^3 + 4^3 + 5^3 = 6^3$

b. $\quad 56^2 + 105^2 = 119^2$ $\qquad$ *e.* $\quad 1^1 + 2^2 + 3^3 = 2^5$

c. $\quad 123^2 + 123^2 + 246^2 = 369^2$ $\qquad$ *f.* $\quad 1^1 + 2^2 + 3^3 + 4^4 = 2^5 \times 3^2$

S4.14. A person borrows $100 from the Hyjack Loan Company, agreeing to repay $10 at the end of each month for 1 year. How much does he repay in addition to the original $100?

S4.15. Mr. *C* bought a house for $27,375, making a down payment of $12,500. How much does he still owe on the house?

S4.16. From a bolt of cloth containing 75 yards of material, 5 cuttings were made as follows: (*a*) 6 yards; (*b*) 4 yards; (*c*) 18 yards; (*d*) 2 yards; (*e*) 9 yards. How many yards remain on the bolt?

S4.17. Denoting loss as negative and profit as positive, a corporation's losses and gains during six consecutive months are listed as follows:

a. $\quad +\$142,857$ $\qquad$ *c.* $\quad -\$285,714$ $\qquad$ *e.* $\quad +\$571,428$

b. $\quad +\$428,571$ $\qquad$ *d.* $\quad +\$857,142$ $\qquad$ *f.* $\quad -\$714,285$

Compute the net profit or loss during this period. The curious bookkeeper observed that the seven numbers occurring in the calculation are the seven multiples of one of them. Verify this fact.

S4.18. A fund-raising program has a goal of $75,000. One generous sponsor donates $12,375; another donates $3,000. During the first half of the drive the program raises an additional $55,389. How much must be raised during the last half of the drive?

S4.19. The endowments of five universities are listed as follows:

Harvard	$1,013,000,000	
Yale	457,052,000	How does the endowment of Harvard com-
Princeton	208,340,000	pare with the sum of the other four endow-
M. I. T.	190,722,000	ments in this list?
Stanford	163,757,033	

S4.20. Which is the shortest road by mileage from Los Angeles to New York, and by how much, according to these two courses?

From Los Angeles to Chicago, 2,175 miles

From Los Angeles to New Orleans, 1,976 miles

From Chicago to New York, 850 miles

From New Orleans to New York, 1,208 miles

S4.21. At the beginning of a vacation trip the automobile odometer registered 3,529 miles; at the end of the five successive days it read, respectively, (day 1) 3,813, (day 2) 4,297, (day 3) 4,507, (day 4) 4,911, (day 5) 5,468. (*a*) Calculate the total mileage driven. (*b*) On which day was the most mileage driven? (*c*) On which day was the least mileage driven?

S4.22. How much change should one receive from a $20 bill on the following purchase of groceries?

4 dozen eggs @ 72 cents per dozen
3 sacks of potatoes @ $1.29 per sack
2 dozen oranges @ 4 cents for each orange
3 cans of peaches @ 43 cents per can
5 loaves of bread @ 38 cents per loaf

S4.23. Compute the average yearly profit realized by the loan company of Problem S4.14, if it makes an average of 200 loans each year, if 3 loans are total losses, and if an average of 12 borrowers each year make only 6 monthly repayments. All other borrowers repay on schedule.

S4.24. Which person earns the higher yearly salary and by how much? Mr. *A* earns $19 per day during each week of 5 days; Mr. *B* earns $16 per day during each week of 6 days (52 weeks = 1 year).

S4.25. Mr. *X* has property worth $45,900, but owes three notes of $4,500 each and two of $5,775 each. How much is he actually worth?

S4.26. What is the difference in elevation between the top of Mt. Everest, which is 29,028 feet above sea level, and the surface of the Dead Sea, which is 1,296 feet below sea level?

S4.27. Which has the greater area, and by how much, New England or Missouri? The New England states are Maine, New Hampshire, Vermont, Massachusetts, Rhode Island, and Connecticut. Their individual populations and areas as of 1965 are listed as follows:

Connecticut	2,830,000	5,009 square miles
Maine	986,000	33,215 square miles
Massachusetts	5,361,000	8,257 square miles
Missouri	4,492,000	69,686 square miles
New Hampshire	673,000	9,304 square miles
Rhode Island	884,000	1,214 square miles
Vermont	404,000	9,609 square miles

S4.28. Which has the greater population, and by how much, the New England states or Missouri?

S4.29. By how much does the area of Alaska exceed the total areas of the next three largest states of the United States, if their areas are listed as follows:

Alaska	586,400 square miles
Texas	267,339 square miles
California	158,693 square miles
Montana	147,138 square miles

S4.30. Compute the difference between the numerical data of the two canals and state what this difference represents.

Panama 1914: 51 miles long, 300 feet minimum width, 40 feet minimum depth
Suez   1869: 104 miles long, 500 feet minimum width, 37 feet minimum depth

S4.31. Compute the difference in the number of transits and tons of cargo passing through these two canals during 1965. Why is there inconsistency in the two results?

Panama: 11,384 transits with 76,573,071 tons
Suez: 6,733 transits with 82,909,000 tons

S4.32. The seating capacity of the major league baseball stadiums in 1967 were listed as follows. By how much did the combined capacity of one league exceed that of the other?

American league		National league	
Cleveland Municipal	78,184	Dodger Stadium	56,000
Yankee Stadium	67,000	Shea Stadium	53,300
Tiger Stadium	53,089	Atlanta Stadium	50,893
Baltimore Memorial	52,185	Busch Stadium	49,491
Comisky Park	46,550	Astrodome	44,500
Minnesota Metropolitan		Candlestick Park	42,561
Stadium	45,182	Wrigley Field	36,644
District of Columbia	45,016	Forbes Field	35,000
Anaheim Stadium	43,204	Connie Mack Stadium	33,608
Fenway Park	33,524	Crosley Field	29,468
Kansas City Municipal			
Stadium	32,561		

S4.33. Check the correctness of the following statements:

a. $2 + 2 = 2^2$ a'. $2 + 2 = 2^2$

b. $2 + 2 + 2^2 = 2^3$ b'. $2^2 + 2^2 = 2^3$

c. $2 + 2 + 2^2 + 2^3 = 2^4$ c'. $2^3 + 2^3 = 2^4$

d. $2 + 2 + 2^2 + 2^3 + 2^4 = 2^5$ d'. $2^4 + 2^4 = 2^5$

Continue these statements as far as $2 + 2 + 2^2 + 2^3 + 2^4 + 2^5 + 2^6 + 2^7 + 2^8 + 2^9 + 2^{10} = 2^{11}$ and $2^{10} + 2^{10} = 2^{11}$.

S4.34. Study the following procedure to prove that the statements in Problem S4.33 are correct as far as one may extend them. Note that:

a. The sum of two equal numbers is equal to twice the number so repeated; thus, $2^n + 2^n = 2 \times 2^n$.

b. $2 \times 2^n = 2^{n+1}$, as this means merely one more use of 2 as a factor.

If $2 + 2 + 2^2 + 2^3 + \cdots + 2^n = 2^{n+1}$, then by adding 2^{n+1} to each member of this equality that is known to be true, the resulting statement must also be true. Thus it must be true that:

$$2 + 2 + 2^2 + 2^3 + \cdots + 2^n + 2^{n+1} = 2^{n+1} + 2^{n+1} = 2^{n+2}$$

Therefore, if any of the statements in Problem S4.33 is correct, the next statement must also be correct. Hence all such statements must be correct, however large the highest exponent of 2 may be that occurs in them.

The following problems (S4.35–S4.42) concern Fibonacci numbers. (See Section S·19.)

S4.35. The Fibonacci numbers are defined as follows, in which F_k represents the kth Fibonacci number: $F_1 = 1$, $F_2 = 1$, $F_3 = 2$, $F_4 = 3$. Quite generally, the sum of any two consecutive Fibonacci numbers is equal to the next ensuing Fibonacci number. Thus, the first 10 such numbers are

1, 1, 2, 3, 5, 8, 13, 21, 34, 55

    a. Extend this list to include the first 30 Fibonacci numbers by noting that $F_n + F_{n+1} = F_{n+2}$.

    b. By reversing the rule of formation of these numbers extend the list backward to 20 Fibonacci numbers preceding F_1, namely, $F_0 = 0$, $F_{-1} = 1$, $F_{-2} = -1, \ldots$.

    c. State the relationship between F_n and F_{-n}.

S4.36. Compute the sums:
$$F_1 + F_2 = ? \qquad F_1 + F_2 + F_3 = ? \qquad F_1 + F_2 + F_3 + F_4 = ?$$
Continue this series of additions until you recognize how to obtain the sum of any arbitrary number of Fibonacci numbers from F_1 to F_n, inclusive, without having to add them.

S4.37. If you have surmised that $F_1 + F_2 + F_3 + \cdots + F_n = F_{n+2} - 1$ in the previous problem, prove that this surmise is universally correct by adding F_{n+1} to each member of the equality and then by replacing the sum of the two terms on the right side of the equality sign, namely, $F_{n+1} + F_{n+2}$ by its equivalent F_{n+3} according to the definition of Fibonacci numbers. Obtain the sum of the 30 Fibonacci numbers in Problem S4.35*a* without adding them.

S4.38. Verify the sums of consecutive Fibonacci numbers:

    a. $F_3 + F_4 + F_5 + F_6 = F_8 - F_4$

    b. $F_9 + F_{10} + F_{11} + F_{12} + F_{13} + F_{14} = F_{16} - F_{10}$

    c. $F_{-4} + F_{-3} + F_{-2} + F_{-1} + F_0 + F_1 + F_2 + F_3 + F_4 + F_5 = F_7 - F_{-3}$

    d. Why should the sum of consecutive Fibonacci numbers from F_k to F_{k+n}, inclusive, be equal to $F_{k+n+2} - F_{k+1}$?

S4.39. Verify that the sum of the even-numbered Fibonacci numbers beginning with F_2 and ending with F_{2k} is equal to $F_{2k+1} - 1$, for the following:
$$F_2 + F_4 = ? \qquad F_2 + F_4 + F_6 = ? \qquad F_2 + F_4 + F_6 + F_8 = ?$$
Show that this relationship is always true.

S4.40. Obtain the rule for the sum of any number of consecutive even-numbered Fibonacci numbers, by testing the sum:
$$F_4 + F_6 = ? \qquad F_6 + F_8 + F_{10} + F_{12} + F_{14} = ?$$
Verify that your rule also holds for the sum of *any* consecutive set of even-numbered Fibonacci numbers. Then test the rule for the sums:
$$F_{-4} + F_{-2} + F_0 + F_2 + F_4 + F_6 = ?$$
$$F_{-10} + F_{-8} + F_{-6} + F_{-4} = ?$$

S4.41. Verify that the sum of odd-numbered Fibonacci numbers beginning with F_1 and ending with F_{2k-1} is equal to F_{2k}, for the following:
$$F_1 + F_3 = ? \qquad F_1 + F_3 + F_5 = ? \qquad F_1 + F_3 + F_5 + F_7 = ?$$

S4.42. Obtain the rule for the sum of any number of consecutive odd-numbered Fibonacci numbers, by first testing the sums:
$$F_3 + F_5 = ? \qquad F_5 + F_7 + F_9 + F_{11} = ?$$
Verify that your rule holds for the sum of *any* set of consecutive odd-numbered Fibonacci numbers. Then test the rule for the sums:
$$F_{-5} + F_{-3} + F_{-1} + F_1 = ? \qquad F_{-9} + F_{-7} + F_{-5} + F_{-3} = ?$$

The remaining problems concern magic squares. (See Sections S·4–S·7.)

S4.43. Insert the correct number in each of the vacant spaces so that the sum of the three numbers in each row, in each column, and in each long diagonal is 15.

a.

	1	
4		2

b.

2		
9	5	

Note that each corner number, such as the 2, is equal to half the sum of two other "remote mid-numbers." Note also that nine consecutive *natural numbers* occur in the completed squares.

Now complete the following three squares by inserting appropriate *integers* so that the sums of rows, columns, and diagonals in them are 0, 3, and 12, respectively. Note the two features indicated in the preceding remarks.

3	−4	
−2		

4		
−1	1	

3	4	
	−1	

S4.44. *a.* Insert the correct natural numbers in the vacant spaces so that the four numbers in each row, column, diagonal, and in each set of four adjoining spaces to form a square have the same sum, namely, 34. Thus, the upper right corner number must be 15, so that the sum 1 + 8 + 10 + 15 is 34. Also the space occupied by letter *a* must contain 11 so that the array of adjoining spaces must have numbers that yield the sum 34, that is, 8 + 10 + 11 + 5 = 34. Note that the completed array must contain 16 consecutive natural numbers.

1	8	10	
	a	5	
		16	

b. Now complete the three squares by supplying appropriate integers so that the four integers in each row, column, diagonal, and set of four adjoining spaces forming squares have the indicated sum +2, −6, 14, respectively.

	−7	0	2
			−3
			8

Sum: 2

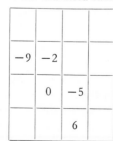

Sum: −6

Sum: 14

S4.45. Let the letters a, b, c, . . . , p, represent the numbers in the magic square, as indicated: Note that the properties of the square survive if adjoining rows are moved from top to bottom of the array, or if adjoining columns are removed from one side to the other of the array. Any particular number in the array may be shifted to any other position of the array. Thus moving the top row to the bottom and then the right column to left, one has:

a	b	c	d
e	f	g	h
i	j	k	l
m	n	o	p

h	e	f	g
l	i	j	k
p	m	n	o
d	a	b	c

Obtain the 16 adjoining numbers

$$\frac{a}{e} \quad \frac{b}{f}, \quad \frac{b}{f} \quad \frac{c}{g}, \quad \cdots, \quad \frac{k}{o} \quad \frac{l}{p}$$

that have the same sum. Obtain also the eight "broken rows" having the same sum, as

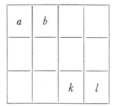 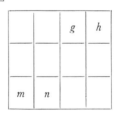 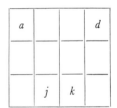

Also obtain the eight "broken columns." Obtain the six broken diagonals, as

a			
			h
		k	
	n		

Also note the eight pairs, $a + k$, $b + l$, $c + i$, and so on, that yield half the required sum. Obtain also the four arrays that yield the correct sum, as

a	c
i	k

LESSON 5 �֍ DIVISION OF NATURAL NUMBERS ✣ FRACTIONS ✣ SYSTEM OF RATIONAL NUMBERS

Gallia est omnis divisa in partes tres.
(The entire extent of Gaul, or Ancient France,
is divided up into three sections.)

—Julius Caesar, *The Gallic War. I*, 1.

5·1 ∿ Division as the inverse operation of multiplication

One recalls that the operation of multiplication of natural numbers a and b, designated by $a \times b$ and read as "a multiplied by b," means obtaining the sum $a + a + a + \cdots + a$, in which a is used b times as an addend. Thus, if $a \times b = c$, the inverse operation $a \times ? = c$, symbolically expressed as $c \div a = ?$, means that a is repeatedly subtracted from c until a final difference of zero is obtained. The required result of the operation, called the *quotient*, is the *number of times* that a must be subtracted to yield 0. If $c - a - a - a - \cdots = 0$, the number of a's used is the required result.

Let 37×4 be read as "37 multiplied by 4," whence 37×4 means $37 + 37 + 37 + 37 = 148$. Accordingly, the inverse operation of *division*, namely, $148 \div 37 = ?$, may be performed as follows:

$$
\begin{aligned}
148 - 37 &= 111 \quad &\text{(First subtraction)} \\
111 - 37 &= 74 \quad &\text{(Second subtraction)} \\
74 - 37 &= 37 \quad &\text{(Third subtraction)} \\
37 - 37 &= 0 \quad &\text{(Fourth subtraction)}
\end{aligned}
$$

As *four* subtractions were required to obtain a final difference of 0, the required result of the division is 4. Thus, $148 \div 37 = 4$. The Latin words describe the character of the three numbers used in the division operation; thus in this example:

148 is the *dividend*, meaning "that which is divided, or separated, or broken asunder."

37 is the *divisor*, or "that which does the separating or dividing."

4 is the *quotient*, meaning "how many times?"

5·2 ∿ Simple methods of performing division of natural numbers

The operation $148 \div 4 = 37$ would be quite tedious by repeatedly subtracting 4, as it would involve 37 individual subtractions. Hence, the work is considerably shortened to involve only two multiplications and subtractions, indicated as follows:

$$
\begin{array}{rl}
148 & \text{The original dividend} \\
100 & \text{Subtracting 25 fours in one step; } 25 \times 4 = 100 \\
\hline
48 & \\
48 & \text{Subtracting 12 fours in one step; } 12 \times 4 = 48 \\
\hline
0 & \text{The required ultimate remainder to complete the division}
\end{array}
$$

As there were altogether 25 and 12 subtractions of 4 to produce a final remainder of 0, the required quotient is $25 + 12$, or 37.

The customary method of performing division by repeated subtractions is called "long division." This procedure in each successive subtraction employs one of the first nine integral multiples of the divisor, which is then multiplied by the highest possible power of 10 to yield the largest possible subtrahend that does not exceed the corresponding minuend. The quotient is written above the dividend, digit by digit, from left to right, as the successive multipliers of the divisor that yield the successive subtrahends, respectively. Two illustrations should clarify the procedure:

$148 \div 4 = ?$

$$
\begin{array}{r}
37 \\
\hline
4\,|\,148
\end{array}
$$

$$
\begin{array}{rl}
120 & (3 \times 4 \times 10 = 120;\ \text{place the multiplier 3, to represent 30, in} \\
\hline
28 & \text{quotient above 4)} \\
28 & (7 \times 4 = 28,\ \text{place the multiplier 7 in quotient above 8)} \\
\hline
0 & \text{Required final remainder}
\end{array}
$$

$197{,}832 \div 8 = ?$

$$
\begin{array}{r}
24729 \\
\hline
8\,|\,197832
\end{array}
$$

$$
\begin{array}{rl}
160000 & (2 \times 8 \times 10^4;\ \text{place the multiplier 2, to represent 20,000, in} \\
\hline
37832 & \text{quotient above 9)} \\
32000 & (4 \times 8 \times 10^3;\ \text{place the multiplier 4, to represent 4,000, in} \\
\hline
5832 & \text{quotient above 7)} \\
5600 & (7 \times 8 \times 10^2;\ \text{place the multiplier 7, to represent 700, in} \\
\hline
232 & \text{quotient above 8)} \\
160 & (2 \times 8 \times 10;\ \text{place the multiplier 2, to represent 20, in quotient} \\
\hline
72 & \text{above 3)} \\
72 & (9 \times 8;\ \text{place the multiplier 9 in quotient above 2)} \\
\hline
0 & \text{Required final remainder}
\end{array}
$$

Thus, the quotient 24,729, as $20{,}000 + 4{,}000 + 700 + 20 + 9$, indicates the total number of 8s that have been subtracted from the dividend 197,832 to yield the final remainder 0.   Each individual digit of the quotient indicates by its *value* and *position* in the quotient the number of times the divisor is subtracted in the corresponding step of the division.

The written portion of the solution may be somewhat shortened by omitting the zeros of the associated appropriate powers of 10 in the successive subtrahends. Thus:

```
       24729
  8│197832
    16
    ──
    37
    32
    ──
     58
     56
     ──
      23
      16
      ──
       72
       72
       ──
        0
```

If the divisor is a number of one digit, as in the two illustrative examples, the written work may be greatly simplified into a form called "short division." One performs the successive multiplications and subtractions mentally and writes only the digits of the quotient as the successive multipliers of the divisor as they are used.

```
     37           24729
  4│148        8│197832
```

If the divisor consists of more than one digit, the long division form is to be used.   To solve $65{,}536 \div 512 = ?$, one proceeds thus:

```
        128
  512│65536
      512          Subtracting 100 five hundred twelves
      ───
      1433
      1024         Subtracting 20 five hundred twelves
      ────
      4096
      4096         Subtracting 8 five hundred twelves
      ────
         0
```

Note again that the zeros are omitted from the successive subtrahends, that each successive digit of the quotient is written precisely above the final written digit of the corresponding subtrahend, and that the next ensuing (unused) digit of the dividend is transferred to the right of each successive difference to complete the ensuing minuend.   Thus the 1 in the quotient is written precisely above the 2 of 512, the next digit 3 of the dividend is transferred to the right of the difference, 143, to complete the ensuing minuend 1,433.

5·3 ∾ DIVISION OF INTEGERS; THREE EXCEPTIONAL SITUATIONS

In extending the division operation from the system of natural numbers to the complete system of integers, three situations must be noted.   Again, if a, b, c are integers, $c \div b = a$ means $a \cdot b = c$.

If the dividend is zero and the divisor not zero, the quotient is zero.   Thus $0 \div a = 0$, if a represents any integer whatever except 0; this follows from Section 3·6, since $0 \times a = 0$.

If the dividend is not zero, the divisor cannot be zero.   For if integers a,b exist so that $a \div 0 = b$, then $b \times 0 = a$, which is also contrary to Section 3·6.

If the dividend and divisor are both zero, the quotient may represent any integer a whatever, for again $a \times 0 = 0$ implies $0 \div 0 = a$.

Henceforth the last two situations must be avoided.

The rules for performing algebraic division follow directly from corresponding rules for performing algebraic multiplication, since $c \div b = a$ is defined as equivalent to $a \cdot b = c$ for all appropriate integers a, b, c.   The two required rules are:

The absolute value of the quotient is equal to the quotient of the absolute values of the dividend and divisor.

If the signs of dividend and divisor are the same, both signs positive or both signs negative, the sign of the quotient is positive; if the signs of the dividend and divisor are not the same, one being positive and the other negative, the sign of the quotient is negative.

Thus: $(+48) \div (+8) = +6$, or 6 $(+56) \div (-7) = -8$
$(-72) \div (-9) = +8$, or 8 $(-144) \div (+9) = -16$

5·4 ∾ DIVISION IS NOT ASSOCIATIVE.   RULE OF PROCEDURE

The operations $(a \div b) \div c$ and $a \div (b \div c)$ quite generally yield different results, as may be noted by specific examples.

$(32 \div 8) \div 2 = 4 \div 2 = 2$ whereas $32 \div (8 \div 2) = 32 \div 4 = 8$

The joint operations of multiplication and division are also generally not associative.

$(72 \div 8) \times 3 = 9 \times 3 = 27$ whereas $72 \div (8 \times 3) = 72 \div 24 = 3$

The following general rule of procedure has been universally adopted to perform such indicated operations as $32 \div 8 \div 2 = ?$ and $72 \div 8 \times 3 = ?$, namely,

In a given series of operations involving algebraic additions, subtractions, multiplications, divisions, and involutions, one must perform first the multiplications and divisions in the order in which they occur, *then the indicated additions and subtractions. The involutions are repeated multiplications.*

EXAMPLE ∾

Perform the indicated operations and evaluate:

$$3 \times (-6) + 15 \times 4 \div 6 + 3^3 - 84 \div 12 \times 2 = ?$$

Performing first the indicated multiplications, divisions, and involution, as they occur:

1. $3 \times (-6) = -18$ 3. $3^3 = 3 \times 3 \times 3 = 27$
2. $15 \times 4 = 60; 60 \div 6 = 10$ 4. $84 \div 12 = 7; 7 \times 2 = 14$

Inserting these four results in the original line, one obtains $(-18) + 10 + 27 - 14 = +5$, or simply 5.

∾ PROBLEMS ∾

5.1. Obtain the sum of the following indicated divisions of natural numbers:

a.	$72 \div 9 = ?$	*f.*	$28 \div 4 = ?$	*k.*	$64 \div 8 = ?$	*p.*	$81 \div 9 = ?$
b.	$56 \div 8 = ?$	*g.*	$27 \div 3 = ?$	*l.*	$42 \div 7 = ?$	*q.*	$36 \div 6 = ?$
c.	$63 \div 7 = ?$	*h.*	$16 \div 2 = ?$	*m.*	$54 \div 6 = ?$	*r.*	$35 \div 7 = ?$
d.	$48 \div 6 = ?$	*i.*	$9 \div 9 = ?$	*n.*	$30 \div 5 = ?$	*s.*	$32 \div 4 = ?$
e.	$45 \div 5 = ?$	*j.*	$63 \div 9 = ?$	*o.*	$8 \div 4 = ?$	*t.*	$24 \div 3 = ?$

5.2. Use the appropriate method to perform the divisions of natural numbers:

a. $65,538 \div 9 = ?$ *d.* $131,072 \div 256 = ?$
b. $1,919,624 \div 7 = ?$ *e.* $229,585 \div 73 = ?$
c. $98,765,432 \div 8 = ?$ *f.* $55,888,888,833 \div 4,527 = ?$

5.3. Perform the indicated operations upon integers:

a. $(-17,835) \div 123 = ?$ *g.* $2 \times 3 \times (-6) - 8 \times 5 -$
b. $(-17,835) \div (-41) = ?$ $(-720) \div 3 + 5 = ?$
c. $17,835 \div (-205) = ?$ *h.* $(-180) \div (-45)(-3) \div 12 \times$
d. $-331,122 \div (-66) = ?$ $8 \div 4 - (-2)(-6)(-9) \div$
e. $662,244 \div (-33) = ?$ $(-27) = ?$
f. $0 \div 235,875 = ?$ *i.* $(-2)^3 + (-3)^4 + (-5)(-3)$
                $(+2) = ?$

5.4. Evaluate the following expressions. Operations enclosed within each pair of parentheses must be performed, yielding a single number, before continuing with operations not enclosed within sets of parentheses.

    a. $(12 \div 4) \times 3 + (8 \times 6) \div 2 \times 4 - 3 = ?$

    b. $12 \div (4 \times 3) + 8 \times (6 \div 2) \times 4 - 3 = ?$

    c. $12 \div 4 \times (3 + 8) \times 6 \div 2 \times (4 - 3) = ?$

    d. $12 \div (4 \times 3 - 8) \times 6 - (2 \times 4 - 3) = ?$

    e. $(12 \div 4 \times 3 + 8 \times 6) - (2 + 4 - 3) = ?$

5.5. A grandfather divided $1,110 equally among fifteen grandchildren (eight grandsons and seven granddaughters). Five of the grandsons spent their shares for books costing $3.70 each; the other grandsons bought books with their shares at $2 each. Each granddaughter placed $50 in a savings account and invested the remainder in books at $4 each. How many books were bought altogether?

5.6. A tourist drove his automobile exactly 4,009 miles on gasoline costing $65.41, averaging 31 cents per gallon. What was his average mileage per gallon?

5.7. If the profit on a commercial transaction is the difference between the wholesale price and the retail price of the commodity involved, what would be the profit on a crate of eggs containing 144 dozen eggs, if the wholesale price of the crate of eggs is $34.56 and the retail price is 60 cents per dozen?

5.8. How long would it take to fly to the moon and return, if the moon is 225,120 miles away and if the spaceship could fly this distance at an average speed of 2,680 miles per hour?

5.9. How many years of 365 days each would it take the spaceship of Problem 5.8 to make a trip to Mars and return, if when Mars is nearest to the earth the distance the spaceship is to travel is 35,215,200 miles each way?

5.10. Six hundred forty pounds of butter @ 78 cents per pound are to be exchanged for fencing costing $1.20 per foot to enclose completely a square field. Calculate the area of the field.

5.11. If $2.34 was spent for meat @ 78 cents per pound, 46 cents for bread @ 23 cents per loaf, $1.66 for butter @ 83 cents per pound, and $1.14 for eggs @ 38 cents per dozen, (*a*) how many items of each (i.e., pounds, dozens, etc.) were purchased, and (*b*) how much change was returned for a $5 bill?

5.12. A clerk worked 8 hours on Monday, 7 hours on Tuesday, 9 hours on Wednesday, 6 hours on Thursday, 8 hours on Friday, and 4 hours on Saturday. What was his take-home pay for this week, if his salary was

$2 per hour, and if $12.37 was deducted for federal income tax, $1.89 for state income tax, and $5.29 for retirement?

5.13. A truckload of onions, in crates, weighed 5,227 pounds. After the truck was unloaded the empty truck weighed 2,419 pounds. How many crates of onions were there, if each crate weighed 72 pounds?

5.14. How many inches are there in 1 mile? If each inch in the mile were replaced by 93,000,000 miles, what would be the resulting length? The 93,000,000 is approximately the average distance between the earth and the sun and is known as *the astronomical unit*. Note that the foregoing resulting length of mile is approximately equal to the length of 1 *light year* (review Problem 3.19). These relationships provide a convenient means of appreciating the vast extent of a light year, a standard unit for estimating distances to stars. The star that is nearest to the solar system, namely, Proxima Centauri, is about $4\frac{1}{4}$ light years away. The North Star, also known as Polaris, is about 1,000 light years away; i.e., it requires about 1,000 years for light to come to us from it, so that we now view it as it appeared 1,000 years ago.

5·5 ∾ BASIC DEFINITIONS AND RELATIONSHIPS PERTAINING TO FRACTIONS

If a, b, c represent three natural numbers such that $ab = c$, then the inverse relations must occur, namely, $c \div b = a$ and $c \div a = b$. Thus if $3 \times 7 = 21$, then $21 \div 3 = 7$ and $21 \div 7 = 3$. However, proposed divisions of natural numbers, such as $21 \div 6 = ?$, or $5 \div 8 = ?$, or $1 \div 2 = ?$, clearly do not yield quotients that are natural numbers. For such divisions to provide suitable quotient numbers, one invents or devises the *fractions*, which are actually pairs of natural numbers, namely, the dividend and the divisor of the proposed division. The solutions of the foregoing proposed divisions are expressed as $2\frac{1}{6}$, $\frac{5}{8}$, and $\frac{1}{2}$, respectively. Other commonly used symbols are $\frac{21}{6}$, $\frac{5}{8}$, $\frac{1}{2}$, and $21:6$, $5:8$, $1:2$; however, the colon, :, is less frequently used. The first of the two natural numbers, the dividend, is now called the *numerator;* the second natural number, the divisor, is now called the *denominator*. This number pair must henceforth be regarded as a single number, just as 23 is regarded as a single natural number twenty-three, although 23 consists of two separate small natural numbers, the 2 and the 3.

If the denominator is larger than the numerator, the fraction is called a *proper fraction;* contrariwise, the fraction is called *improper*. Thus, $\frac{3}{4}$ is a proper fraction, while $\frac{8}{3}$ and $\frac{6}{6}$ are improper fractions.

The significance of the words numerator, denominator, proper, and improper, with reference to fractions, should be apparent from the examples:

1. Let two pies be divided equally among three boys. One may suppose that each pie is cut into three equal slices yielding $2 \times 3 = 6$ slices altogether. Accordingly, 6 (slices) ÷ 3 (boys) = 2 (slices). Each boy should receive two slices of pie, so that 2 (pies) ÷ 3 (boys) = $\frac{2}{3}$ (pies). The numerator 2 indicates how many items are counted off, or *numbered*, the denominator 3 specifies the name, or denomination, of the items that are counted off. Here, the denominator indicates that the items counted off are "thirds" of a pie, the numerator indicates that two of these thirds are counted off for each boy. The quotient, $\frac{2}{3}$, is a *proper fraction*, as it indicates an *appropriate broken part* of a single pie.

2. Let thirteen pies be divided equally among five boys. Here the share of each boy is 13 (pies) ÷ 5 (boys) = $\frac{13}{5}$ (pies). Here $\frac{13}{5}$ is an *improper* fraction, as it indicates one or more entire pies included with a part of a single pie as each boy's share in the division. The division could have been done as follows. Ten of the thirteen pies could have been divided among the five boys, $10 \div 5 = 2$, yielding two entire pies as each boy's share; then the remaining three pies could have been divided, yielding another $\frac{3}{5}$ pie as each boy's fair share. The division yields altogether $2 + \frac{3}{5}$ pies as each boy's part in the equal division. The $2 + \frac{3}{5}$, more frequently written $2\frac{3}{5}$, is called a *mixed number* as it consists of a natural number 2 and a proper fraction $\frac{3}{5}$. The improper fraction $\frac{13}{5}$ and the mixed number $2\frac{3}{5}$ are considered as representing equal numbers. To convert an improper fraction to its equivalent mixed number form, one separates the numerator into two parts, the largest natural number that is exactly divisible by the denominator and the remaining portion; one then performs separately the individual divisions on these two portions. Thus

$$\frac{58}{7} = \frac{56 + 2}{7} = \frac{56}{7} + \frac{2}{7} = 8 + \frac{2}{7} \text{ or } 8\frac{2}{7}$$

Fractional numbers are required for the solution of a wide variety of problems so one must become familiar with their basic properties and master the ensuing rules for their addition, subtraction, multiplication, division, involution, evolution, and indexing. The first four of these operations are presented shortly, the others will be presented later on.

5·6 ∾ LOCATION OF POSITIONS FOR PROPER FRACTIONS ON THE NUMBER LINE

Every proper fraction, a/b, may have a position assigned to it on the number line between the positions of 0 and 1. The actual determination of such positions appears in Figure 5.1.

1. Divide the interval from 0 to 1 into *b* equal parts.

2. The right ends of these individual subdivisions, beginning with the 0, are positions for $1/b$, $2/b$, $3/b$, . . . , $(b-1)/b$, b/b or 1.

3. The *a*th marked position represents a/b.

Now the actual division of the line segment between 0 and 1 may easily be done geometrically (i.e., by using an unmarked straightedge and a pair of compasses). Each of the eight steps in locating the position for the fraction $\frac{3}{5}$ appears in Figure 5.1, thus:

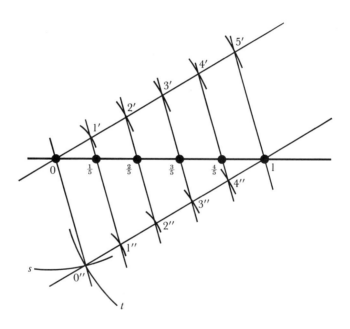

FIGURE 5.1

1. Draw any convenient line through 0 upward toward the right.

2. With the compasses mark off five equal segments on this line from 0 at positions 1′, 2′, 3′, 4′, and 5′.

3. Draw the line segment from 1 to 5′.

4. With compass opening equal to the distance from 1 to 5′, and with compass point at 0, draw the arc indicated by *s*.

5. With compass opening equal to the distance from 0 to 5′, and with compass point at 1, draw the arc indicated by t.   Mark as 0″ the intersection of arcs s and t.

6. With the compass opening equal to the distance from 0 to 1′, lay off equal segments on the line segment joining 0 to 1″ at positions 1″, 2″, 3″, and 4″, starting at 0″.

7. Draw line segments joining 1″ and 1′, 2″ and 2′, 3″ and 3′, 4″ and 4′. These are equally spaced parallel line segments.

8. Mark the positions on the line from 0 to 1 where these parallel line segments cross it as $\frac{1}{5}$, $\frac{2}{5}$, $\frac{3}{5}$, and $\frac{4}{5}$.   The 0 represents $\frac{0}{5}$, and the 1 represents $\frac{5}{5}$.

Similarly, any proper fraction whatever, a/b, may be assigned a position on the number line between the positions of 0 and 1.   To repeat, the denominator b represents the number of equal subdivisions into which the line from 0 to 1 is subdivided; the numerator a represents the number of subdivisions lying between 0 and the position for a/b on the number line.   Thus, the proper fraction $\frac{3}{5}$ has the position at the right end of the *third* subdivision when the interval between 0 and 1 has been marked off into *five* equal subdivisions.

One has a visual image of every proper fraction by its position on the number line.   Specific properties of fractions may be detected from the positional properties of the fractions on the number line; specifically, if two different fractions occupy the same position on the number line, they are to be regarded as equivalent or to have the same number value.   If two fractions occupy different positions on the number line, the larger fraction occupies the position to the right of the other, or smaller, fraction.

To locate the position on the number line for an improper fraction, or for its equivalent mixed-number form, namely, $a + b/c$, one should subdivide the interval on the number line between the positions of the natural numbers a and $a + 1$ into c equal parts, then select the right end of the bth subdivision as the correct position of the mixed number $a + b/c$ or its equivalent improper fractional form, $(ac + b)/c$.

5·7 ∾ THE FUNDAMENTAL PROPERTY OF FRACTIONS

Consider the proper fraction a/b as correctly placed on the number line at the right end of the ath subdivision after the line segment from 0 to 1 has been divided up into b equal subdivisions.

Let each of these b subdivisions be further subdivided into m smaller subdivisions, so that the interval from 0 to 1 has now been divided up into mb small and equal subdivisions.

As the position of the fraction a/b on the number line was originally at the right end of a of the original divisions, it is now at the right end of ma on the smaller subdivisions so that this same position represents the fraction ma/mb. Accordingly, the two fractions a/b and ma/mb must be equal to each other.

One is assured of the validity of the fundamental property of proper fractions, namely, that *the numerator and denominator of any proper fraction may be multiplied by any natural number m without altering the value of the fraction.*

Improper fractions also possess this fundamental property for: The mixed number $a + b/c$ is equivalent to $(ac + b)/c$. Since b/c is a proper fraction, $b/c = mb/mc$. Hence, $a + b/c = a(mb/mc) = (amc + mb)/mc$. Therefore, $(ac + b)/c = (mac + mb)/mc$. Conversely, the value of any fraction is unchanged if one divides its numerator and denominator by the same natural number.

The fundamental property of fractions enables one to reduce any fraction, proper or improper, to higher terms by *multiplying* its numerator and denominator by the same natural number, or to reduce a fraction to lower terms by *dividing* its numerator and denominator by the same natural number. A fraction is said to be in its *lowest terms* if its numerator and denominator have no common divisor; i.e., the numerator and denominator cannot be divided by the same natural number other than 1. Thus $\frac{6}{8}, \frac{9}{12}, \frac{12}{16}, \ldots$ are *higher* terms of $\frac{3}{4}$; contrariwise, $\frac{10}{15}, \frac{4}{6}$ are *lower* terms of $\frac{20}{30}$; $\frac{2}{3}$ and $\frac{3}{4}$ are in their *lowest terms*.

5·8 ∾ THE COMPLETE SYSTEM OF RATIONAL NUMBERS AS PORTRAYED ON THE NUMBER LINE

On a straight line of unlimited extent in both directions one position, or *point*, is selected for the 0; at equal intervals toward the right are the positions for the natural numbers, otherwise called the positive integers, in correct order from 0, namely, 1, 2, 3, 4, . . . , extending without end. To the left of the 0, also at the same equal intervals, are placed the negative integers, -1, -2, -3, -4, ... The positive proper fractions occur properly spaced between 0 and 1; the positive improper fractions or mixed numbers occur between appropriate consecutive positive integers; all positive integers and fractions are of increasing numerical value as they continue to occur farther toward the right of the zero position. The negative proper fractions occur at equal intervals between 0 and -1; thus, $-\frac{1}{2}$ is midway between 0 and -1; $-\frac{1}{3}$ and $-\frac{2}{3}$ are equally spaced between 0 and -1; for negative proper fractions having denominator b, the interval between 0 and -1 is divided up into b equal subdivisions, and the negative fractions $-1/b$, $-2/b$, $-3/b$, . . . are assigned to these division points, respectively, from the 0 toward the left. Likewise, the negative improper fractions, or their equivalent mixed number forms as $-a - b/c$, occur at the division points where the interval between $-a$ and $-(a + 1)$ is subdivided into c equal parts. This complete array of positive and negative integers and fractions and zero constitute the *complete system of rational numbers*.

Throughout this entire array of rational numbers they increase in value from left to right.

The positive sign of quality is unnecessary for positive integers and positive fractions; the negative sign of quality must not be omitted; it may appear before the fraction, or before the numerator of the fraction, as $-\dfrac{2}{3}$ or $\dfrac{-2}{3}$; as $-5\dfrac{2}{3}$ or $\dfrac{-17}{3}$.

৵ PROBLEMS [CONTINUED] ৵

5.15. Reduce the fractions to their lowest terms:

a. $\frac{8}{18}$ d. $\frac{250}{750}$ g. $\frac{24}{42}$ j. $\frac{81}{243}$

b. $\frac{16}{28}$ e. $\frac{12}{18}$ h. $\frac{38}{57}$ k. $\frac{65}{260}$

c. $\frac{14}{35}$ f. $\frac{6}{22}$ i. $\frac{32}{48}$ l. $\frac{102}{306}$

5.16. Reduce the mixed number to equivalent improper fractions:

a. $5\frac{3}{4}$ d. $3\frac{1}{3}$ g. $9\frac{3}{8}$ j. $14\frac{2}{7}$

b. $8\frac{1}{3}$ e. $33\frac{1}{3}$ h. $23\frac{17}{20}$ k. $1,428\frac{4}{7}$

c. $6\frac{1}{4}$ f. $37\frac{1}{2}$ i. $777\frac{7}{9}$ l. $142,857\frac{1}{7}$

5·9 ৵ EQUALITY AND INEQUALITY OF TWO FRACTIONS. APPROPRIATE SYMBOLISM

In observing the positions of the positive and negative fractions on the number line one notes that: If two fractions have the same *denominator*, the *larger* fraction has the *larger* numerator; $\frac{5}{7}$ is larger than $\frac{3}{7}$. If two fractions have the same *numerator*, the fraction nearer 0 has the larger denominator; $\frac{5}{8}$ is smaller than $\frac{5}{7}$.

In making such comparisons the negative fractions must have the negative quality sign written before the numerators; thus, $\dfrac{-5}{7}$ is smaller than $\dfrac{-3}{7}$, $\dfrac{-8}{3}$ is nearer 0 than $\dfrac{-8}{2}$. To determine the larger of two given fractions, one may convert them to the same (higher) denominator and compare the new numerators.

Symbolism. The symbol $>$ is read as "is greater than"; the symbol $<$ is read as "is less than." Thus, $5 > 2$, $3 < 8$. The combined symbol, $\gtreqless$, is to be read as "is greater than, equal to, or less than, respectively."

Thus, $a/b \gtreqless c/b$, according as $a \gtreqless c$. Hence, to identify the larger of two fractions a/b and c/d, one may convert them to the common denominator bd, the fractions becoming respectively ad/bd and bc/bd. Likewise $a/b \gtreqless c/d$, according as $ad \gtreqless bc$. Thus $\frac{2}{3}$ is larger than $\frac{5}{8}$, because 8×2, or 16, is larger than 3×5, or 15.

⤳ PROBLEMS [CONCLUDED] ⤳

5.17. Determine the larger fraction in each pair of fractions:

   a. $\frac{2}{3}$ $\frac{3}{4}$ d. $\frac{12}{5}$ $\frac{17}{7}$ g. $\frac{571,428}{857,142}$ $\frac{2}{3}$

   b. $\frac{7}{12}$ $\frac{11}{21}$ e. $\frac{7}{8}$ $\frac{8}{9}$ h. $\frac{428,571}{857,142}$ $\frac{1}{2}$

   c. $\frac{8}{11}$ $\frac{4}{5}$ f. $\frac{10}{17}$ $\frac{9}{16}$ i. $\frac{285,714}{857,142}$ $\frac{2}{7}$

5.18. Arrange the fractions in a line in order of size, beginning with the smallest fraction at the left end of the line:

$$\frac{2}{3} \quad \frac{1}{2} \quad \frac{3}{7} \quad \frac{2}{5} \quad \frac{3}{4} \quad \frac{1}{6} \quad \frac{5}{8} \quad \frac{5}{9} \quad \frac{7}{10}$$

5.19. Obtain the quotients (i.e., mixed numbers) for the divisions:

   a. $1,993 \div 53 = ?$ e. $16,131,717 \div 71 = ?$

   b. $13,349 \div 17 = ?$ f. $138,617,159 \div 367 = ?$

   c. $188,367 \div 23 = ?$ g. $568,943,375 \div 853 = ?$

   d. $1,002,001 \div 47 = ?$ h. $16,743,985,672 \div 65,537 = ?$

These results may be tested for correctness (i.e., "checked") by reducing mixed numbers back to improper fractions.

5.20. How many small blocks of lead, 5 inches by 3 inches by 2 inches, can be obtained by melting down 11 large blocks of lead, each 5 inches by 6 inches by 7 inches?

5.21. A rectangular solid is 5 feet long, 3 feet wide, and 2 feet high. What *number* is obtained by adding the number of cubic feet in its volume to the total number of square feet in all six of its faces, then subtracting from this sum the total number of feet in all twelve of its edges?

5.22. What is the weight of the solid in Problem 5.21, if it weighs 2 ounces per cubic inch? Give the results in pounds, if 16 ounces are equal to 1 pound.

5.23. How many gallons of liquid are needed to fill a rectangular tank to a depth of 7 feet, if the tank is 12 feet long and 11 feet wide? (By federal statute, 1 gallon contains exactly 231 cubic inches.)

5.24. If the tank in Problem 5.23 contains exactly 300 gallons of liquid, calculate its depth to the *exact* fractional part of an inch.

5.25. The material of which Sirius B, the companion star of Sirius, is composed seems to have a specific gravity of approximately 55,000; i.e., it weighs 55,000 times as much as water. Compute the weight of 1 cubic inch of this material, if water weighs $62\frac{1}{2}$ pounds per cubic foot.

*N*ote 1 ∽ *The system of rational numbers is not discrete, but is dense.*

The system of *integers* is said to be *discrete*, which means that each integer has an immediate predecessor and an immediate successor. Thus 5 is the immediate successor of 4, as no integer whatever can occur between 4 and 5; contrariwise, the system of rational numbers is not discrete, as no rational number can have an immediate successor or immediate predecessor since between any two rational numbers, however nearly equal they may be, there are an unlimited number of fractions. Now if $a/b < c/d$, then $ad < bc$; furthermore, $(a + c)/(b + d)$ lies between a/b and c/d, since $a(b + d) < b(a + c)$ and $(a + c)d < c(b + d)$. For example, $\dfrac{3 + 7}{4 + 9}$, or $\frac{10}{13}$, lies between $\frac{3}{4}$ and $\frac{7}{9}$. Again, $\dfrac{10 + 7}{13 + 9}$, or $\frac{17}{22}$, lies between $\frac{10}{13}$ and $\frac{7}{9}$. By continuing this same procedure, one can obtain as many fractions as one may wish that lie between any two given fractions. Thus, $\frac{13}{17}$ lies between $\frac{3}{4}$ and $\frac{10}{13}$. Then, obtaining new fractions lying between these five fractions, one obtains seven fractions lying between $\frac{3}{4}$ and $\frac{7}{9}$, namely,

$$\tfrac{3}{4} < \tfrac{16}{21} < \tfrac{13}{17} < \tfrac{23}{30} < \tfrac{10}{13} < \tfrac{27}{35} < \tfrac{17}{22} < \tfrac{24}{31} < \tfrac{7}{9}$$

Accordingly, the system of *rational numbers* is *dense*, which means that no rational number has an immediate successor or an immediate predecessor rational number, and that between any two rational numbers, however close their positions on the number line, are an unlimited number of other unequal rational numbers.

More generally, there are just as many fractions between any pair of unequal fractions as there are fractions altogether, for if m,n represent all possible pairs of natural numbers, then m/n must represent all possible fractions, proper and improper. Then, if a/b and c/d are two unequal fractions, necessarily the fraction $(ma + nc)/(mb + nd)$ lies between a/b or ma/mb and c/d or nc/nd; thus the fraction m/n may be paired off with the intermediate fraction $(ma + nc)/(mb + nd)$, thereby exhibiting the validity of the allegation.

*N*ote 2 ∽ *The cardinal number of the set of rational numbers is aleph-zero.*

The cardinal number of the set of all natural numbers is called aleph-zero, $\aleph_0$ (see Note 1 of Lesson 2). Now any other infinite set whose elements may be paired off with the natural numbers must also have this same infinite cardinal number $\aleph_0$. Such sets are called *denumerable* sets. To demonstrate that a specified set is denumerable, one must show how to pair all its elements in a one-to-one correspondence with the natural numbers. Not all infinite sets, however, are denumerable, as will appear in Lesson 11. The following infinite sets *are* denumerable:

1. The set of all integers

2. The set of all positive proper fractions in their lowest terms

3. The set of *all* positive fractions, proper and improper

4. The set of all rational numbers, positive and negative, integral and fractional

5. The set of all fractions that are equivalent to a particular fraction, such as $\frac{3}{4}, \frac{6}{8}, \frac{9}{12}, \frac{12}{16}, \frac{15}{20}, \cdots$

Appropriate one-to-one correspondences between the sets (1), (2), (4), and the natural numbers will demonstrate that these sets are denumerable. The student will set up appropriate correspondences with the natural numbers to prove these other sets also have the same infinite cardinal number $\aleph_0$.

In set 1 above one may pair off all integers with all natural numbers by pairing the positive integers with the *even* natural numbers, and the zero and negative integers with the *odd* natural numbers. In the exhibited pairing, each integer is paired with the natural number that is written below it, and each natural number is paired with the integer that is written above it:

$$\ldots \ -7 \ -6 \ -5 \ -4 \ -3 \ -2 \ -1 \ \ 0 \ +1 \ +2 \ +3 \ +4 \ +5 \ +6 \ldots$$
$$\ldots \ \ 15 \ \ 13 \ \ 11 \ \ \ 9 \ \ \ 7 \ \ \ 5 \ \ \ 3 \ \ 1 \ \ \ 2 \ \ \ 4 \ \ \ 6 \ \ \ 8 \ \ 10 \ \ 12 \ldots$$

The positive integer $+N$ is paired with the natural number $2N$; 0 is paired with the natural number 1; the negative integer $-N$ is paired with the natural number $2N + 1$. This complete pairing off of all integers with all natural numbers proves that the set of integers and the set of cardinal numbers have the same cardinal number, namely, $\aleph_0$. Moreover, any other pairing of integers with natural numbers will establish the fact that the set of integers is denumerable. One other such pairing could be:

$$0 \ 1 \ 2 \ 3 \ -1 \ -2 \ -3 \ 4 \ 5 \ \ 6 \ -4 \ -5 \ -6 \ \ 7 \ \ 8 \ \ 9 \ -7 \ -8 \ -9 \ldots$$
$$1 \ 2 \ 3 \ 4 \ \ \ 5 \ \ \ 6 \ \ \ 7 \ 8 \ 9 \ 10 \ \ 11 \ \ 12 \ \ 13 \ 14 \ 15 \ 16 \ \ 17 \ \ 18 \ \ 19 \ldots$$

In set 2, one scheme of pairing off the positive proper fractions in their lowest terms with the natural numbers is to list the fractions in order of size with increasing denominators; the paired natural numbers are written under the fractions:

$$\frac{1}{2} \quad \frac{1}{3} \quad \frac{2}{3} \quad \frac{1}{4} \quad \frac{3}{4} \quad \frac{1}{5} \quad \frac{2}{5} \quad \frac{3}{5} \quad \frac{4}{5} \quad \frac{1}{6} \quad \frac{5}{6} \quad \frac{1}{7} \quad \frac{2}{7} \ldots$$
$$1 \quad 2 \quad 3 \quad 4 \quad 5 \quad 6 \quad 7 \quad 8 \quad 9 \quad 10 \quad 11 \quad 12 \quad 13 \ldots$$

To prove that the complete set of *all* rational numbers in set 4 is denumerable, one arranges them in vertical columns, placing in the same column the rational numbers having the same denominator. In this arrangement the rational numbers in the first, or left, column represent the integers. All equivalent rational numbers appear in the array, such as $\frac{3}{4}, \frac{6}{8}, \frac{9}{12}, \ldots$; $\frac{1}{1}, \frac{2}{2}, \frac{3}{3}, \ldots$. Positive and negative integers occur in alternate rows.

$$
\begin{array}{cccccc}
\frac{0}{1} & \frac{0}{2} & \frac{0}{3} & \frac{0}{4} & \frac{0}{5} & \frac{0}{6} \quad \cdots \\
-\frac{0}{1} & -\frac{0}{2} & -\frac{0}{3} & -\frac{0}{4} & -\frac{0}{5} & -\frac{0}{6} \quad \cdots \\
\frac{1}{1} & \frac{1}{2} & \frac{1}{3} & \frac{1}{4} & \frac{1}{5} & \frac{1}{6} \quad \cdots \\
-\frac{1}{1} & -\frac{1}{2} & -\frac{1}{3} & -\frac{1}{4} & -\frac{1}{5} & -\frac{1}{6} \quad \cdots \\
\frac{2}{1} & \frac{2}{2} & \frac{2}{3} & \frac{2}{4} & \frac{2}{5} & \frac{2}{6} \quad \cdots \\
-\frac{2}{1} & -\frac{2}{2} & -\frac{2}{3} & -\frac{2}{4} & -\frac{2}{5} & -\frac{2}{6} \quad \cdots \\
\frac{3}{1} & \frac{3}{2} & \frac{3}{3} & \frac{3}{4} & \frac{3}{5} & \frac{3}{6} \quad \cdots \\
-\frac{3}{1} & -\frac{3}{2} & -\frac{3}{3} & -\frac{3}{4} & -\frac{3}{5} & -\frac{3}{6} \quad \cdots \\
\frac{4}{1} & \frac{4}{2} & \frac{4}{3} & \frac{4}{4} & \frac{4}{5} & \frac{4}{6} \quad \cdots \\
-\frac{4}{1} & -\frac{4}{2} & -\frac{4}{3} & -\frac{4}{4} & -\frac{4}{5} & -\frac{4}{6} \quad \cdots \\
\end{array}
$$

The natural numbers are paired with the foregoing integers diagonalwise beginning at upper left corner; each natural number is paired with the integer occupying the same relative position in the array.

1	2	4	7	11	16	. . .
3	5	8	12	17	23	. . .
6	9	13	18	24	31	. . .
10	14	19	25	32	40	. . .
15	20	26	33	41	50	. . .
21	27	34	42	51	61	. . .
28	35	43	52	62	73	. . .
36	44	53	63	74	86	. . .
45	54	64	75	87	100	. . .
55	65	76	88	101	115	. . .

To avoid repetition of equivalent rational numbers, one may omit all fractions that are not in their lowest terms from the array of rational numbers. As the arrays of rational numbers and natural numbers are extended indefinitely, every integer will be paired with one natural number, and each natural number will be paired with an integer, thus establishing the one-to-one correspondence to prove denumerability.

*N*ote 3 ⚬⚬ *The fractions as pairs of integers.*

As the integers were introduced alternately as ordered pairs of natural numbers (Section 4.17), so now the rational numbers may be introduced as ordered pairs of integers. This scheme of introducing the rational numbers as pairs of integers was suggested by the conventional exhibition of fractions as pairs of natural numbers. The first of the two numbers of the number pair is called the numerator, the second number the denominator. Particularly, the second number is a positive integer. As examples of rational numbers, $(2,3)$, $(-4,9)$, $(5,1)$, and $(-13,1)$ represent the familiar $\frac{2}{3}$, $-\frac{4}{9}$, $+5$, and -13, respectively. The basic definitions and relationships are now presented. (a,b) is a rational number; if a,b are integers, $b \neq 0$.

1. Two rational numbers (a,b) and (c,d) are equivalent, if, and only if,
$$ad = bc$$

2. $(a,b) \underset{>}{\overset{\leq}{=}} (c,d)$, if, and only if, $ad \underset{>}{\overset{\leq}{=}} bc$

3. $(a,b) + (c,d) = (ad + bc, bd)$

4. $(a,b) - (c,d) = (ad - bc, bd)$

5. $(a,b)(c,d) = (ac, bd)$

6. $(a,b) \div (c,d) = (ad, bc)$

7. $(a,b)^n = (a^n, b^n)$

8. $(ma, mb) = (a,b)$

By use of these alternate and equivalent definitions of rational numbers and the fundamental operations—addition, subtraction, multiplication, division, and involution—one may prove that the five basic laws of addition and multiplication continue to be valid for rational numbers as well as for natural numbers and for integers. To establish the validity of the commutative law of addition for rational numbers, namely, that $(a,b) + (c,d) = (c,d) + (a,b)$, one notes that $(a,b) + (c,d) = (ad + bc, bd) = (cb + da, db)$, since the commutative laws of addition and multiplication are valid for integers. Also $(c,d) + (a,b) = (cb + da, db)$, which establishes the commutative laws of addition for rational numbers, since a, b, c, d may represent any integers whatever, except that the second integers b,d must not be zero.

The serious student will now construct similarly the proofs that rational numbers observe also the commutative law of multiplication, the associative laws of addition and of multiplication, and the distributive law of multiplication and addition.

∾ SUPPLEMENTARY PROBLEMS ∾

> *King Alfred divided his time into three equal parts: one third to religion and study, another third to sleep and refreshment, and the remaining third to the duties of his kingly office.*
>
> —S. C. Goodrich
> *Pictorial History of England* (1845)

Compute the sum of quotients in Problems S5.1 to S5.11:

S5.1.
a. $72 \div 8 = ?$
b. $72 \div 9 = ?$
c. $72 \div 12 = ?$
d. $72 \div 6 = ?$
e. $72 \div 4 = ?$
f. $72 \div 2 = ?$
g. $72 \div 18 = ?$
h. $72 \div 24 = ?$
i. $72 \div 36 = ?$
j. $72 \div 72 = ?$
k. $72 \div 1 = ?$
l. $72 \div 3 = ?$

S5.2.
a. $16 \div 2 = ?$
b. $26 \div 2 = ?$
c. $36 \div 2 = ?$
d. $51 \div 3 = ?$
e. $15 \div 3 = ?$
f. $57 \div 3 = ?$
g. $52 \div 4 = ?$
h. $36 \div 4 = ?$
i. $92 \div 4 = ?$
j. $60 \div 5 = ?$
k. $30 \div 5 = ?$
l. $80 \div 5 = ?$

S5.3.
a. $78 \div 6 = ?$
b. $42 \div 6 = ?$
c. $96 \div 6 = ?$
d. $56 \div 7 = ?$
e. $84 \div 7 = ?$
f. $98 \div 7 = ?$
g. $256 \div 8 = ?$
h. $704 \div 8 = ?$
i. $992 \div 8 = ?$
j. $117 \div 9 = ?$
k. $171 \div 9 = ?$
l. $711 \div 9 = ?$

S5.4.
a. $562 \div 2 = ?$
b. $308 \div 2 = ?$
c. $550 \div 2 = ?$
d. $111 \div 3 = ?$
e. $501 \div 3 = ?$
f. $105 \div 3 = ?$
g. $748 \div 4 = ?$
h. $396 \div 4 = ?$
i. $112 \div 4 = ?$
j. $125 \div 5 = ?$
k. $240 \div 5 = ?$
l. $900 \div 5 = ?$

S5.5.
a. $552 \div 6 = ?$
b. $738 \div 6 = ?$
c. $876 \div 6 = ?$
d. $161 \div 7 = ?$
e. $343 \div 7 = ?$
f. $952 \div 7 = ?$
g. $16{,}384 \div 8 = ?$
h. $65{,}536 \div 8 = ?$
i. $99{,}544 \div 8 = ?$
j. $3{,}070 \div 2 = ?$
k. $1{,}372 \div 2 = ?$
l. $5{,}070 \div 2 = ?$

S5.6.
a. $42{,}117 \div 3 = ?$
b. $71{,}001 \div 3 = ?$
c. $31{,}416 \div 3 = ?$
d. $57{,}604 \div 4 = ?$
e. $11{,}092 \div 4 = ?$
f. $73{,}532 \div 4 = ?$
g. $24{,}130 \div 5 = ?$
h. $97{,}535 \div 5 = ?$
i. $13{,}700 \div 5 = ?$

S5.7. *a.* 13,458 ÷ 6 = ?   *d.* 88,333 ÷ 7 = ?   *g.* 333,512 ÷ 8 = ?
     b. 77,772 ÷ 6 = ?   *e.* 65,436 ÷ 7 = ?   *h.* 700,904 ÷ 8 = ?
     c. 10,608 ÷ 6 = ?   *f.* 99,099 ÷ 7 = ?   *i.* 456,784 ÷ 8 = ?

S5.8. *a.* 216,459 ÷ 9 = ?   *d.* 123,456,789 ÷ 9 = ?   *g.* 1,003,005 ÷ 9 = ?
     b. 321,651 ÷ 9 = ?   *e.* 987,654,321 ÷ 9 = ?   *h.* 7,000,101 ÷ 9 = ?
     c. 431,262 ÷ 9 = ?   *f.* 135,792,468 ÷ 9 = ?   *i.* 1,111,113 ÷ 9 = ?

S5.9. *a.* 255 ÷ 17 = ?   *d.* 1,751 ÷ 103 = ?   *g.* 34,777 ÷ 83 = ?
     b. 402 ÷ 67 = ?   *e.* 3,956 ÷ 23 = ?   *h.* 93,702 ÷ 46 = ?
     c. 851 ÷ 37 = ?   *f.* 7,155 ÷ 53 = ?   *i.* 75,702 ÷ 74 = ?

S5.10. *a.* 84,690 ÷ 15 = ?   *d.* 112,860 ÷ 76 = ?   *g.* 19,153 ÷ 179 = ?
     b. 43,956 ÷ 66 = ?   *e.* 146,304 ÷ 72 = ?   *h.* 97,237 ÷ 479 = ?
     c. 25,312 ÷ 112 = ?   *f.* 71,104 ÷ 88 = ?   *i.* 26,946 ÷ 499 = ?

S5.11. *a.* 1,757 ÷ 251 = ?   *d.* 1,106,634 ÷ 362 = ?   *g.* 4,049,160 ÷ 12,345 = ?
     b. 1,557 ÷ 173 = ?   *e.* 1,858,238 ÷ 619 = ?   *h.* 6,029,631 ÷ 54,321 = ?
     c. 2,008 ÷ 251 = ?   *f.* 1,759,758 ÷ 879 = ?   *i.* 6,462,954 ÷ 16,077 = ?

S5.12. Perform the divisions, expressing quotients as mixed numbers, or proper fractions in lowest terms, or integers:
     a. 237 ÷ 24 = ?   *g.* 0 ÷ 7 = ?   *m.* 53,333 ÷ 6 = ?
     b. 512 ÷ 36 = ?   *h.* 0 ÷ 12 = ?   *n.* 243,899 ÷ 99 = ?
     c. 345 ÷ 67 = ?   *i.* 1 ÷ 4 = ?   *o.* 763,200 ÷ 123 = ?
     d. 5 ÷ 12 = ?   *j.* 115,770 ÷ 21 = ?   *p.* 150,000 ÷ 617 = ?
     e. 16 ÷ 27 = ?   *k.* 211,091 ÷ 46 = ?   *q.* 432,796,007 ÷ 1,234 = ?
     f. 3 ÷ 10 = ?   *l.* 24,823 ÷ 53 = ?   *r.* 900,800,700 ÷ 65,537 = ?

S5.13. Arrange the sets of fractions in order of size, placing the smallest fraction at the left:
     a. $\frac{3}{4}$ $\frac{2}{3}$ $\frac{5}{8}$ *d.* $\frac{5}{6}$ $\frac{7}{10}$ $\frac{3}{4}$ $\frac{4}{5}$
     b. $\frac{7}{12}$ $\frac{7}{18}$ $\frac{7}{21}$ *e.* $\frac{2}{3}$ $\frac{5}{6}$ $\frac{7}{8}$ $\frac{3}{4}$
     c. $\frac{5}{9}$ $\frac{2}{9}$ $\frac{7}{9}$ *f.* $\frac{1}{2}$ $\frac{3}{8}$ $\frac{2}{5}$ $\frac{4}{15}$ $\frac{3}{5}$

S5.14. Convert the mixed numbers to improper fractions:
     a. $3\frac{1}{2}$ *d.* $15\frac{7}{8}$ *g.* $11\frac{1}{9}$ *j.* $3,333\frac{1}{3}$
     b. $5\frac{3}{8}$ *e.* $21\frac{2}{3}$ *h.* $16\frac{2}{3}$ *k.* $8,851\frac{3}{7}$
     c. $8\frac{1}{4}$ *f.* $62\frac{1}{3}$ *i.* $33\frac{1}{3}$ *l.* $9,090\frac{10}{11}$

S5.15. Divide the difference between 94,321 and 86,247 by 499.

S5.16. Divide the sum of 46,816 and 6,848 by 412.

S5.17. Divide the product of 1,166 and 994 by 8,162.

S5.18. Evaluate (2,832 − 987 + 678) ÷ 841.

S5.19. Multiply the difference between 4,896 and 2,384 by 7^2; then divide the product so obtained by 7×2^4.

S5.20. *a.* Multiply the sum of 478 and 296 by their difference; divide the resulting product by 364.

     b. Divide the difference of the squares of 478 and 296 by 387.

S5.21. Perform the indicated operations upon integers:

    a. $(-1,977) \div (-659) = ?$

    b. $(-6)(-7)(-8) \div (-7) \div (-8) = ?$

    c. $(-8) \div (-8) \div (-7) \div (-7)(-6) = ?$

    d. $(-8)(-8)(-7) \div (-7) \div (-6) = ?$

    e. $(-2)(-3) + (-4) \div (-5) \div (-6)(-7) = ?$

    f. $(4)(5)(9) \div (-60) + (-35)(-4) \div (-70) = ?$

S5.22. At \$1,500 an acre, how many acres of land can be purchased for \$346,500?

S5.23. If a person can walk 26 miles in one day, how long will it take him at this rate to walk a distance of 364 miles?

S5.24. A bequest of \$10,830 is to be divided equally among 19 persons. How much is each person's share?

S5.25. A crop of 9,523 bushels was raised on 107 acres of land. What was the average yield per acre?

S5.26. If one hogshead contains 63 gallons, how many hogsheads are needed to contain 14,868 gallons?

S5.27. The product of two numbers is 6,571,435. If one of the numbers is 1,235, what is the other number?

S5.28. If a donation of \$1 million is divided equally among 269 school libraries, how much does each library receive? Give result to the nearest penny.

S5.29. What would be each person's share, to the nearest penny, of a national debt of 330 billions of dollars, if the country's population is 175 million?

S5.30. Compute to the nearest integer the average number of persons living on each square mile in the following countries having the indicated areas and populations:

	COUNTRY	AREA	POPULATION
a.	Belgium	11,778	9,499,000
b.	Mainland China	3,691,502	735,000,000
c.	Formosa China	13,885	12,819,728
d.	India	1,229,215	486,700,000
e.	United States	3,615,211	179,323,175
f.	Australia	2,971,081	11,537,000
g.	Soviet Russia	8,649,489	230,585,000

S5.31. The earth at its equator is about 24,899 miles in circumference and turns once on its axis in 24 hours. How many miles in one minute would this be at the equator?

S5.32. A certain railroad, 238 miles in length, was constructed at a cost of \$3,731,840. What was this cost per mile?

S5.33. An explosion was set off at a distance of 13,584 feet from an observer at exactly 12 o'clock noon. The observer heard this sound 12 seconds later. State the velocity of the sound in feet per second and in miles per hour.

S5.34. If light travels 186,000 miles per second, how long does it take light to travel from the sun to the earth if the distance between them is 93,000,000 miles? How much longer does it take for light to travel from the sun to the most remote planet Pluto at its greatest distance from the sun, namely, 4,594,000,000 miles?

S5.35. A horse dealer invested $7,560 in horses at $108 each. Later he sold some of them for $259 each, receiving $3,885 for them. Subsequently he recovered his original investment by selling more horses for $175 each. How many horses were then left of his original purchase?

S5.36. A rancher purchased two ranches, ranch *A* for $14,700 at $98 per acre and ranch *B* for $4,655 at $95 per acre. How many acres are there in the combined ranches *A* and *B*?

S5.37. A horse dealer purchased 29 horses at $154 each and sold them for $5,742. What was his profit per horse?

S5.38. A subdivider purchased 25 acres of land for $85,000. He subdivided the land to provide streets and residence lots. How much must he charge for each lot to make a profit of $15,000 on his investment, if there were (*a*) 125 lots? (*b*) 200 lots?

S5.39. To convert a natural number from its decimal form to its binary form, one divides it and the successive quotients by 2. The final quotient, 1, and the successive remainders, 0 or 1, are the required digits of the binary form. To convert the natural number 37 to its decimal form, one proceeds thus:

$$2 | \overline{37}$$
$$2 | \overline{18} \quad \text{Remainder 1}$$
$$2 | \overline{9} \quad \text{Remainder 0}$$
$$2 | \overline{4} \quad \text{Remainder 1}$$
$$2 | \overline{2} \quad \text{Remainder 0}$$
$$1 \quad \text{Remainder 0}$$

Accordingly, the binary form of 37 is 100101 (reading from bottom to top). Using this procedure, convert to the binary form (*a*) 75, (*b*) 150, (*c*) 1,492, (*d*) 1,969.

S5.40. To convert a natural number to the ternary form (base 3), one uses 3 instead of 2 for the successive divisors. The final quotient, 1 or 2, and the successive remainders, 0, 1, or 2, are the required digits of its ternary form. Convert these natural numbers to the ternary form: (*a*) 25, (*b*) 148, (*c*) 1,492, (*d*) 1,776, (*e*) 1,969.

S5.41. A gambler lost on three successive days $1 more than half his original capital for that day. If his original capital was $254, how much did he have at the end of the third day? If his luck continued in precisely this same way, how many more days could he play until his capital became exactly 0?

S5.42. In Problem S5.41 no fractional numbers occurred. Obtain the special numbers that could represent the gambler's original capital to permit such losses without involving fractions. (*Hint:* Convert all numbers that occur in Problem S5.41 to their binary form.)

S5.43. An expeditionary force of 797,160 men encountered severe guerilla opposition and was completely wiped out in 12 days. At the end of each successive day the number of survivors were one less than one-third the number at the beginning of that day. List the number of survivors on each of the 12 days. (Convert these numbers to base 3 to observe why no fractions can occur.)

S5.44. Reconstruct Problem S5.43 after changing 12 days to 10 days and one-third to one-fourth. Obtain the initial number of soldiers.

S5.45. Show how to set up such a problem as the two preceding problems for any arbitrary number of days, d, and for any unit fraction, $1/n$, instead of one-third and one-fourth.

S5.46. Obtain the product of any two natural numbers by use of three operations only: division by 2, multiplication by 2, and addition. The procedure is presented by multiplying 327 by 562.

a.	327	*b.*	562*
	163		1,124*
	81		2,248*
	40		4,496
	20		8,992
	10		17,984
	5		35,968*
	2		71,936
	1		143,872*
			183,774

The numbers in column (*a*) are repeatedly *halved* (divided by 2), ignoring all remainders, 1, that occur, the numbers in column (*b*) are repeatedly *doubled* (multiplied by 2). The numbers in column (*b*) that are in the same line with an odd number in column (*a*) are marked with asterisks. The required product is the sum of the numbers marked with asterisks. Thus, $327 \times 562 = 183,774$. This method of multiplying natural numbers is called the "Russian peasant's method of multiplication."

S5.47. Use the method of Problem S5.46 to obtain the products:

a. $512 \times 511 = ?$ *d.* $1,357 \times 4,096 = ?$

b. $511 \times 512 = ?$ *e.* $129 \times 531 = ?$

c. $4,096 \times 1,357 = ?$ *f.* $16 \times 5,379 = ?$

S5.48. Revise the "Russian peasant's method" to multiply natural numbers by a succession of divisions and multiplications by 3 instead of by 2. The ensuing example should provide necessary clues. Multiply 262 by 213:

262	Remainder 1	213*
87	Remainder 0	639
29	Remainder 2	1,917* + 1,917*
9	Remainder 0	5,751
3	Remainder 0	17,253
1	Remainder 1	51,759*
		55,806

Now use this revised scheme to compute:

a. $728 \times 729 = ?$ *b.* $729 \times 728 = ?$ *c.* $2,187 \times 19 = ?$

S5.49. The joint operation of division followed by multiplication is *not* associative, since $(a \div b)c = a/bc = ac/b$, whereas $a \div (bc) = a \div bc = a/bc$, and these two results are not equivalent.

The joint operation of multiplication followed by division *is* associative, as $(ab) \div c = ab \div c = ab/c$, whereas $a(b \div c) = ab/c$. This latter equality provides easy methods of multiplying by 5, 25, 125, 625, and higher powers of 5.

$5 = 10 \div 2$ Accordingly, if N represents any natural number, $25 = 100 \div 4$ then $N \times 5 = N \times 10 \div 2$, $N \times 25 = N \times 100 \div$ $125 = 1{,}000 \div 8$ 4, $N \times 125 = N \times 1{,}000 \div 8$. And quite gener- $625 = 1{,}000 \div 16$ ally, $N \times 5^{p} = N \times 10^{p} \div 2^{p}$.

. . . .

Use this procedure to multiply 34,567 by: (*a*) 5, (*b*) 25, (*c*) 125.

S5.50. Obtain a fraction whose value is between a/b and c/d as $(a + c)/(b + d)$ for the pairs of fractions: (*a*) $\frac{3}{5}$, $\frac{7}{8}$; (*b*) $\frac{7}{10}$, $\frac{4}{5}$. Note that the intermediate fraction is nearer in value to the fraction that has the larger denominator. Prove that this must always be the situation by using the general representations a/b, c/d, and $(a + c)/(b + d)$.

LESSON 6 ❧ CONCLUSION OF THE BASIC OPERATIONS UPON FRACTIONS ❧ PRIME FACTOR FORMS

6·1 ~ Résumé of common fractions

The common, or vulgar, fractions have been devised and introduced into the number system to make possible the operation of division of natural numbers when the dividend is not a multiple of the divisor. The fractions are represented by positions on the number line. Thus the position of any particular fraction, a/b, is at the right end of the ath interval from 0, if all intervals between the positions of consecutive integers on the number line are subdivided into b equal intervals. The denominator b represents any positive integer, or natural number; the numerator a may be any integer whatever. If a is positive and less than b, the fraction is called *proper* and has its position between 0 and 1; if a is larger than b, the fraction is called *improper* and has a position to the right of 1 on the number line. If a is negative, the position of a/b on the number line lies to the left of 0. If a represents 0, the fraction a/b is equal to 0 itself. Thus the position of the fraction $\frac{5}{8}$ is at the right end of the fifth interval, if the interval between 0 and 1 is divided into eight equal intervals. For the denominator 5, the right ends of consecutive subintervals, beginning at 0 and extending toward the right, are the respective positions of the fractions $\frac{1}{5}, \frac{2}{5}, \frac{3}{5}, \frac{4}{5}, \frac{5}{5}$ or 1, $\frac{6}{5}, \frac{7}{5}, \frac{8}{5}, \frac{9}{5}$, $\frac{10}{5}$ or 2, $\frac{11}{5}, \frac{12}{5}$, ... The negative fractions having the same denominator 5 have positions to the left of the equal intervals extending toward the left of the 0, respectively, for $-\frac{1}{5}, -\frac{2}{5}, -\frac{3}{5}, -\frac{4}{5}, -\frac{5}{5}$ or -1, $-\frac{6}{5}, -\frac{7}{5}, -\frac{8}{5}, -\frac{9}{5}, -\frac{10}{5}$ or $-2, -\frac{11}{5}, -\frac{12}{5}$, ... The set of all fractions having the common denominator 5 uses all integers for numerator and appears graphically thus:

As always, the number line is assumed to extend without end in both directions.

For any denominator other than 5, such as the natural number d, each interval between consecutive integers is divided up into d equal subintervals. The right ends of these subintervals beginning at 0 are positions for the positive fractions $1/d, 2/d, 3/d, 4/d, \ldots$; the left ends of the consecutive subintervals beginning at 0 are the positions for the negative fractions $-1/d, -2/d, -3/d, -4/d, \ldots$. If d is now made to represent, one by one, all natural numbers, 1, 2, 3, 4, $\ldots$, the positions on the number line so obtained represent the *complete system of rational numbers*. Positions on the number line not occupied by rational numbers are said to represent irrational numbers. These will be introduced in Lesson 11.

6·2 ~ ADDITION AND SUBTRACTION OF COMMON FRACTIONS

The equally spaced positions on the number line for fractions with denominator 5, as exhibited in Section 6.1, suggest these two rules for addition and subtraction of fractions:

> *For fractions having the* same natural number *for their* denominators, *the same rules for the addition and subtraction of integers are applied to their numerators; the same common denominator is retained for the resulting sum or difference.*

> *Fractions that have different denominators must be reduced to a common denominator before applying the foregoing rules of addition and subtraction.* (Such necessary reductions to a common denominator are made in accordance with the fundamental property of fractions, Section 5.6.)

EXAMPLES ~

1. $\frac{3}{8} + \frac{11}{8} + \frac{7}{8} + \frac{5}{8} = ?$ Adding the numerators of these fractions that have the common denominator 8, one obtains $3 + 11 + 7 + 5 = 26$. Therefore the required sum is $\frac{26}{8}$, or $\frac{13}{4}$, or $3\frac{1}{4}$.

2. $\frac{7}{12} - \frac{5}{12} = ?$ Subtracting the numerators, $7 - 5 = 2$. Therefore, the required difference is $\frac{2}{12}$ or $\frac{1}{6}$.

3. $\frac{3}{10} + \frac{3}{4} = ?$ The lowest common denominator for 10 and 4 is the smallest natural number that is exactly divisible by both 10 and 4, namely 20. Thus, $\frac{3}{10} = \frac{6}{20}$, $\frac{3}{4} = \frac{15}{20}$. Therefore, $\frac{6}{20} + \frac{15}{20} = \frac{21}{20}$, or $1\frac{1}{20}$.

4. $\frac{1}{4} - \frac{5}{6} = ?$ Converting these fractions to equivalent fractions having the common denominator 12, one obtains $\dfrac{3}{12} - \dfrac{10}{12} = \dfrac{-7}{12}$, or the negative fraction $-\frac{7}{12}$.

6·3 ~ COMMON MULTIPLES OF TWO OR MORE NUMBERS

All *multiples* of a given number are the products of the number by all natural numbers. Then the multiples of

2 are 2, 4, 6, 8, 10, 12, 14, 16, 18, 20, 22, 24, 26, . . .
3 are 3, 6, 9, 12, 15, 18, 21, 24, 27, 30, 33, 36, 39, . . .
4 are 4, 8, 12, 16, 20, 24, 28, 32, 36, 40, 44, 48, 52, . . .
5 are 5, 10, 15, 20, 25, 30, 35, 40, 45, 50, 55, 60, 65, . . .

. . . .

Common multiples of two or more numbers are the multiples that occur simultaneously in the extended lists of their respective multiples. Common multiples of 3 and 4 are 12, 24, 36, ... Also, 12 is the *smallest* or *least common multiple* of 3 and 4. Common multiples of 4, 6, and 7 are 42, 84, ... Their *least* common multiple is 42. One may obtain the least common multiple of two or more numbers by setting forth the complete lists of their multiples until the same number appears in all such lists. One may thus obtain the least common multiple of the denominators of prescribed fractions whose sum or difference is required. This method has been presented to provide a clear understanding of the topic; however, a much easier method is available using prime factors. It will be presented in Section 6.4.

6·4 ~ THE PRIME FACTOR FORM OF A NATURAL NUMBER

The customary form of expressing a natural number involves the operations of multiplication and addition. Thus, 376 means $3 \times 100 + 7 \times 10 + 6$, or $3 \times 10^2 + 7 \times 10 + 6$, or the sum of multiples of powers of the base 10. Each digit in the expression indicates the multiple of the base and also, *by its position*, the power of the base to be used. Again, in 14,652 the digit 1 denotes 10,000, or 1×10^4, the 4 denotes 4×10^3, the 6 denotes 6×10^2, the 5 denotes 5×10^1, the 2 denotes 2 itself.

The *prime factor form* of a natural number involves only multiplications of very special numbers called *prime numbers*. A prime number is a natural number other than 1 that cannot be divided exactly by any natural number except itself and 1. There are 25 prime numbers less than 100, namely, 2, 3, 5, 7, 11, 13, 17, 19, 23, 29, 31, 37, 41, 43, 47, 53, 59, 61, 67, 71, 73, 79, 83, 89, and 97. Natural numbers that are not prime numbers are called *composite numbers;* their prime factor forms consist of the indicated products of the prime numbers that are equal to the numbers themselves. The prime factor forms of the first 60 natural numbers are listed as follows:

1 = the unit of the system of natural numbers, being neither prime nor composite

2 is prime	17 is prime	$32 = 2^5$	47 is prime
3 is prime	$18 = 2 \times 3^2$	$33 = 3 \times 11$	$48 = 2^4 \times 3$
$4 = 2^2$	19 is prime	$34 = 2 \times 17$	$49 = 7^2$
5 is prime	$20 = 2^2 \times 5$	$35 = 5 \times 7$	$50 = 2 \times 5^2$
$6 = 2 \times 3$	$21 = 3 \times 7$	$36 = 2^2 \times 3^2$	$51 = 3 \times 17$
7 is prime	$22 = 2 \times 11$	37 is prime	$52 = 2^2 \times 13$
$8 = 2^3$	23 is prime	$38 = 2 \times 19$	53 is prime
$9 = 3^2$	$24 = 2^3 \times 3$	$39 = 3 \times 13$	$54 = 2 \times 3^3$
$10 = 2 \times 5$	$25 = 5^2$	$40 = 2^3 \times 5$	$55 = 5 \times 11$
11 is prime	$26 = 2 \times 13$	41 is prime	$56 = 2^3 \times 7$
$12 = 2^2 \times 3$	$27 = 3^3$	$42 = 2 \times 3 \times 7$	$57 = 3 \times 19$
13 is prime	$28 = 2^2 \times 7$	43 is prime	$58 = 2 \times 29$
$14 = 2 \times 7$	29 is prime	$44 = 2^2 \times 11$	59 is prime
$15 = 3 \times 5$	$30 = 2 \times 3 \times 5$	$45 = 3^2 \times 5$	$60 = 2^2 \times 3 \times 5$
$16 = 2^4$	31 is prime	$46 = 2 \times 23$	

Note that the prime factor forms exhibit the required prime numbers in order of size; thus 3×5, rather than 5×3, is used for 15.

6·5 ❧ REDUCTION OF A NATURAL NUMBER FROM ITS STANDARD FORM TO ITS PRIME FACTOR FORM

The customary decimal form of expressing a natural number is called its *standard form*. The foregoing table provides the standard forms and the equivalent prime factor forms of the first 60 natural numbers. To obtain the equivalent standard form of a natural number from its equivalent prime factor form, one merely performs the indicated involutions and multiplications as indicated in the prime factor form. To convert $2^2 \times 3 \times 7^2$ to its corresponding standard form, $2^2 = 4$, $7^2 = 49$, $4 \times 3 = 12$, $12 \times 49 = 588$. Contrariwise, to convert a standard form to its prime factor form one must perform a series of appropriate divisions by prime numbers. Two examples follow.

2|360	Dividing 360 by the smallest prime divisor 2
2|180	Dividing the quotient 180 by 2
2| 90	Dividing 90 by 2
3| 45	Dividing 45 by 3, the smallest prime divisor
3| 15	Dividing 15 by 3
5	The final quotient, a prime number

The set of prime divisors and the final prime quotient constitute the factors of the required prime factor form, namely, $2 \times 2 \times 2 \times 3 \times 3 \times 5$, or $2^3 \times 3^2 \times 5$.

Obtain the prime factor form of 188,034:

2	188,034	Divide by the smallest prime divisor 2
3	94,017	Divide by the smallest prime divisor 3
7	31,339	Divide by the smallest prime divisor 7
11	4,477	Divide by the smallest prime divisor 11
11	407	Divide by the smallest prime divisor 11
	37	The final quotient, a prime number

In this example, the prime factor form of 188,034 is $2 \times 3 \times 7 \times 11^2 \times 37$.

6·6 ∾ TESTS FOR DIVISIBILITY OF A NATURAL NUMBER BY PRIME DIVISORS

To convert the standard form of a given natural number to its prime factor form, one must be able to detect the necessary prime divisors that effect exact divisions. Rules for exact divisibility by certain prime numbers are now provided:

1. A natural number is divisible by 2 if its units digit is even, that is, if its units digit is 0, 2, 4, 6, or 8. A natural number is not divisible by 2 if its units digit is odd, 1, 3, 5, 7, or 9.

2. A natural number is exactly divisible by 3 if and only if the sum of its digits is exactly divisible by 3. Thus 501 is divisible by 3 because $5 + 0 + 1$, or 6, which is divisible by 3; 613 is not divisible by 3, because $6 + 1 + 3 = 10$, which is not divisible by 3 exactly.

3. A natural number is divisible by 5 if its units digit is 0 or 5.

4. A natural number is divisible by 7 if and only if the following procedure yields a number that is exactly divisible by 7:
   a. Remove and double the units digit.
   b. Subtract this double from the remaining portion of the original number.
   c. If this final difference is exactly divisible by 7, the original number is divisible by 7; if this final difference is not exactly divisible by 7, the original number also is not exactly divisible by 7. Thus, to test 301 as to divisibility by 7, remove the units digit 1; double 1 to obtain 2; $30 - 2 = 28$; 28 is observed to be divisible by 7. Therefore, 301 is divisible by 7, since $301 \div 7 = 43$, exactly.

5. A natural number is exactly divisible by 11 if and only if the difference between the sums of the two sets of alternate digits is divisible by 11. Thus 1,529 is divisible by 11, since $9 + 5 = 14$, $2 + 1 = 3$, and $14 - 3 = 11$, which is divisible by 11. The figure 83,948,071,526 is also divisible by 11, since the sums of the alternate digits are $6 + 5 + 7 + 8 + 9 + 8 = 43$ and $2 + 1 + 0 + 4 + 3 = 10$; their difference is $43 - 10 = 33$, which is divisible by 11. Again, 235 is instantly noted to be indivisible by 11, since $(5 + 2) - 3 = 4$, which is not divisible by 11. The validity of these and other tests of divisibility may be established by congruence relationships, which will be presented in Lesson 12.

Instead of introducing tests for divisibility by primes larger than 11, the test may be made just as easily by performing the right hand division using successive subtractions of appropriate multiples of the prime divisor. This division is easily made because all prime numbers larger than 5 have for their units digit 1 or 3 or 7 or 9 and because the first nine multiples of numbers ending in these digits have for their units digits all of the digits from 1 to 9, inclusive (Section 3.7).

Test the divisibility of 94,017 by 37:

94017	
37	Subtract 1 thirty-seven, as 1×37 ends in digit 7
9398	(Ignoring the final 0 in each subtraction)
148	Subtract 4 thirty-sevens, as 4×37 ends in digit 8
925	
185	Subtract 5 thirty-sevens, as 5×37 ends in digit 5
74	
74	Subtract 2 thirty-sevens, as 2×37 ends in the digit 4
0	Final remainder is 0, denoting exact division

Incidentally, the quotient is equal to $1 + 40 + 500 + 2,000$, or 2,541.

6·7 ∾ THE FUNDAMENTAL THEOREM OF ARITHMETIC

The *fundamental theorem of arithmetic* asserts that each natural number has only one prime factor form. A valid proof of this theorem, employing congruence relationships, is supplied in the Supplement (S.17). To obtain the *unique* prime factor form of any natural number N, one tests one by one, as divisors, all prime numbers whose squares are less than N. The Sieve of Eratosthenes (S.10) yields as many consecutive prime numbers as desired, namely, 2, 3, 5, 7, ... This same device also yields the factor forms of composite numbers (S.11).

6·8 ∿ Determination of the Lowest Common Multiple by Prime Factor Forms

The use of prime factor forms provides a much simpler method than that presented in Section 6.3 for the determination of the least common multiple of two or more natural numbers. The two ensuing examples should clarify the procedure.

$$
\begin{aligned}
2 &= 2 \\
3 &= 3 \\
4 &= 2^2 \\
6 &= 2 \times 3 \\
\hline
\text{L.C.M.} &= 2^2 \times 3 = 12
\end{aligned}
$$

Obtain the L.C.M. (lowest common multiple) of 2, 3, 4, and 6. Observe that any multiple of the natural number N, namely, mN, must contain all prime factors of N, as is evident by expressing mN in its prime factor form. Thus the L.C.M. of a set of natural numbers must contain only those prime numbers occurring in each prime factor form individually.

$$
\begin{aligned}
18 &= 2 \times 3^2 \\
24 &= 2^3 \times 3 \\
48 &= 2^4 \times 3 \\
60 &= 2^2 \times 3 \times 5 \\
72 &= 2^3 \times 3^2 \\
\hline
\text{L.C.M.} &= 2^4 \times 3^2 \times 5, \text{ or } 720
\end{aligned}
$$

Obtain the L.C.M. of 18, 24, 48, 60, and 72. Observe that the L.C.M. contains each prime number occurring in the individual prime factor forms. Its exponent must be the largest exponent occurring with it in the prime factor forms. The largest exponent of 2 is 4 in the form for 48; the largest exponent of 3 is 2 in the forms for 18 and 72; the largest exponent of 5 is 1 in the form for 60.

6·9 ∿ Multiplication and Division of Natural Numbers in Prime Factor Forms

The exponent indicates how many times its base is to be used in a sequence of multiplications. Thus 3^5 means $3 \times 3 \times 3 \times 3 \times 3$, or 243. Moreover, the product of the prime factor forms $2^5 \times 3^2$ and $2^3 \times 3^7 \times 5$, namely, $(2^5 \times 3^2)(2^3 \times 3^7 \times 5)$, must contain the factors 2, 3, and 5, with individual exponents indicating the total number of times each prime factor occurs, namely, $5 + 3$, $2 + 7$, and 1, respectively. Therefore, the required product is $2^8 \times 3^9 \times 5$. Quite generally, the product of two or more natural numbers in their prime factor form must contain each individual prime number appearing in any of the prime factor forms; the exponent of such a prime number in the product must be equal to the sum of the exponents of that prime number in the original natural numbers.

Contrariwise, exact division of natural numbers is possible if and only if each prime factor of the dividend also occurs in the divisor, and if the exponent of each such prime factor of the dividend is not less than the exponent of that prime factor of the divisor. Furthermore, the exponent of the prime number of the quotient is the difference of the exponents of dividend and divisor. Thus $(2^5 \times 3^4 \times 5^2 \times 7) \div (2^2 \times 3 \times 5^2) = 2^3 \times 3^3 \times 7$.

Since involutions using natural numbers are merely repetitions of multiplications, a single example should reveal the simple rule for performing involution of a natural number in its prime factor form, namely, $(2^3 \times 3^2 \times 5^4 \times 7)^3 = ?$, which means $(2^3 \times 3^2 \times 5^4 \times 7)(2^3 \times 3^2 \times 5^4 \times 7)(2^3 \times 3^2 \times 5^4 \times 7) = 2^9 \times 3^6 \times 5^{12} \times 7^3$. The exponent of each prime factor of the result must be equal to the *product* of the original exponent of the prime factor by the power of the involution. In this example, the exponent of 2 becomes 3×3, or 9; the exponent of 3 becomes 3×2, or 6; the exponent of 5 becomes 3×4, or 12; the exponent of 7 becomes 3×1, or 3. Note that 7 means 7^1.

6·10 ∾ THE LAWS OF EXPONENTS FOR NATURAL NUMBERS

The various situations involving multiplications, divisions, and involutions of natural numbers may be expressed concisely in three forms called laws of exponents for natural numbers:

1. $a^m b^n \cdots h^p \times a^q b^r \cdots h^t = a^{m+q} b^{n+r} \cdots h^{p+t}$
2. $a^m b^n \cdots h^p \div a^q b^r \cdots h^t = a^{m-q} b^{n-r} \cdots h^{p-t}$
3. $(a^m b^n \cdots h^p)^e = a^{em} b^{en} \cdots h^{ep}$

∾ PROBLEMS ∾

6.1. Extend the table of prime factor forms in Section 6.4 as far as 100.

6.2. By use of prime factor forms, obtain in standard form the L.C.M. of the following sets of natural numbers:

 a. 28, 36 *c.* 110, 125 *e.* 36, 72, 144, 288
 b. 54, 64 *d.* 14, 18, 63 *f.* 35, 98, 343

6.3. Perform the indicated operations upon natural numbers, expressing the results in prime factor form and in standard form:

 a. $(2 \times 3)(2^2 \times 7)$ *d.* $(3 \times 5)(2 \times 3)(2^2 \times 5)$
 b. $(2 \times 3 \times 7)(3 \times 5 \times 7)$ *e.* $(2^2 \times 3)^4$
 c. $(3^3 \times 5^2)(3^2 \times 5^2)$ *f.* $(2^3 \times 5^5 \times 7)^3$
 g. $(5^2 \times 13^4 \times 19) \div (5 \times 13^3 \times 19)$

h. $(2 \times 3 \times 5 \times 7 \times 11 \times 13 \times 17) \div (7 \times 11 \times 13 \times 17)$

i. $(2^{12} \times 3^8 \times 5^4) \div (2^6 \times 3^4 \times 5^2)$

j. $(2^3 \times 3^2 \times 5)^3 \times (3^4 \times 5^3 \times 7^2)^4 \div (2^2 \times 3^5 \times 5^3 \times 7^2)^4$

6.4. Obtain the prime factor forms of the following natural numbers:

    a.   141   *c.*   1,001   *e.*   9,216

    b. 5,719   *d.*   899   *f.* 510,510

6·11 ∾ MULTIPLICATION AND DIVISION OF FRACTIONS BY NATURAL NUMBERS

The product of the fraction a/b by the natural number n or the result of multiplying the fraction a/b by n is the sum of the fraction a/b taken n times as an addend. If a represents any integer, and b and n represent any natural numbers, then $n \times a/b = na/b$. Thus $5 \times \frac{3}{4} = \frac{15}{4}$, or $3\frac{3}{4}$. Contrariwise, $na/b \div n = a/b$; i.e., if the numerator is exactly divisible by the integer n, then $a/b \div n = (a \div n)/b$. Thus $\frac{8}{15} \div 4 = \frac{2}{15}$. If the numerator a is not exactly divisible by n, both numerator and denominator of the given fraction a/b may be multiplied by n without altering the value of the fraction. Then $na/nb \div n = a/nb$.

To repeat concisely and symbolically: If a/b represents any fraction, and n represents any natural number, then $a/b \times n = na/b$; $a/b \div n = a/nb$; i.e., to multiply a fraction by a natural number, one multiplies the *numerator* by n; to divide a fraction by a natural number, one multiplies the *denominator* by n.

6·12 ∾ MULTIPLICATION AND DIVISION OF FRACTIONS BY FRACTIONS

Since any fraction a/b has been defined as an indicated division of any integer a by any natural number b, and since $Fa \div b$ has been shown to be associative for integers, that is, $Fa \div b = F(a \div b)$, it is reasonable to define $F(a/b)$ as $Fa \div b$, if F represents any fraction whatever. If F represents the fraction p/q, then $p/q \cdot a/b = (p/q \cdot a) \div b = pa/q \div b = pa/qb$. The rule for multiplication of fractions is:

> *The product of two fractions is the fraction whose numerator is the product of the numerators, and whose denominator is the product of the denominators, respectively, of the two given fractions.*

This rule of multiplication of fractions is justified geometrically in Section 6.16.

Quite generally, the product of any number of fractions is defined as the fraction whose numerator is equal to the product of the numerators and whose denominator is equal to the product of the denominators, respectively, of all of the given fractions.

If now $a/b \cdot p/q = ap/bq$, then inversely $ap/bq \div p/q$ must yield the fraction a/b. This result is accomplished if one multiplies the fraction ap/bq by the fraction q/p, obtained by interchanging the numerator and denominator of the divisor fraction p/q. Thus $ap/bq \cdot q/p = apq/bpq$, which yields a/b by dividing numerator and denominator by pq. The rule for dividing a fraction by a fraction is:

The quotient of two fractions is equal to the product of the dividend fraction by the reciprocal of the divisor fraction; the reciprocal of any given fraction is that fraction obtained by interchanging the numerator and denominator of the given fraction.

$$\tfrac{3}{4} \div \tfrac{5}{6} = \tfrac{3}{4} \times \tfrac{6}{5} = \tfrac{18}{20}, \text{ or } \tfrac{9}{10}, \text{ in lowest terms}$$
$$\tfrac{7}{9} \div \tfrac{2}{3} = \tfrac{7}{9} \times \tfrac{3}{2} = \tfrac{21}{18} = \tfrac{7}{6}, \text{ or } 1\tfrac{1}{6}$$

Multiplications or divisions that involve mixed numbers may be conveniently performed by changing all mixed numbers to improper fractions for performing multiplication or division. To reduce the work of performing the operation of multiplication of fractions, one should remove any common factors that occur in any numerator and any denominator *before* multiplying numerator by numerator and denominator by denominator to obtain the required product of the fractions.

$$\tfrac{3}{4} \div 2\tfrac{1}{4} = \tfrac{3}{4} \div \tfrac{9}{4} = \tfrac{3}{4} \times \tfrac{4}{9} = ?$$

Removing the common factor 3 from the 3 and 9 and removing also the common factor 4 from the numerator and denominator, one obtains:

$$\tfrac{1}{1} \times \tfrac{1}{3} = \tfrac{1}{3}$$

Incidentally, the *reciprocal* of any number is defined as the quotient of 1 divided by that number; accordingly, 0 has no reciprocal.

6·13 ~ Hints for simplifying basic operations upon fractions

Reduce all given fractions to their lowest terms before using them. Thus, $\tfrac{57}{38} - \tfrac{34}{51} = ?$ would require a very large common denominator, namely, 1,938. But, since $\tfrac{57}{38} = \tfrac{3}{2}$ by dividing numerator and denominator by 19, and $\tfrac{34}{51} = \tfrac{2}{3}$ by dividing numerator and denominator by 17, the problem is converted to $\tfrac{3}{2} - \tfrac{2}{3} = \tfrac{9}{6} - \tfrac{4}{6} = \tfrac{5}{6}$.

For addition and subtraction of mixed numbers, one should operate upon the integers and fractions separately rather than to reduce all mixed numbers to improper fractions, for such reductions would introduce unduly large numbers for numerators. Thus $34\tfrac{2}{3} + 76\tfrac{1}{2} + 83\tfrac{5}{6} = ?$ becomes $34 + 76 + 83 = 193$; $\tfrac{2}{3} + \tfrac{1}{2} + \tfrac{5}{6} = \tfrac{4}{6} + \tfrac{3}{6} + \tfrac{5}{6} = \tfrac{12}{6}$, or 2. The required sum is $193 + 2 = 195$. Again, $5,743\tfrac{7}{8} + 8,099\tfrac{5}{6} = ?$ involves $5,743 + 8,099 = 13,842$; $\tfrac{7}{8} + \tfrac{5}{6} = \tfrac{21}{24} + \tfrac{20}{24} = \tfrac{41}{24} = 1\tfrac{17}{24}$, whence $13,842 + 1\tfrac{17}{24} = 13,843\tfrac{17}{24}$.

Likewise, for subtraction, $35\frac{5}{8} - 23\frac{2}{5} = ?$ involves $35 - 23 = 12$; $\frac{5}{8} - \frac{2}{5} = \frac{25}{40} - \frac{16}{40} = \frac{9}{40}$, whence the entire difference is $12\frac{9}{40}$. However, if the fractional portion of the subtrahend is larger than the fractional portion of the minuend, one must transfer a unit from the integral portion of the minuend to its fractional portion to permit the subtraction of the fractional portions. Thus the problem $35\frac{2}{5} - 23\frac{5}{8} = ?$ requires $35\frac{2}{5}$ to be written as $34 + 1 + \frac{2}{5}$, or as $34\frac{7}{5}$, since $\frac{5}{8}$ is larger than $\frac{2}{5}$. Thus $34 - 23 = 11$; $\frac{7}{5} - \frac{5}{8} = \frac{56}{40} - \frac{25}{40} = \frac{31}{40}$, whence the solution $35\frac{2}{5} - 23\frac{5}{8} = 11\frac{31}{40}$.

To reduce a fraction to its lowest terms one must know the prime factor form of numerator *or* denominator. To reduce the fraction $\frac{51}{323}$, one recognizes the factor 3 in 51, as $5 + 1 = 6$ and 6 is divisible by 3. Hence, $51 = 3 \times 17$. But 323 is not divisible by 3, as $3 + 2 + 3 = 8$, which is not divisible by 3. However, 323 is divisible by 17, as $323 \div 17 = 19$, whence $\frac{51}{323} = \frac{3}{19}$. Now if 323 were not divisible by 17, the fraction $\frac{51}{323}$ would have been in its lowest terms since the only prime numbers that can divide 51 are 3 and 17, by the fundamental theorem of arithmetic.

6·14 ∽ Euclid's algorithm

The reduction of the numerator or the denominator to its prime factor form might be quite tedious, involving the testing of many prime numbers as possible prime factors. However, an ancient device known as *Euclid's algorithm* does yield quite simply the largest common divisor of two natural numbers. An example should clarify its operation; proof of its validity is supplied in Section 6.15.

To reduce the fraction $\frac{323}{361}$ to its lowest terms, one must have the largest common divisor of the numerator and denominator; i.e., obtain by Euclid's algorithm the G.C.D. of 323 and 361.

Divide the smaller number into the larger one, obtaining a remainder that is smaller than the divisor:

$$3\ 2\ 3\ \overline{\ \left|\ 3\ 6\ 1\ \right|\ 1}$$
$$\underline{3\ 2\ 3}$$
$$3\ 8$$

Divide the remainder 38 into the previous divisor, 323, obtaining a remainder that is smaller than the divisor:

$$3\ 8\ \overline{\ \left|\ 3\ 2\ 3\ \right|\ 8}$$
$$\underline{3\ 0\ 4}$$
$$1\ 9$$

Continue this procedure, dividing each remainder into the previous divisor, obtaining an ever-smaller remainder.   Finally a remainder of 0 must occur; the divisor that effects that exact division is the G.C.D. of the original two natural numbers.

$$1\ 9\ \overline{|\ 3\ 8\ |}\ 2$$
$$\underline{3\ 8}$$
$$0$$

Now since 19 divides 38 *exactly*, 19 is the G.C.D. of 323 and 361.

In this example, since $323 \div 19 = 17$ and $361 \div 19 = 19$, $\frac{323}{361} = \frac{17}{19}$.

Again, reduce $\frac{252}{553}$ to its lowest terms.   Performing Euclid's algorithm more concisely, one has

$$2\ 5\ 2\ \overline{|\ 5\ 5\ 3\ |}\ 2$$
$$\underline{5\ 0\ 4}$$
$$4\ 9\ \overline{|\ 2\ 5\ 2\ |}\ 5$$
$$\underline{2\ 4\ 5}$$
$$7\ \overline{|\ 4\ 9\ |}\ 7$$
$$\underline{4\ 9}$$
$$0$$

The final divisor 7 is the G.C.D. of 252 and 553.   The successive quotients, 2, 5 and 7, are useless; they are written here to clarify the procedure.   Dividing numerator and denominator by the highest common divisor, 7, one has $\frac{252}{553} = \frac{36}{79}$.

PROBLEMS [CONCLUDED]

6.5. Reduce the following fractions to lowest terms by the prime-factor method:

a. $\frac{98}{119}$ *d.* $\frac{123}{164}$ *g.* $\frac{128}{182}$

b. $\frac{111}{185}$ *e.* $\frac{46}{69}$ *h.* $\frac{270}{405}$

c. $\frac{51}{85}$ *f.* $\frac{154}{203}$ *i.* $\frac{56}{1,001}$

6.6. Reduce the following fractions to lowest terms by use of Euclid's algorithm.   If Euclid's algorithm yields 1 as the G.C.D., the fraction is in its lowest terms.

a. $\frac{256}{384}$ *d.* $\frac{512}{1,536}$ *g.* $\frac{226}{710}$

b. $\frac{777}{1,295}$ *e.* $\frac{889}{1,397}$ *h.* $\frac{2,048}{6,561}$

c. $\frac{101}{297}$ *f.* $\frac{2,565}{4,104}$ *i.* $\frac{428,571}{714,285}$

6.7. Perform the subtractions:

a. $2\frac{1}{4} - 1\frac{1}{8}$ e. $234\frac{9}{11} - 191\frac{1}{4}$ i. $560\frac{1}{9} - 261\frac{1}{8}$

b. $4\frac{2}{3} - 3\frac{1}{2}$ f. $500\frac{5}{6} - 399\frac{2}{3}$ j. $29\frac{11}{37} - 19\frac{95}{111}$

c. $2\frac{4}{5} - 1\frac{1}{3}$ g. $478\frac{3}{5} - 332\frac{9}{10}$ k. $2\frac{3}{11} - 1\frac{15}{17}$

d. $5\frac{1}{8} - 2\frac{3}{4}$ h. $1,456\frac{7}{8} - 1,045\frac{23}{24}$ l. $\frac{19}{38} - \frac{17}{51}$

6.8. Which has the greater sum, and, by how much?

a. $\frac{1}{2} + \frac{1}{4} + \frac{1}{8} + \frac{1}{16} + \frac{1}{32}$ b. $\frac{1}{2} + \frac{1}{3} + \frac{1}{4} + \frac{1}{5} + \frac{1}{6}$

6.9. From the sum of $\frac{2}{3}$, $\frac{3}{4}$, and $\frac{4}{5}$, subtract the sum of $\frac{5}{6}$ and $\frac{7}{12}$.

6.10. A mother wishes to place in a box a number of marbles to be divided equally among the children attending her son's birthday party. The number of children will be 10, 11, or 12. What is the least number of marbles required?

6.11. What is the least number of rectangles, 6 inches by 8 inches, that are required to form a square by placing them side by side and end to end?

6.12. What is the least number of rectangular blocks, 4 inches by 6 inches by 9 inches, that can be stacked into a cubical pile? A cubical pile must have its length, width, and height equal.

6.13. What is the least number of members of a marching club, if they wish to march either four abreast, six abreast, eight abreast, nine abreast, or twelve abreast?

6.14. A father weighs $3\frac{1}{2}$ pounds more than the combined weights of his wife and daughter. His wife weighs $111\frac{1}{4}$ pounds more than this daughter, who weighs $7\frac{1}{2}$ pounds. Calculate their total weight.

6.15. Compute the perimeter of a rectangular field that is $6\frac{7}{8}$ feet longer than its width. The field is $176\frac{3}{4}$ feet wide.

6.16. How many feet of fencing would be needed to surround completely the field in Problem 6.15 and to divide it into three equal rectangular areas? Obtain both solutions.

6.17. Into a pail weighing $2\frac{1}{2}$ pounds, $14\frac{2}{3}$ pounds of water are poured. Then a live fish weighing $1\frac{3}{4}$ pounds is dropped into the pail. If the fish is at rest in the water, what should be the combined weight of the pail and contents?

6.18. The legal length of a meter in the United States is exactly $39\frac{37}{100}$ inches. How does this compare with a length of $39\frac{3}{8}$ inches?

6.19. Two metal balls, A and B, weigh respectively $\frac{7}{16}$ and $\frac{11}{25}$ pounds.

a. Which ball is heavier, and by how much?

b. Compute their total weight.

6.20. A can do a certain job in 15 days; B can do the same job in 12 days.

    a. What part of the job can they do together in one day?

    b. What part of the job remains undone, if A has worked 5 days and B has worked 6 days?

6.21. Check Problem 6.20 if the job to be done were:

    a. Plowing 120 acres of ground   *c.* Sorting 90 tons of mail

    b. Surveying 300 miles of roadway   *d.* Interpreting 60 manuscripts

6.22. Three posts, A, B, C, are placed in a straight line. A and B are $5\frac{3}{8}$ feet apart; B and C are $7\frac{9}{16}$ feet apart. How far apart are A and C if: (*a*) B is between A and C? (*b*) A is between B and C?

6.23. From a board $23\frac{7}{8}$ inches long, three pieces are sawed off. The first piece is $4\frac{7}{8}$ inches long, the second piece is $1\frac{3}{4}$ inches longer than the first piece, the third piece is as long as the other two pieces combined. If $\frac{1}{16}$ inch is lost with each sawing, what is the length of the remaining piece of the original board?

6.24. On one particular day a student spent half of his money for books, a fourth for lunch, an eighth for class dues, and a sixteenth for transportation. What part of his money did he have left?

6.25. A student spends a third of his study time on algebra, a fourth of his study time on English, one-fifth on Spanish, and the remainder on history. How much more of his study time does he spend on history than on Spanish?

6.26. A clerk's beginning salary was $98\frac{1}{2}$ cents per hour. At the end of each year of service his hourly rate was increased by $17\frac{3}{8}$ cents. What was his hourly rate during his seventh year of service?

6.27. On each of five consecutive days a steamship consumed $35\frac{3}{4}$, $39\frac{3}{8}$, $41\frac{1}{2}$, $36\frac{7}{8}$, and $17\frac{5}{8}$ tons of coal, respectively. How much coal was remaining from an original supply of $211\frac{1}{8}$ tons?

6.28. A jet plane made a trip from New York to Salt Lake City in 3 hours and $37\frac{2}{3}$ minutes. If 1 hour and $43\frac{5}{6}$ minutes were required in servicing the plane for the return trip, and if the entire time consumed amounted to $9\frac{1}{2}$ hours, how much time did the return trip require?

6.29. An ice cream company makes an open box to contain 1 gallon (231 cubic inches) of ice cream by cutting equal squares, $4\frac{3}{8}$ inches by $4\frac{3}{8}$ inches, from the corners of a rectangular piece of cardboard $16\frac{3}{4}$ by $15\frac{5}{16}$ inches, then folding up the edges to form a rectangular container. By how much does the content of the box so formed differ from a legal gallon?

6.30. By how much do the squares of the following fractions differ from 2? Obtain two more such fractions if each ensuing fraction is formed from the two preceding fractions as follows: Each numerator or denominator is equal to twice the preceding numerator or denominator, then is increased by the next preceding numerator or denominator. Thus, $17 = 2 \times 7 + 3$. What is peculiar about the difference of consecutive fractions in this series?

$$\tfrac{3}{2}, \ \tfrac{7}{5}, \ \tfrac{17}{12}, \ \tfrac{41}{29}, \ \cdot \ \cdot \ \cdot$$

6.31. Obtain the products of the following sets of fractions:

a. $\frac{1}{2} \times \frac{3}{4}$ *d.* $\frac{3}{4} \times \frac{21}{25}$ *g.* $\frac{2}{3} \times \frac{2}{3} \times \frac{2}{3} \times \frac{2}{3}$

b. $\frac{7}{12} \times \frac{5}{8}$ *e.* $\frac{1}{2} \times \frac{1}{2} \times \frac{1}{2}$ *h.* $\frac{7}{9} \times \frac{11}{15} \times \frac{13}{16}$

c. $\frac{3}{4} \times \frac{7}{8}$ *f.* $\frac{2}{3} \times \frac{4}{5} \times \frac{7}{9}$

6.32. If p, q, r, s, and t represent different prime numbers, reduce the following fractions to lowest terms:

a. $\dfrac{pqr}{rst}$ *d.* $\dfrac{p^3 q^3 s t^5}{p^4 q^2 s^3 t^5}$ *g.* $\dfrac{pqrs}{stqp}$

b. $\dfrac{pq}{pt}$ *e.* $\dfrac{p^4 r^8 t^{12}}{p^2 r^2 t^6}$ *h.* $\dfrac{p^2 q^2 r^2}{r^2 s^2 t^2}$

c. $\dfrac{p^2 q^3 r t^2}{p q^2 s t^3}$ *f.* $\dfrac{pqr}{pqr}$ *i.* $\dfrac{p^2}{q^2}$

6.33. Cancellation of common factors from numerators and denominators should be done before multiplication. Note that the absence of symbols between these fractions implies multiplication. Thus, $\dfrac{\not{p}}{\not{q}} \dfrac{\not{q}}{r} \dfrac{s}{\not{p}} = \dfrac{s}{r}$.

a. $\dfrac{p}{q} \dfrac{pq}{rs} \dfrac{t}{p}$ *c.* $\dfrac{p^3 q}{r^3 s^4} \dfrac{r^5 s^3}{p^3 q^2}$ *e.* $\dfrac{p^4 q^9 r^{16}}{r^2} \dfrac{s^2 t^4}{p^2 q^3 t}$

b. $\dfrac{p}{q} \dfrac{q}{r} \dfrac{r}{s} \dfrac{s}{t}$ *d.* $\dfrac{pq^2 r}{rst} \dfrac{rst}{q^3}$ *f.* $\dfrac{p}{q} \dfrac{p}{q} \dfrac{p}{q} \dfrac{p}{q} \dfrac{p}{q}$

6.34. Perform the multiplications, first making all possible cancellations of common factors from numerators and denominators.

a. $\dfrac{3 \times 5 \times 7}{11 \times 13} \dfrac{2 \times 13}{2 \times 3 \times 7}$ *d.* $\dfrac{3}{2^2 \, 7} \dfrac{2 \times 5}{\times 11} \dfrac{11^2}{3 \times 5}$

b. $\dfrac{2 \times 2 \times 2 \times 3}{5 \times 5 \times 7} \dfrac{5 \times 5 \times 5}{2 \times 2 \times 2 \times 3}$ *e.* $\dfrac{7^2 \times 13}{17 \times 19} \dfrac{19}{2 \times 7} \dfrac{17}{13^2}$

c. $\dfrac{2^3 \times 3^2}{5^3 \times 7} \dfrac{5^4 \times 7^2}{2^4 \times 3}$ *f.* $\dfrac{2^{10}}{3^8} \dfrac{3^4 \, 5^{17}}{5^{12} \, 2^{12}}$

6.35. Perform the indicated operations:

a. $\frac{5}{18} \times \frac{25}{27} \times \frac{9}{40}$ e. $\frac{2}{3} \times \frac{4}{9} \times \frac{8}{27} \times \frac{16}{81}$ i. $2\frac{3}{4} \times 3\frac{7}{8} \times \frac{32}{33}$

b. $\frac{9}{16} \times \frac{6}{7} \times \frac{8}{27}$ f. $\frac{7}{33} \times \frac{6}{13} \times \frac{15}{34}$ j. $3\frac{1}{2} \times 1\frac{1}{3} \times 3\frac{1}{2}$

c. $\frac{93}{68} \times \frac{85}{87} \times \frac{58}{155}$ g. $4\frac{2}{4} \times 2\frac{1}{2} \times 3\frac{1}{2}$ k. $12\frac{1}{2} \times 6\frac{2}{5} \times 7\frac{1}{2}$

d. $\frac{77}{111} \times \frac{9}{14} \times \frac{37}{44}$ h. $3\frac{1}{7} \times 1\frac{4}{11} \times \frac{6}{26}$ l. $2\frac{1}{2} \times 1\frac{2}{3} \times 2\frac{1}{2} \times 1\frac{2}{3}$

6.36. Perform the divisions:

a. $\frac{9}{20} \div \frac{3}{4}$ e. $\frac{2}{3} \div \frac{1}{12}$ i. $\dfrac{pq^2}{rs^2} \div \dfrac{pq}{rs}$

b. $\frac{3}{4} \div \frac{7}{8}$ f. $1\frac{5}{7} \div 4\frac{2}{3}$ j. $\dfrac{pq^2t^3}{r^5s^3} \div \dfrac{rs^2t}{r^5s^2}$

c. $\frac{56}{81} \div \frac{14}{27}$ g. $16\frac{2}{3} \div 12\frac{1}{2}$

d. $\frac{111}{87} \div \frac{37}{58}$ h. $\dfrac{p}{q} \div \dfrac{pq}{st}$

6.37. How many square feet of pavement are in a sidewalk that is $42\frac{1}{3}$ feet long and $4\frac{1}{2}$ feet wide? What would be the cost of removing this pavement at a charge of $7\frac{5}{12}$ cents per square foot?

6.38. A flower bed is $4\frac{1}{4}$ feet long and $1\frac{1}{2}$ feet wide. Calculate the (*a*) area; (*b*) perimeter.

6.39. Compute the volume of a rectangular tank whose inside dimensions are $4\frac{2}{5}$, $4\frac{1}{2}$, and $4\frac{1}{6}$ feet, respectively. (*a*) Express the result in gallons. One gallon contains exactly 231 cubic inches, by federal statute. (*b*) Calculate the weight of fluid that fills the tank, if the fluid weighs $62\frac{1}{2}$ pounds per cubic foot.

6.40. Compute the total cost of this bill of items. Give the result to the nearest cent after obtaining the exact total cost.

$7\frac{3}{4}$ feet of No. A wire at $3\frac{1}{2}$ cents per foot
$12\frac{1}{2}$ feet of No. B wire at $2\frac{2}{3}$ cents per foot
$10\frac{1}{3}$ feet of No. C wire at $1\frac{1}{2}$ cents per foot
$10\frac{2}{3}$ feet of No. D wire at $\frac{15}{16}$ cents per foot

6.41. How many boxes of candy, each of $3\frac{1}{3}$ pounds capacity, can be filled from three trays of candy containing $35\frac{1}{9}$ pounds each? How many additional pounds will be needed to fill the last box?

6.42. A rectangular bin of inside dimensions $3\frac{1}{2}$, $4\frac{2}{3}$, and $7\frac{1}{2}$ feet, respectively, is filled with shelled corn. How long will it take to grind this corn, if the mill can grind $4\frac{1}{5}$ cubic feet of corn per minute?

6.43. How many dozens of storage eggs, worth $37\frac{1}{2}$ cents per dozen, would be equivalent to 27 pounds of butter worth $87\frac{1}{2}$ cents per pound? Solve this problem also for fresh eggs worth $56\frac{1}{4}$ cents per dozen.

6.44. How many books each containing 250 pages can a student read in 30 days, if he can read $1\frac{2}{3}$ pages per minute, if he reads two-thirds of his leisure time, and if he has 2 hours of leisure time each day?

6.45. What is the total cost of carpeting a room, at $\$11\frac{1}{4}$ per square yard, if the entire area of the room, $14\frac{2}{3}$ feet long and $10\frac{1}{2}$ feet wide, is to be covered with carpet?

6.46. Which is greater, and by how much, the cube of $\frac{3}{4}$ or the square of $\frac{5}{8}$?

6.47. What should be the total earnings of a crew that works $7\frac{3}{4}$ hours each day for 5 days, and $4\frac{1}{3}$ hours on the sixth day? Two men are paid $\$5.12\frac{3}{8}$ per hour, seven men are paid $\$3.72\frac{5}{8}$ per hour, and the remainder of the crew, 19 laborers, are paid $\$2.18\frac{3}{4}$ per hour each.

6.48. The force in pounds that is required to slide an object along a level track is equal to the weight of the object in pounds multiplied by the coefficient of sliding friction. (*a*) What force is required to slide a block along a level track, if the block weighs $97\frac{3}{5}$ pounds and the coefficient of sliding friction is $\frac{3}{8}$? (*b*) How heavy a block can a person slide along this track, if he can exert a force of 150 pounds on the block?

6.49. If *A* can do a certain job in 12 days, and *B* can do the same job in 8 days: (*a*) How much of the job remains undone if *A* works 2 days and *B* works 4 days? (*b*) How long will it take them to do the job together?

6.50. *A*, *B*, *C*, and *D* can do a certain job in 9, 8, 7, and 6 days, respectively. If these men work just as efficiently when working together as when working alone, how long would it take them to complete the job working together? Express the result to the nearest minute, if a working day is $6\frac{7}{8}$ hours.

*N*ote 1 ⚬⚬ *Some operational features of the number line.*

The number line is a scale for measurement of distance. Let the distance from the position of 0 to the position of 1 on the number line be the *unit of distance*, such as 1 foot, 1 inch, 1 centimeter, etc. Then any number in its correct position on the number line denotes the precise distance from 0 to its position, in terms of the particular unit employed. Thus, if the unit of distance is the inch, then 8, $\frac{5}{8}$, 25, . . . , represent respectively 8 inches, $\frac{5}{8}$ inch, 25 inches, . . . toward the *right* side of the 0; -7, $-\frac{3}{4}$, -50, . . . denote, respectively, 7 inches, $\frac{3}{4}$ inch, 50 inches toward the *left* side of the 0. Accordingly, any number on the number line represents both its *distance and direction* from the 0.

    An operation is said to be performed *geometrically* if it can be done by use of no other tools than a pair of compasses and an unmarked straightedge. If the

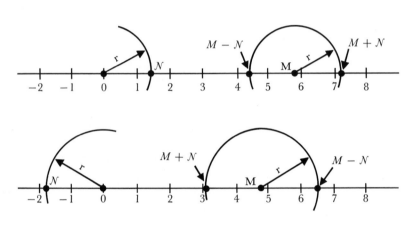

FIGURES 6.1 AND 6.2

positions of 0 and 1 are marked on the number line, one can locate the position for any other rational number geometrically (Section 5.6). Furthermore, if the positions of any two rational numbers are marked on the number line, one may obtain geometrically the positions for their sum, difference, product, and quotient. These geometrical operations follow.

Addition and Subtraction. Let M and N denote positions of the numbers M and N on the number line. With compass point at M, and compass opening the distance from 0 to N, strike two arcs on the number line on opposite sides of M. If N is *positive*, the arc intersection to the *right* of M is the position of $M + N$; if N is *negative*, the arc position to the *left* of M is the position of $M + N$. Now, since $M - (-N) = M + N$, the arc intersection to the left of M represents $M - N$, if N is positive; the arc intersection to the right of M represents $M - N$, if N is negative. (See Figures 6.1 and 6.2.)

Multiplication. Let M and N be positive numbers. The ensuing construction determines the position of MN.

Draw any other arbitrary line through 0. With compass center at 0, and with compass openings equal to distances from 0 to 1, from 0 to M, and from 0 to N, draw the three arcs cutting the number line at 1, M, and N, and the upper portion of the arbitrary line at points $1'$, M', and N', respectively. Draw the line from N' to Q that is parallel to the line from $1'$ to M. This may be done as follows:

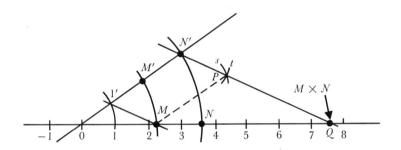

FIGURE 6.3

With compass center at M and compass opening equal to distance from $1'$ to N', draw the arc s; with the compass center at N', and compass opening equal to the distance from $1'$ to M, draw the arc t. Let P denote the intersection point of arcs s and t. The line drawn through points N' and P must be parallel to the line through $1'$ and M. (This fact is established in geometry, namely, that if a quadrilateral, such as the one having its corners at $1'$, N', P, and M, has its opposite sides *equal*, namely, the sides $1'$ to M and N' to P, and the sides $1'$ to N', and M to P, then these same pairs of opposite sides must also be *parallel*.) Accordingly, this line through N' and P must cut the number line at point Q, which represents the number MN. (See Figure 6.3.) If, however, both numbers M and N are negative, one would use the two corresponding positive numbers, since $(-M)(-N) = (+M)(+N)$.

Finally, if M is positive and N negative, the same construction will yield the position of MN, if N' is taken on the lower portion of the arbitrary line through 0, i.e., N' is separated from $1'$ and M' by 0. The point so determined, Q, representing MN if M is positive and N is negative, represents also MN if M is negative and N is positive, as $(-M)(+N) = (+M)(-N)$.

Division. Division is performed geometrically by reversing the steps of the multiplication procedure. Let N and D represent the dividend and divisor, respectively, on the number line. If N and D are both positive, the position of the Q is determined as follows:

Draw an arbitrary line through 0. With compass center at 0, and with compass openings equal to lengths from 0 to 1 and from 0 to D, strike arcs on the upper portion of the arbitrary line at points marked as $1'$ and D', respectively. Draw line through points N and D'; next draw line through $1'$ which is parallel to the line through N and D'. This line intersects the number line in the desired point Q that represents the quotient, $N \div D$. If N and D are both negative, this same point Q represents $N \div D$, since $(-N) \div (-D) = (+N) \div (+D)$. If N is negative and D is positive, the foregoing directions yield the required quotient, although the diagram is slightly different; if, however, N is positive and D is negative, the point D' should be selected on the lower portion of the arbitrary line through 0. The student should encounter no difficulty in making these geometrical constructions. The validity of these constructions for products and quotients follows from properties of similar triangles. For example, in Figure 6.3, the triangles having vertices at points 0, $1'$, M, and at 0, N', Q, are similar.

Therefore, the lengths of corresponding sides form equal triangles, namely, $\dfrac{0 \text{ to } Q}{0 \text{ to } N'} = \dfrac{0 \text{ to } M}{0 \text{ to } 1'}$, or, using their numerical values, $\dfrac{Q}{N} = \dfrac{M}{1}$, or $Q = MN$.

The earnest student will find genuine satisfaction checking these constructions by determining geometrically

$$3 + 5 \qquad 7 - 4 \qquad\qquad -6 + 2$$
$$2 \times 3 \qquad (-3) \times 2 \qquad (+3)(-3)$$
$$6 \div 3 \qquad (-5) \div (+3) \qquad (+3) \div (-4)$$

*N*ote 2 ∾ *Euclid's algorithm.*

The validity of Euclid's algorithm rests upon the fact that the greatest common divisor of two given natural numbers, A and B, is an exact divisor of each divisor and dividend in the successive steps of the ensuing divisions. This assertion may be verified in the illustrative examples in Section 6.13. The following proof of the correctness of Euclid's algorithm is limited to just four divisions. The same discussion would apply to any other number of divisions that terminate in an exact division.

1. The algorithm must always end in an exact division, since each successive remainder is positive and smaller than the previous remainder. Hence the remainder must become ultimately 1 or 0; if a remainder is 1, the next

division must be exact, as 1 is an exact divisor of every natural number; if a remainder is 0, that division is exact. Let the algorithm end with the fourth division:

$$B \;\lfloor\, A \,\rfloor\; q$$
$$\underline{qB}$$
$$C = A - qB$$

$$C \;\lfloor\, B \,\rfloor\; r$$
$$\underline{rC}$$
$$D = B - rC$$

$$D \;\lfloor\, C \,\rfloor\; s$$
$$\underline{sD}$$
$$E = C - sD$$

$$E \;\lfloor\, D \,\rfloor\; t$$
$$\underline{tE}$$
$$0 = D - tE$$

Throughout the entire process only natural numbers occur, namely, q, r, s, t, C, D, and E.

2. If d is any divisor of A and B, then d must be a divisor of each ensuing remainder (ensuing divisor). Accordingly, if d is a divisor of A and B, then $A = dA'$, and $B = dB'$, wherein A' and B' are natural numbers. Therefore:

$$C = A - qB = dA' - qdB' = d(A' - qB') = dC'$$

in which $(A' - qB')$ is represented by C'. Continuing,

$$D = B - rC = dB' - rdC' = d(B' - rC') = dD'$$

in which $(B' - rC')$ is represented by D'. The same argument applies at each ensuing step, so that finally one obtains $E = dE'$, showing that d is a divisor of the ensuing divisors C, D, and E.

3. The final exact divisor E must also be an exact divisor of each previous divisor and dividend, so that E must be an exact divisor of A and B.

$$0 = D - tE \quad \text{or} \quad D = tE \quad \text{then}$$
$$E = C - sD \quad \text{or} \quad C = E + sD = E + s(tE) = E(1 + st) = EM$$
$$D = B - rC \quad \text{or} \quad B = D + rC = tE + r(EM) = E(t + rM) = EN$$
$$C = A - qB \quad \text{or} \quad A = C + qB = EM + q(EN) = E(M + qN) = EP$$

Hence, since $A = EP$ and $B = EN$, the two original numbers A and B are divisible by E.

4. Finally, if every common divisor of A and B, including the greatest common divisor of A and B, is a divisor of E, and if E is an exact divisor of A and of B, then E must be the greatest common divisor of A and B.

$\mathcal{N}$*ote 3* ∽ *A geometrical justification of the rule of multiplication of fractions,*
namely, that a/b·c/d = ac/bd, wherein a, b, c, d are natural numbers.

Consider the rectangle *a* units long and *c* units wide wherein *a* and *c* are natural numbers that represent the number of units of length in the two dimensions of the rectangle. The number of area units contained in this rectangle must be *ac*. Now divide the length of this rectangle into *b* equal parts and the width into *d* equal parts. Drawing parallel lines through the points of equal subdivisions, one obtains *bd* small rectangles of equal area. Hence the area of one of these small rectangles must be equal to *ac* ÷ *bd* area units, or *ac/bd*. That is, the formula for the area of a small rectangle yields $a/b \cdot c/d = ac/db$.

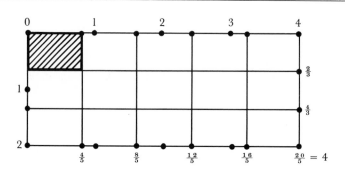

FIGURE 6.4

The foregoing argument is illustrated in Figure 6.4 for the small shaded rectangle of dimensions $\frac{4}{5}$ and $\frac{2}{3}$ length units, respectively, for its length and width, $\frac{4}{5} \times \frac{2}{3} = \frac{8}{15}$ area units for its area. The large rectangle has a length of 4 length units and a width of 2 length units and therefore an area of 4 × 2, or 8, area units. As the length of this rectangle is divided into five equal parts, and the width is divided into three equal parts, the rectangle is divided up into fifteen small equal rectangles, each, accordingly, having an area of 8 ÷ 15, or $\frac{8}{15}$ area units.

∽ $\mathcal{S}$UPPLEMENTARY PROBLEMS ∽   *Discimus agere agendo—*
We learn to do by doing.

S6.1. List all positive multiples of 6, 9, 12, and 60, until a common multiple appears. Then obtain their L.C.M. by the prime factor method.

S6.2. List all multiples of 13 that lie between 100 and 150.

S6.3. Obtain all two-digit multiples of 7 that follow 84.

S6.4. List all multiples of 19 that occur between 100 and 150.

S6.5. Obtain the largest multiple of 19 that does not exceed 1,000.

S6.6. Obtain the smallest positive multiple of 23 that exceeds 23.

S6.7. Obtain the prime factor forms of the following natural numbers:

    a. 396   *c.* 144   *e.* 1,000   *g.* 729   *i.* 2,401

    b. 693   *d.* 441   *f.* 1,625   *h.* 1,024   *j.* 1,331

S6.8. Obtain the unknown prime factor that is indicated by the ?

    a. $899 = 29 \times ?$ *c.* $527 = 17 \times ?$ *e.* $3,599 = 61 \times ?$

    b. $923 = 13 \times ?$ *d.* $949 = 13 \times ?$ *f.* $1,643 = 31 \times ?$

S6.9. Perform the indicated multiplications, simplifying all results to mixed numbers in lowest terms:

    a. $\frac{19}{24} \times 8$ *c.* $\frac{5}{8} \times 7$ *e.* $\frac{7}{12} \times 16$

    b. $\frac{3}{4} \times 14$ *d.* $\frac{2}{3} \times 11$ *f.* $\frac{9}{10} \times 2$

S6.10. Perform the indicated divisions, simplifying all results:

    a. $\frac{15}{19} \div 3$ *c.* $\frac{3}{4} \div 2$ *e.* $2\frac{1}{3} \div 7$

    b. $\frac{18}{19} \div 9$ *d.* $\frac{2}{3} \div 5$ *f.* $3\frac{1}{2} \div 14$

S6.11. Perform the indicated operations, simplifying all results:

    a. $\frac{1}{2} + \frac{2}{3} + \frac{5}{6}$ *c.* $\frac{2}{3} + \frac{3}{4} + \frac{5}{6}$ *e.* $\frac{3}{4} + \frac{4}{5} - \frac{5}{6}$

    b. $\frac{2}{3} + \frac{1}{6} - \frac{1}{2}$ *d.* $\frac{5}{6} - \frac{1}{2} - \frac{1}{4}$ *f.* $\frac{1}{2} + \frac{2}{5} - \frac{3}{7}$

S6.12. Perform the indicated operations, simplifying all results:

    a. $\frac{1}{2} \times \frac{2}{3} \times \frac{5}{6}$ *c.* $\frac{2}{3} \times \frac{3}{4} \times \frac{5}{6}$ *e.* $\frac{3}{4} \times \frac{4}{5} \div \frac{5}{6}$

    b. $\frac{2}{3} \times \frac{1}{6} \div \frac{1}{2}$ *d.* $\frac{5}{6} \div \frac{1}{2} \div \frac{1}{4}$ *f.* $\frac{1}{2} \times \frac{2}{5} \div \frac{3}{7}$

S6.13. Perform all indicated operations upon mixed numbers, simplifying all results:

    a. $24\frac{3}{8} + 46\frac{1}{2} + 91\frac{2}{3} + 37\frac{5}{6} = ?$

    b. $123\frac{4}{5} + 456\frac{7}{8} + 789\frac{11}{12} = ?$

    c. $3,459\frac{8}{10} + 9,401\frac{4}{5} + 7,005\frac{11}{20} = ?$

    d. $401\frac{9}{10} + 691\frac{7}{15} + 119\frac{11}{12} + 599\frac{19}{20} + \frac{29}{30} = ?$

S6.14. *a.* $625\frac{5}{8} - 314\frac{2}{5} = ?$ *d.* $365\frac{3}{4} + 125\frac{5}{8} - 112\frac{11}{12} = ?$

         b. $17\frac{1}{2} - 13\frac{2}{3} = ?$ *e.* $770\frac{1}{3} - 25\frac{1}{2} - 19\frac{7}{8} = ?$

         c. $600\frac{2}{3} - 39\frac{3}{4} = ?$ *f.* $1,000 - 350\frac{3}{4} - 105\frac{3}{8} = ?$

S6.15. *a.* $3\frac{1}{3} \times 5\frac{1}{5} = ?$ *c.* $16\frac{2}{3} \times 39\frac{3}{4} = ?$ *e.* $4\frac{1}{2} \times 3\frac{3}{4} = ?$

         b. $12\frac{1}{2} \times 2\frac{2}{15} = ?$ *d.* $142\frac{6}{7} \times 4\frac{11}{20} = ?$ *f.* $12\frac{1}{2} \times 8\frac{3}{4} = ?$

S6.16. *a.* $2\frac{2}{3} \div 3\frac{1}{2} = ?$ *c.* $14\frac{2}{7} \div 16\frac{2}{3} = ?$ *e.* $\frac{3}{4} \div 2\frac{2}{3} = ?$

         b. $4\frac{1}{2} \div 1\frac{1}{3} = ?$ *d.* $3\frac{3}{5} \div 7\frac{1}{2} = ?$ *f.* $5\frac{2}{3} \div 3\frac{1}{4} = ?$

S6.17. *a.* Obtain the first seven multiples of $\frac{3}{7}$, namely, $\frac{3}{7}, \frac{6}{7}, 1\frac{2}{7}, \ldots$.

         b. Obtain the sum of these seven numbers.

S6.18. *a.* Obtain the sum of the first thirteen multiples of $\frac{5}{13}$.

         b. Obtain the sum of the first thirteen multiples of $\frac{9}{13}$.

         c. Obtain the sum of the first thirteen multiples of $\frac{10}{13}$.

S6.19. From the results of the two previous problems can you surmise what must be the sum of the first eight multiples of $\frac{3}{8}$ and of $\frac{5}{8}$? Check your supposition by computing these two sums.

S6.20. Consider the sum of the first n multiples of a/n, namely, $a/n + 2a/n + 3a/n + \cdots + na/n$. The average size of these n numbers is half the sum of the smallest and largest. Show that this average is $(n + 1)a/2n$. Hence, the sum of these n numbers is $n(n + 1)a/2n$, or $(n + 1)a/2$. Use this formula to check the results of the previous three problems.

S6.21. If one candy bar weighs exactly $1\frac{1}{4}$ ounces, compute the weight of a gross of these candy bars (1 gross = 12 dozen). How many of these candy bars would weigh exactly 5 pounds? (16 ounces = 1 pound.)

S6.22. A garden plot is $16\frac{2}{3}$ feet long and $12\frac{1}{2}$ feet wide. Calculate (*a*) its area, (*b*) its perimeter, (*c*) the area of a path $3\frac{1}{2}$ feet wide that surrounds it.

S6.23. If a lad can saw up $4\frac{3}{4}$ cords of wood in one hour, how long would it take him to saw up $7\frac{1}{8}$ cords at this same rate? Express the result to the *nearest* minute. (A cord is equivalent to a pile 4 feet wide, 4 feet high, and 8 feet long.)

S6.24. How many pieces of cloth, each $3\frac{5}{6}$ yards long, can be cut from a bolt of cloth containing $30\frac{2}{3}$ yards? How many such pieces could be cut from a bolt of 200 yards, and how long would the remnant be?

S6.25. If a motor car can run $12\frac{3}{8}$ miles on 1 gallon of fuel, at this rate how far could the car run on $85\frac{1}{3}$ gallons? How much fuel would the car require to run 5,000 miles at this same rate?

S6.26. A lad worked for a merchant in after-school hours at an hourly rate of $37\frac{1}{2}$ cents. During one week he worked on successive days $3\frac{1}{2}$, $2\frac{1}{3}$, $2\frac{1}{2}$, $4\frac{1}{4}$, and $5\frac{1}{6}$ hours, respectively. How much did he earn for that week? How many hours would he have to work to earn $50?

S6.27. Compute the difference between these two purchases: (a) $19\frac{1}{5}$ tons of grade A steel @ $5\frac{3}{8}$ per ton, or (b) $24\frac{1}{3}$ tons of grade B steel @ $4\frac{1}{2}$ per ton. If all this steel were sold at the same price per ton, what would have been the price?

S6.28. If water weighs $62\frac{1}{2}$ pounds per cubic foot, how many gallons of water would weigh 1 ton, if 2,000 pounds equal 1 ton, and 231 cubic inches are equal to 1 gallon?

S6.29. If a $1 bill is exactly $6\frac{7}{8}$ inches long and $2\frac{5}{8}$ inches wide, how many such bills would be needed to extend for 1 mile, if they are placed end to end? How many if placed side by side? What would be the smallest number of such bills that would be required to form a square, if they are placed side by side and end to end with no overlapping?

S6.30. Which is the largest and the smallest fraction of the set of fractions, $\frac{851}{629}$, $\frac{1219}{954}$, $\frac{1265}{1045}$. (*Hint:* reduce them to their lowest terms.)

S6.31. Obtain the sum of the fractions $\frac{954}{1219}$, $\frac{629}{851}$, $\frac{1045}{1265}$.

S6.32. Which is more expensive and by how much, $90\frac{1}{2}$ pounds of potatoes at $4\frac{1}{2}$ cents per pound or $19\frac{1}{2}$ pounds of apples at $19\frac{1}{2}$ cents per pound?

S6.33. Compute the difference of both perimeters and areas of two rectangles: (*a*) 27 by 12 feet, and (*b*) 25 by 13 feet. (*c*) Re-solve this problem after increasing the lengths of these rectangles by $\frac{1}{2}$ foot, and decreasing their widths by $\frac{1}{2}$ foot.

S6.34. Multiply $4\frac{2}{3}$ by $6\frac{1}{2}$ by two methods:
  a. By converting them to improper fractions.
  b. By using the distributive law $(4 + \frac{2}{3})(6 + \frac{1}{2}) = 4 \times 6 + 4 \times \frac{1}{2} + \frac{2}{3} \times 6 + \frac{2}{3} \times \frac{1}{2}$.

S6.35. Divide $60\frac{2}{3}$ by $6\frac{1}{4}$ by the two methods:
  a. By converting them to improper fractions.
  b. By repeated subtractions of multiples of divisor from the dividend.

S6.36. Perform the indicated operations by two different methods:
  a. $6{,}432\frac{1}{2} \times 154\frac{2}{3} = ?$ b. $993{,}501\frac{1}{3} \div 77\frac{1}{3} = ?$

S6.37. Common fractions having 1 for the numerator are called *unit fractions*. Any unit fraction is equal to the sum of two other unit fractions, such as: (a) $\frac{1}{2} = \frac{1}{3} + \frac{1}{6}$, (b) $\frac{1}{3} = \frac{1}{4} + \frac{1}{12}$, (c) $\frac{1}{5} = \frac{1}{6} + \frac{1}{30}$. (d) Now obtain two unit fractions whose sum is equal to $\frac{1}{7}$, after detecting the rule of formation from the three preceding examples. (e) Obtain two different sets of *three* unit fractions whose sum is $\frac{1}{2}$. Check these sums for correctness.

S6.38. Obtain eight unit fractions whose sum is $\frac{1}{3}$, if the largest denominator used is 90. Note the curious relationship between the denominators of these eight fractions when arranged in order of size.

S6.39. Obtain four unit fractions whose sum is (a) $\frac{1}{4}$, (b) $\frac{1}{5}$, (c) $\frac{1}{6}$. Arrange each set of the four unit fractions in order of size, noting the sequence of three oblong numbers occurring in the denominators. (An oblong number is the product of two consecutive natural numbers.)

S6.40. Write down instantly the (a) five, (b) eight, (c) twenty unit fractions whose sum is $\frac{1}{10}$.

S6.41. Calculate the value of the ? in the successive lines until you detect the rule that yields the ensuing values of the ?

$$\frac{1}{2 \times 3} = \frac{1}{2} - ?$$

$$\frac{1}{2 \times 3} + \frac{1}{3 \times 4} = \frac{1}{2} - ?$$

$$\frac{1}{2 \times 3} + \frac{1}{3 \times 4} + \frac{1}{4 \times 5} = \frac{1}{2} - ?$$

$$\frac{1}{2 \times 3} + \frac{1}{3 \times 4} + \frac{1}{4 \times 5} + \frac{1}{5 \times 6} = \frac{1}{2} - ?$$

$$\cdots \cdots \cdots \cdots \cdots \cdots$$

Now express in words the relationship implied by these examples. The universal validity of this relationship may be proved by mathematical induction which is provided in algebra.

S6.42. Verify the formula for the relationship that may be expressed verbally as follows: The sum of the reciprocals of the oblong numbers from $1/n(n + 1)$ to $1/(m - 1)m$, inclusive, is equal to $1/n - 1/m$, for:
  a. $n = 4,\ m = 7$ c. $n = 1,\ m = 1{,}000{,}000$
  b. $n = 25,\ m = 30$ d. $\frac{1}{2} + \frac{1}{6} + \frac{1}{12} + \cdots$ without end $= ?$

S6.43. Add the following *pairs* of fractions that have a common *numerator*. If possible, discover the rule that yields their sum immediately.

   a. $\frac{1}{7} + \frac{1}{8} = ?$ *c.* $\frac{3}{7} + \frac{3}{8} = ?$ *e.* $\frac{1}{11} + \frac{1}{13} = ?$ *g.* $\frac{7}{19} + \frac{7}{31} = ?$

   b. $\frac{2}{7} + \frac{2}{8} = ?$ *d.* $\frac{5}{7} + \frac{5}{8} = ?$ *f.* $\frac{5}{11} + \frac{5}{13} = ?$ *h.* $\frac{5}{9} + \frac{5}{11} = ?$

S6.44. Reduce 5,083/5,290 to lowest terms if it is known that 13 and 17 are factors of 5,083. Reduce the fraction by use of Euclid's algorithm.

S6.45. One cubic foot is generally stated to be equivalent to $7\frac{1}{2}$ gallons. One gallon, however, has been defined by federal statute to be 231 cubic inches.

   a. Compute the *exact* number of gallons, as a mixed number, in 1 cubic foot.

   b. Compute the exact error in gallons in 1 cubic foot that is committed by using the formula 1 cubic foot = $7\frac{1}{2}$ gallons.

   c. Compute the *exact* number of cubic feet that would be equivalent to 1,500,000 gallons.

   d. Compute the approximate number of cubic feet in 1,500,000 gallons by using the inaccurate formula $7\frac{1}{2}$ gallons = 1 cubic foot.

   e. Calculate the weight of the difference between the results in (*c*) and (*d*), *if* water weighs $62\frac{1}{2}$ pounds per cubic foot.

S6.46. State a valid reason why any power of a fraction, in its lowest terms, must also be in lowest terms. Thus, $\frac{3}{4}$ is in its lowest terms; hence, $(\frac{3}{4})^2$ or $\frac{9}{16}$, $(\frac{3}{4})^3$ or $\frac{27}{64}$, . . . , must be in lowest terms. By these considerations it is evident that no fraction exists whose square is equal to 2; for, if p/q, in lowest terms, is such a fraction then $(p/q)^2 = 2$, or $\frac{2}{1}$. Since $(p/q)^2 = p^2/q^2$, q^2 must be equal to 1, and p^2 must be equal to 2, which is absurd. Fractions may be obtained whose squares differ from 2 by ever smaller amounts, namely, $\frac{3}{2}, \frac{7}{5}, \frac{17}{12}$.

   a. Detect the relationship between three consecutive numerators of this series of fractions; note that the same relationship occurs between three consecutive denominators. Use this relationship to obtain the next three fractions in this series.

   b. Determine the differences between the squares of these fractions and 2. These successive fractions are called convergents to the square root of 2, as they approximate ever closer to the square root of 2.

   c. Noting that m^2/n^2 differs from 2 by exactly $1/n^2$, obtain the first fraction in the above series of convergents whose square differs from 2 by less than $\frac{1}{25,000}$.

   d. Verify the fact that the first, third, fifth, etc., fraction in the series decreases, while the second, fourth, sixth, etc., fraction continues to increase. Note the curious difference between consecutive fractions.

S6.47. Repeat the discussion in the preceding problem to prove that no fraction exists whose square is equal to (*a*) 3, (*b*) 5, (*c*) any natural number that is not a square number.

S6.48. Re-solve Problems S6.46*a*, *b*, *c*, *d*, as applied to:

   a. $\frac{2}{1}, \frac{5}{3}, \frac{7}{4}, \frac{19}{11}, \frac{26}{15}$, whose squares approximate to 3.

   b. $\frac{2}{1}, \frac{9}{4}, \frac{38}{17}, \frac{161}{72}, \frac{682}{305}, \frac{2,889}{1,292}$, whose squares approximate to 5.

S6.49. An indicated division, such as $a \div b$, may be exhibited in the form of a fraction, as a/b, in which the dividend becomes the numerator, and the divisor becomes the denominator. Thus,

$2\frac{3}{4} \div 5$ may be expressed as $\dfrac{2\frac{3}{4}}{5}$

$7 \div \frac{5}{8}$ as $\dfrac{7}{\frac{5}{8}}$ $12\frac{7}{12} \div 62\frac{1}{2}$ as $\dfrac{12\frac{7}{12}}{62\frac{1}{2}}$

These latter forms of fractions whose numerator and denominator may be fractions or mixed numbers are called *complex fractions*. To reduce a complex fraction to its simplest form one merely performs the indicated division denoted by the line separating its numerator and denominator. Thus,

$$\frac{3\frac{2}{3}}{7\frac{3}{4}} = 3\frac{2}{3} \div 7\frac{3}{4} = \frac{11}{3} \div \frac{31}{4} = \frac{11}{3} \times \frac{4}{31} = \frac{44}{93}$$

Now simplify the complex fractions:

a. $\dfrac{2\frac{3}{4}}{5\frac{2}{3}}$ *b.* $\dfrac{\frac{7}{8}}{\frac{5}{12}}$ *c.* $\dfrac{12\frac{7}{8}}{5\frac{5}{9}}$ *d.* $\dfrac{\frac{7}{5}}{\frac{17}{12}}$ *e.* $\dfrac{87\frac{1}{2}}{33\frac{1}{3}}$ *f.* $\dfrac{6\frac{1}{4}}{8\frac{1}{3}}$ *g.* $\dfrac{14\frac{2}{7}}{85\frac{5}{7}}$

S6.50. To convert a given fraction to a specified denominator, one writes the given fraction as the numerator of a complex fraction, and 1 as the denominator of the complex fraction; then one multiplies the numerator and denominator of the complex fraction by the specified denominator. Thus, to reduce the fraction $\frac{11}{13}$ to sixteenths,

$$\frac{11}{13} = \frac{\frac{11}{13}}{1} = \frac{\frac{11}{13} \times 16}{1 \times 16} = \frac{\frac{176}{13}}{16}$$

or $\dfrac{13\frac{7}{13}}{16}$, or $\frac{14}{16}$, since $\frac{7}{13}$ is greater than $\frac{1}{2}$, as the *nearest approximation* to sixteenths.

Now obtain the best approximation of the fraction $\frac{19}{31}$ to sixty-fourths.

S6.51. A student carelessly writes a complex fraction as 3/4/5. What should its value be if he intended to write (*a*) $\dfrac{3/4}{5}$?   (*b*) $\dfrac{3}{4/5}$?

S6.52. An inventor wishes to purchase pieces of a special wire of lengths $5\frac{19}{55}$, $27\frac{11}{49}$, and $43\frac{99}{151}$ inches, respectively. However, the merchant's cutting instrument will cut wire only to the nearest $\frac{1}{128}$ of an inch, which is satisfactory to the inventor. How long will these three pieces be when cut to the nearest $\frac{1}{128}$ of an inch?

S6.53. To learn how many pieces of material of length $a + b/c$ units of length that can be cut from a large piece of material of length $p + q/r$ units of length, one divides $p + q/r$ by $a + b/c$, and obtains the quotient $u + v/w$. Now what does u represent? v/w? $v/w \cdot (a + b/c)$? Here a, b, c, p, q, r, u, v, and w represent appropriate natural numbers.

Identify the corresponding u, v/w, and $v/w \cdot (a + b/c)$ in the following:

a. A milliner cuts from a bolt of cloth containing $115\frac{3}{8}$ yards equal pieces of length $5\frac{2}{3}$ yards.

b. A candy packer packs $3\frac{1}{3}$ pounds of candy in each box from a supply of $38\frac{7}{8}$ pounds of candy.

c. A woodcutter cuts $1\frac{3}{4}$ cords of wood an hour from a supply of wood containing $9\frac{1}{5}$ cords of uncut wood.

d. A student solves 16 problems each hour from a list of 40 problems.

LESSON 7 ✤ RÉSUMÉ OF
THE COMPLETE SYSTEM OF
RATIONAL NUMBERS

Build thee more stately mansions, O my soul,
As the swift seasons roll!
Leave thy low-vaulted past!
Let each new temple, nobler than the last,
Shut thee from heaven with a dome more vast,
Till thou at length art free,
Leaving thine outgrown shell by life's unresting sea!

—Oliver W. Holmes, *The Chambered Nautilus.*

7·1 ∾ GENERALIZATION OF COMMON FRACTIONS

The fraction a/b, as originally presented, indicates the division of the natural number a by the natural number b, whether or not the indicated division is exact. Rules were then formulated to perform operations of addition, subtraction, multiplication, and division upon fractions. To make the operation of subtraction of fractions always possible the numerator was allowed to represent any *integer* whatever, positive, negative, or zero. The definition of fraction is now further generalized as an indicated quotient of any two integers, except that the denominator must not be zero (Section 5.3).

There are three signs associated with every fraction, and again the plus sign need not be written.

$$+\frac{-5}{+8} \quad \text{or} \quad \frac{-5}{8} \qquad -\frac{+7}{-9} \quad \text{or} \quad -\frac{7}{-9}$$

$$+\frac{-3}{-5} \quad \text{or} \quad \frac{-3}{-5} \qquad -\frac{-9}{-13}$$

The individual signs in these examples are identified as follows:

The sign before the fraction, or the sign of the fraction itself. The four examples exhibit them as $+, -, +, -$.

The sign of the numerator. In the four examples they are $-, +, -, -$.

The sign of the denominator. In the four examples they are $+, -, -, -$.

These three signs associated with fractions are *quality* signs; hence eight different arrays of such signs are possible:

$$+\frac{+a}{+b} + \frac{-a}{+b} + \frac{+a}{-b} + \frac{-a}{-b} - \frac{+a}{+b} - \frac{-a}{+b} - \frac{+a}{-b} - \frac{-a}{-b}$$

The $+$ signs may be omitted without altering the value of the fractions. Now each of these eight fractions is equal to one or the other of the two fractions a/b

or $-a/b$, namely, a positive fraction with positive denominator.   This statement may be proved as follows:

Ignoring the quality sign of the fraction itself, the rules of signs for division of integers show that

$$\frac{-a}{-b} = \frac{+a}{+b} \quad \text{or} \quad \frac{a}{b} \qquad \frac{+a}{-b} = \frac{-a}{+b} \quad \text{or} \quad \frac{-a}{b}$$

A negative integer is obtained by subtracting the corresponding positive integer from zero.   Thus, $-1 = 0 - (+1)$.   Extending this same relationship to fractions, one has

$$-\frac{-a}{b} = 0 - \frac{-a}{b} = \frac{0}{b} - \frac{-a}{b} = \frac{a}{b}$$

Therefore, $-\dfrac{-a}{b} = +\dfrac{a}{b}$.   Similarly,

$$-\frac{a}{b} = 0 - \frac{a}{b} = \frac{0}{b} - \frac{a}{b} = \frac{-a}{b}$$

Therefore, $-\dfrac{a}{b} = +\dfrac{-a}{b}$.

Otherwise stated, any pair of the three quality signs associated with a fraction may be changed, $+$ into $-$ and $-$ into $+$, without altering the value.   Accordingly, appropriate changes of signs may be made to make both the sign of the fraction and the sign of the denominator positive.   When so exhibited, the fraction is said to be in *standard form*.   Thus, by changing signs of numerator and denominator:

$$+\frac{-a}{-b} = +\frac{+a}{+b} \quad \text{or} \quad \frac{a}{b} \quad \text{and} \quad +\frac{+a}{-b} = +\frac{-a}{+b} \quad \text{or} \quad \frac{-a}{b}$$

By changing signs of the fraction and the numerator:

$$-\frac{-a}{+b} = +\frac{+a}{+b} \quad \text{or} \quad \frac{a}{b} \quad \text{and} \quad -\frac{+a}{+b} = +\frac{-a}{+b} \quad \text{or} \quad \frac{-a}{b}$$

By changing the signs of the fraction and the denominator:

$$-\frac{+a}{-b} = +\frac{+a}{+b} \quad \text{or} \quad \frac{a}{b} \quad \text{and} \quad -\frac{-a}{-b} = +\frac{-a}{+b} \quad \text{or} \quad \frac{-a}{b}$$

It may be noted that equivalent fractions have an *odd* number of negative signs, one or three, or an *even* number of negative signs, none or two.

Finally, the signs of operation $+$ and $-$ denoting addition and subtraction may serve equally well as signs of quality in the general operation of algebraic addition (Section 4.14, Problem 4.10), as shown in the following two examples.

As signs of operation. Perform the indicated addition and subtraction:

$$\frac{+3}{-4} + \frac{-7}{-8} - \frac{-5}{12} = ? \qquad \text{L.C.D.} = +24$$

$$\frac{+3(-6)}{(-4)(-6)} + \frac{(-7)(-3)}{(-8)(-3)} - \frac{(-5)(+2)}{12(+2)} = \frac{-18}{24} + \frac{21}{24} - \frac{-10}{24} = \frac{+13}{24}$$

since $(-18) + (+21) - (-10) = 13$.

As signs of quality. Add algebraically:

$$\frac{+3}{-4} \quad + \frac{-7}{-8} \quad - \frac{-5}{+12}$$

Reduce each fraction to standard form, $\dfrac{-3}{4}, \dfrac{7}{8}, \dfrac{5}{12}$, i.e., add algebraically the

numerators $\dfrac{-18}{24}, \dfrac{21}{24}, \dfrac{10}{24}$, obtaining again $\dfrac{13}{24}$.

❧ PROBLEMS ❧

7.1. Express the fractions in standard form and in lowest terms:

a. $-\dfrac{8}{-18}$ e. $-\dfrac{-74}{111}$ i. $\dfrac{1}{-2}$

b. $\dfrac{-6}{-15}$ f. $\dfrac{87}{-145}$ j. $-\dfrac{-899}{-930}$

c. $-\dfrac{-24}{-32}$ g. $+\dfrac{-18}{81}$ k. $\dfrac{323}{-357}$

d. $-\dfrac{48}{76}$ h. $-\dfrac{128}{-432}$ l. $-\dfrac{-127}{-255}$

7.2. Perform the indicated operations and express results appropriately:

a. $-\dfrac{5}{12} + \dfrac{-7}{-8} - \dfrac{1}{6} + \dfrac{3}{-4} = ?$ d. $-\dfrac{-12}{-22} + \dfrac{-7}{-12} = ?$

b. $+\dfrac{3}{-4} + \dfrac{-3}{10} - \dfrac{-2}{5} + \dfrac{-1}{-10} = ?$ e. $-\dfrac{7}{-16} - \dfrac{-19}{24} = ?$

c. $-\dfrac{-8}{-11} - \dfrac{5}{-7} = ?$ f. $-\dfrac{13}{-18} + \dfrac{-5}{-9} - \dfrac{1}{6} = ?$

7.3. Add algebraically the sets of numbers:

a. $\dfrac{-5}{12}, \dfrac{7}{8}, \dfrac{-1}{6}, \dfrac{-3}{4}$ d. $\dfrac{-6}{11}, \dfrac{7}{12}$

b. $\dfrac{-3}{4}, \dfrac{-3}{10}, \dfrac{2}{5}, \dfrac{1}{10}$ e. $\dfrac{7}{16}, \dfrac{19}{24}$

c. $\dfrac{-8}{11}, \dfrac{5}{7}$ f. $\dfrac{13}{18}, \dfrac{5}{9}, \dfrac{-1}{6}$

7.4. Express as proper fractions or as mixed numbers in an appropriate form and locate positions for them on the number line:

a. $-\dfrac{-79}{12}$ e. $-5+\dfrac{5}{-7}$ i. $-\dfrac{-171}{21}$ m. $-\dfrac{-71}{-15}$

b. $-\dfrac{-34}{7}$ f. $8+\dfrac{-3}{5}$ j. $\dfrac{333}{-74}$ n. $-4+\dfrac{7}{9}$

c. $-\dfrac{-53}{-11}$ g. $-2+\dfrac{3}{8}$ k. $-\dfrac{50}{-9}$ o. $3-\dfrac{7}{-10}$

d. $\dfrac{187}{-13}$ h. $\dfrac{-301}{-56}$ l. $\dfrac{101}{-707}$ p. $-9-\dfrac{-5}{-8}$

7.5. Add algebraically the sets of numbers:

a. $-2\frac{1}{3},\ -\frac{5}{8},\ -7\frac{1}{6},\ 14$ d. $\dfrac{-35}{-6}, \dfrac{-53}{-9}, \dfrac{-32}{-18},\ -2\frac{3}{4}$

b. $-4,\ 3{,}145,\ -4,\ -4\frac{1}{2},\ 26\frac{1}{2}$ e. $\dfrac{-33}{-4}, \dfrac{-55}{8}, -\dfrac{77}{-8}$

c. $-2\frac{1}{2},\ 3\frac{2}{3},\ -5\frac{5}{6}$ f. $\dfrac{-555}{-27}, \dfrac{-666}{36}, \dfrac{-111}{-9}$

7·2 ⚬ ALGEBRAIC MULTIPLICATION AND DIVISION OF FRACTIONS

A convenient procedure for multiplying or dividing fractions that involve negative numbers is to perform all indicated operations upon the *absolute values* of the numbers involved, then to apply a positive or negative sign to the result according to whether the number of original negative signs is even or odd, respectively. The correctness of this rule of signs appears from the fact that each fraction, proper or improper, containing one or three negative signs, is equivalent to the same configuration of natural numbers with a single negative sign (by changing a pair of negative signs to positive signs), and, if only two negative signs occur with a proper or improper fraction, they may both be changed to positive signs without altering the value of the fraction. When all the fractions are reduced to standard form, the total number of negative signs remains even or odd.

Here a negative mixed number must not exhibit a negative sign between its integral and fractional part. For example, $-2\frac{3}{4}$, although equivalent to $-2 - \frac{3}{4}$, should not be so written with two negative signs, but should be written as an improper fraction with a single negative sign, namely, $-\frac{14}{5}$ or $\frac{-14}{5}$. Here are two illustrations:

$$\left(-\frac{-2}{-5}\right)\left(\frac{-25}{28}\right) = ? \qquad \text{Using absolute values} \qquad \frac{2}{5} \times \frac{25}{28} = \frac{5}{14}$$

As the number of original negative signs is *even*, namely, four, the resulting product is positive, $+\frac{5}{14}$, or simply $\frac{5}{14}$.

$$\left(-\frac{-7}{-16}\right) \div \left(\frac{-3}{-8}\right) = ? \qquad \text{Using absolute values} \qquad \frac{7}{16} \div \frac{3}{8} =$$

$$\frac{7}{16} \times \frac{8}{3} = \frac{7}{6} \qquad \text{or} \qquad 1\frac{1}{6}$$

As the number of negative signs in the original problem is *odd*, namely, five, the sign of the resulting quotient is negative, $-\frac{7}{6}$ or $-1\frac{1}{6}$.

PROBLEMS [CONCLUDED]

7.6. Perform the indicated operations:

a. $\left(-\frac{7}{12}\right)\left(-\frac{15}{21}\right) = ?$

b. $\left(-\frac{-15}{-21}\right)\left(-\frac{-7}{21}\right) = ?$

c. $\left(-\frac{21}{-16}\right)\left(\frac{-12}{35}\right) = ?$

d. $\left(-\frac{13}{-5}\right)(-6\frac{1}{4}) = ?$

e. $\left(-\frac{-8}{15}\right) \div \left(-\frac{-16}{45}\right) = ?$

f. $(-1\frac{3}{5}) \div (\frac{4}{15}) = ?$

g. $\left(-\frac{-87}{100}\right) \div \left(-\frac{-29}{-20}\right) = ?$

h. $\frac{63}{256} \div (-4\frac{1}{5}) = ?$

7.7. Perform the indicated series of operations:

a. $(-3\frac{1}{2})(-2\frac{5}{14}) \div (-2\frac{1}{5}) = ?$

b. $(-21\frac{3}{4}) \div \left(-\frac{-29}{-6}\right)(-5\frac{1}{16}) = ?$

c. $(-\frac{5}{3}) \div (-1\frac{5}{12}) \div \left(-\frac{-13}{-256}\right) \div (-24\frac{8}{21}) = ?$

d. $(-\frac{2}{3}) \div (2\frac{2}{3})\left(-\frac{27}{-64}\right) = ?$

7.8. Evaluate as indicated.   Recall that multiplications and divisions must be performed in the order in which they occur before performing the additions and subtractions.

a. $(-3)(-5) + (-12)(-35) \div (-28) - (-17) = ?$

b. $17 + \frac{3}{5} - 7\frac{2}{3} - 21 + (-37\frac{1}{2}) \div (16\frac{2}{3}) = ?$

c. $\left(-\dfrac{-2}{-3}\right) + (-\frac{3}{8})(-\frac{4}{9}) \div (-\frac{1}{18}) \div \left(\dfrac{5}{-6}\right) = ?$

d. $(-2)(-3)(-\frac{1}{2}) - (-3\frac{1}{2})\left(\dfrac{-4}{-21}\right) \div (-\frac{1}{3}) = ?$

7.9. a.   If a positive number denotes a rise in temperature and a negative number a fall, make a list of temperatures at each of the eight consecutive hours, if the initial temperature was 58° and the change occurring during each ensuing hour was registered as follows:

Hour 1 +6°	Hour 3 −4°	Hour 5 +10°	Hour 7 +5°
Hour 2 +3°	Hour 4 −7°	Hour 6 − 8°	Hour 8 −4°

b.   State the maximum and minimum temperatures in the completed list.

c.   Obtain the total change in temperature by adding algebraically the eight changes listed above.

d.   Check the result in (c) by calculating the difference between the initial and the final temperatures.

7.10. Re-solve Problem 7.9 with the following data, if the initial temperature was $+62\frac{1}{2}°$:

Hour 1 $+7\frac{3}{10}°$	Hour 3 $-3\frac{2}{5}°$	Hour 5 $+11\frac{1}{5}°$	Hour 7 $-13\frac{1}{2}°$
Hour 2 $-5\frac{1}{2}°$	Hour 4 $+4\frac{4}{5}°$	Hour 6 $-\frac{3}{10}°$	Hour 8 $+8\frac{3}{5}°$

7.11. The Utopian Manufacturing Company adjusts all employees at the end of each year on the basis of total rating points that are accumulated by six tests throughout the year.   If an employee's total is negative, he is discharged; if it is positive, he is retained for another year; if it exceeds 10, he is given a liberal bonus and a promotion.

a.   What is done with each of the employees A, B, C, D, and E, whose test scores are listed as follows?

Employee A:	$+2\frac{3}{4}$	$-3\frac{1}{4}$	$+4\frac{1}{2}$	$+4\frac{1}{10}$	$-5\frac{4}{5}$	$+3$
Employee B:	$+5\frac{2}{5}$	$-3\frac{1}{5}$	$-7\frac{3}{5}$	$+4\frac{1}{5}$	$-2\frac{4}{5}$	$-1\frac{1}{2}$
Employee C:	$+2\frac{4}{5}$	$+3\frac{3}{4}$	$-1\frac{1}{4}$	$+4\frac{4}{5}$	$+2\frac{1}{10}$	$-1\frac{1}{2}$
Employee D:	$+2\frac{3}{5}$	$+4\frac{3}{10}$	$+2\frac{7}{10}$	$-8\frac{4}{5}$	$+3\frac{3}{5}$	$+1\frac{1}{10}$
Employee E:	$-1\frac{9}{10}$	$-1\frac{2}{5}$	$-2\frac{1}{5}$	$+9\frac{4}{5}$	$-2\frac{1}{10}$	$-1\frac{1}{5}$

b.   Obtain the algebraic sum of these 30 rating scores.

7.12. On each of six consecutive days a certain stock, originally worth $100\frac{3}{8}$, changed in value as follows:

Day 1 $+1\frac{1}{4}$ Day 3 $+4\frac{3}{4}$ Day 5 $+2\frac{1}{2}$
Day 2 $-3\frac{9}{10}$ Day 4 $-1\frac{5}{8}$ Day 6 -5

   a. On which day did it have its maximum value? What was that value?

   b. On which day did it have its minimum value? What was that value?

   c. Compute the algebraic sum of these six listed numbers. What does this sum denote?

7.13. Interpret movements toward north as positive and those toward south as negative. How does the final position of a traveling salesman compare with his initial position, if his movements on the six consecutive days are listed as follows?

Day 1   Travels north $5\frac{1}{2}$ miles   Day 4   Travels north $43\frac{1}{8}$ miles
Day 2   Travels south $13\frac{7}{10}$ miles   Day 5   Travels south $3\frac{3}{8}$ miles
Day 3   Travels south $11\frac{3}{4}$ miles   Day 6   Travels south $19\frac{4}{5}$ miles

7.14. At the autumnal equinox, generally on September 21, the sun's declination is $0°$. During the next 3 autumn months the sun travels southward $23\frac{1}{2}°$; during the next 6 months, throughout spring and summer, the sun travels northward $47°$ to the summer solstice, generally on June 21. Compare the sun's declination at the summer solstice with that at the autumnal equinox.

7.15. Space rockets have been designed to make the trip from the earth to the moon, a distance of 224,000 miles, in 4 days. (*a*) How long would it require a rocket that maintains this same speed to go to Mars and return, if Mars is 40,000,000 miles away? (*b*) To Pluto and return, if it is 3,600,000,000 miles away?

$7\cdot3$ ∾ R̲ECAPITULATION.   RETROSPECT AND PROSPECT

Natural Numbers, Integers, Rational Numbers. If *a* represents, one by one, all natural numbers, then $-a$, 0, and $+a$ or *a* represent all integers. Furthermore, if *b* also represents, one by one, all natural numbers, then a/b, 0, and $-a/b$ represent all rational numbers. Contrariwise, if a/b, in which *b* is not zero, represents the complete system of rational numbers, then, if $b = 1$, a/b represents the complete system of integers; if $b = 1$ and *a* is positive, a/b represents the complete system of natural numbers. Thus the set of rational numbers contains a proper subset which is the set of integers; the set of integers contains a proper subset which is the set of natural numbers.

The Number Line. The three sets of numbers, namely, the set of natural numbers, the set of integers, and the set of rational numbers, may be represented by positions on a straight line of unlimited extent, known as the *number line*. The natural numbers are represented by equally spaced positions to the right of an arbitrary position which is called the zero position. The positive integers are represented by the same positions as those for natural numbers; the negative integers are represented by equally spaced positions to the left of the zero position. The same spacing is used between all pairs of consecutive integers.

If p and q are both positive or both negative integers, then the position for the positive rational number p/q on the number line is the right end of the pth subinterval to the right of the zero position, if all intervals between positions for consecutive integers on the number line are subdivided into q equal subintervals. If p is positive and q is negative, or if p is negative and q is positive, then the position of the negative rational number p/q is the left end of the pth subinterval to the left of the zero position, if all intervals between positions for consecutive integers on the number line are subdivided into q equal subintervals.

The positions that represent all rational numbers include all positions that represent the integers, which in turn include all positions that represent the natural numbers. Moreover, as soon as one selects the positions for 0 and 1, or for any other two rational numbers, positions are immediately made available for all rational numbers; there are still infinitely many positions on the number line that do not correspond to any rational number whatever, and these will be assigned to the *irrational numbers* to be introduced in subsequent lessons.

Properties of Natural Numbers. The natural numbers have certain specific properties, namely:

1. They are *ordered*, which means that of two different natural numbers, one must be smaller than or larger than the other.

2. They are discrete, which means that every natural number has an immediate successor, or next larger natural number; and that every natural number except 1 has an immediate predecessor or next smaller natural number.

3. They may be pictured graphically by equally spaced positions on the number line; such positions are referred to as *points*.

4. They may be expressed by written symbols in various systems of writing. The familiar "Arabic system" employs ten characters called digit symbols, 0, 1, 2, 3, 4, 5, 6, 7, 8, and 9, by means of which every natural number may be expressed, or "spelled out."

5. The natural numbers may be *counted*, which means that they may be produced in their correct order, either mentally, orally, or by written symbols.

6. They provide a means of measuring, or "sizing up," a set of distinct objects, by matching the natural numbers beginning with *one* in their correct order with the objects of the set. The last natural number so used is called the number of objects of the set.

Definitions of Direct Operations. The direct operations upon natural numbers are defined as follows:

1. Addition is a repeated counting off of two or more natural numbers; the individual natural numbers counted off are called *addends;* the total result of the counting is called their sum. In symbols, $a + b = c$.

2. Multiplication is the repeated adding of the same natural number; the natural number that is repeatedly added is called the multiplicand; the number of times it is added is called the multiplier. In symbols, $a \times b = c$.

3. Involution is the repeated multiplication of the same natural number; the natural number so multiplied is called the base; the number of times it is multiplied is called the exponent. In symbols, $a^b = c$.

Addition and Multiplication. The operations of addition and multiplication of natural numbers obey five laws for any natural numbers whatever, namely:

The commutative law of addition, $a + b = b + a$
The commutative law of multiplication, $ab = ba$
The associative law of addition, $(a + b) + c = a + (b + c)$
The associative law of multiplication, $(ab)c = a(bc)$
The distributive law of multiplication and addition, $a(b + c) = ab + ac$

Involution. The operation of involution does not obey the commutative nor the associative laws. Thus, if a and b are different natural numbers, a^b and b^a yield different natural numbers. For example, $2^3 = 8$ and $3^2 = 9$. Again, a^{b^c} yields different natural numbers for the two different associations of the natural numbers a, b, c. For example, if 2^{3^4} is evaluated as $(2^3)^4$, one obtains $2^3 = 8$, whence $8^4 = 4,096$; and since $3^4 = 81$, $2^{81} = 2,417,851,639,229,258,349,412,352$. Thus, $(2^3)^4$ and $2^{(3^4)}$ yield different resulting natural numbers.

Inverse Operations. Reversing the three foregoing direct operations upon natural numbers yields the four inverse operations, namely:

Subtraction, as the inverse of addition. Thus, inverting $a + b = c$, one has $c = b + ?$, the symbolism for which is $c - b = ?$ Since addition is commutative, $a + b = b + a$; thus, inverting $b + a = c$, one obtains $c = a + ?$, or $c - a = ?$ Hence, $c - b = a$ and $c - a = b$ whenever $a + b = c$, so that c is greater than each of the natural numbers a and b. Such subtractions are possible with natural numbers, $c - b = ?$, and yield the natural number a for the result; here c is called the minuend, b the subtrahend, and the required result the difference. To make possible a subtraction of natural numbers in which the minuend is not larger than the subtrahend, the zero, 0, and the negative integers, -1, -2, -3, . . . , are invented and introduced into the system of numbers. This enlarged system of numbers is called the system of integers. Consistent rules are made available to perform the direct operations of addition, multiplication, and involution upon all numbers of the system of integers.

Division, as the inverse of multiplication. Thus, inverting $ab = c$, one has $c = b \cdot ?$, the symbolism for which is $c \div b = ?$ Since multiplication is commutative, $ab = ba$; thus, inverting $ba = c$, one obtains $c = a \cdot ?$, or $c \div a = ?$ Hence $c \div b = a$ and $c \div a = b$ whenever $ab = c$, so that c is an exact multiple of each of the natural numbers a and b. Accordingly, such divisions are possible with natural numbers, $c \div b = ?$, and yield the natural number a for the result; here c is called the dividend, b the divisor, and the required result the quotient. To make possible a division of natural numbers in which the dividend is not an exact multiple of the divisor, the rational numbers such as $\frac{1}{2}, \frac{1}{3}, \frac{2}{3}$, . . . , are invented and introduced into the number system. This enlarged system of numbers is called the system of rational numbers. Consistent rules are made available to perform the direct operations of addition, multiplication, and involution upon all numbers of the system of rational numbers; however, the divisor must not be 0, and in involution the exponent has thus far been restricted to integers, a restriction to be subsequently removed.

Evolution, or "obtaining the root," as one of the two inverses of involution. Inverting $a^b = c$, one may have $c = ?^b$, the symbolism for which is $\sqrt[b]{c} = a$ whenever $a^b = c$, so that c is an exact power of a. Such evolutions are possible upon natural numbers c and b and yield the natural number a as the required result; here c is called the radicand, b the index, and the required result the bth root of c. If a and b are natural numbers so that a^b yields the natural number c, and if b is an even natural number, the evolution $\sqrt[b]{c}$ yields *two* bth roots of c, namely, the natural number a *and* the negative integer $-a$. However, if c is not an exact bth power of any natural number, then $\sqrt[b]{c}$ cannot have any rational number for its required result. To make possible such evolutions, *surd* numbers are subsequently invented and introduced into the number system.

Indexing, or "obtaining the logarithm," as the other of the two inverses of involution. Involution has *two* distinct inverses since the direct operation of involution is not commutative, as a^b and b^a yield different results if a and b are different natural numbers. Inverting $a^b = c$ into $c = a^?$, one uses the symbolism $\log_a c = ?$ Hence, $\log_a c = b$ whenever $a^b = c$, so that c is an exact power of a. Such indexings are possible upon natural numbers a and c and yield the natural number b as the required result. If no natural number b can serve as a power of a to yield c, then $\log_a c$ cannot have any rational number for its required result. To make possible such solutions, transcendental numbers are invented and introduced into the number system. Convenient rules will also be supplied for performing all direct operations of addition, multiplication, and involution upon surd numbers, transcendental numbers, and the rational numbers; all such operations yield numbers of the *complete system of real numbers*.

Consistent rules are formulated for performing the four inverse operations—subtraction, division, evolution, and indexing—upon real numbers. To make such operations always possible, it is necessary to devise and introduce a final new type of number, called *complex numbers*. All direct and inverse operations may then be performed upon the complex and the real numbers and they always yield real or complex numbers as sum, product, power, difference, quotient, root, or index, so that no further enlargement of the number system is necessary to perform the seven elementary operations upon numbers within the system of complex numbers. As the number line is now completely occupied by positions for the real numbers, one assigns appropriate positions for the complex numbers in the *plane* in which the number line is drawn. The portrayal of positions in this plane for all real and complex numbers is exhibited in Lesson 17. Here it is to be noted that every "point" or position of the plane is assigned to a real or a complex number, and, conversely, every real or complex number is assigned a unique position in the "complex plane."

The system of usable numbers is gradually enlarged by the introduction of new types of numbers and the accompanying rules for performing the basic operations upon them. The name of the successively expanded system of numbers is indicated with the introduction of new kinds of numbers, as follows:

Kind of number	*System of numbers*
Natural number	System of natural numbers
Integer	Complete system of integers
Fraction	Complete system of rational numbers
Irrational numbers	Complete system of real numbers
Complex number	Complete number system of analysis

Incidentally, the irrational numbers are of two distinctive kinds: (*a*) The algebraic irrationals, of which surds such as $\sqrt{5}$, $\sqrt[3]{7}$, $\sqrt[6]{17}$ are a subclass. An algebraic number is defined as any root, rational or irrational, of an algebraic equation. (*b*) The transcendental irrationals, of which irrational logarithms are a subclass. The famous number π, which lies between $3\frac{10}{71}$ and $3\frac{1}{7}$, is a transcendental irrational number.

Some Properties of Rational Numbers. A rational number does not have an immediate predecessor or an immediate successor, as an infinitude of other rational numbers always lie between any two different unequal rational numbers (Section 7.6). Two different rational numbers, such as ka/kb and a/b, in which k, a, b are any integers different from zero, are equivalent and are assigned the same position on the number line.

A fraction can be expressed in standard form by appropriate changes of pairs of signs, so that the sign of the denominator and the sign of the fraction itself are both made positive. If two fractions, a/b and c/d, are in standard form, one may determine their relative size, that is, whether they are equivalent or which is the larger—that is, which has its position to the right of the other on the number line.   The criterion is: $a/b \lesseqgtr c/d$, according as $ad \lesseqgtr bc$.

The five fundamental laws of addition and multiplication given for the natural numbers may also be proved to hold true for *rational* numbers by performing the indicated operations upon a/b, c/d, and e/f, as representing any rational numbers whatever and noting that the five laws are true for integers; a, b, c, d, e, f represent any integers, except that b, d, f may not represent 0.

Commutative law of addition: $a/b + c/d = c/d + a/b$
Commutative law of multiplication: $a/b \cdot c/d = c/d \cdot a/b$
Associative law of addition: $(a/b + c/d) + e/f = a/b + (c/d + e/f)$
Associative law of multiplication: $(a/b \cdot c/d) \cdot e/f = a/b(c/d \cdot e/f)$
Distributive law of multiplication and addition: $a/b(c/d + e/f)$
$$= a/b \cdot c/d + a/b \cdot e/f$$

It can also be proved that if A, B, C represent any numbers whatever, rational, real, or complex, within the complete number system of analysis, these same five fundamental laws are always valid:

$$A + B = B + A \quad\quad AB = BA \quad\quad (A + B) + C = A + (B + C)$$
$$(AB)C = A(BC) \quad\quad \text{and} \quad\quad A(B + C) = AB + AC$$

It must be noted that division is not associative, namely, that $(A \div B) \div C$ is not equal to $A \div (B \div C)$.   Hence $a/b/c$ is ambiguous, as $(a/b)/c = a/bc$ and $a/(b/c) = ac/b$.   Division is not commutative either, as a/b is not equal to b/a if a and b represent different numbers.

*N*ote 1 ∽ *The set of all fractions equivalent to a given fraction is denumerable.*

If a and b are any two natural numbers, then all fractions that are equivalent to a/b must occur in the array of fractions:

$$\frac{a}{b} \quad\quad \frac{2a}{2b} \quad\quad \frac{3a}{3b} \quad\quad \frac{4a}{4b} \cdots$$

$$\frac{-a}{-b} \quad\quad \frac{-2a}{-2b} \quad\quad \frac{-3a}{-3b} \quad\quad \frac{-4a}{-4b} \cdots$$

$$-\frac{a}{-b} \quad\quad -\frac{2a}{-2b} \quad\quad -\frac{3a}{-3b} \quad\quad -\frac{4a}{-4b} \cdots$$

$$-\frac{-a}{b} \quad\quad -\frac{-2a}{2b} \quad\quad -\frac{-3a}{3b} \quad\quad -\frac{-4a}{4b} \cdots$$

Pairing off these fractions with the natural numbers arranged in the same array,

1	5	9	13	. . .
2	6	10	14	. . .
3	7	11	15	. . .
4	8	12	16	. . .

one notes that the cardinal number of the foregoing set of equivalent fractions must be the same as the cardinal number of the set of natural numbers, namely, aleph-zero (Section 5.10).

$\mathcal{N}$*ote 2 ⁓ The set consisting of all fractions, proper, improper, positive, negative, equivalent, nonequivalent, is denumerable.*

Set forth the sets of fractions whose numerators and denominators are natural numbers that have the same sum, beginning with the smallest possible sum, 2. Let the individual fractions within each set be arranged in order of size, beginning with the smallest fraction, thus:

$$\frac{1}{1} \qquad \frac{1}{2} \; \frac{2}{1} \qquad \frac{1}{3} \; \frac{2}{2} \; \frac{3}{1} \qquad \frac{1}{4} \; \frac{2}{3} \; \frac{3}{2} \; \frac{4}{1} \qquad \frac{1}{5} \; \frac{2}{4} \; \frac{3}{3} \; \frac{4}{2} \; \frac{5}{1} \cdots$$

Next, set forth the array of fractions exhibited in the preceding Note 1 in one horizontal line from left to right in the order of the natural numbers with which the fractions are paired off. In this line let the first fraction $\frac{1}{1}$ replace the a/b throughout the horizontal line. Then write out in ensuing horizontal lines this same horizontal line of fractions in which the a/b is successively replaced by ensuing fractions of the sets $\frac{1}{2}$, $\frac{2}{1}$, $\frac{1}{3}$, $\frac{2}{2}$, $\frac{3}{1}$, ... Such successive lines will appear thus:

$$\frac{1}{1} \quad \frac{-1}{-1} \quad -\frac{1}{-1} \quad -\frac{-1}{1} \quad \frac{2}{2} \quad \frac{-2}{-2} \quad -\frac{2}{-2} \quad -\frac{-2}{2} \quad \cdots$$

$$\frac{1}{2} \quad \frac{-1}{-2} \quad -\frac{1}{-2} \quad -\frac{-1}{2} \quad \frac{2}{4} \quad \frac{-2}{-4} \quad -\frac{2}{-4} \quad -\frac{-2}{4} \quad \cdots$$

$$\frac{2}{1} \quad \frac{-2}{-1} \quad -\frac{2}{-1} \quad -\frac{-2}{1} \quad \frac{4}{2} \quad \frac{-4}{-2} \quad -\frac{4}{-2} \quad -\frac{-4}{2} \quad \cdots$$

$$\frac{1}{3} \quad \frac{-1}{-3} \quad -\frac{1}{-3} \quad -\frac{-1}{3} \quad \frac{2}{6} \quad \frac{-2}{-6} \quad -\frac{2}{-6} \quad -\frac{-2}{6} \quad \cdots$$

$$\frac{2}{2} \quad \frac{-2}{-2} \quad -\frac{2}{-2} \quad -\frac{-2}{2} \quad \frac{4}{4} \quad \frac{-4}{-4} \quad -\frac{4}{-4} \quad -\frac{-4}{4} \quad \cdots$$

$$\frac{3}{1} \quad \frac{-3}{-1} \quad -\frac{3}{-1} \quad -\frac{-3}{1} \quad \frac{6}{2} \quad \frac{-6}{-2} \quad -\frac{6}{-2} \quad -\frac{-6}{2} \quad \cdots$$

. . . .

The dots indicate that the array extends without end toward the right and downward.

Finally, pair off the fractions in the foregoing array diagonalwise with the natural numbers thus:

1	2	4	7	11	16	. . .
3	5	8	12	17	. . .	. . .
6	9	13	18	. . .	. . .	. . .
10	14	19	. . .	. . .	. . .	. . .
15	20	. . .	. . .	. . .	. . .	. . .
21	. . .	. . .	. . .	. . .	. . .	. . .

. . . .

The infinitude of all possible fractions, even with repetitions, may be paired off with the natural numbers; to prevent the repetition of the same fraction in the above array one could remove from the array those fractions that have already appeared earlier in the matching with natural numbers. The first such repetition would be $\frac{2}{2}$ in the fifth entry of the first row which is repeated in the first entry in the fifth row and which would be removed before the matching with the natural numbers. The resulting set of all possible different fractions again is denumerable; i.e., the set has the cardinal number aleph-zero, $\aleph_0$.

*N*ote 3 ∞ *The set of unequal fractions lying between two unequal fractions is denumerable.*

The set of unequivalent fractions lying between $\frac{1}{1,001}$ and $\frac{1}{1,000}$, for example, is denumerable; i.e., these fractions may be paired off in a one-to-one correspondence with the natural numbers and thus have the cardinal number aleph-zero, $\aleph_0$.

Observe that each fraction in the ensuing array lies between $\frac{1}{1,001}$ and $\frac{1}{1,000}$.

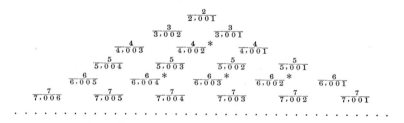

Each fraction marked with * is to be ignored in the matching with natural numbers, as it is equal to a previously occurring fraction in the array. The matching is then done thus:

$$1$$
$$2 \quad 3$$
$$4 \quad * \quad 5$$
$$6 \quad 7 \quad 8 \quad 9$$
$$10 \quad * \quad * \quad * \quad 11$$
$$12 \quad 13 \quad 14 \quad 15 \quad 16 \quad 17$$
$$\cdots \cdots \cdots \cdots \cdots \cdots \cdots \cdots \cdots$$

Moreover, any fraction in its lowest terms that lies between $\frac{1}{1,001}$ and $\frac{1}{1,000}$, such as p/q, must be the $(p \times 1001 - q)$th fraction in the pth row in the foregoing array of fractions. For, since $\dfrac{1}{1,001} < \dfrac{p}{q} < \dfrac{1}{1,000}$, then $\dfrac{p}{p \times 1,001} < \dfrac{p}{q}$

$< \dfrac{p}{p \times 1,000}$. Hence q must lie between $p \times 1,000$ and $p \times 1,001$. Now, since the denominators of the fractions in the pth row of the foregoing array are *all* of the consecutive natural numbers between $p \times 1,000$ and $p \times 1,001$, q must be one of them, thereby proving that the fraction p/q must appear in the array. The correspondence between the different fractions in lowest terms lying between $\frac{1}{1001}$ and $\frac{1}{1000}$ and the natural numbers is established.

To prove quite generally that a denumerable set of unequal fractions lies between any two unequal fractions whatever, namely, a/b and c/d, in standard form and lowest terms, one may use advantageously two lemmas, or preliminary propositions, which are easily proved.

LEMMA 1 ∾

The set of all fractions in lowest terms and standard form is denumerable. The reader may prove this lemma by using the methods set forth in the previous notes.

LEMMA 2 ∾

If m/n and m'/n' are unequal fractions, and if a/b and c/d are also unequal fractions, then $\dfrac{ma + nc}{mb + nd}$ and $\dfrac{m'a + n'c}{m'b + n'd}$ are unequal fractions.

PROOF ∾

If $\dfrac{m}{n} \ne \dfrac{m'}{n'}$, then $mn' \ne m'n$, or $mn' - m'n \ne 0$. If $\dfrac{a}{b} \ne \dfrac{c}{d}$, then $ad \ne bc$, or $ad - bc \ne 0$. Therefore, $(ad - bc)(mn' - m'n) \ne 0$. That is,

$$admn' - adm'n - bcmn' + bcm'n \ne 0$$
or $\quad admn' - adm'n - bcmn' + bcm'n \ne admn' - admn' + cdnn' - cdnn'$
or $\quad mm'ab + nn'cd + mn'ad + m'nbc \ne mm'ab + nn'cd + m'nad + mn'bc$

or $(ma + nc)(m'b + n'd) \neq (m'a + n'c)(mb + nd)$

or $\dfrac{ma + nc}{mb + nd} \neq \dfrac{m'a + n'd}{m'b + n'd}$

thus proving the lemma.

The reader may supply the complete proof of the original proposition that a denumerable set of unequal fractions lies between any two unequal fractions, a/b and c/d, by showing first that if m and n are any two integers, the fraction $\dfrac{ma + nc}{mb + nd}$ lies between a/b and c/d; secondly, that there is a one-to-one correspondence between $\dfrac{ma + nc}{mb + nd}$ and m/n; and hence the set of intermediate fractions $\dfrac{ma + nc}{mb + nd}$ is denumerable, since the set of unequal fractions m/n is denumerable.

⤳ SUPPLEMENTARY PROBLEMS ⤳

> *"Take some more tea,"* the March Hare said to Alice, very earnestly. *"I've had nothing yet,"* Alice replied in an offended tone, *"so I can't take more."*   *"You mean you can't take* less" said the Hatter, *"it's very easy to take more than nothing."*
>
> —*Alice in Wonderland.*

S7.1. Reduce the fractions to standard form in their lowest terms:

a. $-\dfrac{-6}{16}$ g. $-\dfrac{-37}{222}$ m. $-\dfrac{119}{245}$ s. $\dfrac{-141}{-376}$

b. $-\dfrac{12}{-27}$ h. $-\dfrac{-65}{91}$ n. $-\dfrac{-238}{-595}$ t. $-\dfrac{1,001}{-1,365}$

c. $-\dfrac{-24}{-64}$ i. $-\dfrac{-57}{-95}$ o. $-\dfrac{247}{-988}$ u. $\dfrac{2,002}{-4,620}$

d. $\dfrac{-28}{-63}$ j. $\dfrac{36}{-73}$ p. $\dfrac{-294}{-441}$ v. $\dfrac{1,234}{-4,567}$

e. $+\dfrac{72}{-96}$ k. $\dfrac{-27}{-72}$ q. $\dfrac{144}{-492}$ w. $-\dfrac{-899}{3,100}$

f. $-\dfrac{27}{-69}$ l. $-\dfrac{77}{-98}$ r. $-\dfrac{-1,649}{1,940}$ x. $\dfrac{-4,096}{-5,832}$

S7.2. Reduce to mixed numbers in appropriate form:

a. $\dfrac{47}{-7}$ d. $\dfrac{100}{-7}$ g. $\dfrac{-1,333}{-17}$ j. $-\dfrac{-625}{-875}$

b. $\dfrac{-111}{-21}$ e. $\dfrac{-99}{-2}$ h. $\dfrac{1,342}{-242}$ k. $\dfrac{1,000,000}{-448}$

c. $\dfrac{-29}{6}$ f. $\dfrac{-99}{-12}$ i. $\dfrac{-1,000}{56}$ l. $\dfrac{-1,299}{-2,165}$

S7.3. Reduce the complex fractions to simple fractions in appropriate form:

a. $\dfrac{\frac{3}{4}}{9}$ d. $\dfrac{\frac{2}{3}}{\frac{3}{4}}$ g. $\dfrac{3}{\frac{3}{4}}$ j. $\dfrac{\frac{19}{35}}{\frac{38}{105}}$

b. $\dfrac{\frac{2}{3}}{4}$ e. $\dfrac{\frac{7}{8}}{\frac{1}{4}}$ h. $\dfrac{30}{\frac{2}{3}}$ k. $\dfrac{\frac{35}{38}}{\frac{19}{105}}$

c. $\dfrac{\frac{5}{8}}{50}$ f. $\dfrac{\frac{5}{12}}{\frac{15}{16}}$ i. $\dfrac{13}{\frac{3}{4}}$ l. $\dfrac{\frac{16}{27}}{\frac{4}{9}}$

S7.4. Reduce to appropriate simple form:

a. $\dfrac{37\frac{1}{2}}{63\frac{1}{2}}$ d. $\dfrac{14\frac{2}{7}}{71\frac{3}{7}}$ g. $\dfrac{133\frac{1}{3}}{71\frac{1}{7}}$ j. $\dfrac{2\frac{3}{4}}{3\frac{4}{5}}$

b. $\dfrac{33\frac{1}{3}}{200}$ e. $\dfrac{428\frac{4}{7}}{857\frac{1}{7}}$ h. $\dfrac{34\frac{2}{5}}{51\frac{3}{5}}$ k. $\dfrac{3\frac{1}{7}}{2\frac{5}{14}}$

c. $\dfrac{16\frac{2}{3}}{66\frac{2}{3}}$ f. $\dfrac{83\frac{1}{3}}{100}$ i. $\dfrac{3\frac{1}{3}}{\frac{2}{3}}$ l. $\dfrac{7,777\frac{7}{9}}{555\frac{5}{9}}$

S7.5. At $62\frac{1}{2}$ cents per hour, how many hours would be required to earn $44?

S7.6. A teacher works 178 school days during a calendar year at an annual salary of $10,000. Calculate the hourly rate of pay if each working day contains 6 hours.

S7.7. If a clerk earns $61\frac{1}{4}$ in a week of 35 hours, what is his hourly rate of pay?

S7.8. Compute the overtime pay of the teacher and the clerk in Problems S7.6 and S7.7, if the teacher teaches 4 hours of evening classes at her same hourly rate, and the clerk works 8 hours on Sunday at double his hourly rate.

S7.9. If a gambler loses money at a rate of $4\frac{1}{5}$ an hour, what would be his financial status in $8\frac{3}{4}$ hours if his original capital was $25?

S7.10. The eighty-eighth Congress consisted of 258 Democrats and 117 Republicans. What fractional part of the total membership was Republican? Which of the three fractions $\frac{1}{2}$, $\frac{4}{9}$, $\frac{5}{11}$ most nearly represents this fractional part?

S7.11. What fractional part of the eighty-eighth Congress consisted of Democrats? Which of the following fractions most nearly represents this fractional part: $\frac{1}{2}$, $\frac{6}{11}$, $\frac{11}{19}$?

S7.12. Two-thirds of the membership of Congress must vote to override a presidential veto of a bill. How many Democrats must vote to override a veto if all Republicans vote to override the veto?

S7.13. How many pieces of wire $2\frac{3}{4}$ inches long can be cut from a wire that is $16\frac{1}{2}$ inches long? How many smaller pieces of length $1\frac{1}{4}$ inches could be cut from the original length of $16\frac{1}{2}$ inches?

S7.14. Three boys agree to work off a debt of \$52.50 at hourly rates of $62\frac{1}{2}$ cents, $87\frac{1}{2}$ cents, and \$1.12$\frac{1}{2}$, respectively. How long would it take them to accomplish this, if they all work together?

S7.15. Verify the associative and the distributive laws of addition and multiplication on the sets of three numbers: (a) -2, -3, $+7$; (b) $\frac{2}{3}$, $\frac{3}{4}$, $\frac{5}{6}$; (c) $-3\frac{1}{3}$, $+6\frac{1}{4}$, $3\frac{3}{4}$.

S7.16. A ship develops a leak which admits $2\frac{3}{4}$ tons of water each hour; the pumps immediately start pumping out this water at the rate of $1\frac{2}{3}$ tons per hour. If 40 tons of water will sink the ship, how long will it stay afloat?

S7.17. Evaluate the configurations. Compute the value contained within a set of parentheses before continuing with the evaluation. What do the results illustrate?

a. $\left(\dfrac{-3\frac{2}{5}}{-1\frac{2}{3}}+\dfrac{7\frac{1}{2}}{-8\frac{1}{3}}\right)+\dfrac{8\frac{1}{3}}{33\frac{1}{3}}$
b. $\dfrac{-3\frac{2}{5}}{-1\frac{2}{3}}\left(\dfrac{7\frac{1}{2}}{-8\frac{1}{3}}+\dfrac{8\frac{1}{3}}{33\frac{1}{3}}\right)$

a'. $\dfrac{-3\frac{2}{5}}{-1\frac{2}{3}}+\left(\dfrac{7\frac{1}{2}}{-8\frac{1}{3}}+\dfrac{8\frac{1}{3}}{33\frac{1}{3}}\right)$
b'. $\dfrac{-3\frac{2}{5}}{-1\frac{2}{3}}\dfrac{7\frac{1}{2}}{-8\frac{1}{3}}+\dfrac{-3\frac{2}{5}}{-1\frac{2}{3}}\dfrac{8\frac{1}{3}}{33\frac{1}{3}}$

S7.18. What is the smallest length of wire that could be divided up into lengths of 6, 8, 9, 12, 18, 24, and 36 inches, respectively?

S7.19. What is the smallest length of wire that could be divided up into lengths of $1\frac{2}{3}$, $5\frac{6}{7}$, or $8\frac{9}{10}$ inches, respectively?

S7.20. Evaluate as a simple fraction the following continued fractions. Note that each individual numerator is 1.

a. $\dfrac{1}{2+\frac{1}{4}}$
b. $\dfrac{1}{5+\dfrac{1}{3+\frac{1}{8}}}$
c. $\dfrac{1}{2+\dfrac{1}{3+\dfrac{1}{5+\dfrac{1}{2\frac{1}{2}}}}}$

Hint: Work upward from the bottom. Thus, $2\frac{1}{2}=\frac{5}{2}$; $\dfrac{1}{\frac{5}{2}}=\frac{2}{5}$; then $3+\frac{2}{5}=$

$\frac{17}{5}$; $\dfrac{1}{\frac{17}{5}}=\frac{5}{17}$; $\ldots$

S7.21. Evaluate as a simple fraction: $\dfrac{-5\frac{1}{3}}{-1\frac{7}{9}}+\left(\dfrac{5\frac{1}{3}}{-1\frac{7}{9}}\right)^2+\left(\dfrac{8\frac{1}{3}}{25}\right)^3$.

S7.22. Which is the greater and by how much?

a. $\dfrac{1}{2+\dfrac{1}{3+\dfrac{1}{1+\frac{1}{2}}}}$
b. $\dfrac{1}{2+\dfrac{1}{1+\dfrac{1}{3+\frac{1}{2}}}}$

S7.23. Which of the following fractions most nearly approximates S7.22a: $\frac{1}{2}, \frac{3}{7}$, or $\frac{4}{9}$?

S7.24. Which of the following fractions most nearly approximates S7.22b: $\frac{1}{2}, \frac{1}{3}$, or $\frac{4}{11}$?

S7.25. Calculate the sum of the six numbers, noting that each number after the first number is obtained by multiplying the preceding number by $-\frac{1}{2}$:

$$10\tfrac{2}{3} \qquad -5\tfrac{1}{3} \qquad 2\tfrac{2}{3} \qquad -1\tfrac{1}{3} \qquad \tfrac{2}{3} \qquad -\tfrac{1}{3}$$

Such a series of numbers is called a geometric progression, in which:

a represents the first number of the series; here $a = 10\tfrac{2}{3}$.

r represents the multiplier used to obtain successive terms; here $r = -\tfrac{1}{2}$.

n represents the number of terms in the series; here $n = 6$.

L represents the last term of the series; here $L = -\tfrac{1}{3}$.

S represents the sum of all terms of the series.

S7.26. The formula $L = Ar^{n-1}$ yields the last, or *n*th, term of a geometrical progression, without computing the intermediate terms. Its correctness is apparent by considering the calculation of successive terms, thus:

Let a = first term

Then ar = second term

And $arr = ar^2$ = third term

And $ar^2r = ar^3$ = fourth term

Again $ar^3r = ar^4$ = fifth term

One notes that the exponent of r is one less than the cardinal number of the particular term so obtained. The formula for the *n*th term must be ar^{n-1}. Hence, $L = ar^{n-1}$.

Compute the sixth term of the geometrical progression whose first term is $10\tfrac{2}{3}$ and whose multiplier r is $-\tfrac{1}{2}$. Also obtain the sum of the six terms.

S7.27. Compute the fifth term of the geometric progression whose leading (first) term is $6\tfrac{3}{4}$ and whose multiplier is $\tfrac{1}{3}$. Check your result by obtaining each term from the preceding term until the fifth term is so obtained.

S7.28. One may calculate by formula the sum S of all the terms of a geometrical progression, if one knows a, n, and r, or if he knows a, L, and r. These formulas may be obtained as follows:

$$S = a + ar + ar^2 + ar^3 + \cdots + ar^{n-1}$$

then $\quad rS = \qquad ar + ar^2 + ar^3 + \cdots + ar^{n-1} + ar^n$

then $S - rS = a + 0 + 0 + 0 + \cdots + \quad 0 \quad - ar^n$

obtained by subtracting termwise the lower equal values from the upper equal values. That is,

$$S - rS = a - a \cdot r^n \qquad \text{or} \qquad S - rS = a - ar^{n-1}r = a - Lr$$
$$S(1 - r) = a(1 - r^n) \qquad \text{or} \qquad S(1 - r) = a - rL$$

which yield the two required formulas, namely,

$$S = \frac{a(1 - r^n)}{1 - r} \qquad \text{and} \qquad S = \frac{a - rL}{1 - r}$$

Now use these formulas to verify the sums obtained in Problems S7.25 and S7.27.

S7.29. By two methods compute the sum of five terms of the geometric progression whose first two terms are $3\frac{3}{8}$ and $2\frac{1}{4}$.

S7.30. If a certain germ divides itself into two separate germs one hour after it was produced from a previous division, and if the reproduction continues at this hourly rate, how many germs would one germ produce in 24 hours? Also compute and interpret S in this situation.

S7.31. Miners A and B are panning for gold. On their first day A panned $2\frac{10}{27}$ ounces of gold, and on each succeeding day A panned half as much as on the preceding day; meanwhile, B panned $1\frac{7}{8}$ ounces on the first day and on each succeeding day two-thirds as much as on the preceding day. (*a*) How much did they pan together during their first four days of panning? (*b*) How much did each pan on the fifth day?

S7.32. Evaluate the continued fraction by successively replacing the bottom-most complex fraction, as $\dfrac{1}{3+\frac{1}{5}}$, by the equivalent simple fraction $\frac{5}{16}$.

$$\cfrac{1}{2+\cfrac{1}{1+\cfrac{1}{3+\frac{1}{5}}}}$$

S7.33. Apply Euclid's algorithm to obtain the greatest common divisor of numerator and denominator of the fraction $\frac{21}{58}$, noting especially the *quotients* that occur in the successive divisions. Observe how these quotients appear in the continued fraction of Problem S7.32.

S7.34. *a.* Reduce to a simple fraction the continued fraction:

$$\cfrac{1}{6+\cfrac{1}{2+\cfrac{1}{5+\frac{1}{3}}}}$$

 b. Apply Euclid's algorithm to obtain the G.C.D. of numerator and denominator of $\frac{35}{226}$. Identify the successive quotients with certain numbers in the foregoing continued fraction.

S7.35. Evaluate the successive larger portions of the continued fraction in Problem S7.34, namely,

a. $\frac{1}{6}$ *b.* $\dfrac{1}{6+\frac{1}{2}}$ *c.* $\dfrac{1}{6+\cfrac{1}{2+\frac{1}{5}}}$

These simple fractions are called, respectively, the first, second, and third convergents of the fraction $\frac{35}{226}$. Each convergent is the best possible approximation to the fraction $\frac{35}{226}$ that exists employing no smaller natural numbers than those occurring in that particular convergent.

S7.36. *a.* Compute the differences between $\frac{35}{226}$ and its three convergents.

    b. Show that $\frac{35}{226}$ lies between each pair of successive convergents.

    c. Show that the difference between each pair of successive convergents of $\frac{35}{226}$ is a unit fraction; i.e., having 1 for its numerator.

S7.37. Obtain the three convergents of $\frac{21}{58}$ from the continued fraction in Problem S7.32.

S7.38. Use Euclid's algorithm to form the continued fraction that is equal to the simple fraction $\frac{56}{127}$. Then compute the five convergents of $\frac{56}{127}$. Show that these convergents are alternately greater than and less than $\frac{56}{127}$, that their values are ever closer to $\frac{56}{127}$, and that the differences between consecutive convergents are unit fractions.

S7.39. *a.* Examine understandingly the procedure that yields the convergents of $\frac{19}{43}$.

$$\frac{19}{43} = \frac{1}{\frac{43}{19}} = \frac{1}{2 + \frac{5}{19}}$$

Ignoring the final $\frac{5}{19}$, one obtains the *first convergent* of $\frac{19}{43}$, namely, $\frac{1}{2}$. But

$$\frac{5}{19} = \frac{1}{\frac{19}{5}} = \frac{1}{3 + \frac{4}{5}}$$

Ignoring the final $\frac{4}{5}$, one obtains

$$\frac{1}{2 + \frac{1}{3}}$$

which yields the *second convergent* of $\frac{19}{43}$, namely, $\frac{3}{7}$. But

$$\frac{4}{5} = \frac{1}{\frac{5}{4}} = \frac{1}{1 + \frac{1}{4}}$$

Ignoring the final $\frac{1}{4}$, one obtains

$$\frac{1}{2 + \dfrac{1}{3 + \frac{1}{1}}}$$

which yields the *third convergent*, namely, $\frac{4}{9}$. Retaining the final $\frac{1}{4}$, one has the completed continued fraction

$$\frac{1}{2 + \dfrac{1}{3 + \dfrac{1}{1 + \frac{1}{4}}}}$$

which yields the original $\frac{19}{43}$, so that the *fourth convergent* of $\frac{19}{43}$ is the fraction itself, $\frac{19}{43}$.

    b. The successive convergents are alternately greater than and less than $\frac{19}{43}$, as their differences indicate.

$$\frac{1}{2} - \frac{19}{43} = \frac{5}{86}$$

$$\frac{19}{43} - \frac{3}{7} = \frac{4}{301}$$

$$\frac{4}{9} - \frac{19}{43} = \frac{1}{387}$$

c.   The successive convergents are ever closer to $\frac{19}{43}$, as the successive differences become ever smaller, namely, $\frac{5}{86}$, $\frac{4}{301}$, and $\frac{1}{387}$.

S7.40.   Re-solve Problem 7.39a, b, c for these fractions: (a) $\frac{16}{45}$, (b) $\frac{31}{38}$, (c) $\frac{30}{43}$, (d) $\frac{10}{43}$, (e) $\frac{3}{5}$, (f) $\frac{8}{13}$.

S7.41.   Examine understandingly the ensuing much simpler method of obtaining the successive convergents of $\frac{19}{43}$.

a.   Obtain the successive quotients in Euclid's algorithm upon 19 and 43, namely, 2, 3, 1, 4.

$$
\begin{array}{c}
19 \ \lfloor\,43\,\lfloor\, 2 \\
\ 38 \\[2pt]
\ \overline{5} \ \lfloor\,19\,\lfloor\,3 \\
\ 15 \\[2pt]
\ \overline{4}\ \lfloor\,5\,\lfloor\,1 \\
\ 4 \\[2pt]
\ \overline{1}\ \lfloor\,4\,\lfloor\,4 \\
\ 4 \\[2pt]
\ \overline{0}
\end{array}
$$

b.   Prepare two columns for numbers headed by *D* for denominators and *N* for numerators of the successive convergents.   Under the *D* column list 0 and 1; under the *N* column list 1 and 0.   In a third column to the left headed by *Q*, list the successive quotients that were obtained by Euclid's algorithm.

Q	*D*	*N*
	0	1
	1	0
2	2*	1*
3	7*	3*
1	9*	4*
4	43*	19*

These quotients should begin in the next line after the 0s and 1s of the *D* and *N* columns.   Now each new entry in the *D* (or *N*) column is the product of the last entry in the *D* (or *N*) column by the next entry in the *Q* column, increased by the preceding entry in the *D* (or *N*) column.   Thus, the successive new entries in the *D* and *N* columns, marked by *, are obtained as follows:

In D column	*In N column*
$2 \times 1 + 0 = 2^*$	$2 \times 0 + 1 = 1^*$
$3 \times 2^* + 1 = 7^*$	$3 \times 1^* + 0 = 3^*$
$1 \times 7^* + 2^* = 9^*$	$1 \times 3^* + 1^* = 4^*$
$4 \times 9^* + 7^* = 43^*$	$4 \times 4^* + 3^* = 19^*$

These new entries in the *D* and *N* columns are denominator and numerator of the successive convergents of $\frac{19}{43}$, namely, $\frac{1}{2}$, $\frac{3}{7}$, $\frac{4}{9}$, and $\frac{19}{43}$.   By the foregoing procedure obtain the convergents of the fractions listed in Problem S7.40a to f, inclusive, and for this fraction: $\frac{163}{201}$.

S7.42. *a.* Show that the successive convergents for $\frac{163}{201}$ are alternately greater than and less than $\frac{163}{201}$.

b. Show that each convergent is a better approximation to $\frac{163}{201}$ than its preceding convergent; i.e., show that the successive differences between $\frac{163}{201}$ and its convergents decrease.

c. Show that the differences between consecutive convergents are unit fractions.

S7.43. Obtain the best possible fractional approximations to the following fractions, if the numerators and denominators must not exceed 20. The convergents are the best possible approximations for the size of numbers appearing in them. (a) $\frac{453}{777}$, (b) $\frac{88}{103}$, (c) $\frac{31,416}{10,000}$.

S7.44. *a.* Obtain all convergents of $\frac{8}{13}$.

b. Show that the differences between successive convergents are unit fractions.

c. Show that these convergents are alternately greater than and less than $\frac{8}{13}$.

d. Show that each convergent of $\frac{8}{13}$ is nearer to $\frac{8}{13}$ than the preceding convergent.

S7.45. The four properties of $\frac{8}{13}$ as established in (*a*) to (*d*) in Problem S7.44 are now established for all arithmetical fractions. Examine understandingly the following proofs.

Let M and N represent any natural numbers whatever. Let the fraction M/N have the continued fractional form:

$$\cfrac{1}{a + \cfrac{1}{b + \cfrac{1}{c + \cfrac{1}{d + \cdots}}}}$$

That is,

Q	D	E
	0	1
	1	0
a	a	1
b	$ab + 1$	b
c	$abc + c + a$	$bc + 1$
. . . .		
. . .	H	K
. . .	L	P
t	R	S
. . . .		

Thus, successive convergents are $1/a$, $b/(ab + 1)$, $(bc + 1)/(abc + c + a)$, . . . , K/H, P/L, S/R, . . .

a. Prove that the difference between consecutive fractions is always a unit fraction. Note that:

$$\frac{1}{a} - \frac{b}{ab + 1} = \frac{ab + 1}{a(ab + 1)} - \frac{ab}{a(ab + 1)} = \frac{1}{a(ab + 1)}$$

Thus the difference between the first two convergents is a unit fraction whose denominator is the product of the denominators of the convergents. Again:

$$\frac{b}{ab + 1} - \frac{bc + 1}{abc + c + a} = \frac{(bc + 1)(ab + 1) - b(abc + c + a)}{(ab + 1)(abc + c + a)}$$

which reduces to

$$\frac{1}{(ab+1)(abd+c+a)}$$

which again is a unit fraction whose denominator is the product of the denominators of the convergents. This property holds for the first three convergents of any proper fraction. Assume now that the property holds for all convergents as far as P/L. This is a safe assumption if P/L is the third convergent. That is,

$$\frac{P}{L} - \frac{K}{H} = \frac{PH - LK}{LH} = \frac{1}{LH} \qquad \text{so that} \qquad PH - LK = 1$$

Then the very next convergent, represented by S/R, must be of form $(tP + K)/(tL + H)$. Now compute the difference between this new convergent and the preceding convergent, P/L. Thus,

$$\frac{P}{L} - \frac{tP+K}{tL+H} = \frac{tLP + HP - tPL - LK}{L(tL+H)} = \frac{PH - LK}{L(tL+H)} = \frac{1}{L(tL+H)}$$

since $PH = LK = 1$, as assumed above. Therefore, if the property holds for any two pairs of consecutive convergents, it must hold for the next pair of convergents, and, as the property is seen to hold for the first three pairs of convergents, it must hold for all ensuing pairs of convergents.

b. Each convergent is in its lowest terms. Let P/L and K/H be two consecutive convergents. Now $P/L - K/H = (PH - LK)/LH = 1/LH$, since the difference between two consecutive convergents is a unit fraction. As $PH - LK = 1$, and the divisor of the numerator and denominator of P/L must also divide 1, the only possible common divisor of P and L can be 1, so that P/L must be in its lowest terms.

c. The odd-numbered convergents, the first, third, fifth, etc., are greater than the original fraction; the even-numbered convergents, the second, fourth, sixth, etc., are less than the original fraction. Let M/N be the original proper fraction. Then $M/N = 1/(N/M)$, in which N/M is an improper fraction, so that $N/M = a + r/M$; hence $M/N = 1/(a + r/M)$. Therefore, $1/a$, the first convergent, is greater than M/N, since the fraction $1/(a + r/M)$ is increased by diminishing its denominator by subtracting r/M from the denominator.

Since r/M is a proper fraction, M/r must be an improper fraction, so that $M/r = b + s/r$. Now $r/M = 1/(M/r) = 1/(b + s/r)$; accordingly, $1/b$ is greater than r/M, as the fraction $1/(b + s/r)$ is increased by diminishing its denominator by subtracting s/r from the denominator. Hence, the entire denominator of

$$\frac{1}{a + \dfrac{1}{b + \dfrac{s}{r}}} \qquad \text{namely} \qquad a + \dfrac{1}{b + \dfrac{s}{r}}$$

is increased, as $1/(b + s/r)$ is increased by subtracting s/r from $b + s/r$. Therefore, the second convergent, namely,

$$\cfrac{1}{a + \cfrac{1}{b}} \quad \text{is smaller than} \quad \cfrac{1}{a + \cfrac{1}{b + \cfrac{s}{r}}}$$

which is equal to the original fraction, M/N. Continuing the same argument step by step, the third convergent, namely,

$$\cfrac{1}{a + \cfrac{1}{b + \cfrac{1}{c}}} \quad \text{is larger than} \quad \cfrac{1}{a + \cfrac{1}{b + \cfrac{1}{c + \cfrac{t}{s}}}}$$

which is equal to the original fraction M/N. Again, the fourth convergent, namely,

$$\cfrac{1}{a + \cfrac{1}{b + \cfrac{1}{c + \cfrac{1}{d}}}} \quad \text{is smaller than} \quad \cfrac{1}{a + \cfrac{1}{b + \cfrac{1}{c + \cfrac{1}{d + \cfrac{u}{t}}}}}$$

which is equal to the original fraction M/N. By extending the continued fraction to ensuing stages, the continued fraction that always equals the original fraction M/N is noted to be increased or decreased alternately by omitting the final remainder: r/M, s/r, t/s, u/t, ... Therefore, the odd-numbered convergents are all greater than the original fraction, and the even-numbered convergents are all less than the original fraction.

d. The odd-numbered convergents successively decrease in value; the even-numbered convergents successively increase in value. Let P/Q, R/S, T/U, V/W be four consecutive convergents of the fraction M/N and let P/Q, T/U be odd-numbered convergents and hence larger than M/N; then R/S and V/W are even-numbered convergents and hence smaller than M/N. Add:

$$P/Q - R/S = 1/QS, \text{ a positive fraction}$$
$$\text{and} \quad R/S - T/U = -1/SU, \text{ a negative fraction}$$
$$\overline{P/Q - T/U = 1/QS - 1/SU = (U - Q)/QSU, \text{ a positive}}$$
fraction

The odd-numbered convergent T/U is smaller than its preceding odd-numbered convergent P/Q. Similarly, adding

$$R/S - T/U = -1/SU, \text{ a negative fraction}$$
$$\text{and} \quad T/U - V/W = 1/UW, \text{ a positive fraction}$$
$$\overline{R/S - V/W = -1/SU + 1/UW = (S - W)/SUW, \text{ a negative}}$$
fraction

The even-numbered convergent R/S is less than its next ensuing even-numbered convergent. While the successive numerators and denominators of all convergents continue to increase, P, R, T, V, . . . and Q, S, U, W, . . . , the odd-numbered convergents continue to decrease, thereby closing in on the original fraction M/N.

e. Finally, if K/H is a convergent of the fraction M/N, then K/H is nearer in value to M/N than any fraction having a smaller denominator than H.

Let K/H and R/S be two consecutive convergents of the fraction M/N, and let R/S be an odd-numbered convergent; hence K/H must be an even-numbered convergent. In either situation, whether K/H follows or precedes R/S, $R/S - K/H = 1/SH$. Now suppose that the fraction p/q is a closer approximation to M/N than either K/H or R/S. The ensuing argument proves that q must be larger than H and S. Two situations must be considered:

1. If R/S *precedes* K/H, then S is smaller than H. Now because $R/S - K/H = 1/SH$, and because p/q lies between R/S and K/H,

$$\frac{p}{q} - \frac{K}{H} < \frac{1}{SH} \quad \text{or} \quad \frac{pH - qK}{qH} < \frac{1}{SH} \quad \text{that is} \quad \frac{pH - qK}{q} < \frac{1}{S}$$

Since $pR - qH$ must be equal to 1 or exceed 1, it is necessary that q be larger than S.

2. If R/S *follows* K/H, then S is larger than H. Now because $R/S - K/H = 1/SH$, and because p/q lies between R/S and K/H,

$$\frac{R}{S} - \frac{p}{q} < \frac{1}{SH} \quad \text{or} \quad \frac{qR - pS}{qS} < \frac{1}{SH} \quad \text{that is} \quad \frac{qR - pS}{q} < \frac{1}{H}$$

Since $qR - pS$ must be equal to 1 or exceed 1, it is necessary that q be larger than H.

Therefore, if p/q is any approximation to the fraction M/N and is a better approximation than any convergent K/H, then the denominator q must exceed the denominator H.

S7.46. The length of a meter in the United States has been defined by federal statute as exactly $39\frac{37}{100}$ inches. Obtain the best possible approximation for the fraction $\frac{37}{100}$, using a fraction having a single digit in its numerator and denominator. Compute the error committed by using this approximation for the length of the meter.

S7.47. Verify the properties in Problem S7.45a to e, inclusive, for the fraction $\frac{37}{100}$. Compare $\frac{5}{17}$ with the two nearest convergents.

S7.48. Obtain all convergents of $\frac{972}{1,393}$. The final convergent must be the fraction itself, as a check against errors of calculation.

S7.49. A very accurate value of the important number π is given as $\frac{31,415,927}{10,000,000}$. Obtain the best approximation for this fraction using for numerator and denominator: (a) one-digit numbers, (b) two-digit numbers, (c) three-digit numbers.

S7.50. An inventor requires small pieces of wire of unusual lengths, namely, $\frac{39}{53}$, $\frac{23}{37}$, $\frac{47}{99}$, and $\frac{119}{141}$ inches, respectively. His cutting instrument can cut wire segments to the nearest $\frac{1}{64}$ of an inch, which is an acceptable tolerance. Obtain the lengths so obtained by two different methods:

a. Convert the given fraction a/b to sixty-fourths by considering the complex fraction $\dfrac{(a/b) \times 64}{64}$, then take the nearest natural number to this numerator.

b. Use for a/b the convergent whose denominator is the largest number not exceeding 64.

S7.51. Obtain the exact number of gallons in 1 cubic foot, if 1 gallon contains 231 cubic inches and 1 cubic foot contains 1,728 cubic inches. Obtain the best fractional approximation in the required mixed number whose numerator and denominator are single-digit numbers. How great an error does this introduce?

S7.52. Obtain the best possible fractional approximations for the following fractions, if their numerators and denominators have no more than two digits: (a) $\frac{97}{345}$, (b) $\frac{2.718}{1.000}$ (the fractional part), (c) $\frac{1.728}{6.543}$.

LESSON 8 ❧ REVIEW OF THE COMPLETE SYSTEM OF RATIONAL NUMBERS AND OPERATIONS UPON THEM

I leave this rule for others when I'm dead, BE ALWAYS SURE YOU'RE RIGHT, THEN GO AHEAD.

—David Crockett, *Autobiography*, 1834.

8·1 ↢ THE THREE DIRECT ARITHMETICAL OPERATIONS UPON NATURAL NUMBERS

Arithmetic begins with the natural numbers and the operation of counting; that is, reciting or writing them in their proper order, as "one, two, three, four, . . . ," or 1, 2, 3, 4, ... Three direct operations are then performed upon these natural numbers, namely,

Addition, or repeated counting

Multiplication, or repeated addition

Involution, or repeated multiplication

These three direct operations, when performed upon natural numbers, always lead to only one correct result, called respectively the *sum*, *product*, and *power*, which is itself a natural number. This situation is described by stating that these three operations are always possible upon the natural numbers, or that the system of natural numbers is *closed under the operations of addition, multiplication, and involution*.

↢ PROBLEM ↢

8.1.   *a.*   Add the natural numbers 876, 2, 575, 1,000,000, 5,280, and 987,642.

   b. $78 + 93 + 11 + 875 + 777 + 1,001 + 250 = ?$

   c.   Multiply 987,324 by 4,936.

   d. $45,376,998,625 \times 4,096 = ?$

   e.   Obtain the fourth power of 34.

   f. $2^{10} = ?$

   g. $10^2 = ?$

8·2 ∽ Direct operations versus inverse operations upon the natural numbers

Addition, multiplication, and involution are the three fundamental or basic direct operations of arithmetic. In each of these operations one obtains from two natural numbers a and b a third natural number c as the result of the operation. These three operations are expressed symbolically, thus:

Addition, $a + b = c$
Multiplication, $a \cdot b = c$, or $ab = c$
Involution, $a^b = c$

The operations of addition and multiplication are *commutative*, which means that the result is the same if a and b are interchanged; that is, $a + b = b + a$, and $ab = ba$. Involution is not commutative, since a^b and b^a yield different results, if a and b represent different natural numbers.

Definition. An operation performed upon the number resulting from a direct operation and one of the original numbers of the operation, which yields the other original number of the direct operation, is called an *inverse operation* of the given direct operation. The inverse operation of addition is called subtraction; it is the operation of finding the missing number ? in the indicated additions: $a + ? = c$ or $? + b = c$. In appropriate symbols these subtractions are expressed as $c - a = ?$ and $c - b = ?$, respectively. Since addition is commutative, the two forms of inverse operations, $a + ? = c$ and $? + b = c$, are the same inverse operation, namely, subtraction. As multiplication is also commutative, the two forms of inverse operation, namely, $a \cdot ? = c$ and $? \cdot b = c$, which, in appropriate symbols, $c \div a = ?$ and $c \div b = ?$, respectively, are a single inverse operation known as *division*.

Contrariwise, the direct operation of involution is not commutative since, if a and b are different natural numbers, $a^b = c$ and $b^a = d$, wherein c and d are different natural numbers. Involution has two inverse operations:

Evolution, the determination of the missing number ? in the relationship $?^b = c$, which is expressed in appropriate form as $\sqrt[b]{c} = ?$ and is expressed verbally as "the bth root of c equals what."

Indexing, the determination of the missing number ? in the relationship $a^? = b$, which is expressed in appropriate symbols as $\log_a b = ?$ and is expressed verbally as "the logarithm of b for the base a equals what."

To illustrate the two inverse operations of the involution $3^5 = 243$, wherein 3^5 means $3 \times 3 \times 3 \times 3 \times 3$, the repeated multiplication of 3: $\sqrt[5]{243} = 3$, read as "the fifth root of 243 equals 3"; $\log_3 243 = 5$, read as "the logarithm of 243 with base 3 is 5."

The system of natural numbers is not closed under the inverse operations of subtraction, division, evolution, and indexing; i.e., if a and b represent any natural numbers whatever, the operations $a - b = ?$, $a \div b = ?$, $\sqrt[a]{b} = ?$, and $\log_a b = ?$ may or may not yield a natural number as a result.

⟶ Problems [CONTINUED] ⟵

8.2. Perform the indicated operations that are possible with natural numbers.

a. $7{,}895 + ? = 9{,}342$

b. $1{,}000{,}132 - 785{,}845 = ?$

c. $512 \times ? = 65{,}536$

d. $950{,}898 \div 1{,}898 = ?$

e. $?^2 = 144$

f. $\sqrt{121} = ?$

g. $\sqrt[3]{125} = ?$

h. $7^? = 343$

i. $4^? = 64$

j. $\log_2 32 = ?$

8·3 ⟶ Enlargement of the system of natural numbers to include all rational numbers

Inverse operations upon natural numbers that do not yield natural numbers for results are said to be "impossible within the system of natural numbers." Such inverse operations are made possible by inventing new kinds of numbers and introducing them into the system of usable numbers. Thus, to make subtraction always possible upon natural numbers, one introduces the *zero* and the *negative integers;* to make division always possible upon natural numbers, one introduces the *fractions* into the system of usable numbers. With the introduction of these new kinds of numbers as the zero, negative integers, and fractions, one extends the definitions of the fundamental direct operations and the inverse operations of subtraction and division upon all such numbers and upon the resulting numbers. All such numbers so encountered comprise the *complete system of rational numbers.* This system consists of all positive and negative integers and zero, and of all fractions, proper and improper, positive and negative.

At this stage of arithmetic the student can perform correctly the following operations, under the indicated restrictions:

Addition, $a + b = ?$
Subtraction, $a - b = ?$
Multiplication, $ab = ?$
Division, $a \div c = ?$
Involution, $a^d = ?$

Here a and b may represent any rational number whatever, c may be any rational number *except zero,* d is restricted to *natural numbers.*

8·4 ∽ Scope of exponents enlarged to include all integers

The exponent d in a^d is defined as the number of times a is to be used in a continued product. Thus $7^5 = 7 \times 7 \times 7 \times 7 \times 7$; $(\frac{2}{3})^4 = \frac{2}{3} \cdot \frac{2}{3} \cdot \frac{2}{3} \cdot \frac{2}{3}$. This restrictive definition requires that the exponent be a natural number. New definitions must be formulated for the operation of involution if the exponent is not a natural number. Such definitions are now provided for all *integral* exponents as follows: (1) For any rational number a, *except zero*, $a^\circ = 1$. Thus, $3^\circ = 1$; $(5\frac{2}{3}^\circ) = 1$; $(-\frac{5}{8})^\circ = 1$; $1{,}000{,}000^\circ = 1$. (2) The expression 0° may represent any number whatever. Expressions that may represent any number whatever are called *indeterminates*. The seven commonly occurring *indeterminates* are presented in S.21. (3) If a represents any rational number *except zero* and if $-d$ represents any negative integer, then $a^{-d} = \dfrac{1}{a^{+d}}$. Accordingly,

$$2^{-3} = \frac{1}{2^3} \quad \text{or} \quad \tfrac{1}{8} \qquad (\tfrac{2}{3})^{-2} = \frac{1}{(\tfrac{2}{3})^2} = \frac{1}{\tfrac{4}{9}} = \tfrac{9}{4} = 2\tfrac{1}{4}$$

The meaning of a^d for any rational value of a *except zero* and for any rational value of d will be presented in Section 16.1. These extended definitions of a^d are formulated to harmonize with previous rules of involution and division.

8·5 ∽ The complete number system of analysis

The complete system of rational numbers is quite sufficient to provide solutions for very many but not all problems that arise in life situations—science, industry, commerce, etc. These rational numbers are inadequate to provide results for all inverse operations upon natural numbers or integers. As examples, $\sqrt{3}$, $\sqrt{-2}$, $\log_2 3$, $\log_5 (-1)$ are not equal to any rational number; to perform these indicated operations as stated or in their analogous forms, $?^2 = 3$, $?^2 = -2$, $2^? = 3$, $5^? = -1$, one must invent two new kinds of number, namely, the *irrational numbers* and the *complex numbers*. Extending the definitions of the three direct and the four inverse operations upon these new irrational and complex numbers, one requires no new kinds of number to perform the operations. The enlarged system of numbers consisting of rational, irrational, and complex numbers is called the complete number system of analysis; this system of numbers is *closed under all seven fundamental direct and inverse operations*, namely, addition, multiplication, involution, and subtraction, division, evolution, indexing. The single operation of division by zero must be excluded as an impossible operation within the complete number system of analysis.

   It may be added that the pursuit of abstruse mathematical researches has led scholars to invent and to operate upon still other new kinds of numbers that are not contained within the complete number system of analysis. As such examples, one may cite the quaternions of higher algebra and the ideal numbers of algebraic number theory.

∾ PROBLEMS [CONTINUED] ∾

8.3. Perform the following subtractions:

a. $78,154 - 81,259 = ?$ e. $(-34) - (4\frac{1}{4}) = ?$

b. $23\frac{4}{5} - 72\frac{3}{8} = ?$ f. $(2\frac{3}{7}) - (-5\frac{1}{2}) = ?$

c. $(-45,765) - 85,334 = ?$ g. $(-234\frac{7}{8}) - (-365\frac{5}{12}) = ?$

d. $0 - (-23) = ?$ h. $234\frac{1}{2} - 243\frac{1}{3} = ?$

8.4. Perform the following multiplications:

a. $(-23)(56) = ?$ e. $(34,987)(65,872\frac{1}{2})(0) = ?$

b. $(-2\frac{1}{3})(-3\frac{1}{2}) = ?$ f. $(-\frac{3}{5})(-\frac{4}{5})(-7\frac{1}{7}) = ?$

c. $(-25)(-35)(-45) = ?$ g. $(-3)(+4)(-5)(+6)(-7) = ?$

d. $(-6\frac{1}{4})(-3\frac{1}{5})(13) = ?$ h. $(-3\frac{2}{3})(+4\frac{1}{4})(-24) = ?$

8.5. Perform the divisions that are possible (one is impossible):

a. $58 \div 13 = ?$ f. $12 \div 0 = ?$

b. $2 \div 5 = ?$ g. $(-5\frac{5}{6}) \div 70 = ?$

c. $(-7) \div (-12) = ?$ h. $(-11) \div (-111) = ?$

d. $(-8\frac{3}{4}) \div (-33\frac{1}{3}) = ?$ i. $(-74) \div 185 = ?$

e. $0 \div 7 = ?$ j. $(-555\frac{5}{9}) \div (7,777\frac{7}{9}) = ?$

8.6. Perform the following involutions:

a. $3^6 = ?$ e. $(-11)^3 = ?$ i. $(1\frac{7}{8})^3 = ?$

b. $(-5)^4 = ?$ f. $(-7\frac{1}{2})^2 = ?$ j. $(123\frac{1}{2})^0 = ?$

c. $(-1\frac{2}{3})^3 = ?$ g. $(-2)^6 = ?$ k. $(2\frac{1}{2})^{-2} = ?$

d. $(-\frac{1}{2})^7 = ?$ h. $(-10)^5 = ?$ l. $(-3\frac{1}{3})^{-3} = ?$

8.7. Perform the indicated operations in the order in which they occur; then add algebraically the five results in each of the following:

a. $(-2)(-9) \div (-6)$ $(-4)^4$ $\frac{343}{49}$ $72 \div 6 \div (-3)$ $2^2 \times 5^2$

b. $(-4\frac{1}{2})(-3\frac{1}{6})$ $-13\frac{7}{8} \div 9\frac{1}{4}$ $\sqrt{\frac{9}{16}}$ $\sqrt[3]{-8}$ $(-\frac{3}{2})^2$

c. $(2\frac{1}{2})(-1\frac{3}{5})$ $12\frac{3}{4} \div (-2\frac{1}{8})$ $(-3)^2(-2)^2$ $\sqrt{25}$ $-\frac{-87}{-3}$

d. $\frac{-57}{-19}$ $-2 \div 3$ $\frac{-220}{55}$ $\log_3 27$ $\log_2 16$

8·6 ～ ORDER OF PERFORMING THE SEVEN FUNDAMENTAL OPERATIONS OF ARITHMETIC

To simplify or to evaluate an expression involving the fundamental operations (addition, subtraction, multiplication, division, involution, evolution, and indexing), one must perform all operations in the order in which they occur *excepting the additions and subtractions* which are performed last. The necessity for observing this rule arises from the fact that various different operations are generally *not associative*. Thus, it is true that $ab \div c = a(b \div c)$, since each of these expressions yields the same result, namely, $\dfrac{ab}{c}$; however, $(a \div b)c = \dfrac{ac}{b}$, whereas $a \div bc = \dfrac{a}{bc}$ so that $(a \div b)c$ and $a \div bc$ are quite unlike. To illustrate, evaluate the expression:

$$5 + \underline{7 \times 3} - \underline{4 \times 6 \div 8} + 7 - \underline{8^2} + \underline{4 \times 3} - \underline{36 \div 9 \times 4} = ?$$

The underlined expressions must first be evaluated: $7 \times 3 = 21$; $4 \times 6 = 24$, $24 \div 8 = 3$; $8^2 = 64$; $4 \times 3 = 12$; and $36 \div 9 = 4$, $4 \times 4 = 16$. Inserting these results in the original line, one obtains $5 + 21 - 3 + 7 - 64 + 12 - 16$. Finally, performing these indicated additions and subtractions, or adding algebraically $+5$, $+21$, -3, $+7$, -64, $+12$, -16, one obtains the required result, namely, -38.

～ PROBLEMS [CONTINUED] ～

8.8. Evaluate the following expressions:

a. $5 \times 3 + 7 - 4 \times 9 \div 2 + 5^3 - 3^5 + 28 \div 7 - 3 = ?$

b. $(-1\frac{1}{2})(-3\frac{3}{4}) \div (-22\frac{1}{2}) - (-3\frac{1}{2})^2 = ?$

c. $(-2)(-3) + (-3) \div (-4) - (-5) \div (-6) + (-\frac{3}{8}) \div 48^{-1} = ?$

d. $(+3)^3 - 3^3 \times 2 + 3^2 \times 2^2 - 2^3 = ?$

e. $(2\frac{1}{2})^2 - 5 \times 1\frac{1}{4} + (1\frac{1}{4})^2 = ?$

8·7 ～ GRAPHICAL REPRESENTATION OF THE SYSTEM OF RATIONAL NUMBERS

Let equally spaced tickmarks be placed along a straight line, thus:

Now select an intermediate tickmark to represent 0; identify it by writing 0 above it. Identify the consecutive tickmarks to the right of 0 by the consecutive natural numbers, beginning with 1. Thus one provides a graphical representation of *all natural numbers*, assuming that the straight line extends without end toward the right, thus:

$$0 \quad 1 \quad 2 \quad 3 \quad 4 \quad 5 \ldots$$

By identifying the tickmarks toward the left of the 0 with the negative integers, consecutively, beginning with -1 for the tickmark immediately to the left of 0, one obtains a graphical representation of the *complete system of integers*, thus:

$$\ldots -5 \quad -4 \quad -3 \quad -2 \quad -1 \quad 0 \quad 1 \quad 2 \quad 3 \quad 4 \quad 5 \ldots$$

The line is assumed to extend without end in both directions; the positive integers are the same numbers as the natural numbers.

All positive proper and improper fractions having the same denominator d, namely, $1/d, 2/d, 3/d, 4/d, \ldots$, may be given graphical representation by points on this line by subdividing the intervals between 0 and 1 and those between each pair of natural numbers into d equal subintervals, and by assigning these positive fractions, in order, to these new points of subdivision beginning with the first new point to the right of the 0. Similarly the negative fractions $-1/d, -2/d, -3/d, \ldots$, are assigned to points of subdivision similarly obtained to the left of the 0. Letting $d = 12$, one obtains graphical representation for $\frac{1}{12}, \frac{2}{12}, \frac{3}{12}, \frac{4}{12}, \ldots$, and $-\frac{1}{12}, -\frac{2}{12}, -\frac{3}{12}, -\frac{4}{12}, \ldots$, enlarging for convenience the intervals between consecutive integers on the line:

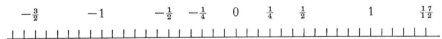

The marked tickmarks to the right of the 0 are identified, in order, with $\frac{1}{12}$, $\frac{2}{12}$ or $\frac{1}{6}$, $\frac{3}{12}$ or $\frac{1}{4}$, $\frac{4}{12}$ or $\frac{1}{3}$, $\frac{5}{12}$, $\frac{6}{12}$ or $\frac{1}{2}$, $\frac{7}{12}$, $\frac{8}{12}$ or $\frac{2}{3}$, $\frac{9}{12}$ or $\frac{3}{4}$, $\frac{10}{12}$ or $\frac{5}{6}$, $\frac{11}{12}$, $\frac{12}{12}$ or 1, $\frac{13}{12}$ or $1\frac{1}{12}$, $\frac{14}{12}$ or $1\frac{1}{5}$, $\frac{15}{12}$ or $1\frac{1}{4}$, $\frac{16}{12}$ or $1\frac{1}{3}$, ... The marked tickmarks to the left of the 0 are identified, in order toward the left, with $-\frac{1}{12}$, $-\frac{2}{12}$ or $-\frac{1}{6}$, $-\frac{3}{12}$ or $-\frac{1}{4}$, $-\frac{4}{12}$ or $-\frac{1}{3}$, $-\frac{5}{12}$, $-\frac{6}{12}$ or $-\frac{1}{2}$, $-\frac{7}{12}$, $-\frac{8}{12}$ or $-\frac{2}{3}$, $-\frac{9}{12}$ or $-\frac{3}{4}$, $-\frac{10}{12}$ or $-\frac{5}{6}$, $-\frac{11}{12}$, $-\frac{12}{12}$ or -1, $-\frac{13}{12}$ or $-1\frac{1}{12}$, $-\frac{14}{12}$ or $-2\frac{1}{6}$, $-\frac{15}{12}$ or $-1\frac{1}{4}$, $-\frac{16}{12}$ or $-1\frac{1}{3}$, $-\frac{17}{12}$ or $-1\frac{5}{12}$, ...

Repeating the process with $d = 2, 3, 4, 5, \ldots$, one obtains graphical representations for all rational numbers. The same tickmark represents all equal rational numbers, such as $\frac{3}{4} = \frac{6}{8} = \frac{9}{12} = \frac{12}{16} = \frac{15}{20}, \ldots$.

Assuming that all rational numbers are identified with their corresponding position tickmarks on the line, the rational numbers increase in value as their corresponding tickmarks extend farther toward the right; the rational numbers decrease in value as their corresponding points, or tickmarks, extend farther toward the left.

The actual distance between two corresponding integers is called the *units distance* and may represent arbitrarily "1 inch" or "1 foot," "1 meter" or "1 mile," etc. The distance between two tickmarks on the number line, as measured from the left tickmark to the right tickmark, is equal to the difference obtained by subtracting the smaller number representing the left tickmark, from the larger number representing the right tickmark. Thus, the distance between the tickmarks representing the numbers $-2\frac{1}{2}$ and $5\frac{2}{3}$ is computed as $5\frac{2}{3} - (-2\frac{1}{2}) = 8\frac{1}{6}$.

Problems [concluded] ᦇ

8.9. Compute the distance between each pair of positions representing the pairs of rational numbers:

a.	35, 63	*e.*	$6\frac{8}{9}, -4\frac{2}{3}$	*i.*	$-56, -59$
b.	$-19, +7$	*f.*	$0, -7$	*j.*	$+56, -59$
c.	$-37, -23$	*g.*	$-1, +1$		
d.	$-2\frac{3}{4}, +5\frac{1}{6}$	*h.*	56, 59		

8.10. Obtain the arithmetic mean of the following pairs of numbers. (The arithmetic mean of two numbers is half their sum.) Then locate on the appropriate portion of the number line the pair of given numbers and their arithmetic mean:

a.	$+3, +7$	*e.*	$-8\frac{1}{4}, -11$	*i.*	$-2\frac{5}{6}, +1\frac{3}{4}$
b.	$1\frac{1}{2}, 2\frac{3}{4}$	*f.*	$+2, -1$	*j.*	$+17, -5$
c.	$-3\frac{1}{3}, 4\frac{1}{2}$	*g.*	$+3, 0$		
d.	$-5, +1$	*h.*	$-2, +2$		

8.11. Obtain the algebraic sum of the two sets of numbers of Problem 8.10:
a. $+3, 1\frac{1}{2}, -3\frac{1}{3}, -5, -8\frac{1}{4}, 2, 3, -2, -2\frac{5}{6}, 17$
b. $+7, 2\frac{3}{4}, 4\frac{1}{2}, +1, -11, -1, 0, +2, +1\frac{3}{4}, -5$

8.12. *a.* Obtain the algebraic sum of the 10 arithmetic means obtained in Problem 8.10.

  b. Obtain the arithmetic mean of the two answers obtained in Problem 8.11.

  c. State the fact that the two foregoing results seem to imply.

  d. Illustrate this fact for the three pairs of numbers: 5, 7; $-3, -11$; $+4, -10$.

*N*ote 1 ↝ *A suggestion pertaining*
to an extensive long division.

Before undertaking any extensive long division, it may be convenient to list the first nine multiples of the divisor. For example, obtain the quotient of 1,397,467,293,765 divided by 47,392.

Multiples of
divisor

47,392	
94,784	
142,176	
189,568	
236,960	
284,352	
331,744	
379,136	
426,528	

$$
\begin{array}{r}
29107598 \\
47392\overline{)1379467293765} \\
94784 \\
\hline
431627 \\
426528 \\
\hline
50992 \\
47392 \\
\hline
360093 \\
331744 \\
\hline
283497 \\
236960 \\
\hline
465376 \\
426528 \\
\hline
388485 \\
379136 \\
\hline
9349
\end{array}
$$

*N*ote 2 ↝ *The roman system*
of writing natural numbers.

It is convenient to be familiar with the Roman scheme of writing the natural numbers from 1 to 3,999,999, as these numerals frequently occur on monuments, on cornerstones of buildings, chapter headings, on the faces of many clocks and watches, etc.

Seven letters are used in the Roman system, namely, I, V, X, L, C, D, M, representing respectively 1, 5, 10, 50, 100, 500, 1,000. A horizontal line placed above a letter multiplies its value by 1,000. Thus, $\bar{I}$, $\bar{V}$, $\bar{X}$, $\bar{L}$, $\bar{C}$, $\bar{D}$, $\bar{M}$ represent respectively 1,000, 5,000, 10,000, 50,000, 100,000, 500,000, 1,000,000. The multiplicative principle occurs in overlining. The Roman system of numerals employs two other principles:

The *subtractive* principle of writing I or X or C before (to the left of) particular symbols as follows:

I to the left of V, as IV, denotes 5 − 1, or 4
I to the left of X, as IX, denotes 10 − 1, or 9

X to the left of L, as XL, denotes 50 − 10, or 40
X to the left of C, as XC, denotes 100 − 10, or 90
C to the left of D, as CD, denotes 500 − 100, or 400
C to the left of M, as CM, denotes 1,000 − 100, or 900

The *additive* principle in which symbols for smaller numbers are placed to the right of symbols for larger numbers, or the repetition of the same symbol two or three times, indicates an addition of their numerical values.

VII denotes 5 + 1 + 1, or 7
CCLXXXVII denotes 100 + 100 + 50 + 10 + 10 + 10 + 5 + 1 + 1 = 287
MCMLXVIII denotes 1,000 + 900 + 50 + 10 + 5 + 1 + 1 + 1 = 1,968
$\overline{\text{XXV}}$ denotes 1,000(10 + 10 + 5) = 25,000

Without further modifications the Roman system of writing natural numbers is confined to the writing of natural numbers less than 4 million, if one adheres to the practice of writing the same letter not more than three times consecutively in any number. There is just one noteworthy exception to this practice, namely, in writing IIII for 4 on the faces of clocks and watches instead of the orthodox IV. Just why IIII should appear here rather than IV is unknown. It has been surmised that the original clockmakers preferred IIII to IV in displaying a more balanced array of characters on the face of the clock.

The ensuing table of equivalences should enable one to formulate the Roman expression for any natural number from 1 to 3,999,999 (the largest expressible Roman number) inclusive:

1	I	38	XXXVIII	99	XCIX
2	II	39	XXXIX	100	C
3	III	40	XL	256	CCLVI
4	IV	41	XLI	398	CCCXCVIII
5	V	42	XLII	444	CDXLIV
6	VI	44	XLIV	499	CDXCIX
7	VII	49	XLIX	879	DCCCLXXIX
8	VIII	50	L	999	CMXCIX
9	IX	51	LI	1,492	MCDXCII
10	X	59	LIX	3,999	MMMCMXCIX
31	XXXI	84	LXXXIV	5,000	$\overline{\text{V}}$
32	XXXII	89	LXXXIX	5,284	$\overline{\text{V}}$CCLXXXIV
33	XXXIII	90	XC	38,796	$\overline{\text{XXXVIII}}$DCCXCVI
34	XXXIV	91	XCI	808,927	$\overline{\text{DCCCVIII}}$CMXXVII
35	XXXV	92	XCII	999,999	$\overline{\text{CMXCIX}}$CMXCIX
36	XXXVI	94	XCIV	3,597,623	$\overline{\text{MMMDXCVII}}$DCXXIII
37	XXXVII	98	XCVIII	3,999,999	$\overline{\text{MMMCMXCIX}}$CMXCIX

One may perform the rational arithmetical operations (addition, subtraction, multiplication, division, and involution) upon natural numbers in Roman forms quite effectively, provided the numbers that are used do not exceed 3,999,999. Such computations with small Roman numbers will greatly increase one's admiration and appreciation of the beautiful simplicity of our familiar Arabic number system of writing natural numbers.

Note 3 ↝ Conversion of natural numbers from one base to another base.

The symbolism for natural numbers employing bases other than 10 was presented in Section 1.12. The conversion of a natural number N in the familiar decimal system to its equivalent form with base b instead of 10 is accomplished by repeatedly dividing N and the ensuing integral portions of the successive quotients by b. The final quotient and the remainders, in reverse order, are the digits of the required expression for the natural number with base b.

To illustrate, convert the decimal form 1,160 of the natural number to its equivalent form with base 7.

$7\underline{	1160}$		Therefore, the required form is 3245, $3(7)^3 +$
$7\underline{	165}$	Remainder 5	$2(7)^2 + 4(7) + 5$, which is equivalent to the
$7\underline{	23}$	Remainder 4	decimal form 1,160, or $1(10)^3 + 1(10)^2 +$
3	Remainder 2	$6(10) + 0$.

The correctness of this successive division algorithm is verified by reversing the successive steps in the division, namely, $23 = 7 \times 3 + 2$; $165 = 7 \times 23 + 4$, or, replacing the 23 by its previously obtained form, $7 \times 3 + 2$, one has

$$165 = 7(7 \times 3 + 2) + 4, \text{ or } (7^2 \times 3) + (7 \times 2) + 4$$
$$1,160 = 7 \times 165 + 5$$

or, replacing the 165 by its previously obtained form, $(7^2 \times 3) + (7 \times 2) + 4$, one has $1,160 = 7(7^2 \times 3 + 7 \times 2 + 4) + 5$, or $7^3 \times 3 + 7^2 \times 2 + 7 \times 4 + 5$ whence

$$1,160 = 3 \times 7^3 + 2 \times 7^2 + 4 \times 7 + 5$$

Accordingly, when expressed to base seven, 1,160 appears as 3,245.

The foregoing procedure, yielding 1,160 as equivalent to $3 \times 7^3 + 2 \times 7^2 + 4 \times 7 + 5$, or $7\{7(3 \times 7 + 2) + 4\} + 5$, reveals the convenient method of converting back to the decimal form (with base 10) any form of the natural number when written to a different base. To recapitulate briefly, using one by one the digits from the left end:

1. Multiply the left end digit by the base.

2. Add the second digit from the left to this product.

3. Multiply the sum obtained in (2) by the base.

4. Add the third digit from the left to the product obtained in (3).

5. Multiply the sum obtained in (4) by the base.

6. Add the next (fourth) digit from the left to the product obtained in (5).

Quite generally, one continues this procedure of successive multiplications by the base and subsequent additions of products to the next ensuing digit until all digits are used. The final number so obtained is the required *decimal* form.

To illustrate, let the septimic number 3,245 (base 7) be converted to its equivalent decimal form (base 10).

$$7 \times 3 = 21 \qquad 21 + 2 = 23$$
$$7 \times 23 = 161 \qquad 161 + 4 = 165$$
$$7 \times 161 = 1155 \qquad 1155 + 5 = 1,160 \qquad \text{The required decimal form}$$

The foregoing steps may be performed compactly in the convenient algorithm, which becomes clear by identifying the numbers occurring in it with those used in converting the septimic 3,245 to the decimal 1,160.

3	2	4	5	$\lfloor 7$ (The given base)
	21	161	1155	
3	23	165	1160	(1,160 has base 10 as required)

Again, to convert the binary or dyadic form (of base 2), 101101, to the corresponding decimal form (of base 10), identify the successive multiplications and additions $2 \times 1 = 2$, $2 + 0 = 2$, $2 \times 2 = 4$, $4 + 1 = 5$, $2 \times 5 = 10$, $10 + 1 = 11$, $2 \times 11 = 22$, $22 + 0 = 22$, $2 \times 22 = 44$, $44 + 1 = 45$:

1	0	1	1	0	1	$\lfloor 2$ (Old base)
	2	4	10	22	44	
1	2	5	11	22	45	(45 has base 10)

Thus, 101101 means $2^5 + 2^3 + 2^2 + 1 = 32 + 8 + 4 + 1 = 45$.

Finally, to convert a number from one base to another, neither base being 10, it is convenient to convert the given number to its equivalent *decimal* form, then convert this decimal form to the equivalent form of the specified new base. As an example, convert 4,352, of base 8, to the corresponding form of base 9.

4	3	5	2	$\lfloor 8$
	32	280	2280	
4	35	285	2282	(2,282 is of base 10)

$9 \lfloor 2282$
$9 \lfloor 253$ With remainder 5
$9 \lfloor 28$ With remainder 1
$ 3$ With remainder 1

The required form with base 9 is 3,115, as its digits are the final quotient 3 and the successive remainders 1, 1, 5 taken in reverse order of their occurrence.

~ SUPPLEMENTARY PROBLEMS ~

This above all: to thine own self be true,
And it must follow, as the night the day,
Thou canst not then be false to any man.

—*Hamlet, I,* 3.

S8.1. How many natural numbers are less than 19? How many between 29 and 43? How many two-digit natural numbers contain the digit 1?

The following 12 problems concern arithmetical progressions.

S8.2. Continue the arithmetical progressions as far as possible without exceeding 100.

     a. 7, 13, 19, . . .   *b.* 9, 16, 23, . . .   *c.* 13, 25, 37, . . .

Note that each successive term (number) in an arithmetical progression is obtained by adding algebraically the same number to its preceding term.

S8.3. Continue the arithmetical progressions as far as possible by using natural numbers only.

     a. 93, 84, 75, . . .   *b.* 95, 88, 81, . . .   *c.* 90, 75, 60, . . .

S8.4. Continue the arithmetical progressions as far as possible by using negative integers only.

     a. $-59, -48, -37,$ . . .   *b.* $-27, -22,$ . . .   *c.* $-350, -275,$ . . .

S8.5. Continue the arithmetical progressions until each progression contains ten terms.

     a. 23, 17, 11, . . .   *b.* 8, 5, 2, . . .   *c.* $-5, -13, -21,$ . . .

S8.6. The nth term of an arithmetical progression is equal to the sum of the first term and $(n-1)$ times the *common difference;* the common difference is the number that is added to any term to obtain the next ensuing term. For the progression 5, 12, 19, . . . , the common difference is $12-5$, or 7. Hence the fifteenth term is equal to $5 + 14 \times 7$ or 103. Verify this result by extending the series to the fifteenth term.

S8.7. Compute the twelfth term in each progression of Problems S8.2-5, inclusive.

S8.8. The sum of n consecutive terms of an arithmetical progression is equal to the product of the arithmetical mean of the first and nth term of the progression by n. To compute the sum of the 10 terms of the progression 7, 14, 21, . . . , one computes the tenth term as $7 + 9 \times 7$, or 70. Then the arithmetical mean of 7 and 70 is $\frac{1}{2}(7 + 70) = \frac{77}{2}$. Finally, the sum of the 10 terms from 7 to 70, inclusive, is $\frac{77}{2} \times 10$, or 385. Verify this by extending the progression 7, 14, 21, to 10 terms, then obtain the sum of the 10 terms.

S8.9. Obtain the sum of the arithmetical progressions in Problems S8.2-5.

S8.10. Compute the sum of all positive multiples of 7 that do not exceed 100.

S8.11. What is the largest multiple of 7 that does not exceed 1,000? 10,000? 100,000? 1,000,000? Is this statement true: "If n represents any natural number, then the largest multiple of 7 that does not exceed 10^n is $10^n - 2$"? Why not?

S8.12. Show that the formula $\dfrac{(10^n + 2)(10^n - 1)}{6}$ yields the sum of all positive multiples of 3 that do not exceed 10^n, if n represents 1, 2, 3, and 4. Without extensive calculations, what would one surmise the sum of all positive multiples of 3 less than 1,000,000,000 to be?

S8.13. To provide for his son's college expenses, a father places in a Credit Union savings account as many $10 bills as the son's age on each birthday until his eighteenth, inclusive. If the account earns 6 percent interest compounded annually and yields a final amount, including the eighteenth deposit, of $2,461.66, how much of this total accumulation is interest?

S8.14. A lot is three times as long as its width. Calculate its area and its perimeter, if it is 53 feet wide.

S8.15. Re-solve Problem S8.14 if the length of the lot is 111 yards.

S8.16. The length of a lot is $5\frac{2}{3}$ times its width. Compute its area and perimeter if it is $19\frac{1}{2}$ feet wide and $119\frac{1}{2}$ feet long.

S8.17. Solve the following five problems:

$$
\begin{array}{ccccc}
-14 & -24 & +36 & 72 & -96 \\
+\ 7 & -\ 8 & -12 & 18 & -24 \\
\hline
\end{array}
$$

and obtain the algebraic sum of the five results, if the operation is: (*a*) algebraic addition, (*b*) algebraic subtraction, (*c*) algebraic multiplication, (*d*) algebraic division of upper by lower number.

S8.18. Obtain the sum of the fractions in each set:

a. $\frac{1}{2}, \frac{2}{3}, \frac{3}{4}, \frac{5}{6}, \frac{11}{12}$

b. $\frac{3}{4}, \frac{5}{8}, \frac{1}{2}, \frac{9}{16}, \frac{29}{32}$

c. $\frac{3}{5}, \frac{7}{10}, \frac{11}{20}, \frac{80}{100}$

S8.19. Obtain the sum of the mixed numbers in each set:

a. $12\frac{3}{4}, 18\frac{2}{3}, 11\frac{1}{6}, 5\frac{7}{12}$

b. $12,365\frac{3}{5}, 19,001\frac{7}{10}, 19,440\frac{11}{20}$

c. $56\frac{7}{12}, 43\frac{2}{3}, 83\frac{1}{3}, 4\frac{1}{4}$

S8.20. Add algebraically:

a. $-1\frac{3}{8}, 4\frac{1}{2}, -6, -2\frac{3}{4}, \frac{5}{16}$

b. $23\frac{7}{12}, -58\frac{2}{3}, -101\frac{1}{4}, +12\frac{1}{2}, 1\frac{5}{6}$

c. $-\frac{1}{2}, +\frac{2}{3}, -\frac{3}{4}, +\frac{5}{6}, -\frac{9}{10}, +\frac{7}{12}, -\frac{13}{15}, +\frac{29}{30}$

S8.21. Evaluate:

a. $3 + 9 \times 6 \div 2 + 9 \times 2 \div 6 - 12 \times 12 \div 32$

b. $3 + 9 \times (6 \div 2 + 9) + (6 - 12) \div 2$

c. $(3 \times 5 - 2) \div 13 + (7 \times 71 + 3) \div 125$

S8.22. Reduce to lowest terms:

a. $\frac{39}{91}$ *d.* $\frac{427}{671}$ *g.* $\frac{635}{1,143}$

b. $\frac{560}{784}$ *e.* $\frac{279}{930}$ *h.* $\frac{1,855}{2,226}$

c. $\frac{123}{328}$ *f.* $\frac{783}{1,566}$ *i.* $\frac{679}{1,164}$

Arrange the nine fractions in order of size, beginning with the smallest on the left. *Hint:* Use their lowest terms.

S8.23. Which fraction in each of the following pairs is the larger fraction?

a. $\frac{3}{4}, \frac{2}{3}$ d. $\frac{5}{6}, \frac{6}{7}$ g. $\frac{5}{16}, \frac{16}{51}$

b. $\frac{3}{5}, \frac{4}{7}$ e. $\frac{5}{16}, \frac{6}{19}$ h. $\frac{5}{26}, \frac{4}{21}$

c. $\frac{6}{9}, \frac{16}{24}$ f. $\frac{7}{17}, \frac{5}{12}$ i. $\frac{3}{11}, \frac{10}{37}$

S8.24. How many gallons of water are needed to fill a rectangular swimming pool that is 20 feet wide, 40 feet long, with a level bottom 12 feet below the surface of the water? (231 cubic inches = 1 gallon.)

S8.25. The average, or arithmetic mean, of a set of numbers is obtained by dividing the sum of the numbers by the number of numbers of the set.   Obtain the arithmetic mean of the following sets of numbers:

a. 34, 29, 53, 99, 12, 8, 72, 23

b. $23\frac{1}{2}, 41\frac{2}{3}, 29\frac{5}{6}, 16\frac{1}{4}$

c. 28, -53, 200, -320, 299, -12

d. $41\frac{2}{3}, -16\frac{3}{4}, -12\frac{1}{2}, 83\frac{1}{3}, -56\frac{1}{4}$

e. $\frac{1}{2}, \frac{1}{3}, \frac{1}{4}, \frac{1}{6}, \frac{1}{12}$

S8.26. Calculate the cost of $1\frac{3}{4}$ yards of cloth at $16\frac{2}{3}$ cents per yard.

S8.27. How much gasoline costing $34\frac{9}{10}$ cents per gallon can one buy for $10?   Obtain the *exact* fractional number.   Express the result also to the nearest tenth of a gallon.

S8.28. Mr. *A* drives his car a distance of 2,000 miles, using gasoline that costs 30 cents per gallon, which yields a mileage of $12\frac{1}{2}$ miles per gallon.   Mr. *B* drives the same distance, but uses gasoline that costs 36 cents per gallon, yielding him a mileage of $16\frac{2}{3}$ miles per gallon.   Compute the difference in the amounts the two men paid for gasoline on this trip.

S8.29. A baseball diamond is square measuring 90 feet on each side.   If a player can run at an average speed of 100 yards in 11 seconds, how many seconds would he require to make a home run, that is, run completely around the square diamond?

S8.30. A set of three equal volumes stands side by side on a bookshelf; volume I is to the left of volume II, volume III to the right of volume II.   How far is the first page of volume I from the last page of volume III, if each cover of each book is $\frac{1}{8}$ inch thick, if each book contains 800 pages, if each page is $\frac{1}{400}$ inch thick? (*Caution:* The distance is less than three inches.)

S8.31. Mr. *A* is employed at a beginning annual salary of $4,096, with an assured annual increase each successive year of one-sixteenth his previous yearly salary. Mr. *B* is hired at the same time at a beginning annual salary of $3,800 with an assured annual increase each successive year of one-tenth his previous annual salary.   If these men began service on January 1, 1968, in what year will Mr. *B*'s salary surpass Mr. *A*'s annual salary?   In how many complete years will Mr. *B*'s total earnings surpass those of Mr. *A*?

S8.32. Five north-south highways, 1 mile apart, intersect five east-west highways, also 1 mile apart.   At each intersection there are traffic signals that must be serviced once each month.   The inspector lives at the intersection of the two middle roads and inspects one intersectional system each day, returning home each evening.   How much total mileage does one complete inspection require?

S8.33. A *geometric progression* is a series of numbers in which each number after the first number is obtained by multiplying its predecessor by the same multiplier throughout the series. Thus, if a denotes the first term, m the common multiplier, and n the number of terms of the progression, and if $a = 3$, $m = 2$, and $n = 5$, the geometric progression is the series of numbers 3, 6, 12, 24, 48. Now write out the geometrical progressions for the indicated data:

a. $a = 5$, $m = 3$, $n = 4$ 　　　　c. $a = 81$, $m = -\frac{2}{3}$, $n = 5$

b. $a = 512$, $m = \frac{1}{2}$, $n = 10$ 　　d. $a = 160$, $m = 1\frac{1}{2}$, $n = 6$

S8.34. If $a = 3$ and $m = 2$, the second term is 3×2; the third term is $3 \times 2 \times 2$ or 3×2^2; the fourth term is $3 \times 2^2 \times 2$ or 3×2^3. Thus, the nth term is the product of the first term by a power of 2 which is 1 less than the n. For example the fifth term is 3×2^4, the twelfth term is 3×2^{11}, ... Or, quite generally, the nth term of the geometric progression whose first term is a and whose common multiplier is m must be $a \times m^{n-1}$. Now write these terms:

a. Fifth term of the geometric progression 7, 14, . . .

b. Sixth term of the geometric progression 5, 15, . . .

c. Eighth term of the geometric progression $\frac{3}{8}$, $\frac{3}{4}$, . . .

d. First term of the geometric progression if its fourth and fifth terms are 112, 224

e. Seventh term of the geometric progression 384, 192, . . .

S8.35. The sum S of all terms of the geometric progression may be expressed compactly, or in a "closed form," as follows:

Let $S = a + ar + ar^2 + \cdots + ar^{n-1}$ 　　　that is

$$S = \frac{(a + ar + ar^2 + ar^3 + \cdots + ar^{n-1})(r - 1)}{r - 1}$$

Multiplying out the numerator by use of the distributive law of multiplication and addition one obtains:

$$S = \frac{ar + ar^2 + \cdots + ar^n - a - ar - ar^2 - \cdots - ar^{n-1}}{r - 1}$$

which condenses to $S = \dfrac{ar^n - a}{r - 1}$

Now use this formula to verify the sums of the four geometric progressions in Problem S8.33.

S8.36. Discover a very simple rule to compute the sum of any number of consecutive terms of a *given* geometrical progression by dividing the difference between two terms of the progression by $r - 1$. Then apply the rule to compute: (a) the sum of all terms, (b) the sum of the four terms beginning with the third term, and (c) the sum of the first eight terms of each of the geometric progressions:

i.   1, 2, 4, 8, 16, 32, 64, 128, 256, 512, 1,024, 2,048

ii. 1, 3, 9, 27, 81, 243, 729, 2,187, 6,561, 19,683

iii. 1, 4, 16, 64, 256, 1,024, 4,096, 16,384, 65,536

iv. 1, 5, 25, 125, 625, 3,125, 15,625, 78,125, 390,625

S8.37. Discover a very simple rule for writing down immediately the sum of any number of consecutive terms of a geometric progression consisting of powers of a unit fraction, such as:

a. $\frac{1}{2}$, $\frac{1}{4}$, $\frac{1}{8}$, $\frac{1}{16}$, $\frac{1}{32}$, . . . 　　　c. $\frac{1}{4}$, $\frac{1}{16}$, $\frac{1}{64}$, $\frac{1}{128}$, $\frac{1}{512}$, . . .

b. $\frac{1}{3}$, $\frac{1}{9}$, $\frac{1}{27}$, $\frac{1}{81}$, $\frac{1}{243}$, . . . 　　d. $\frac{1}{6}$, $\frac{1}{36}$, $\frac{1}{216}$, $\frac{1}{1,296}$, . . .

Write down immediately the sums of the terms appearing in these four progressions.

S8.38. As the geometric progression in Problem S8.37a is extended indefinitely, the sum of the terms becomes ever nearer to 1. Obtain the number toward which the sum approaches in each of the other progressions in Problem S8.37, if the number of terms is increased indefinitely.

The following several problems deal with figurate numbers.

S8.39. The product of any natural number by itself is called a *square number*. The series of square numbers is: 1, 4, 9, 16, 25, 36, 49, 64, ... They are called square numbers because they represent the numbers of dots that can be arranged in a square array, as

a. Obtain the other square numbers that are smaller than 200.

b. Write the series of numbers that are the differences between consecutive square numbers. What kind of numbers are these differences?

c. By use of the information revealed in (b) write down immediately the remaining square numbers that are less than 1,000.

S8.40. Write the first 10 terms of the series that consists of the sums of the sets of the consecutive square numbers beginning with 1. Thus, letting 1 be the first term of the series, $1 + 4 = 5$ the second term, $1 + 4 + 9 = 14$ the third term, the series would appear as 1, 5, 14, ...

a. Extend this series to 10 terms.

b. If S represents the sum of the square numbers from 1 to n^2, then

$$S = \frac{n(n + 1)(2n + 1)}{6}$$

Verify this formula for the terms occurring in (a).

c. Compute the sum of the first 1,000 square numbers.

S8.41. The product of any natural number by its successor is called an *oblong* number. The series of oblong numbers is $1 \times 2, 2 \times 3, 3 \times 4, 4 \times 5, . . .$ or 2, 6, 12, 20, 30, 42, ... These numbers are called oblong numbers because they represent the numbers of dots that can be arranged in a rectangular array that is one unit longer than wide, as

a. Write the series that consists of the first 10 oblong numbers.

b. Write the series that consists of the differences between consecutive oblong numbers. What kind of numbers are these differences?

c. By use of the information revealed in (b) write down the series of oblong numbers that are less than 500.

S8.42. a. Write the first 10 terms of the series that consists of the sums of the sets of consecutive oblong numbers beginning with 2. Thus, letting 2 be the first term of this series, the second term must be $2 + 6 = 8$; the third term of the series must be $2 + 6 + 12 = 20$; hence the series appears as 2, 8, 20, 40, ...

b. If S represents the sum of the first n consecutive oblong numbers, beginning with 2, then

$$S = \frac{n(n + 1)(n + 2)}{3}$$

That is, the sum of n consecutive oblong numbers, beginning with 2, is equal to one-third of the product of three consecutive natural numbers, the smallest natural number being n.

c. Verify this formula for the sums of oblong numbers in (a).

d. Compute the sum of the first 1,000 oblong numbers.

S8.43. The halves of the oblong numbers are called *triangular* numbers. The series of consecutive triangular numbers is 1, 3, 6, 10, 15, ... These numbers are called triangular numbers because they represent the numbers of dots that can be arranged in a triangular array, as

. .   or   . .   etc.
. . .

a. Write the series of numbers that are differences between consecutive triangular numbers. What kind of numbers are they?

b. Write the series of numbers that are sums of two consecutive triangular numbers. What kind of numbers are they?

c. By use of the information revealed in (a) write down the first 20 triangular numbers.

d. Write down the two-thousandth triangular number immediately by noting its definition.

S8.44. a. Write the first 10 terms of the series that consists of the sums of the sets of consecutive triangular numbers, beginning with 1. Thus, letting 1 be the first term of this series, the second term must be $1 + 3 = 4$, the third term must be $1 + 3 + 6 = 10$; hence this series appears as 1, 4, 10, 20, ...

b. Now let S represent the sum of the first n terms of the series in (c); then

$$S = \frac{n(n + 1)(n + 2)}{6}$$

Verify this formula for $n = 3$, 4, and 5. Compute the sum of the first 1,000 triangular numbers.

S8.45. Consider the series consisting of reciprocals of the oblong numbers, namely,

$$\frac{1}{1 \times 2} \qquad \frac{1}{2 \times 3} \qquad \frac{1}{3 \times 4} \qquad \frac{1}{4 \times 5} \qquad . . .$$

a. Write out the first five terms of the series consisting of the sums of sets of consecutive terms of this series, beginning with $\frac{1}{1 \times 2}$, namely,

$$\frac{1}{1 \times 2} \qquad \frac{1}{1 \times 2} + \frac{1}{2 \times 3} \qquad \frac{1}{1 \times 2} + \frac{1}{2 \times 3} + \frac{1}{3 \times 4} \qquad . . .$$

evaluating each term of this new series. Then write down immediately the one-thousandth term of this new series.

   b. The astonishing fact revealed in (*a*) becomes clear if one writes out the series consisting of differences of consecutive unit fractions, namely, $\frac{1}{1} - \frac{1}{2}$, $\frac{1}{2} - \frac{1}{3}$, $\frac{1}{3} - \frac{1}{4}$, $\frac{1}{4} - \frac{1}{5}$, ... Now write down immediately the sum of the reciprocals of the first million oblong numbers.

S8.46.   *a.* If gold weighs $19\frac{1}{3}$ times as much as water, and if water weighs $62\frac{1}{2}$ pounds per cubic foot, calculate the weight of 1 cubic foot of gold.

   b. What would be the value of 1 cubic inch of gold if gold is worth $30 an ounce?   (16 ounces = 1 pound)

S8.47. In 1965 the average family income in Montgomery County, Md., was $9,317, as compared with $1,453 in Holmes County, Miss.   Comparison of these two average family incomes may be expressed fractionalwise as $\frac{1,453}{9,317}$.

   a. Which of the following fractions is most nearly equal to this ratio? $\frac{1}{6}$, $\frac{2}{13}$, $\frac{5}{32}$, $\frac{12}{77}$, $\frac{29}{109}$.

   b. Arrange these fractions in order of size.

   c. Which of these fractions are greater than $\frac{1,453}{9,317}$?

S8.48. In 1965 the total population of the United States was 179,323,175.   At that time the public debt was $286,741 million.

   a. How much would have been "each person's fair share" of the debt then?

   b. If this debt rose to $321,681 million by 1967, while the population increased by 20 million, what would have been each person's fair share of the debt in 1967?

S8.49. A set of numbers is said to be *closed under an operation,* if the operation and its result also involve only numbers of the set.   Under which of the operations of *addition, subtraction, multiplication, division,* and *involution* is each of the following sets of numbers closed?

   a. Natural numbers: 1, 2, 3, 4, 5, 6, 7, 8, 9, 10, 11, . . .

   b. Integers: . . . -5, -4, -3, -2, -1, 0, 1, 2, 3, 4, 5, . . .

   c. Even natural numbers: 2, 4, 6, 8, 10, 12, 14, . . .

   d. Odd integers: . . . -7, -5, -3, -1, 1, 3, 5, 7, . . .

   e. All proper fractions, positive and negative

   f. All square numbers: 1, 4, 9, 16, 25, 36, 49, . . .

   g. All rational numbers

S8.50. On a television program in Los Angeles, Calif., on Sunday, March 24, 1968, the following automobiles were offered for sale.   Calculate the total amount of interest and carrying charges a buyer would be expected to pay on each sale.

   a. $2,868 $717 down and $77 each month for 36 months

   b. $2,568 $642 down and $69 each month for 36 months

   c. $2,268 $567 down and $61 each month for 36 months

   d. $2,168 $542 down and $58 each month for 36 months

   e. $2,068 $517 down and $55 each month for 36 months

   f. $1,766 $ 61 down and $61 each month for 36 months

   g. $1,666 $ 58 down and $58 each month for 36 months

   h. $1,466 $ 51 down and $51 each month for 36 months

   i. $ 966 $ 34 down and $34 each month for 36 months

LESSON 9 ❧ EQUIVALENCE OF COMMON AND DECIMAL FRACTIONS ❧ PROPERTIES OF DECIMAL FRACTIONS

What's in a name?   That which we call a rose
By any other name would smell as sweet.

—Shakespeare, *Romeo and Juliet, II*, 1 (85).

9·1 ~ Some advantages of decimal fractions over common fractions

The fractions that occur in the previous lessons are known as common or vulgar fractions. The basic operations upon fractions are more complicated and more liable to errors than the corresponding operations upon integers. To avoid these troublesome operations upon fractions, one may use special forms of fractions known as *decimal fractions* which, except for one feature—the decimal point, look exactly like integers and are operated on as if they were integers. It will be observed in converting common fractions into their equivalent decimal fractional forms that *certain small errors sometimes arise*. But since these errors can be made as small as one may wish, but not equal to zero, and since the various computations made upon decimal fractions are as easy as computations of integers, and since the correctness of results of calculations made upon decimal fractions may be checked easily by tests (to be presented in Lesson 12) which are inapplicable to the results of calculations made upon common fractions, one will prefer in many instances to use decimal fractions rather than common fractions.

9·2 ~ Definition and symbolism of decimal fractions

A decimal fraction is a proper or improper fraction whose denominator is a power of 10. As the powers of 10 are $10^1 = 10$, $10^2 = 100$, $10^3 = 1,000$, $10^4 = 10,000$, . . . , there are as many zeros in any power of 10 as the exponent that indicates the particular power. Some examples of decimal fractions are: $\frac{7}{10}, \frac{539}{100}, \frac{3}{1,000}, \frac{3,937}{100}, \frac{31,416}{10,000}$.

The *symbol*, or form, of a decimal fraction is the numerator containing a dot called the *decimal point*, which is inserted before (to the left of) as many digits of the numerator as the specified power of 10 (the number of zeros) in the denominator. Thus, the appropriate symbols for the foregoing five examples of decimal fractions are:

0.7   The decimal point, . , is placed before *one* digit of the numerator, as the denominator is the *first* power of 10; a valueless 0 is also placed before the decimal point to emphasize its presence.

5.39   The point is placed to the left of *two* digits of the numerator, as the denominator is the *second* power of 10, containing two 0s.

0.003   As the denominator is the *third* power of 10, two 0s are inserted between the decimal point and the 3 to provide *three* digits to the right of the decimal point; again the extra 0 is placed to the left of the decimal point to emphasize its presence.

39.37   The decimal point is placed to the left of two digits, 37, as the denominator is the second power of 10. By federal statute in the United States 1 meter is *exactly* equivalent to 39.37 inches.

3.1416   As the denominator 10,000 is the *fourth* power of 10, *four* digits of the numerator appear to the right of the decimal point. The number 3.1416 is a very good approximation for the length of the circumference of a circle, if the diameter of the circle is 1.

9·3 ∾ CONVERTING A DECIMAL FRACTION TO ITS EQUIVALENT COMMON FRACTIONAL FORM

A decimal fraction may be reduced to, or expressed in, its *exactly* equivalent common fractional form by using *for its numerator* the decimal form without the decimal point and *for its denominator* the appropriate power of 10, namely, 1 followed by as many 0s as there are digits in the decimal form to the right of the decimal point. The common fraction so formed should be reduced to its lowest terms if it is so reducible. Thus,

$$0.28 = \tfrac{28}{100} = \tfrac{7}{25} \qquad 2.375 = \tfrac{2,375}{1,000} = \tfrac{19}{8} = 2\tfrac{3}{8}$$

9·4 ∾ CONVERTING A COMMON FRACTION TO ITS EQUIVALENT DECIMAL FRACTIONAL FORM

Only those common fractions which, in their lowest terms, have no prime factors other than 2 or 5 in their denominators have exactly equivalent decimal fractional forms, for only such denominators can be converted to powers of 10 by appropriately reducing the common fractions to higher terms. The common fraction $\tfrac{17}{40}$ does have an exactly equivalent decimal fractional form, as the denominator 40 has $2^3 \times 5$ for its prime factor form and contains *no other prime factor* than 2 and 5 (the fundamental theorem of arithmetic, S.17). Now

$2^3 \times 5$ may be made into the third power of 10 by multiplying it by 5^2, becoming thereby $2^3 \times 5^3$, or 10^3. Clearly, any natural number is a power of 10 if and only if its prime factor form contains the same number of 2s as 5s, since each individual pair of 2 and 5 yields 10 and each factor 10 in 10^n yields a single 2 and a single 5. Thus $10 = 2 \times 5$, $10^2 = 2^2 \times 5^2$, $10^3 = 2^3 \times 5^3$, and quite generally $10^n = 2^n \times 5^n$.

By multiplying the numerator and denominator of $\frac{17}{40}$ or $\dfrac{17}{2^3 \times 5}$ by 5^2, one

obtains $\dfrac{17 \times 5^2}{2^3 \times 5^2}$, or $\frac{425}{1,000}$, or 0.425 in appropriate form. Again, to reduce $\frac{19}{50}$ to its equivalent decimal form, one notes that the denominator 50 has the prime factor form 2×5^2; hence a single factor 2 is required to make the number of 2s and 5s the same. Hence, $\frac{19}{50} = \dfrac{19 \times 2}{50 \times 2} = \frac{38}{100} = 0.38$, the required exactly equivalent decimal fractional form.

The common fraction $\frac{5}{12}$ has no exactly equivalent decimal fractional form, since the denominator 12 in prime factor form, namely $2^2 \times 3$, contains the prime factor 3, which is different from 2 and 5. The presence of the prime factor 3 prevents the denominator 12 from ever becoming a power of 10 by raising the fraction $\frac{5}{12}$ to higher terms. Therefore, the fraction $\frac{5}{12}$ has no exactly equivalent decimal fractional form. It will be shown later in this lesson how to obtain decimal fractions that differ from $\frac{5}{12}$ by as small a number as desired, *but not zero*. To repeat, a common fraction may be converted into an *exactly* equivalent decimal fractional form if the denominator, when in lowest terms, has a factored form $2^m \times 5^n$ in which m or n (but not both m and n) may be 0. The number of digits to the right of the decimal point is m or n, whichever is the larger, or to both m and n if they are equal. No other common fraction has an exactly equivalent decimal fractional form.

∾ PROBLEMS ∾

9.1. Convert the given decimal fractions to their exactly equivalent common fractional form (or to mixed numbers) in their lowest terms:

a.	0.75	f.	0.00025	k.	456.45	p.	99.44
b.	0.85	g.	56.125	l.	0.095	q.	6.400
c.	0.5625	h.	7.15625	m.	0.102	r.	7.040
d.	9.875	i.	3.7	n.	0.092	s.	8.008
e.	0.0625	j.	0.35	o.	5.07	t.	0.055

9.2. By observing the prime factor forms of the following fractions, *in their lowest terms*, state which of them have exactly equivalent decimal fractional forms and how many digits must occur in their exactly equivalent decimal fractional forms. *Then* obtain the exactly equivalent decimal fractional forms.

a. $\frac{9}{16}$ *d.* $\frac{37}{625}$ *g.* $\frac{11}{320}$ *j.* $\frac{65}{28}$

b. $\frac{11}{24}$ *e.* $\frac{5}{15}$ *h.* $\frac{87}{48}$ *k.* $\frac{39}{128}$

c. $\frac{7}{125}$ *f.* $\frac{19}{55}$ *i.* $\frac{28}{65}$ *l.* $\frac{32}{125}$

9·5 ∽ Converting a common fraction to its equivalent decimal fractional form by division

The prescribed procedure for converting $\frac{37}{80}$ to its equivalent decimal fractional form suggests the convenient usual method of dividing the denominator into the numerator, supplying sufficient 0s to the right of the numerator to permit exact division; then the quotient is the required decimal form if a decimal point is placed before (to the left of) as many digits of the quotient as the number of 0s that were supplied to the numerator. The following discussion will show that this procedure is valid for $\frac{37}{80}$. It is to be noted that the same argument will apply to any other fraction which in its lowest terms has a denominator whose prime factor form contains no prime factor other than 2 or 5.

The denominator 80 has the prime factor form $2^4 \times 5$. Hence the fraction $\frac{37}{80}$, which is in its lowest terms, does have an exactly equivalent decimal fractional form as the prime factor form of 80 contains no prime factor other than 2 or 5.

Multiply the numerator and denominator of $\frac{37}{80}$ by 10^4, namely, the power of 10 that corresponds to the higher power of 2 or 5 that occurs in the prime factor form of the denominator 80. Hence

$$\frac{37}{80} = \frac{37 \times 10 \times 10 \times 10 \times 10}{2^4 \times 5 \times 10,000}$$

Now each 10, or 2×5, introduced into the numerator admits the cancellation of one 2 and one 5 of the original denominator 80, or $2^4 \times 5$. Exhibiting this cancellation

$$\frac{37 \times (2 \times 5) \times (2 \times 5) \times (2 \times 5) \times (2 \times 5)}{(2 \times 2 \times 2 \times 2 \times 5) \times 10,000} = \frac{37 \times 5^3}{10,000} = \frac{4,625}{10,000}$$

Thus it is clear that 37×10^4, or 370,000, is exactly divisible by 80.

$$\frac{37}{80} = \frac{37 \times 10,000}{80 \times 10,000} = \frac{370,000}{80 \times 10,000} = \frac{370,000 \div 80}{10,000} = \frac{4,625}{10,000} \quad \text{or} \quad 0.4625$$

Again, convert $\frac{9}{32}$ to its exact decimal fractional equivalent by the division method. Note that $32 = 2^5$. Supply *five* 0s and perform the division 900,000 ÷ 32 = 28,125. Therefore, $\frac{9}{32} = 0.28125$.

∾ PROBLEMS [CONTINUED] ∾

9.3. Obtain the exactly equivalent decimal fractional form for the following common fractions by the division method. Supply the precise number of 0s to the numerator (dividend) *before* beginning the division.

a. $\frac{39}{64}$ c. $\frac{7}{8}$ e. $\frac{37}{40}$ g. $\frac{13}{1,024}$

b. $\frac{26}{32}$ d. $\frac{123}{125}$ f. $\frac{311}{250}$ h. $\frac{399}{525}$

9·6 ∾ CONVERTING A MIXED DECIMAL FRACTION TO ITS EQUIVALENT COMMON FRACTIONAL FORM

A *mixed decimal fraction* is a decimal fraction followed immediately by a proper common fraction, for example, $1.6\frac{2}{3}$, $0.23\frac{5}{6}$, $0.00007\frac{8}{9}$. The common fractional portion of mixed decimal fractions, in these examples $\frac{2}{3}$, $\frac{5}{6}$, and $\frac{8}{9}$, do not occupy separate digit positions but share the position of the digit immediately to the left. The rule for converting a mixed decimal fraction to a common fraction is:

Remove the decimal point, divide the resulting number by the power of 10 which is equal to the number of digit spaces to the right of the decimal point in the original mixed decimal fraction.

Accordingly, $1.6\frac{2}{3} = \dfrac{16\frac{2}{3}}{10} = 16\frac{2}{3} \div 10 = \frac{50}{3} \times \frac{1}{10} = \frac{5}{3} = 1\frac{2}{3}$

$0.23\frac{5}{6} = \dfrac{23\frac{5}{6}}{100} = 23\frac{5}{6} \div 100 = \frac{143}{6} \times \frac{1}{100} = \frac{143}{600}$

$0.00007\frac{8}{9} = \dfrac{7\frac{8}{9}}{100,000} = 7\frac{8}{9} \div 100,000 = \frac{71}{9} \times \frac{1}{100,000} = \frac{71}{900,000}$

∾ PROBLEMS [CONTINUED] ∾

9.4. Convert the following mixed decimal fractions to their equivalent common fractions in their lowest terms, or to appropriate mixed numbers:

a. $1.33\frac{1}{3}$ g. $0.1\frac{3}{7}$ m. $10.00\frac{1}{3}$

b. $0.28\frac{4}{7}$ h. $1.\frac{3}{7} = 1\frac{3}{7}$ n. $0.000\frac{5}{7}$

c. $34.2\frac{5}{6}$ i. $7.7\frac{1}{2}$ o. $0.00\frac{3}{7}$

d. $0.06\frac{2}{3}$ j. $8.6\frac{1}{4}$ p. $0.00000\frac{3}{17}$

e. $6.6\frac{2}{3}$ k. $78.1\frac{3}{8}$ q. $0.000000000\frac{1}{3}$

f. $0.01\frac{3}{7}$ l. $0.5555\frac{5}{9}$ r. $0.142857\frac{1}{7}$

9·7 ↝ Conversion of common fractions to mixed decimal fractions

If a/b represents any common fraction, then a/b is clearly equal to $(a/b)(10^n) \div 10^n$ if n represents any natural number. This valid associative law of multiplication and division by any power of 10 provides the method of converting any common fraction to a mixed or unmixed decimal fraction. Thus,

$$\tfrac{5}{8} = \tfrac{5}{8} \times 10 \div 10 = \frac{\overset{5\,0}{\tfrac{8}{}}}{10} = \frac{6\tfrac{1}{4}}{10} = 0.6\tfrac{1}{4}$$

$$= \tfrac{5}{8} \times 100 \div 100 = \frac{\overset{5\,0\,0}{\tfrac{8}{}}}{100} = \frac{6\tfrac{1}{4}}{100} = 0.62\tfrac{1}{2}$$

$$= \tfrac{5}{8} \times 1{,}000 \div 1{,}000 = \frac{\overset{5\cdot0\,0\,0}{\tfrac{8}{}}}{1{,}000} = \tfrac{625}{1000} = 0.625$$

Accordingly, $\tfrac{5}{8} = 0.6\tfrac{1}{4} = 0.62\tfrac{1}{2} = 0.625$. Since the denominator is $8 = 2^3$, the fraction $\tfrac{5}{8}$ does have an equivalent *unmixed* decimal fractional form.

All equivalent decimal forms of $\tfrac{3}{7}$ must be *mixed* decimal fractions, since the denominator 7 is a prime number different from 2 and 5. Thus,

$$\tfrac{3}{7} = \tfrac{3}{7} \times 10 \div 10 = \frac{\overset{3\,0}{\tfrac{7}{}}}{10} = \frac{4\tfrac{2}{7}}{10} = 0.4\tfrac{2}{7}$$

$$= \tfrac{3}{7} \times 100 \div 100 = \frac{\overset{3\,0\,0}{\tfrac{7}{}}}{100} = \frac{42\tfrac{6}{7}}{100} = 0.42\tfrac{6}{7}$$

$$= \tfrac{3}{7} \times 1{,}000 \div 1{,}000 = \frac{\overset{3\,0\,0\,0}{\tfrac{7}{}}}{1{,}000} = \frac{428\tfrac{4}{7}}{1{,}000} = 0.428\tfrac{4}{7}$$

$$= \tfrac{3}{7} \times 10{,}000 \div 10{,}000 = \frac{\overset{3\,0\cdot0\,0\,0}{\tfrac{7}{}}}{10{,}000} = \frac{4{,}285\tfrac{5}{7}}{10{,}000} = 0.4285\tfrac{5}{7}$$

$$= \tfrac{3}{7} \times 100{,}000 \div 100{,}000 = \frac{42{,}857\tfrac{1}{7}}{100{,}000} = 0.42857\tfrac{1}{7}$$

The common fractional parts of the mixed decimal fractions, namely, $0.0\tfrac{2}{7}$, $0.00\tfrac{6}{7}$, $0.000\tfrac{4}{7}$, $0.0000\tfrac{5}{7}$, and $0.00000\tfrac{1}{7}$, may be evaluated respectively as follows:

$$0.0\tfrac{2}{7} = \frac{\tfrac{2}{7}}{10} = \tfrac{2}{7} \times 0.1$$

$$0.00\tfrac{6}{7} = \frac{\tfrac{6}{7}}{100} = \tfrac{6}{7} \times 0.01$$

$$0.000\tfrac{4}{7} = \frac{\tfrac{4}{7}}{1{,}000} = \tfrac{4}{7} \times 0.001$$

$$0.0000\tfrac{5}{7} = \frac{\tfrac{5}{7}}{10{,}000} = \tfrac{5}{7} \times 0.0001$$

$$0.00000\tfrac{1}{7} = \frac{\tfrac{1}{7}}{100{,}000} = \tfrac{1}{7} \times 0.00001$$

The actual value of these fractions depends upon how many digit spaces they occur from the decimal point and are equal to the product of that fractional part of a unit in the digit position immediately preceding the fraction; accordingly, $0.0\frac{2}{7}$ is less than 0.1; $0.00\frac{6}{7}$ is less than 0.01; $0.000\frac{4}{7}$ is less than 0.001; $0.0000\frac{5}{7}$ is less than 0.0001; $0.00000\frac{1}{7}$ is less than 0.00001. Consequently, if the fractional part of a mixed decimal fraction is omitted, the decimal fraction is diminished by less than a unit in the final digital position of the decimal fraction. Such considerations permit one to state that

$\frac{3}{7}$ is approximately equal to 0.4, with error less than 0.1
$\frac{3}{7}$ is approximately equal to 0.42, with error less than 0.01
$\frac{3}{7}$ is approximately equal to 0.428, with error less than 0.001
$\frac{3}{7}$ is approximately equal to 0.4285, with error less than 0.0001
$\frac{3}{7}$ is approximately equal to 0.42857, with error less than 0.00001

The foregoing decimal approximations for $\frac{3}{7}$ are all slightly smaller than $\frac{3}{7}$; one may also use decimal approximations for $\frac{3}{7}$ that are slightly larger than $\frac{3}{7}$ by increasing the final digit of the decimal fraction by 1, with the same indicated magnitude of error.

To obtain the *best* decimal fractional approximation for any common fraction, one should increase by 1 the final digit in the decimal fraction, if the common fractional part of the mixed fraction to be omitted is greater than $\frac{1}{2}$. The *best* decimal fractional approximations for $\frac{3}{7}$ for the indicated number of digits are 0.4, 0.43, 0.429, 0.4286, 0.42857.

To repeat, the *best* decimal approximation for the common fraction a/b, employing n digits to the right of the decimal point, is the quotient of $a \times 10^n \div b$, omitting the remainder if the remainder is less than half the divisor b or increasing by 1 the final digit of the quotient if the remainder is greater than half the divisor b.

Obtain the successive *best* decimal fractional approximations for the common fraction $\frac{9}{13}$. Note the successive remainders that are greater than 6, which occasion the increase of the corresponding digit in the quotient, for the corresponding decimal approximation of $\frac{9}{13}$.

		Corresponding best decimal approximation is:
0.692307		
13)9.000000		
78		
120	Note remainder 12	0.7
117		
30	Remainder 3	0.69
26		
40	Remainder 4	0.692
39		
1	Remainder 1	0.6923
100	Remainder 10	0.69231
91		
9	Remainder 9	0.692308

Მ PROBLEMS [CONTINUED] Მ

9.5. Obtain the *best* four-digit decimal approximation for each of the common fractions, i.e., with error less than 0.0001:

a. $\frac{8}{13}$ *c.* $\frac{12}{19}$ *e.* $\frac{4}{23}$ *g.* $\frac{11}{29}$ *i.* $\frac{3}{11}$

b. $\frac{16}{17}$ *d.* $\frac{5}{21}$ *f.* $\frac{3}{7}$ *h.* $\frac{7}{9}$ *j.* $\frac{529}{777}$

9·8 Მ Ʀᴇᴘᴇᴀᴛɪɴɢ ᴅᴇᴄɪᴍᴀʟ ꜰʀᴀᴄᴛɪᴏɴꜱ, ᴀʟꜱᴏ ᴄᴀʟʟᴇᴅ ᴘᴇʀɪᴏᴅɪᴄ ᴏʀ ᴄɪʀᴄᴜʟᴀᴛɪɴɢ ᴅᴇᴄɪᴍᴀʟ ꜰʀᴀᴄᴛɪᴏɴꜱ

If a fraction is in its lowest terms and if the prime factor form of the denominator is $2^m \times 5^n$ in which m or n (but not both m and n) may be 0, then the fraction has an exact equivalent decimal fraction form. Such decimal fractions are called *terminating* decimal fractions; the number of digits to the left of the decimal point is equal to the larger of the numbers m or n (Section 9.4). Contrariwise, if the prime factor form of the denominator of a fraction, in its lowest terms, contains one or more prime factors different from 2 or 5, the fraction cannot be converted to an exactly equivalent *unmixed* decimal fractional form. Each exactly equivalent decimal fractional form must be a *mixed* decimal fraction having any arbitrary number of digits to the right of the decimal point. Furthermore, each appended common fraction at the right end of the mixed decimal fraction cannot have a numerator larger than the denominator of the original fraction. Sooner or later an appended fraction must recur in the array of mixed decimal fractions that are listed in order of the increasing number of digits that they contain. Therefore, if the decimal fractional form is indefinitely extended toward the right from the decimal point, the very same array of digits must recur that did occur between the first two identical appended fractions.

EXAMPLES Მ

Obtain the successive exactly mixed decimal fractions for the common fractions $\frac{5}{7}$, $\frac{111}{175}$, and $\frac{101}{296}$.

1. $\frac{5}{7} = 0.\frac{5}{7}$*   Observe the first repetition of an appended common
      $= 0.7\frac{1}{7}$ fraction, the $\frac{5}{7}$, marked by *. Therefore, if the decimal
      $= 0.71\frac{3}{7}$ expression were indefinitely extended, the same set of
      $= 0.714\frac{2}{7}$ digits, 714285, must continually recur. The repeating
      $= 0.7142\frac{6}{7}$ portion of the extended decimal form is called its
      $= 0.71428\frac{4}{7}$ *period* and is identified by the overline.
      $= 0.714285\frac{5}{7}$*

Therefore, $\frac{5}{7} = 0.\overline{714285}714285714285$ . . . , the dots indicating that the decimal may be extended without end.

2. $\frac{111}{175} = 0.\overset{.}{1}\frac{111}{175}$

     $= 0.6\frac{12}{35}$

     $= 0.63\frac{3}{7}$ *

     $= 0.634\frac{2}{7}$

     $= 0.6342\frac{6}{7}$

     $= 0.63428\frac{4}{7}$

     $= 0.634285\frac{5}{7}$

     $= 0.6342857\frac{1}{7}$

     $= 0.63428571\frac{3}{7}$ *

Again note the first reappearance of the appended fraction $\frac{3}{7}$, marked by *. The six new digits evolving in the decimal fraction between these two same appended fractions constitute the *period* of the decimal fraction, for this same set of digits must always recur between consecutive recurrences of $\frac{3}{7}$ as the appended common fraction.

Accordingly, the decimal fraction form for $\frac{111}{175}$ is 0.63$\overline{428571}$ . . . . The dots indicate that the period, indicated by the line over 428571, continues to recur without change.

3. $\frac{101}{296} = 0.\overset{.}{2}\frac{101}{296}$

     $= 0.3\frac{61}{148}$

     $= 0.34\frac{9}{74}$

     $= 0.341\frac{8}{37}$ *

     $= 0.3412\frac{6}{37}$

     $= 0.34121\frac{23}{37}$

     $= 0.341216\frac{8}{37}$ *

     $= 0.3412162\frac{6}{37}$

     $= 0.34121621\frac{23}{37}$

     $= 0.341216216\frac{8}{37}$ *

Note again the first reappearance of an appended fraction, the $\frac{8}{37}$ marked by *, which identifies the three new digits in the decimal fraction as the period 216. Note also the repetition of new digits 216 from the second to the third occurrence of the $\frac{8}{37}$ *. The decimal fractional form of $\frac{101}{296}$ is 0.341$\overline{216}$ . . . .

It is to be noted that the decimal fractional period of $\frac{5}{7}$ begins at the decimal point, while the period of $\frac{111}{175}$ begins after the *second* digit following the decimal point, and the period of $\frac{101}{296}$ begins after the *third* digit following the decimal point. These latter two decimal fractions are called *delayed* repeating decimal fractions. These delays are caused by the presence of the factors 2 or 5 in the prime factor forms of the denominator. Thus, $175 = 7 \times 5^2$ and $296 = 37 \times 2^3$ (Section 9.9).

ᴘ PROBLEMS [CONTINUED] ᴖ

9.6. Obtain the equivalent decimal fractional forms of the following common fractions, overlining the period in each decimal fraction:

a. $\frac{13}{37}$	*e.* $\frac{5}{9}$	*i.* $\frac{7}{11}$	*m.* $\frac{9}{28}$
b. $\frac{5}{7}$	*f.* $\frac{8}{13}$	*j.* $\frac{7}{17}$	*n.* $\frac{17}{24}$
c. $\frac{2}{7}$	*g.* $\frac{1}{13}$	*k.* $\frac{5}{19}$	*o.* $\frac{123}{175}$
d. $\frac{7}{9}$	*h.* $\frac{2}{13}$	*l.* $\frac{19}{23}$	

Note that the period begins at the decimal point if the denominator does not contain the prime factors 2 or 5; observe also the delay in the period of those listed in (*m*), (*n*), (*o*). Why must the number of digits in the period be less than the denominator of the corresponding common fraction?

p. $\frac{17}{21}$ *r.* $\frac{16}{27}$ *t.* $\frac{14}{33}$

q. $\frac{37}{49}$ *s.* $\frac{11}{39}$ *u.* $\frac{64}{77}$

9.7. Convert to decimal fractions, correctly overlining the period. Account also for the delay of the period in each decimal fraction.

a. $\frac{11}{52}$ *d.* $\frac{123}{484}$ *g.* $\frac{1}{6}$ *j.* $\frac{625}{10,000}$

b. $\frac{19}{75}$ *e.* $\frac{7}{15}$ *h.* $\frac{119}{150}$

c. $\frac{23}{28}$ *f.* $\frac{5}{6}$ *i.* $\frac{72}{8,000}$

9·9 ∽ Delayed periodic decimal fractions

Nonterminating Decimal Fractions. The period of the decimal fractional form of the proper fraction a/p, if p is a *prime number*, begins at the decimal point.

Since $a/2$ and $a/5$ yield terminating decimal fractions, p cannot be 2 or 5, so that p cannot be an exact divisor of 10. The successive digits of the nonterminating decimal fraction that is equivalent to a/p, represented by $a_1, a_2, a_3, \ldots$, are obtained by successive steps in the division of $a \times 1000 \cdots 0$ by p. Let each successive remainder in the division algorithm be represented by $r_1, r_2, r_3, \ldots$.

The successive steps in the division provide the relationships between the individual digits of the decimal fractional form (the quotient) and the corresponding numerical remainders, as follows:

$$a = p \times 0 + a$$
$$10a = pa_1 + r_1$$
$$10r_1 = pa_2 + r_2$$
$$\cdots \cdots \cdots$$
$$10r_{k-1} = pa_k + r_k$$
$$\cdots \cdots \cdots \cdots$$
$$10r_{k+h-1} = pa_{k+h} + r_{k+h}$$
$$\cdots \cdots \cdots \cdots \cdots$$

Now if the first remainder to recur is a, the period must begin with a_1 at the decimal point; however, suppose that the first remainder to recur is r_k which recurs h steps later as r_{k+h}, so that $r_{k+h} = r_k$, so that the period must begin with the digit a_{k+1}.   Subtract

$$10r_{k-1} = pa_k + r_k$$
$$10r_{k+h-1} = pa_{k+h} + r_{k+h}$$
$$\overline{10r_{k-1} - 10r_{k+h-1} = pa_k - pa_{k+h}} \qquad \text{(Since } r_{k+h} = r_k\text{)}$$

This answer, by the distributive law, becomes $10(r_{k-1} - r_{k+h-1}) = p(a_k - a_{k+h})$. The two numbers represented by the expressions on the two sides of the sign of equality, $=$, are the same number.   Since p is a factor of the right side number, p must be a factor, or exact divisor, of $r_{k-1} - r_{k+h-1}$.   Since each remainder is less than p, this difference between two of them must also be less than p.   Therefore, $r_{k-1} - r_{k+h-1}$ must be 0 to be exactly divisible by p.   Thus, $r_{k-1} = r_{k+h-1}$, so that r_k is *not* the first remainder to recur, thereby making the period begin at the decimal point for the fraction a/p, if p is a prime number other than 2 or 5.

Delayed Period.   The period of the decimal fraction form of the proper fraction, in its lowest terms, $\dfrac{a}{2^m \times 5^n \times q}$, if q is not divisible by 2 or 5, is *delayed* by m or n digits, whichever is the larger.   Suppose that m is larger than n.   Then multiply the numerator and denominator of the given fraction by 5^{m-n}, obtaining

$$\frac{5^{m-n} \times a}{2^m \times 5^m \times q} \qquad \text{or} \qquad \frac{A}{10^m \times q} \qquad \text{or} \qquad \frac{A/q}{10^m}$$

Since q does not contain 2 or 5 as factors, the numerator A/q may be reduced to a periodic (repeating) decimal fraction whose period $a_1, a_2, \ldots, a_k$ begins at the decimal point.   Hence the fraction $(A/q)/10^m$ may be reduced to the following fraction:

$$\frac{c_1 c_2 c_3 \; \cdots \; c_m.a_1 a_2 a_3 \; \cdots \; \overline{a_k a_1 a_2 a_3 \; \cdots \; a_k a_1 a_2} \; \cdots}{10^m}$$

The period is overlined, beginning at the decimal point; some or all the consecutive c's beginning at the left end may be 0.

Finally, to remove the 10^m from the denominator, one must divide the numerator and denominator by 10^m.   Dividing the numerator by 10^m moves the decimal point m digit spaces toward the left, so that the original fraction $\dfrac{a}{2^m \times 5^n \times q} = 0.c_1 c_2 c_3 \; \cdots \; c_m \overline{a_1 a_2 a_3 \; \cdots \; a_k} \; \cdots$.   Thus the period is delayed m digit spaces from the decimal point.

If n is larger than m, one multiplies numerator and denominator of $\dfrac{a}{2^m \times 5^n \times q}$ by 2^{n-m}.   Similar argument shows that the period is delayed in this case n digital spaces from the decimal point, as n is here supposed to be larger than m.

9·10 ∽ TWO REMARKABLE PROPERTIES OF THE PERIOD OF A DECIMAL FRACTION WHOSE EQUIVALENT COMMON FRACTION, IN ITS LOWEST TERMS, CONTAINS IN ITS DENOMINATOR ONLY ONE PRIME FACTOR p THAT IS DIFFERENT FROM 2 OR 5

(1) The number of digits in the period is an exact divisor of $p - 1$.   (2) If the number of digits in the period is even, the number obtained by adding the two equal halves of the period consists of nines only.

Consider the decimal fractional form for $\frac{27}{52}$.   Note that the denominator, $52 = 2^2 \times 13$, contains $p = 13$.

```
      0.51923076
  52|27.00000000
    260
    ‾‾‾
    100
     52
    ‾‾‾
    480*
    468
    ‾‾‾
    120
    104
    ‾‾‾
    160
    156
    ‾‾‾
    400
    364
    ‾‾‾
    360
    312
    ‾‾‾
    48*     48* is the recurring remainder, determining the period
            923076
```

The number of digits in the period, 6, is an exact divisor of 12, as p here is 13 and $p - 1 = 12$.   Add the two equal halves of the period $923 + 076 = 999$. These two properties of such periods are established in the supplement, S.19.

∽ **P**ROBLEMS [CONTINUED] ∽

9.8.   Verify the first two statements of Section 9.10 for the fractions in Problems 9.6 and 9.7.   For which of these 31 fractions are these statements inapplicable?

9.9. *a.* Add the common fractions $\frac{3}{7}$, $\frac{2}{13}$, and $\frac{3}{17}$ by using lowest common denominator.

b. Obtain the best four-digit decimal approximations of each of these three fractions. Now add these approximations as if they were integers, keeping the decimal points in vertical line under one another.

c. Obtain the best four-digit decimal approximation of the common fraction obtained in (*a*).

d. Which of the two sums (*a*) or (*c*) is the more accurate as the sum of the three common fractions? Which was more laborious?

9.10. *a.* Obtain the periods of the decimal fractional forms for $\frac{1}{7}$, $\frac{2}{7}$, $\frac{3}{7}$, $\frac{4}{7}$, $\frac{5}{7}$, and $\frac{6}{7}$. What curious relationship have these six periods to one another?

b. Repeat the investigation upon the set of 12 proper fractions having denominator 13.

9·11 ∿ THREE APPROPRIATE METHODS OF READING DECIMAL FRACTIONS

Reading Digits in Order. The simplest method of reading a decimal expression is to state in order, from left to right, the names of the digit symbols occurring and also to pronounce the word "dot" or "point" for the decimal point at its place in the decimal expression; for a mixed decimal expression, one pronounces the word "and" just before reading the final appended common fraction in its customary way.

One may read 34,397.80331 as "three four three nine seven point eight zero three three one." One may read $105.46\frac{2}{3}$ as "one zero five period four six and two-thirds."

The two other methods of reading decimal expressions require a knowledge of the "principle of position," or "place value" of the digital positions, and the names of the individual digit positions in every decimal expression. Thus, $83,704.49287\frac{3}{4}$ means the indicated sum:

$$8 \times 10^4 + 3 \times 10^3 + 7 \times 10^2 + 0 \times 10 + 4 + \frac{4}{10} + \frac{9}{10^2} + \frac{2}{10^3} + \frac{8}{10^4} + \frac{7\frac{3}{4}}{10^5}$$

The value of any digital position of the decimal expression is 10 times as great as the position immediately on its right. This feature persists throughout decimal positions endlessly in both directions, decimal positions becoming indefinitely large toward the left, indefinitely small toward the right. Beginning at the decimal point, the digit place values are named toward the left, successively, units, tens, hundreds, thousands, ten thousands, hundred thousands, millions, etc.; toward the right the digit place values are named successively, tenths, hundredths, thousandths, ten thousandths, hundred thousandths, millionths, etc.

Reading Decimal Fractions as Natural Numbers. In this most commonly used method, one reads two individual numbers separated by the decimal point as if they were ordinary natural numbers, or as a natural number and a mixed number, supplying these two additions: one pronounces the word "and" between the reading of the two portions separated by the decimal point; one pronounces the name of the position occupied by the right end digit of the decimal fractional form.

One reads 145,678.69,547,301 as "one hundred forty-five thousand, six hundred seventy-eight *and* sixty-nine million, five hundred forty-seven thousand, three hundred one *hundred millionths.*"

In reading a *mixed* decimal expression, such as 43,500.3,556$\frac{3}{8}$, one pronounces the word "and" before the appended fraction $\frac{3}{8}$ somewhat less vigorously than the *and* for the decimal point. This decimal expression would be read as "forty-three thousand, five hundred *and* three thousand, five hundred fifty-six and three-eighths *ten thousandths.*"

Reading Digit Sets. This method is the logical extension of the method of reading natural numbers; the sets of digits are marked off in sets of threes in both directions from the decimal point. One reads the entire decimal expression from left to right, pronouncing the name of each set of digits. Again, the extreme sets of digits may include only one or two digits, as well as three digits; in reading the final right end set of digits the name of the final digit space on the right is named. Likewise the conjunction *and* is used for the decimal point and before the appended common fractional part of a mixed decimal expression.

To illustrate, one reads, with appropriate comma placements, 23.567,010$\frac{2}{3}$ as twenty-three *and* five hundred sixty-seven thousandths, ten and two-thirds millionths; 1,023.765,16$\frac{5}{7}$ as one thousand, twenty-three *and* seven hundred sixty-five thousandths, sixteen and five-sevenths hundred thousandths; 30,000.000,2 as thirty thousand *and* two ten thousandths.

↬ PROBLEMS [CONCLUDED] ↫

9.11. Write out fully the names of the following decimal expressions in accordance with the foregoing three methods.

a.	34.765	*g.*	0.0001$\frac{2}{3}$
b.	203040.50607	*h.*	0.00$\frac{4}{5}$
c.	65477090.12345678	*i.*	0.000$\frac{5}{6}$
d.	9866.2$\frac{3}{5}$	*j.*	0.0000$\frac{7}{8}$
e.	34.56$\frac{7}{8}$	*k.*	1002000050.0500201
f.	190.358$\frac{7}{12}$	*l.*	1.420$\frac{3}{8}$

9.12. Write the decimal fractional expressions that would be read by the logical method described last in the foregoing section.

    a. One thousand, thirty-six *and* sixty-three and two-thirds hundredths

    b. One billion, two hundred *and* twenty-six and one-fifth thousandths

    c. Thirty-six thousand *and* thirty-five and two-fifths millionths

    d. Three *and* one hundred forty-one thousandths, six ten thousandths

    e. One *and* four hundred fourteen thousandths, two hundred fourteen millionths

    f. One hundred forty-two thousandths, eighty-five and one-seventh hundred thousandths

*N*ote 1 ∽ *Scientific notation.*

One may express extremely large or extremely small numbers by the use of positive or negative powers of 10. The mass of the earth is estimated to be approximately 6,000,000,000,000,000,000,000 long tons. (A long ton is equal to 2,200 pounds.) This large number, read as "six sextillion" in the United States, may be concisely written as 6×10^{21}. Again, the length of a light year is approximately 5,880,000,000,000 miles, namely, five trillion, eight hundred eighty billion miles. In scientific notation this number appears as 5.88×10^{12}. The number of years required for a radioactive substance to disintegrate to half its present amount is called its *half-life*. The half-life of uranium is 4.5×10^9, or 4,500,000,000 years.

A convenient unit for expressing extremely small lengths is the angstrom, represented by Å, and defined as one-hundred-millionth of a centimeter. This small unit of length has been named in honor of the Swedish physicist A. J. Angstrom, 1814–74. Otherwise expressed, 100,000,000 Å = 1 cm = 0.393,7 inches *exactly*, by definition. Thus, green light in a mercury spectrum has a wavelength of 0.000,054,61 centimeters, or 5,461 Å, since 1 Å = 10^{-8} cm. Other extreme measurements are the following:

1. The diameter of the nucleus of a gold atom is 10^{-12} cm, or 10^{-4} Å.

2. The distance from center of sun to center of earth averages very slightly more than 93,000,000 miles, or 93×10^6 miles.

3. The mass of a hydrogen atom, consisting of its center proton and its revolving electron, is calculated to be 1.662×10^{-24} grams; the mass of the electron alone at rest is 9.11×10^{-28} grams; the least radius of the electron in its orbit around the proton, or nucleus, is 0.5×10^{-8} cm, or $\frac{1}{2}$ Å.

4.   The probability of any particular player receiving 13 cards of the same suit, i.e., all hearts, all spades, all diamonds, or all c'ubs, in one dealing of a shuffled standard deck of cards among four players, is approximately 192.3×10^{-50}.

*N**ote 2 ⤙ Some mysteries cleared by rational operations upon numbers.*

The operations of addition, subtraction, multiplication, and division are called the *rational operations.*   From the definitions of these four operations as applied to rational numbers, it is now understood that:

If any rational number is added to, subtracted from, multiplied by, or divided by, any rational number, the result of the operation is always one correct rational number, except for division by zero, which is impossible in arithmetic.

The universal validity of the foregoing statement enables one to clarify a great variety of intriguing arithmetical problems, such as the following.

Jack Dudley's Numerical Puzzle.   Jack challenges his classmate to:

1.   "Think of any number.

2.   Double it.

3.   Add 8 to your result.

4.   Divide what you now have by 2.

5.   Subtract the number you started with.

6.   And now I know that your answer is 4," said Jack, astonishing his friends.

How did Jack know the correct answer?   Jack repeated his challenge, and in step (3) he directed his classmate to add other numbers, such as 12, 6, 14, and called out correctly in each case the correct result, such as 6, 3, 7, respectively.

"Oh, I see," exclaimed little Lummy Risdale, "your answer is just half of what you tell us to add."

"Not so fast," cried Jack, clapping his hand over Lummy's mouth, "you'll give away my secret."

By way of explanation, each successive step yields only one correct number, which is known to Jack's schoolmate but which is *not* known to Jack, except the number that the final step (6) yields.

1.   Let N represent the original number, unknown to Jack.

2.   Doubling N yields $2N$.

3. Adding the number represented by k, *which is known to Jack*, yields the sum $2N + k$; this sum is not known to Jack.

4. Dividing $2N + k$ by 2 yields $N + \frac{1}{2}k$.

5. Subtracting the original number N from $N + \frac{1}{2}k$ yields $\frac{1}{2}k$. Since Jack did know the number he directed his classmate to add in step (3), represented here by k, he surely knows the value of $\frac{1}{2}k$.

If Jack had directed his friend in step (2) to multiply by some other number, represented by m, and in step (4) to divide by m, the final number he should call out in step (5) must be k/m. The successive steps are: (1) N; (2) mN; (3) $mN + k$; (4) $N + k/m$; (5) $(N + k/m) - N$, or k/m.

To repeat, each step involves a rational operation upon numbers, which must yield one correct result; when Jack finally knows the result of step (5) it must be the only possible correct number and hence must be the same number that is in his classmate's mind.

Captain Lindenburn's Card Trick. The captain distributes the cards of an ordinary shuffled deck into separate piles, all face down. Each picture card counts as 10, the other cards according to the number on them, the ace as 1, deuce as 2, etc. The captain directs someone to place one card face down, noting its number. Mentally calling this card by its number, he is to count off additional cards, all face down, counting them by ensuing numbers until he reaches 12. Thus, if the first card were 8, he would place ensuing cards on it all face down, counting them mentally as "nine," "ten," "eleven," "twelve," thereby putting altogether five cards on this pile. He continues to form other piles in the same way until the entire deck is exhausted, or until he has remaining insufficient cards to form another pile by this counting process. Thereupon the captain notes the number of piles, all face down, and the number of unused cards, and promptly calls out the *sum of the numbers on the bottom cards* of all of the piles. How did he do this? The explanation is as follows:

Each bottom card on each finished pile has a specific number, which the captain cannot know. Let these individual numbers be represented by A, B, C, . . . , K. Without knowing these individual numbers, the captain can obtain the *sum* of them, represented by $A + B + D + \cdots + K$. He does know the number of piles, represented by N, which he determines simply by counting the piles. He must be told also the number of unused cards, which is represented by U. The captain knows there are thirteen each of four kinds of cards in the deck.

Each pile has a specific number of cards in it, namely, $13 - A$, $13 - B$, $13 - C$, . . . , $13 - K$. As there are exactly N piles, the total number of cards in these N piles must be the sum $(13 - A) + (13 - B) + (13 - C) + \cdots + (13 - K)$; these N numbers may be regrouped as $N \times 13 - A - B - C - \cdots - K$, or $N \times 13 - (A + B + C + \cdots + K)$.

The total number of cards in the N piles, added to the number of unused cards, U, must equal the total number of cards in the deck, namely, 52, or 4×13. Therefore, the two numbers, as *underlined*, must be *the same number; i.e.,*

$$\underline{4 \times 13} = \underline{13N - (A + B + C + \cdots + K) + U}$$

Adding the number represented by $(A + B + C + \cdots + K) - 4 \times 13$ to this same number in the two forms, as underlined, one again obtains the same number in the two different forms on opposite sides of the sign of equality, $=$. Thus,

$$\underline{4 \times 13 + (A + B + C + \cdots + K) - 4 \times 13}$$
$$= \underline{13N - (A + B + C + \cdots + K) + U + (A + B + C + \cdots + K)}$$
$$- 4 \times 13$$

Since $4 \times 13 - 4 \times 13 = 0$, $13N - 4 \times 13 = 13(N - 4)$, and $(A + B + C + \cdots + K) - (A + B + C + \cdots + K) = 0$, this lengthy expression condenses to $(A + B + C + \cdots + K) = 13(N - 4) + U$, which is the symbolic solution for the captain's puzzling trick.

To determine the sum of the bottom cards in the layout, one must diminish the number of piles by 4, obtaining $N - 4$; multiply this difference by 13; add to this product the number of unused cards. The final number so obtained is the required sum of the numbers on the bottom cards.

*N*ote 3 ⚭ *Terminating and repeating (periodic) forms for fractions using a base different from 10.*

In any system of numbers employing a base different from 10, the fractions that are analogous to the decimal fractions are those fractions whose denominators are powers of the base of the number system. For the specific base, 2, 3, 4, $\ldots$, these fractions are referred to respectively as binary fractions, ternary fractions, quaternary fractions, etc., or, quite generally, as *basal* fractions. These basal fractions in lowest terms have the same properties as the terminating and repeating decimal fractions, as explained in these four statements:

1. If the denominator of the fraction contains no other prime factors than the *prime factors of the base*, the basal fraction is terminating. Such basal fractions contain as many digits to the right of the basal point as the largest power of these primes that are present.

2. If the denominator contains prime factors different from the prime factors contained in the base, the basal fraction is a repeating, or periodic, basal fraction. The presence of prime factors of the base also in the denominator

causes the period to be delayed by as many digits as the highest power of these prime factors of the base of the number system.

3. If the denominator contains *only one prime factor*, besides possibly powers of the prime factors of the base of the number system, and if the period contains an *even* number of digits, then the sum of the two equal halves of the period consists entirely of the digit that is one less than the base of the number system.

4. If the denominator contains only one prime factor, p, besides possibly powers of the prime factors of the base of the number system, the number of digits in the period of the basal fraction must be an exact divisor of $p - 1$.

EXAMPLES ᠊ᢗᠸᠤ

Verify the four foregoing statements with the examples below.

Binary system: 1, 10, 11, 100, 101, 110, 111, 1000, 1001, . . .

Statement 1. $\frac{1}{2}$ converts to $\frac{1}{10} = 0.1$

              $\frac{3}{4}$ converts to $\frac{11}{100} = 0.11$

              $\frac{13}{16}$ converts to $\frac{1101}{10000} = 0.1101$

Statement 2. $\frac{43}{60}$ converts to $\frac{101011}{111100} = 0.101101 \ldots$

              $\frac{11}{120}$ converts to $\frac{1011}{1111000} = 0.0001011 \ldots$

Statements 3, 4. $\frac{13}{20}$ converts to $\frac{1101}{10100} = 0.101001 \ldots$

              $10 + 01 = 11$.   5 is the only prime factor of 20; 4 must be an exact divisor of $5 - 1$.

Ternary system: 1, 2, 10, 11, 12, 20, 21, 22, 100, 101, 102, 110, . . .

Statement 1. $\frac{5}{9}$ converts to $\frac{12}{100} = 0.12$

              $\frac{11}{27}$ converts to $\frac{102}{1000} = 0.102$ (Terminating basal fractions)

Statement 2. $\frac{17}{30}$ converts to $\frac{122}{1010} = 0.12002 \ldots$ (Delayed period)

Statements 3, 4. $\frac{19}{63}$ converts to $\frac{201}{2100} = 0.02201021 \ldots$

              7 is the only prime factor of 63 other than powers of 3. Period 201021 has six digits.   Therefore, 6 must be an exact divisor of $7 - 1$.   Moreover, $201 + 021 = 222$.

Septimal system: 1, 2, 3, 4, 5, 6, 10, 11, 12, 13, 14, 15, 16, 20, . . .

              The decimal fraction $\frac{1}{13}$ (base 10) takes the form $\frac{1}{16}$ when expressed in the system of base seven.

Statements 3, 4. $\frac{1}{13}$ converts to $\frac{1}{16} = 0.\overline{035245631421} \ldots$

The septimal period 035245631421 contains 12 digits; 12 is an exact divisor of the denominator less 1, or 12.   Again, the sum of the two halves of the period, $035245 + 631421 = 666666$, a number consisting of 6s only, as 6 is one less than the base 7.

In dividing 1.000,0 . . . by 16 to obtain the septimal fractional form for $\frac{1}{16}$, it is convenient to exhibit the six multiples of 16 (Section 8.7).

```
Multiples of
 the divisor        0.035245631421
  1    16       16|1.000000000000
  2    35          54
  3    54          130
  4   103          122
  5   122           50
  6   141           35
                   120
                   103
                    140
                    122
                     150
                     141
                      60
                      54
                      30
                      16
                     110
                     103
                      40
                      35
                      20
                      16
                       1
```

If the denominator contains a single prime factor that does not occur in the base of the employed number system, then these two remarkable properties are present:

The number of digits in the period is an exact divisor of one less than that single prime factor.

If the number of digits of the period is even, the sum of the two equal halves of the period must consist entirely of the digit that is one less than the base itself.

These two statements are proved in the Supplement (S.19) for base 10. The proofs can readily be modified to apply to any legitimate base; i.e., to any natural number except 1.

Contrariwise, these properties of the period must identify a number as composite, if either relationship fails to be true. The period of $\frac{1}{143}$ is 006993, and

$006 + 993 = 999$, but the number of digits of the period, namely six, is not an exact divisor of 142. Therefore, 143 cannot be a prime number ($143 = 11 \times 13$). Again, $\frac{1}{259} = 0.\overline{003,861}$ . . . . Since $003 + 861 - 864 \neq 999$, the number 259 cannot be prime ($259 = 7 \times 37$).

To recapitulate, if p is a prime number, then: (1) The number of digits in the decimal (basal) period of $1/p$ must be an exact division of $p - 1$. (2) If the number of digits in the period is even, the sum of two equal portions of the period must consist of 9s only. (If the number p is expressed in number system of base b, the period must consist of the digit $b - 1$ only.)

These two tests are merely *necessary* tests for the primality of any natural number N; i.e., if either test fails, N cannot be prime. These tests are not sufficient for primality of N; i.e., both tests may be met for some composite numbers.

Thus $\frac{1}{91} = 0.\overline{010,989}$ . . . . Here $010 + 989 = 999$, and the number of digits of the period, 6, is an exact divisor of $91 - 1$, or 90, as $90 \div 6 = 15$. But $91 = 7 \times 13$. However, the tests show 91 to be composite by using another base, such as 6. For base 6 one has $\frac{1}{231} = 0.\overline{002,212,411,525}$. Now both tests show the number cannot be prime, since $002212 + 411525 = 414141$, not consisting of 5s only. The number of digits of the period is not an exact divisor of 90 (90 is not exactly divisible by 12).

⁓ CHALLENGES

1. By investigation of the decimal period of $\frac{1}{N}$, show that N cannot be a prime number, if N is: (*a*) 111, (*b*) 133, (*c*) 899.

2. Show that the following numbers cannot be prime: (*a*) 9,331, (*b*) 435,356,-467. (*Hint:* use system of numbers with base 6.)

3. Examine for primality: (*a*) 8,403, (*b*) 6,725,601. (*Hint:* change to base 7.)

⁓ SUPPLEMENTARY PROBLEMS ⁓

Jabberwocky
'*Twas brillig, and the slithy toves*
Did gyre and gimble in the wabe;
All mimsy were the borogroves,
And the mome raths outgrabe.

—Lewis Carroll, *Through the Looking-Glass.*

S9.1. Reduce to decimal fractional forms, overlining the periods of the repeating decimal fractions:

a.	$\frac{1}{2}$	*h.*	$\frac{1}{9}$	*n.*	$\frac{1}{15}$	*t.*	$\frac{1}{21}$
b.	$\frac{1}{3}$	*i.*	$\frac{1}{10}$	*o.*	$\frac{1}{16}$	*u.*	$\frac{1}{22}$
c.	$\frac{1}{4}$	*j.*	$\frac{1}{11}$	*p.*	$\frac{1}{17}$	*v.*	$\frac{1}{23}$
d.	$\frac{1}{5}$	*k.*	$\frac{1}{12}$	*q.*	$\frac{1}{18}$	*w.*	$\frac{1}{24}$
e.	$\frac{1}{6}$	*l.*	$\frac{1}{13}$	*r.*	$\frac{1}{19}$	*x.*	$\frac{1}{25}$
f.	$\frac{1}{7}$	*m.*	$\frac{1}{14}$	*s.*	$\frac{1}{20}$	*y.*	$\frac{1}{26}$
g.	$\frac{1}{8}$						

S9.2. Using the periods obtained in S9.1*f*, *p*, *r*, and with no computations whatever, list in order the decimal forms for all proper fractions having the denominators: (*a*) 7, (*b*) 17, (*c*) 19.

S9.3. Using the periods obtained in S9.1*h*, *j*, and with a minimum of computation, list the decimal forms for all proper fractions having the denominators: (*a*) 9, (*b*) 11.

S9.4. Obtain the periods of the six unit fractions whose denominators contain two of the primes 3, 7, 11, 13, namely, $\frac{1}{21}$, $\frac{1}{33}$, $\frac{1}{39}$, $\frac{1}{77}$, $\frac{1}{91}$, $\frac{1}{143}$. Test their periods for the two properties of Section 9.9.

S9.5. Obtain the periods of the three unit fractions whose denominators contain three of the primes 3, 7, 11, 13, namely, $\frac{1}{231}$, $\frac{1}{273}$, $\frac{1}{429}$, and $\frac{1}{1001}$. Test their periods for the two properties of Section 9.9.

S9.6. Obtain the periods of the fractions whose denominators are powers of:

a. 3, namely, $\frac{1}{9}$, $\frac{1}{27}$, $\frac{1}{81}$

b. 7, namely, $\frac{1}{49}$, $\frac{1}{343}$

c. 11, namely, $\frac{1}{121}$, $\frac{1}{1331}$

Test their periods for the two properties of Section 9.9.

S9.7. Obtain the mixed decimal fractional forms to *thousandths* for:

a.	$\frac{3}{7}$	*d.*	$\frac{4}{13}$	*g.*	$\frac{10}{21}$	*j.*	$\frac{11}{27}$	*m.*	$\frac{17}{30}$
b.	$\frac{5}{9}$	*e.*	$\frac{6}{17}$	*h.*	$\frac{12}{23}$	*k.*	$\frac{13}{28}$	*n.*	$\frac{21}{31}$
c.	$\frac{7}{11}$	*f.*	$\frac{8}{19}$	*i.*	$\frac{14}{25}$	*l.*	$\frac{15}{29}$	*o.*	$\frac{25}{33}$

S9.8. Obtain the *best* decimal fractional forms, to the nearest ten thousandth:

a.	$\frac{355}{113}$	*d.*	$\frac{1.111}{1.331}$	*g.*	$\frac{231}{361}$
b.	$\frac{113}{355}$	*e.*	$\frac{6.677}{8.300}$	*h.*	$\frac{555}{778}$
c.	$\frac{101}{131}$	*f.*	$\frac{3.800}{6.677}$	*i.*	$\frac{143}{1.001}$

S9.9. Obtain the exact unmixed decimal fractional form for the fractions:

a.	$\frac{411}{625}$	*d.*	$\frac{1.274}{8.125}$	*g.*	$\frac{91}{520}$
b.	$\frac{101}{128}$	*e.*	$\frac{1.001}{9.100}$	*h.*	$\frac{111}{148}$
c.	$\frac{123}{250}$	*f.*	$\frac{3.157}{7.700}$	*i.*	$\frac{473}{550}$

The fractions listed in (*d*) to (*i*), inclusive, have prime factors in their denominators that are different from 2 and 5. Do the results conflict with Section 9.4? Why not?

S9.10. Convert to equivalent common fractional form in lowest terms:

a. 0.15	*f.* 0.45	*k.* 0.75	*p.* 0.375	*u.* 0.525
b. 0.2	*g.* 0.5	*l.* 0.80	*q.* 0.625	*v.* 0.575
c. 0.25	*h.* 0.55	*m.* 0.85	*r.* 0.875	*w.* 0.675
d. 0.35	*i.* 0.6	*n.* 0.95	*s.* 0.325	*x.* 0.725
e. 0.40	*j.* 0.65	*o.* 0.125	*t.* 0.475	*y.* 0.775

S9.11. Convert to equivalent common fractional form in lowest terms:

a. $0.33\frac{1}{3}$	*f.* $0.16\frac{2}{3}$	*k.* $0.55\frac{5}{9}$	*p.* $0.52\frac{16}{17}$
b. $0.03\frac{1}{3}$	*g.* $0.83\frac{1}{3}$	*l.* $0.07\frac{7}{9}$	*q.* $0.76\frac{12}{13}$
c. $0.6\frac{2}{3}$	*h.* $0.06\frac{1}{4}$	*m.* $0.888\frac{8}{9}$	*r.* $0.56\frac{2}{3}$
d. $0.666\frac{2}{3}$	*i.* $0.18\frac{3}{4}$	*n.* $0.57\frac{1}{7}$	*s.* $0.111\frac{1}{9}$
e. $0.31\frac{3}{4}$	*j.* $0.56\frac{1}{4}$	*o.* $0.93\frac{3}{4}$	*t.* $0.86\frac{2}{3}$

S9.12. Reduce to the equivalent mixed number in lowest terms:

a. Fifty-eight *and* eight and four-seventeenths tenths

b. Fifty-eight *and* eighty-two and six-seventeenths hundredths

c. Fifty-eight *and* eight hundred twenty-three and nine-seventeenths thousandths

d. Fifty-eight *and* eight hundred twenty-three thousandths, five and five-seventeenths ten thousandths

e. Fifty-eight *and* eight hundred twenty-three thousandths, fifty-two and sixteen-seventeenths hundred thousandths

f. Fifty-eight *and* eight hundred twenty-three thousandths, five hundred twenty-nine and seven-seventeenths millionths

g. Fifty-eight *and* eight hundred twenty-three thousandths, five hundred twenty-nine millionths, four hundred eleven billionths, seven hundred sixty-four and twelve-seventeenths trillionths

S9.13. Point off with commas and write out the names in accordance with the last two methods of Section 9.11.

a. 3.3872	*e.* 78501.10587	*i.* $6805520.0255086\frac{2}{3}$
b. 38.80379	*f.* 667789.8974284	*j.* $45656723.85685611\frac{5}{12}$
c. 138.09783	*g.* $3114.4113\frac{3}{4}$	*k.* $3000.00002\frac{3}{4}$
d. 4009.3007	*h.* $64537.78546\frac{7}{8}$	*l.* $3141633.9786756\frac{1}{2}$

S9.14. Examine the period of the basal form of $\dfrac{1}{p}$ for the properties given in Section 9.9 for bases other than 10 for the indicated values of p and specified bases. Thus,

For $p = 17$, b (base) = 2, one has $\frac{1}{10001} = 0.\overline{00001111} \ldots$

For base 3, 17 appears as 122, whence $\frac{1}{122} = 0.\overline{0011202122110201} \ldots$

For base 4, 17 appears as 101, whence $\frac{1}{101} = \overline{0.0033} \ldots$

For base 5, $\frac{1}{17}$ appears as 32, whence $\frac{1}{32} = 0.0121340243231042 \ldots$

a. $p = 5, b = 2, 3, 4, 6$

b. $p = 7, b = 2, 3, 4, 5, 6, 8, 9$

c. $p = 11, b = 2, 3, 4, 5, 6, 7, 8, 9$;
   $10 = t, 11 = u$ for base 12

d. $p = 13, b = 2, 3, 4, 5, 6, 7, 8, 9, 11, 12$

e. $p = 17, b = 15$, in which t, u, v, w, x represent, respectively, digit symbols for numbers 10, 11, 12, 13, 14

S9.15. If the decimal period of $\frac{1}{p}$, if p is prime, consists of an even number of digits, then if the first half of the period is multiplied by $p - 1$, and the resulting product is increased by $p - 2$, the resulting difference is the second half of the period. Thus, if $\frac{1}{7} = 0.142,857 \ldots$, then $6 \times 142 + 5 = 857$.

a. Verify this property of the decimal periods for $\frac{1}{13}, \frac{1}{101}, \frac{1}{17}$.

b. Verify this property for the basal periods of the fractions in the previous problem for the various bases indicated there.

S9.16. A repeating decimal fraction may be regarded as an unending geometric progression (Problem S8.35). For example, $\frac{1}{37} = 0.\overline{027,027} \ldots$ or $0.027 + 0.000,027 + 0.000,000,027 + 0.000,000,000,027 \ldots$, which may be written as $0.027(1 + 0.001 + 0.001^2 + 0.001^3 + \cdots)$. The sum of n terms of a geometric progression is given by the formula $S = \dfrac{a(1 - r^n)}{1 - r}$ wherein a represents the first term, n the number of terms, and r the common multiplier. If r is less than 1, r^n becomes ever nearer to zero as n is increased in value. If n becomes indefinitely large, r^n must become indefinitely small if r is less than 1, as it is for the repeating decimals. If a represents the period of a repeating decimal consisting of k digits, and if the period is not delayed but starts at the decimal point, the repeating decimal fraction may also be represented by $\dfrac{a(1 - 0)}{1 - (0.1)^k}$ or simply as $\dfrac{a}{0.999 \ldots 9}$ in which the decimal point is included with the period, and there are k 9s in the denominator. This affords an easy way of converting an undelayed repeating decimal fraction to its equivalent common fractional fraction. Thus $0.\overline{027} \ldots = \frac{0.027}{0.999} = \frac{1}{37}$ in lowest terms. Using this procedure obtain the common fractional equivalents of:

a. $0.\overline{135,135,135} \ldots$ (Note that the period is 135)

b. $0.\overline{009,900,990,099} \ldots$

c. $0.\overline{108,910,891,089} \ldots$

d. $0.\overline{144,144,144} \ldots$

e. $0.\overline{128,712,871,287} \ldots$

Check resulting common fraction by reconverting it to a decimal fraction.

S9.17. Obtain the equivalent common fractional form in lowest terms, and check results.

a. $0.\overline{243} \ldots$

b. $0.\overline{72} \ldots$

c. $0.\overline{259} \ldots$

d. $0.\overline{037} \ldots$

e. $0.\overline{538,461} \ldots$

f. $0.\overline{461,538} \ldots$

g. $0.\overline{384,615} \ldots$

h. $0.\overline{153,846} \ldots$

i. $0.\overline{207} \ldots$

j. $0.\overline{300,6} \ldots$

k. $0.\overline{445,5} \ldots$

l. $0.\overline{554,4} \ldots$

S9.18. Show that if the period of a decimal fraction consists of 1 digit, the *prime* denominator of the equivalent common fraction must be 3. If the decimal period is

d, the common fractional equivalent must be $\dfrac{d}{9}$; the only *prime* factor of 9 is 3,

thus, the only composite denominator of a common fraction in its lowest terms that yields a decimal fraction of undelayed period of one digit must be 9. Check this statement for the decimal forms for $\frac{1}{3}, \frac{2}{3}, \frac{1}{9}, \frac{2}{9}, \frac{4}{9}, \frac{5}{9}, \frac{7}{9}$, and $\frac{8}{9}$.

S9.19. Show that only common fractions in their lowest terms that yield repeated undelayed decimal fractions whose period contains exactly two digits are those whose denominators are 11, 33, and 99.

S9.20. Obtain the only possible denominators of fractions in their lowest terms that yield undelayed periodic decimal fractions whose period consists of exactly: (*a*) three digits, (*b*) four digits, (*c*) five digits, (*d*) six digits.

S9.21. Obtain all possible denominators of binary fractions in their lowest terms whose undelayed period consists of: (*a*) one digit, (*b*) two digits, (*c*) three digits, (*d*) four digits, (*e*) five digits, (*f*) six digits, (*g*) seven digits, (*h*) eight digits.

S9.22. Solve Problem S9.21 if the fractions are expressed in the number system of base: (*a*) 3, (*b*) 4, (*c*) 5, (*d*) 6, (*e*) 7, (*f*) 8, (*g*) 9, (*h*) 11, using t to denote the digit 10.

S9.23. Obtain the periods of the decimal fractions for $\frac{1}{37}, \frac{1}{31}, \frac{1}{43}$. These periods do not contain an even number of digits. However, the *number* of digits in the period is divisible by three. Add the three equal sections of these periods to discover the curious property of such periods.

S9.24. By consideration of various periods of repeating fractions arising from common

fractions $\dfrac{1}{p}$, for p a prime number, complete the statement: If the decimal

period of $\dfrac{1}{p}$, for p a prime number, consists of n digits, and if $n = ab$, then the

sum of the equal sections of the period, each section consisting of b digits, consists of . . . , or of . . . .

S9.25. Show that $1 = 0.999 \ldots .$ Then show how to write down immediately the decimal period for $(p - h)/p$ from the known period of h/p. How does this apply for bases other than 10?

LESSON 10 ❧ THE FOUR RATIONAL OPERATIONS WITH DECIMAL FRACTIONS

A little onward lend thy guiding hand
To these dark steps, a little farther on . . .

—John Milton, *Samson Agonistes*, lines 1, 2.

10·1 ∞ THE DECIMAL POINT ASSIGNS POSITIONAL VALUES AS POSITIVE AND NEGATIVE POWERS OF TEN

One observes that the location of the decimal point determines the positional values of all digits in any integer or decimal fraction. For example, in the decimal fraction 87,542.631, the digit immediately to the *left* of the point, the 2, is in the *units* position and represents 2 itself; the next digit to its left, the 4, is in the *tens* position and here represents the value 40 or 10 fours; the 5 is in the *hundreds* position and here represents the value 500 or 100 fives; the next ensuing positions to the left, occupied by the 7 and the 8, are in the *thousands* and *ten-thousands* positions, as was outlined in Lesson 9.

Now the first digit to the *right* of the decimal point, the 6, is in the *tenths* position and here represents $\frac{6}{10}$; the next digit to the right, the 3, is in the *hundredths* position and here represents $\frac{3}{100}$; the 1 is in the *thousandths* position and here represents $\frac{1}{1000}$, as was presented in Lesson 9. By this convenient device the basic characteristic of the decimal numeration for natural numbers is extended to decimal fractions, namely, each digit occupies a position in the decimal expression that is 10 times as valuable, or as large, as the adjoining position on its right. The digit 2 in the foregoing illustration would have the value 20 if it were in the position occupied by the 4; the digit 1, which represents $\frac{1}{1000}$, or 0.001, would have the value 0.01 or $\frac{1}{100}$ if it were in the position of the 3. Likewise the digit 3, which denotes a value of 0.03 or $\frac{3}{100}$, would have the value of 0.3 or $\frac{3}{10}$, or be 10 times as great if it were in the position occupied by 6.

10·2 ∞ ADDITION AND SUBTRACTION OF DECIMAL FRACTIONS

The extension of the important positional feature of natural numbers to the digits on the right of the decimal point in decimal fractions allows one to perform addition and subtraction of decimal fractions in the same algorithm as that of natural numbers themselves; i.e., in performing the individual additions or subtractions upon the digits in the same digital positions. This is facilitated by placing the decimal fractions in a vertical column with the decimal points under one another. Supplying the valueless zeros on the right of the several decimal fractions to make them all of equal extent is equivalent to reducing the fractional portions to a common denominator. For an example of addition add the numbers 1.43, 0.236,4, 84.717, and 0.001,62.

$$
\begin{array}{lllll}
1.43 & \text{or} & 1.430,00 & \text{or} & 1\frac{43,000}{100,000} \\
0.236,4 & & 0.236,40 & & \frac{23,640}{100,000} \\
84.717 & & 84.717,00 & & 84\frac{71,700}{100,000} \\
\underline{0.001,62} & & \underline{0.001,62} & & \frac{162}{100,000} \\
86.385,02 & & 86.385,02 & & 86\frac{38,502}{100,000}
\end{array}
$$

Placing the summands (numbers to be added) in a vertical column with the decimal points directly under one another makes the insertion of zeros on the right unnecessary; however, for horizontal addition, the insertion of zeros is highly convenient to preserve one's perspective, if one underlines the individual digits as one adds them (note Problem 2.22).

For an example of subtraction, subtract 7.693,8 from 84.051.

$$
\begin{array}{lllll}
84.051 & \text{or} & 84.051,0 & \text{or} & 84\frac{510}{10,000} \\
\underline{7.693,8} & & \underline{7.693,8} & & 7\frac{6,938}{10,000} \\
76.357,2 & & 76.357,2 & & 76\frac{3,572}{10,000}
\end{array}
$$

The observations regarding the insertion of zeros on the right are also true for both vertical and horizontal subtraction.

10·3 ~ Multiplication and division of decimal fractions

The following examples will provide appropriate simple rules of operation.

EXAMPLES ~

1. Multiply 1.732,4 by 46.6. Replacing these two decimal expressions by their equivalent common improper fractional forms, one has

$$
\frac{17,324}{10,000} \cdot \frac{466}{10} = \frac{8,072,984}{100,000} = 80.729,84
$$

Here the multiplication of the common fractions is performed in accordance with the definition (Section 6.12), and the reconversion of the common fraction in the product is then made to its decimal form (Section 9.2). The rule for multiplication of decimal fractional expressions is:

Multiply the numbers without regard for the decimal point; then point off in the product from the right as many digits as the sum of the number of digits pointed off from the right in the two original numbers.

In this example:

  4   Number of digits pointed off in the multiplicand
+1   Number of digits pointed off in the multiplier
  5   Number of digits pointed off in the product

2. Divide 80.729,84 by 4.66. Performing the indicated operation upon the equivalent common fractional forms, one has

$$\frac{8,072,984}{100,000} \div \frac{466}{100} = \frac{8,072,984}{100,000} \frac{100}{466}$$

or, cancelling equal powers of 10 from numerators and denominators,

$$\frac{8,072,984}{100,0\cancel{00}} \frac{1\cancel{00}}{466} = \frac{8,072,984 \div 466}{1,000} = \frac{17,324}{1,000} = 17.324$$

3. Divide 655.36 by 1.28 using equivalent common fractional forms:

$$\frac{65,536}{100} \div \frac{128}{100} = \frac{65,536}{1\cancel{00}} \frac{1\cancel{00}}{128} = \frac{65,536}{128} = 512$$

4. Divide 6553.6 by 0.0512 using equivalent common fractional forms:

$$\frac{65,536}{10} \div \frac{512}{10,000} = \frac{65,536}{1\cancel{0}} \frac{10,0\cancel{00}}{512} = \frac{65,536,000}{512} = 128,000$$

The rule for division of decimal fractional expressions is:

Divide the dividend by the divisor without regard for the decimal point; then point off in the quotient from the right as many digits as difference obtained by subtracting the number of digits pointed off from the right in the divisor from the number of digits pointed off from the right in the dividend.

In example (2): $5 - 2 = 3$; in example (3): $2 - 2 = 3$. However, in example (4), the number of digits pointed off in the divisor is *greater* than the number of digits pointed off from the right in the dividend; accordingly, one may supply as many valueless zeros to the right of the dividend as needed to equal the number of digits pointed off in the divisor. Thus, one has $6553.600,0 - 0.051,2 = 65,536,000 - 512 = 128,000$. Incidentally, if the number of digits pointed off from the right in the dividend and divisor is the same, the decimal point can be completely ignored in the division.

5. Obtain the *best* possible quotient, to the nearest 0.001, of 12.732 by 56.83. Supply to the right of the dividend enough valueless zeros so that the dividend contains three more digits pointed off than the divisor. Then obtain the quotient according to the foregoing rules. Again, if the remainder in the division is greater than half the divisor, the final digit of the quotient is increased by 1.

$$
\begin{array}{r}
0.224 \\
\overline{56.83\,)\,12.73200} \\
11366 \\
\hline
13660 \\
11366 \\
\hline
22940 \\
22732 \\
\hline
208
\end{array}
$$

Since the remainder 208 is less than half of 5683, the remainder is ignored. Accordingly, $12.732 \div 56.83 = 0.224$, with inaccuracy less than 0.0005.

◦◦ PROBLEMS ◦◦

10.1. Add the following sets of positive decimal fractions:

a.	56.098	7.964,3	0.000,34	9.070,5	56
b.	2.718,2	3.141,6	0.301	0.477,1	0.497,2
c.	67.432	98.999	76.401	99.99	2.000,1

d. Add the three foregoing sums.

10.2. Perform the indicated subtractions:

a. $45.003 - 39.772$ *d.* $56.009 - 60$

b. $10 - 8.764,09$ *e.* $37.987,6 - 45.687,65$

c. $9.987,65 - 5.889,98$ *f.* $7,142.85 - 28,571.4$

10.3. Add (algebraically) the following sets of decimal expressions:

a.	98.65	-439.4	78.098	$-2,345.87$	$-1,024.785,4$
b.	89.698	777.01	$-1,000.99$	98.453	35.829
c.	198.765,4	-78.009	-56.5	6,000	$-7,175.367,5$

10.4. Perform the indicated multiplications:

a. 4.76×1.032 *d.* $(-23.75)(-23.45)$

b. $(-811.79)(-0.023)$ *e.* $1.732,051^2$

c. $0.002,01 \times (-1,001)$ *f.* $(-1.25)^4$

10.5. Perform the following exact divisions:

a. $84.76 \div 16.3$ *d.* $(-19.784,49) \div 3.949$

b. $(-19.785,9) \div (-0.653)$ *e.* $0.165,9 \div 7,900$

c. $2,646.4 \div 0.082,7$ *f.* $8.07 \div 134.5$

10.6. Perform the following divisions to obtain the *best* quotients to the nearest 0.001:

> *a.* 8.765 ÷ 9.651   *d.* 2 ÷ 56.8
> *b.* 56.98 ÷ 6.998   *e.* 100.654 ÷ 49
> *c.* 0.006,75 ÷ 1.098   *f.* 0.000,007 ÷ 0.000,012,5

10.7. Arrange in order of size from left to right, beginning with the smallest: $\frac{34}{55}$, $\frac{55}{89}$, $\frac{76}{123}$, $\frac{21}{34}$. (*Hint:* Convert to decimals.)

10.8. If the length of our standard solar day (now 24 hours long) continues to increase at the present rate of 0.002 seconds per century, in how many years will the day become exactly twice as long as it now is? One century is equal to 100 years.

10·4 ∾ THE REDUCTION OF REPEATING (PERIODIC) DECIMAL FRACTIONS TO THEIR EQUIVALENT COMMON FRACTIONAL FORMS

It is to be noted that all equivalent common fractions have the identical equivalent decimal fractional form. If two equivalent common fractions *did* have different decimal fractional forms, one would have as the two equivalences:

$a/b = 0.d_1d_2d_3d_4 \ldots$
$ka/kb = 0.e_1e_2e_3e_4 \ldots$

wherein the *d*'s and *e*'s represent the digits in the two different decimal fractional expressions. Now if these two decimal expressions were different, their difference would not be equal to zero; one would then have

$$0 = a/b - ka/kb = (0.d_1d_2d_3 \ldots) - (0.e_1e_2e_3 \ldots) = N \neq 0$$

an absurd statement that N is both equal to zero and not equal to zero. All equivalent common fractions must have the same equivalent decimal fractional form. The decimal fraction that is equivalent to each fraction of the set of fractions that are equivalent to a/b must be a periodic decimal fraction, if a/b in its lowest terms contains at least one prime factor that is different from 2 and 5.

Contrariwise, every periodic decimal fraction (pure or delayed) is equivalent to a unique (only one) common fraction in its lowest terms. This important fact is established by use of the principle of the uniqueness of results of the rational operations (Section 9.13).

The present discussion is limited to the determination of a common fraction that is equivalent to the delayed decimal fraction 0.260135135135 . . . . It should be clear that the procedure here used is also applicable in determining a common fraction that is equivalent to any other periodic decimal fraction.

Now let N represent a common fraction that hopefully is equivalent to 0.260,135,135,135 . . . . Note that the period contains 3 digits, 135. Then $10^3 \times N$ would be equal to 260.135,135,135 . . . . Now if N were equal to 0.260,135,135 . . . , then by subtraction, $10^3 N - N$, or $999N$, should be equal to 259.875,000,000 . . . .   Now if $999N = 259.875$, then N must be equal to $\frac{259.875}{999}$ or $\frac{259.875}{999,000}$ or $\frac{77}{296}$ in its lowest terms.   Consequently, if 0.260,135,135 . . . were equivalent to any common fraction in its lowest terms, that fraction must be $\frac{77}{296}$.   But $\frac{77}{296}$ has a unique decimal fractional equivalent; hence $\frac{77}{296}$ must be equivalent to 0.260,135,135 . . . , as may be verified by reducing $\frac{77}{296}$ to its decimal fractional equivalent form.

To repeat, one may obtain the equivalent common fraction in its lowest terms for any repeating decimal fraction, as follows:

1. Multiply the decimal fraction by 10^n, wherein n is equal to the number of digits in the period; i.e., remove the decimal point n digits toward the right.

2. Subtract the original decimal fraction from the result in (1).

3. Form the fraction whose numerator is the result in (2), and whose denominator is equal to $10^n - 1$, or the natural number consisting of n nines.

4. Multiply the numerator and denominator of the fraction formed in (3) by 10^d wherein d is equal to the number of digits between the decimal point and the period in the original decimal fraction.

5. Reduce to lowest terms the fraction obtained in (4).

Moreover, if the given periodic decimal fraction were not a *delayed* periodic decimal fraction, d would be equal to zero in step (4), so that one could obtain immediately an equivalent common fraction by using the period for its numerator and using for the denominator the natural number consisting of n nines, wherein n is equal to the number of digits of the period.   Thus,

$$0.428,571,428,571 \ldots = \frac{428571}{999999} \quad \text{or} \quad \frac{3}{7} \text{ in lowest terms}$$

As a final illustration,

$$0.000,545,454 \ldots = \frac{54}{99000} = \frac{3}{5500}$$

One may thus obtain an equivalent common fraction for a delayed periodic decimal fraction if m zeros occur between the decimal point and the period by using the period for its numerator (let the period consist of n digits) and using for the denominator the natural number consisting of n nines followed by m zeros.

∾ PROBLEMS [CONTINUED] ∾

10.9.   Reduce to the equivalent common fraction in lowest terms:

a. 0.272,727 . . .	c. 0.393,939 . . .	e. 0.878,787 . . .
b. 0.403,740,37 . . .	d. 0.185,185 . . .	f. 0.090,909 . . .

Use the five-step method of reducing the delayed decimal fractions to verify the correctness of the immediately preceding two-step method:

g.   0.000,727,272 . . .   h.   0.006,363,63 . . .   i.   0.000,011,11 . . .

10.10. Obtain equivalent common fractions in their lowest terms:

    a. 0.625,636,363 . . .   *d.* 0.123,451,11 . . .

    b. 0.832,730,730 . . .   *e.* 0.870,456,363,63 . . .

    c. 0.425,727,272 . . .   *f.* 0.372,121,212 . . .

10·5 ∽ Rational numbers versus irrational numbers

A rational number is any number that can be expressed as a common fraction, i.e., as an indicated quotient of two integers. Hence, every common fraction, proper or improper, and every terminating or repeating decimal fraction, is a rational number. Contrariwise, a decimal fraction that does not terminate nor repeat periodically cannot be a rational number. Positions are to be provided on the number line for all these irrational numbers (Section 11.8).

A very important irrational number to be encountered in many unexpected—and surprising—mathematical situations is that number representing the length of the circumference of the circle whose diameter is represented by one. This famous irrational number is represented by the Greek letter π, equivalent to our letter p, for *perimeter* of the circle of diameter *one*. The letter π is pronounced generally as "pi." Modern electronic computers can very quickly supply as many digits as one may wish for this irrational number. Working out as far as the sixty-fourth digit to the right of the decimal point, one finds that

π = 3.141,592,653,589,793,238,462,643,383,279,502,884,197,169,399,375,
105,820,974,944,592,3 . . .

10·6 ∽ Four very important formulas involving π that pertain to circles and spheres

Valid proofs of the ensuing relationships are to be found in books dealing with plane and solid geometry. These formulas are to be accepted here without proof of their assured universal validity and are to be used with complete confidence.

Circumference of a Circle. The number of units of length in the circumference (boundary) of every circle (in inches, feet, centimeters, miles, etc.) is equal to the product of the number of units of length in its diameter (in inches, feet, centimeters, miles, etc., respectively) times π. To facilitate the memory, this relationship is expressed symbolically as $C = \pi d$. Here C denotes the number of units of length in the circumference and d the number of the *same* units of length in the diameter. If r represents the number of the same units of length in the radius, and as $d = 2r$, the formula $C = \pi d$ may also occur as $C = 2\pi r$.

Area of a Circle. The number of units of area enclosed within the circumference of a circle (in square inches, square feet, etc.) is equal to the product of the *square* of the number of units of length in the radius (in inches, feet, etc., respectively) by π.

In symbols, if A represents the number of units of area within the circle, $A = \pi r^2$. Now, as $r = \frac{1}{2}d$, then $r^2 = (\frac{1}{2}d)^2 = \frac{1}{4}d^2$, one has also $A = \frac{1}{4}\pi d^2$.

Surface of a Sphere. The number of units of area on the surface of a sphere (a perfectly round ball) is exactly four times as large as the number of units of area within a circle whose diameter is equal to the diameter of the sphere. Thus, if S equals the number of units of area on the surface of a sphere and r and d the number of corresponding length units in the radius and diameter, respectively, the symbolic relationships are

$$S = 4\pi r^2 \qquad \text{and} \qquad S = \pi d^2$$

Volume of a Sphere. The number of units of volume contained within a sphere (in cubic inches, cubic feet, etc.) is equal to the product of one-sixth of π multiplied by the *cube* of the number of corresponding units of length in the diameter (in inches, feet, etc., respectively). Thus, if V equals the number of units of volume comprising the sphere and r and d the number of corresponding units of length of the radius and diameter, respectively, the relationships appear symbolically as

$$V = \frac{1}{6}\pi d^3 \qquad \text{and} \qquad V = \frac{4}{3}\pi r^3$$

If the radius of a circle is 5 inches, its circumference is $2 \times 5 \times \pi$ inches, or 10π inches. Its area is equal to $5^2\pi$ square inches, or 25π square inches.

If the diameter of a sphere is 12 centimeters in length, the area of the sphere must be $12^2\pi$ square centimeters, or 144π square centimeters. The volume of this same sphere must be $\frac{1}{6} \times 12^3\pi$ cubic centimeters, or 288π cubic centimeters.

To express the foregoing two answers decimally one must use *approximate* values of π; these results cannot be expressed *exactly* in terms of proper or improper fractions; one must be content with an approximate result. However, the approximation may be made as good as desired (but not perfect) by using sufficient digits to the right of the decimal point for π.

➤ PROBLEMS [CONCLUDED] ➤

10.11. Which is the most accurate of the following three commonly used approximations for π? *Hint:* Convert them to decimal fractional form and note how many of their digits agree with the expression for π that is given above correct to sixty-four digits to the right of the decimal point. (*a*) $\frac{22}{7}$, (*b*) 3.141,6, (*c*) $\frac{355}{113}$.

10.12. Obtain the area of the circle if its radius is: (*a*) 14 inches, (*b*) 35 feet, (*c*) 1.25 yards. Use the approximation 3.141,6 for π in these three examples.

10.13. Obtain the circumferences of the three circles in Problem 10.12, using the same approximation for π.

10.14. Compute the area of the sphere whose radius is: (*a*) 6 feet, (*b*) 2.15 inches, (*c*) 1.102 centimeters. Use $\pi = 3.141,6$.

10.15. Compute the volumes of the three spheres in Problem 10.14, using the same approximate value for π.

10.16. What is the weight of a medicine ball that is 5 feet in diameter if it is made of cork that weighs $14\frac{3}{4}$ pounds per cubic foot? Use $\pi = 3.141,6$.

10.17. *a.* How many iron balls of 2 inches diameter can be packed into a cubical box 1 foot long, 1 foot wide, and 1 foot high in its inside dimensions if the balls are packed evenly with the same number of balls in each row and resting on top of one another?

     b. What will these balls weigh if iron weighs 490 pounds per cubic foot?

     c. Re-solve parts (*a*) and (*b*) for iron balls that are 6 inches in diameter.

     d. Re-solve parts (*a*) and (*b*) for balls that are 1 foot in diameter. Use $\pi = 3.141,6$.

10.18. Re-solve Problem 10.17 using (*a*) $\pi = \frac{22}{7}$, (*b*) $\pi = \frac{355}{113}$. Which of the three sets of answers is most nearly correct? Convert the three sets of answers to decimal form; for how many digits do they agree?

*N*ote 1 ∽ *The operation of partitioning applied to natural numbers.*

The operation of subtraction of natural numbers was introduced as the inverse operation of addition of natural numbers. This inverse operation was defined as the determination of the unknown number represented by ? in the relationship $a + ? = c$, or $? + a = c$, in which a and c represent known natural numbers. A more general inverse operation of addition, namely, the operation of *partitioning* natural numbers, is now defined as the determination of natural numbers represented by ? in such relationships as $? + ? = a$, $? + ? + ? = a$, $? + ? + ? + ? = a$, . . . , in which a represents a known natural number, and two or more unknown numbers represented by ? appear in the relationship. Moreover, a prescribed character is assigned to the ?'s.

EXAMPLES ∽

1. Partition 9 to yield three consecutive natural numbers; i.e., $9 = ? + ? + ?$, in which the three ?'s represent three consecutive natural numbers. *Solution:* Let n represent the middle natural number. The three consecutive natural numbers would appear symbolically as $n - 1$, n, and $n + 1$; their sum, $n - 1 + n + n + 1 = 3n$, must be equivalent to 9. Hence, if $3 \times n = 9$,

then n itself must be equivalent to 3, $n - 1$ must be equivalent to 2, and $n + 1$ to 4. Therefore, this prescribed partition of 9 is indicated by $9 = 2 + 3 + 4$.

2. Partition 15 to yield three consecutive odd numbers. A direct solution, similar to that in (1), or a few trials will yield the appropriate partitioning, namely, $15 = 3 + 5 + 7$.

3. Partition 12 into divisors of itself. All possible exact divisors of 12 are 1, 2, 3, 4, 6, and 12. A few trials will yield the desired partitioning in this case, namely, $12 = 2 + 4 + 6$.

4. Partition 28 into all divisors of 28 except 28 itself. Here one readily obtains the prescribed partitioning, namely, $28 = 1 + 2 + 4 + 7 + 14$. Any natural number that yields a partitioning into all of its exact divisors, exclusive of the number itself, was called by the ancient Greek mathematicians a *perfect number.* Thus, 6 is the smallest perfect number, since $2 \neq 1$, $3 \neq 1$, $4 \neq 1 + 2$, $5 \neq 1$, but $6 = 1 + 2 + 3$.

5. Partition 65 into two square natural numbers. By adding all pairs of square numbers less than 65, namely, 1, 4, 9, 16, 25, 36, 49, and 64, one readily finds the two required pairs yielding two possible partitionings as prescribed, namely, $65 = 1 + 64$ and $65 = 16 + 49$. Indeed, if a natural number can be partitioned into two square numbers in two ways, the natural number cannot be a prime number. Hence, since $221 = 10^2 + 11^2$ and $221 = 5^2 + 14^2$, it follows that 221 cannot be a prime. Actually, $221 = 13 \times 17$.[1]

6. Partition $2^{2^n} + 1$ into two square numbers if n exceeds 5.

While still a teenager the famous mathematician C. F. Gauss made the remarkable discovery that if the number $2^{2^n} + 1$ is a prime number, it is possible to construct by elementary geometry a regular polygon having that prime number of sides. Thus, if $n = 0$, $2^{2^0} + 1 = 3$. Therefore the triangle having three equal sides can be constructed. The actual simple construction appears as the first proposition in Euclid's Elements of Geometry (*circa* 300 B.C.).

If $n = 1$, $2^{2^1} + 1 = 2^2 + 1 = 4 + 1 = 5$. The construction of the polygon of five equal sides and five equal angles was probably discovered by Pythagoras (*circa* 550 B.C.) and seems to be used as the emblem of the ancient Secret Society of the Pythagoreans, which he founded. The actual construction appears as Proposition 11 of Book 4 of Euclid's Elements.

If $n = 2$, $2^{2^2} + 1 = 2^4 + 1 = 16 + 1 = 17$; if $n = 3$, $2^{2^3} + 1 = 2^8 + 1 = 257$; if $n = 4$, $2^{2^4} + 1 = 2^{16} + 1 = 65,637$. Since 17, 257, and 65,537 are prime numbers, one may construct by the postulates of elementary geometry (i.e., by Euclidean geometry) regular polygons having 17, 257, and 65,537 sides, respectively.

[1] Oystein Ore, "Number Theory and Its History," p. 59, McGraw-Hill Book Company, New York, 1948.

For any larger values of n it is not known at present whether $2^{2^n} + 1$ ever yields a prime number, as these numbers become rapidly extremely large and are difficult to investigate. However, it has been determined that for certain values, namely $n = 5, 6, 7, 8, 9, 11, 12, 15, 18, 23, 36, 38$, and 73, $2^{2^n} + 1$ is not prime but composite; for example, in 1732 Euler showed that $2^{2^5} + 1$, or 4,294,967,297, is equal to $641 \times 6,700,417$.

Now if it can be shown how to extend by appropriate induction the following partitionings into two pairs of squares, this famous unsolved problem will be solved:

$A = 2^{2^5} + 1 = (2 \times 25 \times 409 - 1)^2 + (2^{2^4} - 2 \times 4 \times 409)^2$
$B = 2^{2^6} + 1 = (20 \times 516 \times 139{,}418 - 1)^2 + (2^{2^5} - 20 \times 89 \times 139{,}418)^2$

Caution: Not all proposed partitionings are possible.

⌁ CHALLENGES

1. *a.* Evaluate A as $(2^{2^4})^2 + 1^2$ and as $(2 \times 25 \times 409 - 1)^2 + (2^{2^4} - 2 \times 4 \times 409)^2$.

   b. Evaluate B as the two indicated sums of pairs of squares.

2. Obtain the first four perfect numbers. The rule for finding them appears as Proposition 36 of Book 9 of Euclid's Elements, namely (using modern symbolism): If $2^n - 1$ is a prime number, then $(2^n - 1) \times 2^{n-1}$ is a perfect number. Evaluate this expression for $n = 1, 2, 3, 4, \ldots$, and review the foregoing definition of a perfect number.

N*ote 2 ⌁ Partitioning a proper fraction
into two or more fractions.*

The operation of partitioning a proper fraction into two or more positive or negative proper fractions, whose algebraic sum is the given fraction, is also called *resolving a fraction into its partial fractions.*

A valid partitioning of a given fraction a/b into partial fractions yields new fractions whose denominators are smaller numbers than the denominator b. Such partitioning is not possible if b is a single prime number or any power of a single prime. However, if b is a product of two or more powers of prime numbers, such as p^m, q^n, $\ldots$, the new fractions will have these powers of primes as denominators. Such partitioning is always possible into one or more different sets of partial fractions.

EXAMPLES ⌁

1. $\frac{43}{72} = \dfrac{43}{2^3 \times 3^2} = \dfrac{3}{2^3} + \dfrac{2}{3^2} = \tfrac{3}{8} + \tfrac{2}{9}$

2. $\frac{13}{15} = \tfrac{2}{3} + \tfrac{1}{5}$

3. $\frac{89}{120} = \frac{2}{3} - \frac{1}{8} + \frac{1}{5} = \frac{2}{3} + \frac{7}{8} - \frac{4}{5}$

4. $\frac{7}{24} = \frac{5}{8} - \frac{1}{3} = -\frac{3}{8} + \frac{2}{3}$

A method of resolving a proper fraction in its lowest terms into its partial fractions may be obtained by noting the resolution of $\frac{19}{72}$ into its partial fractions. Factor the denominator $72 = 2^3 \times 3^2$. The denominators of the required partial fractions are 2^3 and 3^2, or 8 and 9.

One must next determine the required numerators, represented by the letters A and B, so that

$$\frac{19}{72} = \frac{A}{8} + \frac{B}{9} \quad \text{or} \quad \frac{19}{72} - \frac{A}{8} = \frac{19 - 9A}{72} = \frac{B}{9} \quad \text{or} \quad \frac{19 - 9A}{8} = B$$

Hence, one must repeatedly add multiples of 9 to 19, or subtract multiples of 9 from 19 until an exact multiple of 8 is produced. If m denotes the successful *added* multiple of 9, then $A = -m$; if m denotes the successful *subtracted* multiple of 9, then $A = +m$. The exact multiple of 8 so obtained is the value of B.

This result is always achieved for an absolute value of m that is less than 8. The regimen, or algorithm, appears as follows:

Additions	Multiple	Subtractions
19		19
9		9
28	1	10
9		9
37	2	1
9		9
46	3	−8 *

Thus, -8, arising from the third multiple of 9, by *subtraction* is exactly divisible by 8. Therefore, $A = +3$; $B = -\frac{8}{8} = -1$.

Continuing the additions, $46 + 9 = 55$; $55 + 9 = 64$, which is exactly divisible by 8. For $m = 5$, whence $A = -5$, $B = 8$, whence

$$\frac{19}{72} = \frac{3}{8} + \frac{-1}{9} = \frac{-5}{8} + \frac{8}{9}$$

If the denominator of the given fraction contains more than two different prime factors, the required partial fractions may be obtained, one by one, from a series of resolutions into *two* fractions, one of which is a required partial fraction. To illustrate, let the fraction $\frac{764}{3,465}$ be resolved into its partial fractions. Note that $3,465 = 3^2 \times 5 \times 7 \times 11$.

First resolution: $\frac{764}{3,465} = \frac{A}{9} + \frac{B}{385}$

Additions	Multiple	Subtractions
764		764
385		385
1149	1	379
385		385
1534	2	−6
385		385
1919	3	−391
385		385
2304*	4	−776

Therefore $A = -4$ $B = 2{,}304 \div 9 = 256$ whence $\frac{764}{3465} = \frac{-4}{9} + \frac{256}{385}$

Second resolution: $\frac{256}{385} = \frac{A}{5} + \frac{B}{77}$

Additions	Multiple	Subtractions
256		256
77		77
333	1	179
77		77
410*	2	102

But $B = 410 \div 5 = 82$, and $\frac{82}{77}$ is an improper fraction. Continuing the additions and subtractions:

410	2	102
77		77
487	3	25*

Therefore $A = +3$ $B = 25 \div 5 = 5$ whence $\frac{256}{385} = \frac{3}{5} + \frac{5}{77}$

Third resolution: $\frac{5}{77} = \frac{A}{7} + \frac{B}{11}$

Additions	Multiple	Subtractions
5		5
11		11
16	1	−6
11		11
27	2	−17
11		11
38	3	−28*

Therefore $A = 3$ $B = -28 \div 7 = -4$ whence $\frac{5}{77} = \frac{3}{7} + \frac{-4}{11}$

Accordingly, one complete resolution yields

$$\frac{764}{3,465} = \frac{-4}{9} + \frac{3}{5} + \frac{3}{7} + \frac{-4}{11}$$

↭ CHALLENGES [CONTINUED]

3. Resolve into its partial fractions: (*a*) $\frac{1}{6}$, (*b*) $\frac{1}{28}$, (*c*) $\frac{1}{496}$.   (*d*) What relationship do these partitions suggest?

4. Resolve into partial fractions: (*a*) $\frac{1}{15}$, (*b*) $\frac{1}{63}$, (*c*) $\frac{1}{48}$, (*d*) $\frac{1}{24}$, (*e*) $\frac{1}{35}$.   (*f*) What do these resolutions suggest?

5. Verify the resolution into partial fractions:

$$\frac{1}{2^{32} + 1} = \frac{102}{641} + \frac{-1,066,213}{6,700,417}$$

(*Hint:* Combine the partial fractions.)

*N*ote 3 ↭ *Lists of periods of repeating decimal fractions.*

The periods of all fractions whose denominators are prime numbers, or powers of prime numbers, from 2 to 97 are listed in the Disquisitiones Arithmeticae of Gauss (1801); the list is extended as far as 347 in a subsequent Memoire of Gauss, published posthumously in 1863.   The list enables one to convert easily any fraction into its decimal form if the denominator of the given fraction contains no other prime factor, or power of a prime number, than those appearing in the table.

The earlier part of the table may be readily computed and is inserted here as far as 49 or 7².

D	Period of 1/D, or periods of A/D, if A and D have no common factor (digits are grouped in sets of fives for convenience)
3	3 6
7	14285,7
9	1 2 4 5 7 8
11	09 18 27 36 45
13	07692,3 46153,8

17	05882,35294,11764,7
19	05263,15789,47368,421
23	04347,82608,69565,21739,13
27	037 074 148 185 259 296
29	03448,27586,20689,65517,24137,931
31	03225,80645,16129 54838,70967,74193
37	027 054 081 135 162 189 243 297 378 459 486 567
41	02439 04878 07317 09756 12195 14634 26829 36585
43	02325,58139,53488,37209,3 65116,27906,97674,41860,4
47	02127,65957,44680,85106,38297,87234,04255,31914,89361,7
49	02040,81632,65306,12244,89795,91836,73469,38775,51

To obtain the period of any proper fraction whose denominator occurs in the list, such as $\frac{10}{13}$, one need compute only one or two, or possibly three, digits of the period to recognize the rest of the period in the table. Thus, $\frac{10}{13} = 0.7****$. As 7 occurs only once in the two possible periods for denominator 13, namely, in 076923, one writes out the entire period for $\frac{10}{13}$ by these six digits in cyclic order, beginning with the 7; therefore, $\frac{10}{13} = 0.769,230 \ldots$. Similarly, $\frac{3}{13} = 0.2*$, whence the table entry for denominator 13 yields $\frac{3}{13} = 0.230,769 \ldots$.

The period of the decimal form of a proper fraction (in its lowest terms) whose denominator involves factors that are primes and powers of primes may be obtained by combining appropriately the periods of the partial fractions into which the given proper fraction is resolved. Thus, to obtain the decimal fractional period of $\frac{115}{231}$, one obtains $\frac{115}{231} = \frac{2}{7} + \frac{2}{3} - \frac{5}{11}$. From the tables, $\frac{2}{7} = 0.285,714$; $\frac{2}{3} = 0.\overline{6}$; $\frac{5}{11} = 0.\overline{45}$.

	0.285714
	0.666666
Adding	0.952380
	0.454545
Subtracting	0.497835

therefore, $\frac{115}{231} = 0.\overline{497,835} \ldots$

It is to be noted that the period of a fraction having a composite base contains as many digits in its period as the lowest common multiple of the numbers of digits in the periods of the partial fractions into which the given fraction has been resolved.

⌘ CHALLENGES [CONCLUDED]

6. Obtain the period of the decimal form of $\frac{764}{3465}$ by use of tables.

7. Obtain the two next entries of the above table to extend the table to 60.

8. By use of table and partial fractions, obtain the decimal form of $\frac{53}{112}$, overlining the period.

~ **S**UPPLEMENTARY PROBLEMS ~

> *"You seem very clever at explaining words,*
> *Sir," said Alice. "Would you kindly tell*
> *me the meaning of the poem called 'Jabberwocky'?"*
> *"Let's hear it," said Humpty Dumpty. "I can*
> *explain all the poems that ever were invented—*
> *and a good many that haven't been invented just*
> *yet."*
>
> —*Through the Looking-Glass, VI.*

S10.1. Perform the indicated additions of the exact decimal forms:

    a. 10.45 + 4.662 + 0.011   *d.* 578.398 + 36.009,4 + 0.000,749

    b. 3.980 + 92.49 + 875.09   *e.* 900.032 + 5,265.1 + 1,728

    c. 0.661 + 0.055 + 0.003,2   *f.* 78.904,16 + 19.600,04 + 62.5

S10.2. Obtain the sums of the following:

    a. Three and twenty-five hundredths; nine and five-tenths; two thousandths

    b. Ninety-nine and forty-four hundredths; thirty-nine and thirty-seven hundredths; eight hundred seventy-five thousandths

    c. Seventeen and thirty-five thousandths; thirty-five and seventeen ten thousandths; three thousand two hundred fifty-six ten thousandths

S10.3. Add horizontally and vertically, as indicated:

    a.

      48.7   +   1.703   + 12.62   +   98.700,1 =

    119.853 + 87.33   +   8.112 + 6,285.16   =

     43.59 + 28.000,9 + 456.970,2 +   500.032 =

   666.713 + 117.343,1 + 985.46   +   780.0   =

    b.

      1.234,6 +   56.789 + 246.89   +   0.678,1 =

   57.904 +   8.460,2 + 9,006.5   +   890.22   =

   755.29 + 8,733.8   +   0.181,3 + 7,865.9   =

 2,503.1   + 763.88   + 83.191 + 664,422.0 =

    1.003,9 +   25.375 + 3,125.6   +   111.77   =

    c. +12.45 + −85.933 + +682.87 + −3.981 =

    −56.75 + +45.875 + −235.33 + +9.019 =

    +31.25 + −77.512 + +915.22 + −7.761 =

    −11.22 + +33.445 + −566.77 + +8.899 =

S10.4. Perform the indicated subtractions. Then obtain the sum of the individual minuends, the subtrahends, and the differences. Note that the sum of the latter two sums must equal the sum of the minuends.

    a. 87.329   *c.* 6,823.9   *e.* 35.729

        49.571   5,975.7   16.858

    b. 593.21   *d.* 4.362,1   *f.* 123.456

        104.55   1.004,7   789.789

S10.5. Use same directions as given in Problem S10.4:

a.	-34.62	c.	-17.25	e.
	-21.88		$+23.75$	

a. $\begin{array}{r} -34.62 \\ -21.88 \end{array}$ c. $\begin{array}{r} -17.25 \\ +23.75 \end{array}$ e. $\begin{array}{r} +10.37 \\ -65.43 \end{array}$ g. $\begin{array}{r} -75.31 \\ +24.69 \end{array}$

b. $\begin{array}{r} +43.01 \\ +55.33 \end{array}$ d. $\begin{array}{r} +42.61 \\ +76.29 \end{array}$ f. $\begin{array}{r} -12.46 \\ -99.44 \end{array}$ h. $\begin{array}{r} +10.01 \\ +97.71 \end{array}$

S10.6. Perform the indicated multiplications:

a. $(32.51)(125.4)$ d. $(-100.23)(-62.5)$ g. $(5.006)(-120.9)$
b. $(31.25)(4.096)$ e. $(55.312)(0.016)$ h. $(-72.99)(-87.5)$
c. $(9.375)(15.36)$ f. $(-7.128)(+1.007)$ i. $(0.007)(0.009)$

S10.7. Perform the exact divisions:

a. $5,898.24 \div 1.125$ e. $31.416 \div 2,640$
b. $548.625 \div 8.75$ f. $314.16 \div 6,160$
c. $3.141,6 \div 0.001,19$ g. $3,141.6 \div 0.119$
d. $3.141,6 \div 13.09$ h. $39.27 \div 31,416$

S10.8. Obtain the products to the nearest, tenth, hundredth, and thousandth:

a. 4.123×39.27 d. $5,637 \times 0.072,9$ g. 1.071×32.19
b. 51.99×9.871 e. $762.9 \times 0.119,1$ h. 62.97×4.311
c. 3.333×67.77 f. $1,700 \times 0.989,9$ i. 543.2×0.951

S10.9. Obtain the quotients to the nearest tenth, hundredth, and thousandth:

a. $6.135 \div 59.71$ d. $45.13 \div 917.23$ g. $62.7 \div 512.9$
b. $7.499 \div 60.03$ e. $78.67 \div 877.64$ h. $11.7 \div 733.1$
c. $3.141 \div 719.1$ f. $10.07 \div 376.11$ i. $51.2 \div 409.6$

S10.10. The Reader's Digest *Almanac* and yearbook for 1968,[1] page 713, states ". . . 1 meter = 39.37 inches, which was established by an act of Congress in July 1866. Thus, the yard is defined as follows: 1 yard = 0.914,4 meter. The inch is therefore exactly equal to 25.4 millimeters." If the definition of the equivalence by act of Congress is correct, why must the next two statements necessarily be incorrect? Replace the decimal fractions 0.914,4 and 25.4 by appropriate mixed decimal fractions to make the statements absolutely correct.

S10.11.   a.   Compute the number of meters, to the nearest 0.1 meter, that is equivalent to 1,000 miles. Correct equivalence: 1 meter = 39.37 inches.

    b.   Compute the number of meters, to the nearest 0.1 meter, using the alleged equivalence 1 yard = 0.914,4 meters.

    c.   Explain the difference between these two results.

S10.12. Calculate the (a) area and (b) circumference of the circle whose radius is exactly 28 feet. Use $\pi = \frac{22}{7}$.

S10.13. Solve Problem S10.12, using $\pi = 3.141,6$.

S10.14. Solve Problem S10.12, using $\pi = \frac{355}{113}$.

S10.15. Compute to the nearest 0.1 inch the circumference of the circle whose radius is 1 mile long, using (a) $\pi = 3.141,6$; (b) $\pi = \frac{355}{113}$.

S10.16. Compute to the nearest 0.1 square inch the area of the circle whose radius is 1 mile long, using $\pi = 3.141,6$; $\pi = \frac{355}{113}$.

[1] The *Almanac* credits the National Bureau of Standards as the source of this information.

S10.17. Use enough digits from the approximation given for π in Section 10.5 to compute the circumference and area of the circle in Problems S10.15 and S10.16 to the nearest 0.1 inch and 0.1 square inch, respectively.

S10.18. Compute the number of gallons of water that a hollow sphere, of inside diameter 2 feet, can contain.   Use $\pi = 3.141,6$.   One gallon = 231 cubic inches.

S10.19. How many cubic inches of metal are contained in the sphere in Problem S10.18 if the metal is 0.75 inch thick?

S10.20. Compute the cost of paving a path 5 feet wide that surrounds a circle of diameter 50 feet, if the paving is to cost 30 cents per square foot.   Use $\pi = 3.141,6$.

S10.21. How many circles of diameter 3 feet would be exactly equivalent in area to one large circle of radius 12 feet?   Does the result depend upon the particular value one uses for π?

S10.22. Compute the area and circumference of a circle whose radius is 3.97 inches long, using $\pi = 3.141,6$.

S10.23. Compute the area and volume of a sphere whose diameter is 72.35 centimeters long, using $\pi = 3.141,6$.

S10.24. What must be the radius of the circle whose circumference is exactly 1 foot long?   Use $\pi = 3.141,6$ and obtain the result to the nearest 0.1 inch.

S10.25. The *number* of units of volume (cubic inches, cubic feet, cubic centimeters, etc.) contained within a rectangular solid is equal to the *number* of units of area (square inches, square feet, square centimeters, etc.) contained in the base, multiplied by the *number* of corresponding units of length (inches, feet, centimeters, etc.) contained within its altitude.   To aid the memory, the relationship is expressed symbolically as $A = bh$ and is read "Volume equals base times altitude."

Compute to the nearest 0.1 cubic inch the volume of a rectangular solid that is exactly 43.48 inches long, 29.01 inches wide, and 4.69 inches high.

S10.26. How many gallons of water can a cylindrical water tank hold, if its diameter is 10 feet long and its height is 8 feet?   The volume of a cylindrical tank is expressed symbolically as $V = bh$, which means that the number of units of volume it contains (cubic inches, etc.) is equal to the product of the number of area units (square inches, etc.) contained in the circular base multiplied by the number of length units (inches, etc.) contained in its height.   Use $\pi = 3.141,6$.

S10.27. Compute to the nearest 0.1 cubic inch the volume of the cylinder whose diameter is 3.41 inches long, and whose height is 7.29 inches long.   The dimensions and $\pi = 3.141,6$ are assumed to be *exactly* stated.

S10.28. The volume of a right circular cone is given by the formula $V = \dfrac{\pi r^2 \times h}{3}$ in which r and h represent the number of units of length in the radius of the base and in the height, respectively; V represents the number of corresponding units of volume.   The top of a right circular cone is directly above the center of the circular base.

  a. Compute the volume of the cone whose height is 14 feet and radius of base is 6 feet.   Use $\pi = \frac{22}{7}$.

b. Compute the volume of the cone to the nearest 0.1 cubic inch, if its exact dimensions are given as $r = 23.51$ and $h = 43.97$. Use $\pi = 3.141{,}6$.

S10.29. If \$1 is placed in a savings account at the end of each month for 8 years, theoretically the account will amount to \$122.828,541,7 at 6 percent interest compounded monthly. How much should the account amount to if monthly payments of \$37.85 were made instead of the \$1? Give result to the nearest cent.

S10.30. If a deposit of \$1, made at the end of each year, would amount to \$37.786,075,6 in 21 years, at interest of $5\frac{1}{2}$ percent compounded annually, what must be the annual deposit to accumulate \$20,000? Calculate the yearly deposit to the nearest cent.

S10.31. Which is greater and by how much?
  a. 9.76^2 or 4.57^3
  b. 21.2^3 or 97.6^2
  c. 97.6^2 or $4.57^3 \times 21.2^3$

S10.32. An acre is divided up into small enclosures 22 feet long and 19.8 feet wide. How many such enclosures are there? One square mile contains exactly 640 acres. What should be the dimensions of this acre?

S10.33. The official bushel in the United States is the so-called *Winchester bushel*, which is equivalent to the volume of a right circular cylinder of inside dimensions, diameter $18\frac{1}{2}$ inches and height 8 inches. Use the appropriate number of digits of the decimal expression for the number of cubic inches in a bushel which is correct to the nearest 0.000,1. Criticize the statement: 1 bushel = 2150.42 cubic inches exactly.

S10.34. The length of the tropical year, the year of the seasons, upon which our calendar is based is generally given as equal to 365 days, 5 hours, 48 minutes, 46 seconds, and also as 365.242,20 days. Which of these lengths of time is the larger, and by how much? Give the exact number of seconds, expressed as a decimal fraction.

S10.35. The tropical year appears to be decreasing at the rate of 0.53 seconds per century, approximately. In how many years would our year be just half as long as it now is, if this rate of decrease continues precisely at 0.53 seconds per century?

S10.36. The same source cited in Problem S10.10 gives the equivalences:
  1 cable length = 120 fathoms
              = 219.456 meters (exactly)
  Now if 1 meter is equal to 39.37 inches, by act of Congress (July 1866), how many feet must be equal to 1 fathom? Comment on the above word "exactly."

S10.37. If 1 troy ounce of gold is worth exactly \$32 and if 1 troy ounce is equivalent to 1.097 avoirdupois ounces (to nearest 0.001), and if 16 avoirdupois ounces are equivalent to 1 avoirdupois pound, compute to the nearest cent the value of 1 pound avoirdupois of gold.

S10.38. If 1 British quart contains 69.354 cubic inches, how many American gallons are equivalent to 1,000 British gallons (4 quarts = 1 gallon)? One American gallon contains 231 cubic inches. Give result to nearest 0.1 gallon.

LESSON 11 ☙ EVOLUTION—
THE INVERSE OPERATION
OF INVOLUTION

Ah, but a man's reach should exceed his grasp,
Or what's a heaven for?

—Robert Browning, *Andrea del Sarto.*

11·1 ∾ Definitions and Symbolism Pertaining to Evolution

Involution is the process of raising a given number, the base, by repeated multiplications to a given power as indicated by the exponent. Thus 3^5 or $3 \times 3 \times 3 \times 3 \times 3 = 243$; $(\frac{3}{4})^2 = \frac{3}{4} \times \frac{3}{4} = \frac{9}{16}$; $1.25^3 = 1.25 \times 1.25 \times 1.25 = 1.953,125$; $5^0 = 1$; $0^5 = 0$; $7^{-1} = \frac{1}{7}$; $12^{-2} = \dfrac{1}{12^2} = \dfrac{1}{12 \times 12} = \frac{1}{144}$. Hence, the two given numbers are the base and the exponent; the required number is the power.

Contrariwise, *evolution* is the inverse of involution and yields the unknown base from a given, or known, exponent and power. It is the operation of obtaining the number denoted by ? in such indicated involutions as the following:

$$?^5 = 243 \qquad ?^3 = 1.953,125 \qquad ?^{-1} = \tfrac{1}{7}$$
$$?^2 = \tfrac{9}{16} \qquad ?^0 = 1 \qquad ?^{-2} = \tfrac{1}{144}$$

The customary symbol for such evolutions, or "root extractions," is the radical sign, $\sqrt{}$. The foregoing evolutions appear appropriately as

$$\sqrt[5]{243} = ? \qquad \sqrt{\tfrac{9}{16}} = ? \qquad \sqrt[3]{1.953,125} = ?$$

The ? in $?^0 = 1$ is indeterminate, which means that any number whatever when raised to the power 0 yields 1; the -1 exponent always denotes a reciprocal, as 7^{-1} means $\frac{1}{7}$; finally $?^{-2} = 144$ means $\dfrac{1}{\sqrt{144}} = ?$ These four expressions employing radical signs are read, respectively, as "fifth root of 243," "square root of $\frac{9}{16}$," "cube root of 1.953,125," "one over the square root of 144." Note that the index, the number written above the radical, as the 5 and the 3, need not be written above square root radicals.

The operation of evolution as applied to rational numbers, i.e., integers and fractions, does not always yield a rational number as the result, or root. Evolutions that do yield rational results can usually be done by inspection, or by a few simple trials, if the rational numbers involved are small. Thus, $\sqrt{81} = 9$, since it is known that $9^2 = 81$; $\sqrt[3]{64} = 4$, since it is known that $4^3 = 64$; $\sqrt{\frac{16}{25}} = \frac{4}{5}$, since $4^2 = 16$ and $5^2 = 25$.

ᴄᴏ Pʀᴏʙʟᴇᴍs ᴄᴏ

11.1. Perform by inspection, or by simple trials, the involutions that yield positive rational roots. *Hint:* Convert the mixed radicand to an improper fraction.

a. $\sqrt{100}$	*e.* $\sqrt{144}$	*i.* $\sqrt{1\frac{7}{9}}$	*m.* $\sqrt[3]{\frac{8}{27}}$
b. $\sqrt[3]{343}$	*f.* $\sqrt[4]{441}$	*j.* $\sqrt[4]{81}$	*n.* $\sqrt{0.008,1}$
c. $\sqrt{169}$	*g.* $\sqrt{\frac{25}{49}}$	*k.* $\sqrt[5]{32}$	*o.* $\sqrt[3]{0.008}$
d. $\sqrt{961}$	*h.* $\sqrt{\frac{9}{16}}$	*l.* $\sqrt[6]{729}$	*p.* $\sqrt[5]{0.000,01}$

11·2 ᴄᴏ Iɴᴠᴏʟᴜᴛɪᴏɴ ᴅᴏᴇs ɴᴏᴛ ʏɪᴇʟᴅ ᴜɴɪǫᴜᴇ ʀᴇsᴜʟᴛs

Since $(+a)^2 = +a^2$ and $(-a)^2 = +a^2$, if a^2 represents any rational number, it must follow that $\sqrt{+a^2}$ has two values, namely, $+a$ and $-a$. Accordingly, there are *two* rational roots for parts (a), (c), (d), (e), (f), (g), (h), (i), and (n) of the preceding problem. Moreover, parts (j) and (l) also have two rational solutions, since any *even* power of a rational number is positive. To indicate which root is required in such ambiguous cases, it is customary to place before the radical sign the positive sign $+$, the negative sign $-$, or the double sign $\pm$ if the positive root, the negative root, or both roots must be obtained. Thus, $\sqrt{25} = 5$ or -5; for emphasis $+\sqrt{25} = +5$; $-\sqrt{25} = -5$; and $\pm\sqrt{25} = \pm5$ if both roots are required.

Contrariwise, an odd root of any rational number has only one (real) solution; thus, (b), (k), (m), (o), and (p) do not have negative solutions; $\sqrt[5]{-32} = -2$, not $+2$. Subsequently it will be demonstrated that $\sqrt[n]{a}$ has n different roots (Lesson 17); at that time the number system will be enlarged for the final time to admit the complex numbers to provide for these roots other than the positive and negative roots.

The indicated evolution of an even root of a negative number has no solution among the rational numbers. To solve $\sqrt{-4} = ?$ or $\sqrt[4]{-81} = ?$, or even $\sqrt{3} = ?$, one requires other kinds of numbers than the rational numbers.

11·3 ∽ ONE KIND OF IRRATIONAL NUMBER: THE SURD NUMBERS

In Lesson 5 the fractions were introduced into the number system to provide appropriate numbers to serve for quotients whenever a prescribed division upon natural numbers is impossible. The operation $2 \div 3 = ?$ cannot yield a natural number for the quotient, as 2 does not occur among the multiples of 3. To make division upon natural numbers always possible, the fractions were invented and introduced into the system of available numbers; hence $2 \div 3 = \frac{2}{3}$. This new number is really a pair of natural numbers but is *regarded as a single number* and is given a *unique* position on the number line. To make these numbers serviceable, the basic operations were extended to apply also to them, and rules for performing the basic operations upon fractions were devised which are adequate and consistent.

Now if a represents any rational number whatever, and if n represents any natural number whatever, then a^n must also be equal to a rational number. Thus, if $a^n = b$, then $\sqrt[n]{b} = a$. Since $2^3 = 8$, then it must follow that $\sqrt[3]{8} = 2$. However, if n represents any natural number and if b represents any rational number, it is not always true that $\sqrt[n]{b}$ can yield a rational number; indeed, $\sqrt[n]{b}$ can be equal to a rational number, a, if and only if $a^n = b$.

To illustrate, consider $\sqrt{2}$. Now $\sqrt{2}$ cannot be equal to an *integer*, since $(\pm 1)^2 = 1$, $(\pm 2)^2 = 4$, and the squares of all other integers are greater than 2. To demonstrate that $\sqrt{2}$ cannot be equal to a *fraction*, the assumption that $\sqrt{2}$ can be equal to some fraction, say p/q, leads to an impossible situation. If one assumes that $\sqrt{2} = p/q$ in its lowest terms, then $(p/q)^2 = p^2/q^2$, which must also be in its lowest terms, for if p and q do not have any common factor other than 1, then p^2 merely contains each factor of p repeated just once, and q^2 contains each factor of q repeated just once, so that p^2 and q^2 cannot have any common factor either. Again, if $\sqrt{2} = p/q$, then $p^2/q^2 = 2$, or $\frac{2}{1}$. But $\frac{2}{1}$ is in its lowest terms, so the equivalent fraction p^2/q^2 in its lowest terms must have $q^2 = 1$ and $p^2 = 2$, for a common fraction can have *only one form* for its lowest terms. But $\sqrt{2}$ cannot be equal to p^2 if p is an integer, so $\sqrt{2}$ cannot be equal to any fraction. Otherwise stated, $\sqrt{2}$ cannot be equal to any rational number. Such indicated roots of rational numbers that cannot be equal to any rational numbers are called *surds* or *surd numbers*. Surds are the first kind of irrational number to be encountered. A surd, then, is a number pair also, namely, one natural number called the *index* and one rational number called the *radicand*. In $\sqrt[3]{7}$ the 3 is the index, the 7 is the radicand; the expression $\sqrt[3]{7}$ represents a single number, a particular kind of irrational number known as a *surd*. Although no rational number exists that is exactly equal to a surd, it is possible to obtain two appropriate rational numbers as near to each other as one may desire and which contain any given surd number within the interval between them.

11·4 ∾ THE SIX BASIC OPERATIONS, ADDITION, SUBTRACTION, MULTIPLICATION, DIVISION, INVOLUTION, AND EVOLUTION, PERFORMED UPON SURD NUMBERS

Addition of Surds.   *Similar* surds may be added to yield a surd as the sum. Two or more surds are said to be similar, or *like surds*, if they have the same index and the same radicand.   Thus, $2\sqrt[3]{5}$ and $6\sqrt[3]{5}$ are similar surds as they contain the same radicand 5 and have the same index 3.   Similar surds are added thus: $\sqrt[3]{5} + \sqrt[3]{5} = 2\sqrt[3]{5}; 2\sqrt[3]{5} + \sqrt[3]{5} = 3\sqrt[3]{5}; 3\sqrt[3]{5} + 3\sqrt[3]{5} = 6\sqrt[3]{5}; 6\sqrt[3]{5} + 4\sqrt[3]{5} = 10\sqrt[3]{5}$.   Quite generally, if a, b, and c represent rational numbers, and n represents a natural number, than $a\sqrt[n]{c} + b\sqrt[n]{c} = (a + b)\sqrt[n]{c}$, which may be read as "$a$ times the nth root of c and b times the nth root of c equals the sum of a and b times the nth root of c."

The number written under the radical sign has been named the radicand, the number appearing before the radical sign is the surd's coefficient.   The number written above the radical is the index.   Hence the rule for addition of surds:

The coefficient of the sum of two like surds is equal to the sum of the coefficients of the like surds; the radicand and index remain unchanged.

The sum of two *unlike* surds is represented by the two or more given surds as joined with the sign of addition, $+$.   The sum of the unlike, or dissimilar, surds $\sqrt[3]{5}, \sqrt[3]{5}$, and $\sqrt[3]{7}$ is $\sqrt[3]{5} + \sqrt[3]{5} + \sqrt[3]{7}$; the sum of $4\sqrt[4]{7}, 3\sqrt[3]{7}, 8\sqrt[3]{7}$, and $9\sqrt[3]{7}$ is $11\sqrt[3]{7} + 9\sqrt[3]{7} + 4\sqrt[4]{7}$.   Such sums, consisting of two or more different radicals, are to be *regarded as a single number;* they may also be represented approximately as decimal fractions as accurately as one may desire. These two sums are equal, respectively, to 5.585,97 and 52.825,94, with inaccuracy less than 0.000,01, as may be determined later in this lesson.

Subtraction of Surds.   As in addition, the difference of two similar surds is expressible as a single surd that is also similar to the two given surds.   Thus, $12\sqrt[3]{17} - 9\sqrt[3]{17} = 3\sqrt[3]{17}$ exactly, or 7.713,85, with error less than 0.000,01, since $\sqrt[3]{17} = 2.571,282, \ldots$.

The difference of two unlike surds must be expressed as the indicated subtraction of the subtrahend surd from the minuend.   To subtract $13\sqrt[3]{6}$ from $19\sqrt[3]{5}$ one obtains $19\sqrt[3]{5} - 13\sqrt[3]{6}$ as the appropriate difference, which is to be regarded as a single irrational number, or as the *approximate* decimal fraction, 8.866,97, with error less than 0.000,01.

Symbolically expressed, if a, b, c are rational numbers, and m, n are natural numbers, then $a\sqrt[n]{c} - b\sqrt[n]{c} = (a - b)\sqrt[n]{c}$; but $b\sqrt[n]{c}$ subtracted from $a\sqrt[m]{c}$ yields $a\sqrt[m]{c} - b\sqrt[n]{c}$, which is to be regarded as a single irrational number in the same sense that 23 and $\frac{2}{3}$ and 2^3 are regarded as single numbers, although made up of two different numbers, the 2 and the 3.

Multiplication of Surds.   At present the operation of multiplication is defined only for surds having the same index.   The rule is:

The product of two surds having the same index is a surd whose coefficient is equal to the product of the coefficients of the two surds; the radicand of the product is equal to the product of the radicands of the two given surds.   The index is retained unchanged.

Thus, $5 \sqrt[3]{7} \times 6 \sqrt[3]{2} = 30 \sqrt[3]{14}$.   The rule of multiplication of surds having a common index is immediately extended to the product of more than two such surds.   Thus, $2 \sqrt{3} \times 4 \sqrt{5} \times 7 \sqrt{8} \times 8 \sqrt{11} = 448 \sqrt{1,320}$.

The restriction of multiplication of surds to surds having a common (same) index may now be removed.   The procedure is analogous to the reduction of common fractions to a common denominator to permit the operation of addition of fractions.   The product of surds having different indices may be obtained by reducing the indices to their lowest common multiple as their least common index.   The following pertinent relationship allows this to be done: $\sqrt[n]{a} = \sqrt[kn]{a^k}$.   The rule for multiplying surds with different indices is:

The index of any surd may be multiplied by any natural number, k, without altering the value of the surd, if the radicand is also raised to the same power, k.

The validity of this rule can be established as follows.   Let $\sqrt[n]{a} = b$, in which n represents any natural number.   If a and b were rational numbers, then $b^n = a$.   Raising these two equal numbers to the same power, k, their results must be equal, namely, $a^k = (b^n)^k$.   But $(b^n)^k = b^n b^n b^n \cdots b^n$, or b^{nk}, in which b^n is repeated as a factor k times.   Hence, $b^{nk} = a^k$, which appears in the inverse form as $\sqrt[nk]{a^k} = b$.   Moreover, if a is rational and b is not rational but is irrational, and if one assumes that $\sqrt[n]{a} = b$ and $b^n = a$ are equivalent relationships, then b^n must be rational, so that the foregoing argument is applicable.

For example, let $\sqrt[3]{2} = b$, in which b is not rational but an irrational number so that $b^3 = 2$.   Then $(b^3)^4 = 2^4$, or $b^{12} = 2^4$, or $\sqrt[12]{2^4} = b$; that is, $\sqrt[3]{2} = \sqrt[12]{16}$.   Therefore, to multiply $\sqrt[2]{3}$ by $\sqrt[3]{5}$, the lowest common multiple of the indices 2 and 3 is 6.   Then $\sqrt[2]{3} = \sqrt[2 \times 3]{3^3} = \sqrt[6]{27}$, and $\sqrt[3]{5} = \sqrt[3 \times 2]{5^2} = \sqrt[6]{25}$.   Hence $\sqrt[2]{3} \times \sqrt[3]{5} = \sqrt[6]{27} \times \sqrt[6]{25} = \sqrt[6]{675}$.

Division of Surds.   Division of surds may be regarded as the inverse of multiplication of surds.   The rule is:

The coefficient of the quotient of two surds having the same index is equal to the quotient of their coefficients; the radicand of the quotient is equal to the quotient of the two radicands. Moreover, if the indices of the two given surds are different, the indices may be reduced to their least common multiple by raising the two radicands to appropriate powers.

Thus, $3 \sqrt[3]{7} \div 5 \sqrt[3]{2} = \frac{3}{5} \sqrt[3]{3\frac{1}{2}}$. Again, $12 \sqrt[2]{4} \div 6 \sqrt[3]{2} = 12 \sqrt[6]{64} \div 6 \sqrt[6]{4} = 2 \sqrt[6]{16}$ or $2^2 \times \sqrt[3]{4^2} = 2 \sqrt[3]{4}$, in its simplest form.

Involution of Surds. For all integral exponents, involution of a surd may be performed as follows. In the example $(a \sqrt[n]{c})^p = ?$, a and c are rational, n is a natural number, and p is an integer:

Let p be a positive integer. The involution is performed by repeatedly multiplying the surd by itself p times as a factor.

Let $p = 0$. Then, by extending the property of the zero exponent to surds, one has $(a \sqrt[n]{c})^0 = 1$.

Let $-p$ be a negative integer. Then let $(a \sqrt[n]{c})^{-p} = \dfrac{1}{(a \sqrt[n]{c})^p}$.

Evolution of Surds. To perform the evolution of surds for this example, $\sqrt[m]{a \sqrt[n]{b}} = ?$, assume that $\sqrt[m]{a \sqrt[n]{b}}$ has a numerical value, represented by x, which is either rational or irrational, but such that $a \sqrt[n]{b} = x^m$. Also assume that $\sqrt[n]{b}$ has a numerical value, y, rational or irrational, so that $b = y^n$. Raising these two equal numbers, $a \sqrt[n]{b}$ and x^m to the nth power, the results must be equal. That is,

$$(a \cdot \sqrt[n]{b})^n = (ay)^n = a^n y^n = a^n b = (x^m)^n = x^{mn}$$

Therefore, if $a^n b = x^{mn}$, then $x = \sqrt[mn]{a^n b}$. Thus, symbolically,

$$\sqrt[m]{a \sqrt[n]{b}} = \sqrt[mn]{a^n b}$$

For example,

$$\sqrt[3]{2 \sqrt[5]{7}} = \sqrt[15]{2^5 \times 7} \quad \text{or} \quad \sqrt[15]{224}$$

To summarize, if all radicands of surds of even indices are positive numbers, then the foregoing six basic operations upon surds always yield rational numbers or surds for the results; i.e., no further extension of the number system is necessary at this point to perform all these basic operations upon such surds. However, if a radicand of a surd of even index is negative, the evaluation of such a surd requires a further extension of the number system to include the complex numbers. With these new numbers, it will appear that a surd has as many different values as the index. To anticipate, $\sqrt{4}$ has two values, $+2$ and -2; $\sqrt[8]{-256}$ has eight different values, namely, $+2, -2, +2i, -2i, (+1 + i)/\sqrt{2}$,

$(-1 - i)/\sqrt{2}$, $(+1 - i)/\sqrt{2}$, and $(-1 + i)/\sqrt{2}$, in which i represents the new unit, namely, such a number that $i^2 = -1$. These beautiful unifying concepts will be presented in Lesson 17.

∽ PROBLEMS [CONTINUED] ∽

11.2. Perform the indicated operations upon surds:

a. $5\sqrt{3} + 7\sqrt{3} = ?$

b. $\frac{2}{3}\sqrt[3]{5} + \frac{3}{4}\sqrt[3]{5} = ?$

c. $1.34\sqrt{\frac{2}{3}} - 0.85\sqrt{\frac{2}{3}} = ?$

d. $3\frac{3}{4}\sqrt{2} - 3.375\sqrt{2} = ?$

e. $16\sqrt[3]{10} \times 25\sqrt[3]{3} = ?$

f. $2\sqrt{2} \times 3\sqrt{3} - 5\sqrt{6} = ?$

g. $91\sqrt[3]{111} \div 13\sqrt[3]{37} = ?$

h. $(2\sqrt[3]{3})^3 = ?$

i. Obtain the sum of $2\sqrt[3]{3}$, $5\sqrt{7}$, $3\sqrt{7}$, $10\sqrt[3]{3}$, and $\sqrt{7}$

j. Obtain the sum of $2\sqrt{3} + 3\sqrt[3]{4} + 5\sqrt[3]{6}$, and $12\sqrt[3]{3}$

k. Subtract the result in (*i*) from the result in (*j*)

l. Obtain a single surd as the product of $2\sqrt[3]{3}$ and $3\sqrt[2]{2}$

m. Obtain a single surd as the quotient of $15\sqrt[4]{4}$ divided by $5\sqrt{2}$

n. Obtain a single surd as the square root of $2\sqrt[3]{5}$

o. Obtain the cube root of $2\sqrt{7}$

p. Divide the result of (*o*) by the result of (*n*)

11·5 ∽ USING DECIMAL APPROXIMATIONS FOR SURDS

Instead of using surds in required rational computations, it is common practice to replace them by decimal approximations. As such decimal approximations entail certain small errors, the results of the calculations will also involve small errors. Lesson 15 provides methods of determining the possible errors in such calculations upon inaccurate original numbers. To solve Problem 11.2*a*, one may replace $\sqrt{3}$ by its rational approximation, 1.732,051, which involves an error that is less than 0.000,001. Thus, adding

$$5\sqrt{3} = 5(1.732,051) = 8.660,255$$
$$\text{and} \quad 7\sqrt{3} = 7(1.732,051) = \underline{12.124,357}$$
$$20.784,612$$

The sum $12\sqrt{3}$ may be checked, as $12(1.732,051) = 20.784,612$.

∽ PROBLEMS [CONTINUED] ∽

11.3. Check all parts of the preceding problem if it is known that, to the nearest 0.000,001,

$$\sqrt{\tfrac{2}{3}} = 0.816,497 \qquad \sqrt[3]{5} = 1.709,976 \qquad \sqrt[4]{64} = 2.828,427$$

$$\sqrt{2} = 1.414,214 \qquad \sqrt[3]{6} = 1.817,121 \qquad \sqrt[6]{0.7} = 0.942,286$$

$$\sqrt{3} = 1.732,051 \qquad \sqrt[3]{10} = 2.154,435 \qquad \sqrt[6]{28} = 1.742,581$$

$$\sqrt{6} = 2.449,490 \qquad \sqrt[3]{30} = 3.107,233 \qquad \sqrt[6]{40} = 1.849,311$$

$$\sqrt{7} = 2.645,751 \qquad \sqrt[3]{37} = 3.332,222 \qquad \sqrt[6]{72} = 2.039,649$$

$$\sqrt[3]{3} = 1.442,250 \qquad \sqrt[3]{111} = 4.805,896 \qquad \sqrt[6]{1\tfrac{3}{7}} = 1.061,248$$

$$\sqrt[3]{4} = 1.587,401$$

11.4. *a.* Show that the squares of the following numbers are less than 2 but ever nearer to 2: 1.4; 1.41; 1.414; 1.414,2; 1.414,21; 1.414,213.

b. Show that the squares of the following numbers are greater than 2 but ever nearer to 2: 1.5; 1.42; 1.415; 1.414,3; 1.414,22; 1.414,214.

11.5. Show that the following fractions are ever better approximations to 2, i.e., show that their squares are ever nearer to 2; compute also the differences of consecutive fractions in the series of fractions: $\tfrac{3}{2}, \tfrac{7}{5}, \tfrac{17}{12}, \tfrac{41}{29}, \tfrac{99}{70}, \tfrac{239}{169}$. How are these differences related to errors in the approximations to $\sqrt{2}$?

11·6 ∽ Obtaining the Square Root of a Natural Number

One may easily compute the square of 374 to obtain 139,876. That is, $374^2 = ?$ is solved simply by multiplying 374 by 374. The present task is to provide a method of solving the inverse problem, namely $?^2 = 139,876$, or $\sqrt{139,876} = ?$ Using these same numbers in a physical situation, one may state that the area of a square field 374 feet long and 374 feet wide is $374 \times 374 = 139,876$ square feet. The present problem is to determine the dimensions of the square field from its known area, namely, 139,876. This is done by determining successively the individual digits of the required number. Note that $300^2 = 90,000$, which is smaller than 139,876, and that $400^2 = 160,000$, which is larger than 139,876. Therefore the first digit of the required number is 3.

Next, computing $310^2, 320^2, 330^2, \ldots, 390^2$, one notes that $370^2 = 136,900$, which is smaller than 139,876, and that $380^2 = 144,400$, which is larger than 139,876. Therefore, the first two digits of the required number are 37. Now, computing $371^2, 372^2, 373^2, 374^2$, one obtains $374^2 = 139,876$, which is the given area itself. Therefore, 374 is the required number of feet in the length and width of the square field.∎

A closer examination of the geometrical aspect of these successive steps will reduce the number of trials of possible digits and present a concise method of computing the square root of any natural number or of any decimal fraction, proper or improper. Grouping the digits into pairs by overlinings beginning at the decimal point, namely 13 98 76, one readily notes that the left hand pair, 13, lies between the square numbers 9 and 16; therefore the first digit of the required square root of 139,876 must be 3, as $3^2 = 9$ and $4^2 = 16$.

The large square in Figure 11.1 represents the square field of area 139,876 square feet. Removing from it the smaller square of side 300 feet, or area 90,000 square feet, one has remaining an L-shaped area of 139,876 − 90,000, or 49,876 square feet.

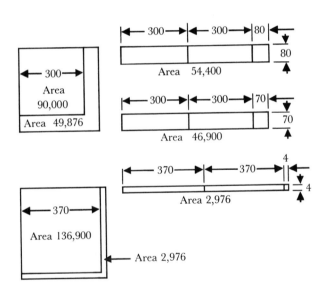

FIGURE II.I

One must find next the largest number of 10s to be added to the length of the side of the smaller square, 300, so that the resulting area of this enlarged square does not exceed in size the original square of area 169,876. Reassemble the L-shaped area into two long rectangles and a tiny square, forming one long rectangle of length 300 + 300 + ? and width ? wherein the ? represents the length of the side of the tiny square. As the area of this long rectangle is 49,876, its *approximate* width would be 49,876 ÷ 600 = 83.12 . . . , ignoring the length of the side of the tiny square, the ?. Now, testing 80 as the nearest possible 10s digit, the area of the L-shaped configuration would be (300 +

$300 + 80) \times 80 = 54{,}400$, which is too large. Testing the ? as 70, one obtains $(300 + 300 + 70) \times 70 = 46{,}900$, which is smaller than the area of the L-shaped configuration. Therefore, 370 represents the side of the largest square to the nearest 10s that can be removed from the large original square.

Repeating the discussion with the larger interior square of side 370, the resulting L-shaped figure has an area of $139{,}876 - 370^2 = 2{,}976$. Reassembling this L-shaped figure into a long, thin rectangle of length $370 + 370 + h$ and width h, the approximate width h is equal to $2{,}976 \div 740 = 4.02 \ldots$. Testing $h = 4$, one obtains $(370 + 370 + 4) \times 4 = 2{,}976$. Therefore h must be 4, the number of units in the required square root of 139,876, whence $\sqrt{139{,}876} = 374$.

The foregoing steps leading to the required square root of 139,876 may be arranged into a convenient algorithm for the extraction of the square root of any natural number, or decimal proper or improper fraction. The ensuing pattern is used because it may be readily developed into the corresponding similar algorithm for obtaining higher roots, namely, cube roots, fourth roots, fifth roots, etc. The customary orthodox forms for performing square and cube roots are presented presently.

For the extraction of square roots, one must know that $1^2 = 1$, $2^2 = 4$, $3^3 = 9$, $4^2 = 16$, $5^2 = 25$, $6^2 = 36$, $7^2 = 49$, $8^2 = 64$, and $9^2 = 81$. Array 1 with 000 and 139,876. Use 300 as the working number, as 300^2 is the largest square of hundreds not exceeding 139,876.

The successive steps leading to the first double line are the following. For identification, the working number 300 is printed in italic, *300*. Rewrite the original 1 as 1^*; $1^* \times 300 = 300$, which is written under the 000; add $000 + 300 = 300^*$; $300^* \times 300 = 90{,}000$, which is written under 139,876; subtract $139{,}876 - 90{,}000 = 49{,}876$. Again write 1^* under the previous 1^*; $1^* \times 300 = 300$, which is written under the 300^*; add $300^* + 300 = 600$.

1	000	139,876	*300*
	300	90,000	
1^*	300^*	49,876	
	300		
1^*	600		

For the second working number, use the largest number of 10s obtained from $49{,}876 \div 600$, namely, 80. Thus, write the 1^{**} under the 1^*; $1^{**} \times 80 = 80$, which is written under the 600; add $600 + 80 = 680$; $680 \times 80 = 52{,}400$, which is too large, as it exceeds 49,876. Now test the next lower number of 10s, namely 70, as a working number.

1^*	600	49,876	*80*
	80	52,400	
1^{**}	680		

Use *70* as a working number. Write the 1** under the 1*; 1** × 70 = 70, which is written under the 600; add 600 + 70 = 670; 670 × 70 = 46,900, which is written under the 49,876; subtract 49,876 − 46,900 = 2,976. Again write 1** under the previous 1**; 1** × 70 = 70, which is written under 670; add 670 + 70 = 740. Write under the next double line the first three numbers occurring above it.

1*	600	49,876	$\boxed{70}$
	70	46,900	
1**	670	2,976	
	70		
1**	740		

To obtain the next likely number, divide 2,976 by the 740, obtaining 4.02 . . . . Using the 4 as the working number, the algorithm terminates with the zero occurring in the subtraction 2,976 − 2,976 = 0. The sum of the appropriate working numbers, namely, 300 + 70 + 4, or 374, is the required square root of 139,876.

1**	740	2,976	$\boxed{4}$
	4	2,976	
1***	744	0	

The validity of the prescribed algorithm is to be established by noting that the successive steps are precisely those used in the previous discussion, leading to the determination of the size of the side of the square field of known area 139,876 square feet. The student is urged to identify the corresponding steps in the two foregoing presentations.

To calculate the square root of 2 by this procedure, one knows that the algorithm will never terminate nor yield a periodic decimal fraction, since 2 is not equal to the square of any rational number. However, by continuing the algorithm sufficiently far, one may compute the square root of 2 as accurately as desired; i.e., with an error as small as one may specify, *but not zero*. Note again that the successive working numbers are the successive digits of the required square root of 2.

1	0	2	$\boxed{1}$
	1	1	
1	1		
	1		
1	2		

1 is the working number, as it is the largest square number not exceeding 2.

1	2	1
	0.4	0.96
1	2.4	0.04
	0.4	
1	2.8	

0.4 Note that $1 \div 2 = 0.5$; but 0.5 is too large as a working number; hence try *0.4*.

1	2.80	0.04
	0.01	0.028,1
1	2.81	0.011,9
	0.01	
1	2.82	

0.01 Note that $0.04 \div 2.8$ yields *0.01* as the largest possible working number.

1	2.82	0.011,9
	0.004	0.011,296
1	2.824	0.000,604
	0.004	
1	2.828	

0.004 Note that $0.011,9 \div 2.82$ yields *0.004* as the largest possible working number.

1	2.828	0.000,604
	0.000,2	0.000,565,64
1	2.828,2	0.000,038,36
	0.000,2	
1	2.828,4	

0.000,2 Note that $0.000,604 \div 2.828$ yields *0.000,2* as the largest possible working number.

1	2.828,4	0.000,038,36
	0.000,01	0.000,028,284,1
1	2.828,41	0.000,010,075,9
	0.000,01	
1	2.828,42	

0.000,01 Note that $0.000,038,36 \div 2.828,4$ yields the largest possible working number, namely, *0.000,01*.

1	2.828,42	0.000,010,075,9
	0.000,003	0.000,008,485,269
1	2.828,423	0.000,001,590,631
	0.000,003	
1	2.828,426	

0.000,003

1	2.828,426	0.000,001,590,631

Thus the correct value for $\sqrt{2}$ is 1.414,213, with error less than 0.000,001. However, it may be proved that if the last used successful working number contains k digits to the right of the decimal point (in this case 0.000,003 contains $k = 6$ digits, the five 0s and the 3 to the right of the decimal), then k more correct digits may be obtained by dividing the right end number by the middle number below the next ensuing double line. Thus, dividing 0.000,001,590,631 by 2.828,426 yields 0.000,000,562,372 . . . , or six more correct digits of the required square root of 2. That is, $\sqrt{2} = 1.414,213,562,372$, with error less than 0.000,000,000,001.

The foregoing algorithm for the extraction of square roots, as demonstrated for obtaining the square root of 139,876 and of 2 may be condensed into the conventional form. The student should follow through the steps carefully and identify the numbers as they occur with the same numbers in the foregoing algorithm.

To compute the square root of 139,876 by the conventional algorithm, mark off the given number whose square root is desired into *pairs* of digits, beginning at the decimal point. If no decimal point is written it is understood to be at the right end of the given number. The number of pairs of digits so marked off is the number of digits in the computed root. Thus: $\overline{13}\ \overline{98}\ \overline{76}$ shows three pairs of digits by the three overlines that mark off the given digits; hence there must be three digits in the calculated square root.

Select the largest square natural number that does not exceed the number in the left end set (this left end set may be a pair of digits, as in this instance $\overline{13}$, or it may be a single digit, as in the ensuing example). Here the largest square not exceeding 13 is 9. Place the 3, whose square is 9, in the divisor position, which will assemble the digits for the required square root; place the 9 under the 13; subtract the 9 from the 13, obtaining the 4; transfer the next pair of digits, the $\overline{98}$, to a new position adjoining the 4, thereby forming the new remainder 498. The orthodox form of the algorithm now appears thus:

$$\begin{array}{r|l}
\overline{13}\ \overline{98}\ \overline{76} & \underline{\ 3} \\
9 & \\
\hline
68 \qquad 4\ 9\ 8 &
\end{array}$$

Form the "trial divisor," which is *double* the portion of the root that has been found, the 3, thus obtaining 6 for the trial divisor. Obtain the units digit of the quotient of $49 \div 6$, ignoring the right end digit of the 498. Thus, $49 \div 6 = 8.125$. By placing this *8* to the right of the trial divisor 6, one forms the complete divisor, 68. Now multiply the complete divisor 68 by its right end digit, 8. Thus $68 \times 8 = 544$. But 544 is unsatisfactory, as 544 is larger than 498. Hence, use the next smaller digit, 7, instead of 8 to form the complete divisor 67. Then $67 \times 7 = 469$. Place the 7 beside the 3 in the divisor position.

Subtract the 469 from 498, obtaining 29; transfer the next (and last) pair of digits, the 76, to its new position to the right of the 29, thus forming the new remainder, 2976. The orthodox or conventional form of the square root algorithm now appears thus:

$$
\begin{array}{r}
\overline{13}\ \overline{98}\ \overline{76}\ \quad \underline{\quad 37} \\
9 \\
67 \qquad \overline{4\ 9\ 8} \\
7 \qquad 4\ 6\ 9 \\
\overline{\qquad\qquad 29\ 76}
\end{array}
$$

Form the next trial divisor by doubling the portion of the square root that has now been found, the 37, obtaining 74. This new trial divisor may also be found quite simply by *adding* the previous complete divisor, 67 and 7, as these numbers appear in the immediately preceding multiplication which yielded the 469.

Obtain the units digit of the quotient of $297 \div 74$, ignoring the right end digit of the 2976. Thus $297 \div 74 = 4$. Append this 4 to the trial divisor to form the complete divisor, 744. Obtaining the product of the complete divisor 744 by its right end digit 4, one has $744 \times 4 = 2976$. Subtracting this product from the latest remainder, 2976, one obtains the final remainder 0.

The complete conventional algorithm for the extraction of the square root of 139,876 appears compactly as follows. The successive multiplications of the complete divisors by their right end digits are done mentally, thus facilitating the formation of the ensuing trial divisors.

$$
\begin{array}{r}
\overline{13}\ \overline{98}\ \overline{76}\ \quad \underline{\quad 374} \\
9 \\
67 \qquad \overline{4\ 9\ 8} \\
7 \qquad 4\ 6\ 9 \\
\overline{744} \qquad \overline{2\ 9\ 76} \\
4 \qquad 2\ 9\ 76 \\
\overline{\qquad\qquad 0}
\end{array}
$$

Compute the square root of 2 to 12 digits to the right of the decimal point. The conventional algorithm yields the first six digits to the right of the decimal point; division of the final remainder by the associated trial divisor yields six more digits of the required square root.

	$\overline{2.00}\ \overline{00}\ \overline{00}\ \overline{00}\ \overline{00}\ \overline{00}$	*1.414213*
	1	
24	1 00	
4	96	
281	4 00	
1	2 81	
2824	1 19 00	
4	1 12 96	
28282	6 04 00	
2	5 65 64	
282841	38 36 00	
1	28 28 41	
2828423	10 07 59 00	
3	8 48 52 69	
2828426	1 59 06 31	

Six more digits of the square root of 2 may be obtained by dividing the last remainder, which actually is 0.000,001,590,631, by the latest trial divisor, which actually is 2,828,426, thereby obtaining the quotient, 0.000,000,562,372, . . . , of six more digits of the square root; that is to say, $\sqrt{2} = 1.414,213,562,372$. It may be of interest to verify the fact that the quotient of any remainder by the corresponding trial divisor yields as many more digits of the required square root as the number of digits to the right of the decimal point already obtained at that stage.

⚭ PROBLEMS [CONTINUED] ⚭

11.6. Compute the square root of the following numbers. These numbers are square numbers and hence have rational square roots.

    a.   927,369   *c.*   217.857,6   *e.*   65,536

    b.   7,378.81   *d.*   539.725,824   *f.*   0.072,9

11.7. Obtain the best rational approximation for $\sqrt{3}$ to the nearest 0.000,001. One may use the conventional algorithm to compute the square root of 3 to the seventh digit to the right of the decimal point, then round off the result to six digits to the right of the decimal point; or one may use the conventional algorithm to compute the square root of 3 to the fourth digit to the right of the decimal point, *then* divide the remainder by the corresponding trial divisor at that stage to obtain four additional digits to the right of the decimal point, thereby having eight digits of the square root of 3 to the right of the decimal point. Correctly rounding off this result to the required number of digits yields the required result.

11.8. Obtain the best rational approximations of the square roots of the following numbers, with the indicated allowable errors.

a. 380, with error less than 0.001

b. 5.79, with error less than 0.001

c. 986.713, with error less than 0.000,1

d. 5, with error less than 0.000,001

e. 1,020,304,050.473,77, with error less than 0.000,1

11·7 ∾ THE PYTHAGOREAN RELATIONSHIP

The number of units of length in the diagonal and in the two sides of every rectangle are related to one another by a most remarkable relationship whose discovery has been attributed to the ancient Greek philosopher Pythagoras, about 550 B.C. The diagonal separates the rectangle into two equal triangles called *right triangles*, as each triangle contains one right angle of the original rectangle. The longest side of each right triangle formed by the diagonal of the rectangle is called the *hypotenuse*, connoting in Greek "lying opposite to" the right angle. The Pythagorean relationship, as proved in Euclid's Elements of Geometry, Book 1, Proposition 47, states that in every right triangle the square of the hypotenuse is equal to the sum of the squares of the other two sides. Incidentally, Proposition 48, the last proposition of Book 1, proves the converse, namely, that if the square on one side of a triangle is equal to the sum of the squares of the other two sides, the triangle must be a right triangle.

If the length of the two sides of a rectangle are 5 inches by 12 inches, respectively, the length of the diagonal may be computed by use of the Pythagorean relationship, namely, that the square of the number of units of length of the diagonal represented by d^2 must be equal to the sum of the *squares* of 12 and of 5, or $12^2 + 5^2$. Hence, if $d^2 = 12^2 + 5^2$, or $d^2 = 144 + 25$, or $d^2 = 169$, then d must be equal to $\sqrt{169}$, or 13. Therefore, the diagonal is 13 inches in length.

∾ PROBLEMS [CONTINUED] ∾

11.9. Calculate the length of the diagonal of each rectangle of the indicated dimensions. Calculate also the perimeter and the area specifying the unit for each.

a. Length 15 feet, width 8 feet

b. Length 80 yards, width 39 yards

c. Length 308 meters, width 75 meters

d. Length $21\frac{2}{3}$ feet, width $5\frac{3}{4}$ feet

To avoid fractions, one may convert feet into inches: 1 foot = 12 inches.

11.10. A field is 56 yards long and contains an area of 1,848 square yards. Calculate its width and the length of its diagonals.

11.11. The diagonals of a rectangle are 113 centimeters long. The rectangle is 15 centimeters wide. Calculate the length and the area of the rectangle.

11.12. Post A is 7 rods north of post B and 24 rods west of post C. How far apart are B and C?

11.13. A ladder 17 feet long leans against a vertical wall with its feet on level ground. If the feet of the ladder are 8 feet from the wall, how high upon the wall does the ladder reach?

11.14. Calculate to the nearest 0.001 inch the length of the diagonals of a square whose area is 7 square inches.

$11 \cdot 8$ ～ Obtaining the cube root of a natural number

Let the cube of 637 be $637 \times 637 \times 637$, or 258,474,853. Now the problem is to devise a method of computing $\sqrt[3]{258,474,853}$ without knowing that this number is to be 637. In geometrical language, if the length of the edge of a cubical block is 637 inches, its volume must be 258,474,853 cubic inches. The present problem is to determine the length of an edge of a cubical block whose volume is 258,474,853 cubic inches. One must know that $1^3 = 1$, $2^3 = 8$, $3^3 = 27$, $4^3 = 64$, $5^3 = 125$, $6^3 = 216$, $7^3 = 343$, $8^3 = 512$, and $9^3 = 729$.

Now to extract the cube root of 258,474,853, one must first determine the correct number of hundreds, namely 600, then the correct number of tens, namely 30, and finally the correct number of units, namely 7, thus obtaining the complete cube root, $600 + 30 + 7$, or 637. The foregoing list of cubes shows that six is the number of hundreds required, as $600^3 = 216,000,000$, while $700^3 = 343,000,000$, which exceeds the given cube, 258,474,853. Again the geometrical aspect of the solution will clarify the details.

Removing the cube of volume 216,000,000 from the given cube (Figure 11.2) leaves a cave-shaped volume containing 258,474,853–216,000,000 = 42,474,853 cubic inches. This remaining volume consists of three slabs, three sticks, and one tiny cubical block. Figure 11.2 also shows these seven pieces reassembled into one rectangular block with a tiny cubical projection in the lower right corner. Since the three large square slabs contain by far the greater portion of this rectangular volume, the unknown thickness of this rectangular block cannot be greater than its volume, 42,474,853 cubic inches, divided by the combined area of the square faces of the three slabs (instead of the entire top area of this rectangular configuration); thus the thickness cannot be greater than 42,474,853 $\div$ (3×600^2), or 42,474,853 $\div$ 1,080,000 = 39.4 . . . . Using 3 tens as the possible number of tens, for the thickness of these seven pieces, one obtains the

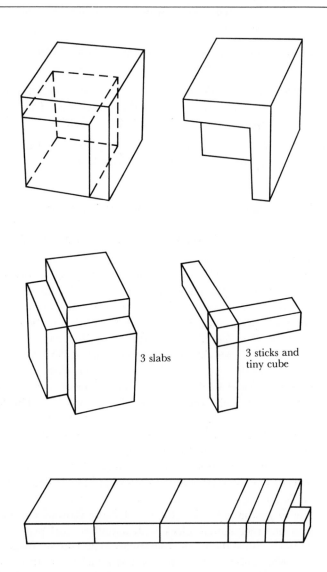

FIGURE 11.2

combined volume of the seven pieces as $3 \times 30 \times 600^2 + 3 \times 600 \times 30^2 + 30^3$, or 34,047,000. Subtracting this volume, 34,047,000 cubic inches, from the previous remaining volume, 42,474,853 cubic inches, one obtains 42,474,853 − 34,047,000 = 8,427,853 cubic inches, which represents the volume of a much thinner cave-shaped volume; i.e., removing a cube of edge 600 + 30, or 630 cubic inches, from the original cube of volume 258,474,853 cubic inches, one obtains 258,474,853 − 630³ = 8,427,853 cubic inches, which represents the volume again of three slabs, three sticks, and one tiny cube; these latter, however, are much thinner than the previous seven pieces. Again the three large square slabs of larger edges 630 inches constitute the greater portion of the entire volume, so that the thickness cannot exceed 8,427,853 ÷ (3 × 630²) = 7.8 . . . . Using 7 inches for the thickness, the volume of these seven pieces would be $3 \times 630^2 \times 7 + 3 \times 630 \times 7^2 + 7^3 = 8,427,853$, which is precisely equal to the remaining cave-shaped volume. Therefore, the exact cube root of 258,474,853 is 600 + 30 + 7, or 637.

The various necessary arithmetical operations that were performed in determining the required 637 may be assembled in the following convenient algorithm, which is patterned exactly like that used for the extraction of square roots except that there are *two* insertions of sets of zeros in the first line and three sets of additions before reaching the ensuing double lines, instead of *one* set of zeros and two sets of additions.

1	000	000,000	258,474,853		600
	600	360,000	216,000,000		
1	600	360,000	42,474,853		
	600	720,000			
1	1,200	1,080,000			
	600				
1	1,800				

The first working number, 600, is determined from the list of cubes, $7^3 = 343$, whence $700^3 = 343,000,000$, which is too large as it exceeds the 258,474,853; however, $6^3 = 216$, whence $600^3 = 216,000,000$, which is smaller than 258,474,853.

1	1,800	1,080,000	42,474,853		30
	30	54,900	34,047,000		
1	1,830	1,134,900	8,427,853		
	30	55,800			
1	1,860	1,190,700			
	30				
1	1,890				

Working numbers after the first one are determined as not exceeding the right end number under the double line, here 42,747,853, divided by the number preceding it, here 1,080,000. Hence 43,474,853 ÷ 1,080,000 = 39+. Use 30 as the largest multiple of 10.

1	1,890	1,190,700	8,427,853	7
	7	13,279	8,427,853	
1	1,897	1,203,979	0	

The working number 7 is the largest unit not exceeding $8,427,853 \div 1,190,700 = 7.8 \ldots$. Use 7.

As the subtraction yields 0, the extraction yields an exact cube root.

The foregoing algorithm for the extraction of the cube root of 258,474,853 may be condensed into the more compact conventional algorithm. One should examine it carefully, step by step, to note the exact equivalence of the two algorithms and to master the conventional one. The first step is to group the digits into sets of threes beginning at the decimal point.

$$
\begin{array}{r}
258,474,853 \\
216 \\
\hline
\end{array}
\begin{array}{l}
\underline{637}
\end{array}
$$

	42 474
108	
54	
9	
$11349 \times 3 =$	34 047
	8 427 853
11907	
1323	
49	
$1203979 \times 7 =$	8 427 853
	0

Note that the largest cube is 6^3, or 216, that does not exceed the left set of overlined digits, $\overline{258}$, as $7^3 = 343$, which exceeds 258. Subtract 216 from 258; place the 6 in the answer; bring down the next set of three digits, $\overline{474}$, into juxtaposition with the remainder, 42, thus forming 42,474.

The trial divisor is always three times the square of the current portion of the answer, here 6, hence the trial divisor is 3×6^2 or 108. Divide 108 into 42,47̶4̶ (ignoring the final two digits); $424 \div 108 = 3.9 \ldots$. Hence the next digit of the required root cannot exceed 3. Now use this *3* to form the complete divisor, as follows: $3 \times 3 \times 6^2 = 54$; place 54 under 108, extending the 54 one digit's place toward the right; $3^2 = 9$, so place this 9 under the 54, extending it one digit's place toward the right. Thus,

$$
\begin{array}{r}
108 \\
54 \\
9 \\
\hline
\end{array}
$$

The sum   11349   is the *complete* divisor

Finally, multiply the complete divisor by the *3*, obtaining 34,047, which is usable, as 34,047 does not exceed 42,474. If this latest product *did* exceed the remainder 42,474, the complete divisor would have to be formed by using the next smaller digit than the *3*, namely, the *2*. Since *3* yielded a usable complete divisor, place the *3* in the divisor position.

Subtract 34,047 from 42,474, obtaining 8,427. Bring down the next set of three digits, 853, into juxtaposition with the remainder, 8,427, forming 8,427,853. Form the new trial divisor by obtaining three times the square of the portion of the root already found, 63. Thus $3 \times 63^2 = 11,907$. Indeed, the new trial divisor may be found more easily by adding to the former complete divisor the former addends:

$$
\begin{array}{r}
54 \\
9 \\
9 \\
11349 \\
\hline
11907
\end{array}
$$

(to the right of the second 9) (Repeating the final addend 9)

Divide this trial divisor, 11,907, into the remainder, 8,427,8̶5̶3̶, ignoring the final digits 5̶3̶, obtaining 7.8 . . . . Hence the next digit of the required root cannot exceed 7.

$$
\begin{array}{ll}
11907 & \text{The trial divisor} \\
1323 & \text{Which is } 3 \times 63 \times 7 \text{ one place to the right} \\
49 & \text{Which is } 7^2 \text{ one more place to the right} \\
\hline
1203979 & \text{The complete divisor}
\end{array}
$$

Finally, multiplying the complete divisor by the multiplier 7, one obtains 8,427,853, which does not exceed the current remainder 8,427,853, so the 7 is a correct digit to be placed in the divisor position. Subtracting this new product from the current remainder, one obtains 0, thus noting that the root is the exact cube root of 258,474,853. The entire required cube root has been assembled in the divisor 637.

As another illustration of these two algorithms of cube root extraction, one may examine the calculation of the cube root of 2 to the nearest 0.000,001.

1	0	0	2	⌊1
	1	1	1	
1	1	1	1	
	1	2		
1	2	3		
	1			
1	3			

Each ensuing working number must not exceed the first (left hand) digit of the quotient of the right end number under the double line by the number preceding it.

1	3.0	3.00	1.000	0.3
	0.3	0.99	1.197	
1	3.3	3.99	(Impossible as 1.197 exceeds 1.000)	

As a possible working number use 0.3, the first digit different from 0 in the quotient of $1 \div 3 = 0.33 \ldots$. As 0.3 is too large to serve as a working number, repeat this line of operations with a working number of 0.2, the next available working number smaller than 0.3.

1	3.0	3.00	1.000	0.2
	0.2	0.64	0.728	
1	3.2	3.64	0.272	
	0.2	0.68		
1	3.4	4.32		
	0.2			
1	3.6			

1	3.60	4.32	0.272,000	0.06
	0.06	2.196	0.909,6	
1	3.66	6.516	Impossible	

As a possible working number, note that $0.272 \div 4.32 = 0.062 \ldots$. Hence one should test 0.06 as a possible working number.

One finds 0.06 too large to serve as a working number, so one must test the next smaller one-digit working number, 0.05. Again rewriting the array of numbers under the latest double line, one proceeds thus:

1	3.60	4.320	0.272,000	0.05
	0.05	0.182,5	0.225,125	
1	3.65	4.502,5	0.046,875	
	0.05	0.185,0		
1	3.70	4.687,5		
	0.05			
1	3.75			

As $0.046,875 \div 4.687,5 = 0.009 \ldots$, one should test 0.009 as a possible working number, which does prove to be correct.

1	3.750	4.687,500	0.046,875,000		0.009
	0.009	0.033,831	0.042,491,979		
1	3.759	4.721,331	0.004,383,021		
	0.009	0.033,912			
1	3.768	4.755,243			
	0.009				
1	3.777				

Note that 0.004,38 . . . ÷ 4.75 . . . yields 0.000,9 . . . . Hence test 0.000,9 as a possible working number.

1	3.777,0	4.755,243,00	0.004,383,021,000		0.000,9
	0.000,9	0.003,400,92	0.004,282,778,799		
1	3.777,9	4.758,643,11	0.000,100,242,201		
	0.000,9	0.003,400,92			
1	3.778,8	4.762,044,03			
	0.000,9				
1	3.779,7				

Note that 0.000,100,2 . . . ÷ 4.76 . . . yields 0.000,02 as a likely working number.

1	3.779,70	4.762,044,030,0	0.000,100,242,201,000		0.000,02
	0.000,02	0.000,075,594,4	0.000,095,242,392,488		
1	3.779,72	4.762,119,624,4	0.000,004,999,808,512		
	0.000,02	0.000,075,594,8			
1	3.779,74	4.762,195,219,2			
	0.000,02				
1	3.779,76				

1	3.779,760	4.762,195,219,200	0.000,004,999,808,512,000		0.000,001
	0.000,001	0.000,003,779,761	0.000,004,762,198,998,961		
1	3.779,761	4.762,198,998,961	0.000,000,237,609,513,039		
	0.000,001	0.000,003,779,762			
1	3.779,762	4.762,202,778,723			

One may anticipate the next working number as the first digit in 0.000,000, 237, . . . ÷ 4.76 . . . = 0.000,000,049, . . . , so that the cube root of 2 has been calculated as 1.259,921,04 . . . .

Furthermore, it may be proved that if the numbers under any double line are $\overline{\overline{1 \quad A \quad B \quad C}}$, and if the last used working number contains n digits, including the 0s, to the right of the decimal point, then one may divide B into C to obtain as many more digits of the required cube root immediately to the right of the last used working number as there are 0s immediately following the decimal point in the number $A \times (0.1)^{2n}$.

In the foregoing example the last working number is 0.000,001, containing to the right of the decimal point six digits. Moreover, $A \times 0.1^{2n}$ becomes 3.779,63 × 0.000,000,000,001, or 0.000,000,000,003,7 . . . , which contains eleven 0s immediately following the decimal point. Hence, using 11 digits of C, one divides 0.000,000,237,60 by 4.762,2 . . . . Omitting the useless digits, the division appears thus:

$$
\begin{array}{r}
0.000,000,049,89 \\
4.762,2\overline{\smash{\big)}0.000,000,237,60} \\
190,48 \\ \hline
47,12 \\
42,85 \\ \hline
4,27 \\
3,80 \\ \hline
47 \\
42 \\ \hline
\end{array}
$$

The final digit uncertain as 9 or 8

Accordingly, $\sqrt[3]{2}$ = 1.259,921,049,89 with error less than 0.000,000,000,01.

Using the conventional algorithm for the calculation of the cube root of 2 to *five* decimal places to the right of the decimal point, one supplies *five* sets of three 0s to the right of the decimal point at the outset. One must recall that each ensuing trial divisor is three times the square of the portion of the required cube root that has been obtained at that stage. However, each new trial divisor may be obtained much less laboriously by adding to the previous complete divisor the two corrective numbers that were added to the previous trial divisor to form the previous complete divisor, adding twice the last of the two corrective numbers. To master the process one must identify each number as it occurs in the ensuing presentation.

$$\overline{2}.\overline{000},\overline{000},\overline{000},\overline{000} \quad \Big| \; \textit{1.259,92}$$

	1
3	$\overline{1\ 000}$
6	
4	
$\overline{364} \times 2 =$	728
6	$\overline{272\ 000}$
4	
4	
$\overline{432}$	
180	
25	
$\overline{45025} \times 5 =$	225 125
180	$\overline{46\ 875\ 000}$
25	
25	
$\overline{46875}$	
3375	
81	
$\overline{4721331} \times 9 =$	42 491 979
3375	$\overline{4\ 383\ 021\ 000}$
81	
81	
$\overline{4755243}$	
33993	
81	
$\overline{475864311} \times 9 =$	4 282 778 799
33993	$\overline{100\ 242\ 201\ 000}$
81	
81	
$\overline{476204403}$	
75594	
4	
$\overline{47621196244} \times 2 =$	95 242 392 488
	$\overline{4\ 999\ 808\ 512}$

Clearly, the next digit of the root must be 1, so that the cube root of 2 is equal to 1.259,92, with error less than 0.000,005.

Comment: If only two or three digits of a cube root are required, the conventional method should prove quite satisfactory. But if the required cube root involves an extensive number of digits, the algorithm involving successive working numbers is recommended as less tedious.

11.15. Compute the cube roots of the following perfect cube numbers:

a.	17,576	*e.*	85,184	*h.*	438,976
b.	250,047	*f.*	226,981	*i.*	704,969
c.	778,688	*g.*	941,192	*j.*	205,379
d.	32,768				

Note that these cube roots could have been obtained *mentally* with no writing whatever. This is possible by knowing only the cubes of the first nine natural numbers and the peculiar feature of the final digit of these nine cube numbers.

11.16. Using both methods, compute the cube roots of the following numbers:

a.	80,062,991	*d.*	476,379,541	*g.*	201,436,163,924
b.	100,544,625	*e.*	949,862,087	*h.*	26,145,183,232
c.	273,359,449	*f.*	799,178,752	*i.*	12,891,914,491,392

11.17. Compute to the nearest 0.001 the cube roots of the following numbers:

a.	63.876,721,44	*c.*	0.066,462,119,7	*e.*	0.000,064,368
b.	0.563,876,105	*d.*	0.003,101,22	*f.*	100,056,999,783.1

11.18. Compute the volume of the cube if the area of one face is 289 square inches. Note especially the relationship between the length of an edge, the area of a face, and the volume of the cube.

11.19. Compute to the nearest 0.000,1 the volume of the cube if the total area of all its six faces is equal to 35 square inches.

11.20. Calculate the radius of the circle whose circumference is 15.708 inches in length. Compute also the area of this circle. (Use $\pi = 3.141,6$.)

11.21. Compute the radius of the sphere whose area is 78.54 square inches. Compute also the volume of this sphere. (Use $\pi = 3.141,6$.)

11.22. If the relationship between the diameter and the volume of a sphere may be expressed as $V = \pi D^3/6$, or as $D = \sqrt[3]{6V/\pi}$, compute to the nearest 0.01 inch the inner diameter of a hollow sphere that contains exactly 40 gallons. Use $\pi = 3.141,6$ and the fact that 231 cubic inches are equal to 1 gallon. Convert the fractional part of the result to the nearest $\frac{1}{64}$ part of an inch, noting that 64 sixty-fourths equal 1 inch.

11·9 ∾ Obtaining higher roots of natural numbers than square and cube roots

The first of the two algorithms for extracting square roots and cube roots as previously presented can be extended directly to the calculation of all higher roots of natural numbers or to decimal fraction, namely, to the extraction of fourth roots, fifth roots, sixth roots, etc. There is no simple method of exhibiting the validity of these root extractions by geometrical illustrations as was done for square roots and cube roots when they refer to the area of a square or the volume of a cubical block. The validity of these higher root extractions will be provided in advanced algebra.

In arraying the work for the extraction of fourth, fifth, sixth, or higher roots, one merely inserts between the 1 and the given power number three, four, five or more 0s instead of the one or two 0s used for the extraction of square roots or the cube roots.

The ensuing algorithm illustrates how one may compute the *fifth* root of 222,620,278,176. Marking this number off into sets of *five* digits from the decimal point, as $\overline{22}\ \overline{26202}\ \overline{78176}$, one obtains *three* sets, indicating that the fifth root of this number must contain *three* digits. To obtain the left end digit, or the hundreds digit, of the required fifth root, one must know the fifth powers of the single-digit natural numbers, to wit: $1^5 = 1$, $2^5 = 32$, $3^5 = 243$, $4^5 = 1,024$, $5^5 = 3,125$, $6^5 = 7,776$, $7^5 = 16,807$, $8^5 = 32,768$, $9^5 = 59,049$.

Clearly, the hundreds digit of the required fifth root must be 1, as 1 is the largest fifth power that does not exceed $\overline{22}$, for $2^5 = 32$. Accordingly, 100 is the first working number in this fifth-root algorithm.

1	0	0	0	0	222,620,278,176	$\lfloor$ 100
	100	10,000	1,000,000	100,000,000	10,000,000,000	
1	100	10,000	1,000,000	100,000,000	212,620,278,176	
	100	20,000	3,000,000	400,000,000		
1	200	30,000	4,000,000	500,000,000		
	100	30,000	6,000,000			
1	300	60,000	10,000,000			
	100	40,000				
1	400	100,000				
	100					
1	500					

To obtain 80 as the largest number of tens to be used as the working number, one notes that this maximum number of tens cannot exceed the quotient of

212,620,278 ÷ 500,000,000 = 425.24 . . . , or 42 tens, but since one cannot use more than 9 tens, one tries 90 as a working number, which is found to be too large.   Hence one tries 80, which is the correct working number.

1	500	100,000	10,000,000	500,000,000	212,620,278,176	80
	80	46,400	11,712,000	1,736,960,000	178,956,800,000	
1	580	146,400	21,712,000	2,236,960,000	33,663,478,176	
	80	52,800	15,936,000	3,011,840,000		
1	660	199,200	37,648,000	5,248,800,000		
	80	59,200	20,672,000			
1	740	258,400	58,320,000			
	80	65,600				
1	820	324,000				
	80					
1	900					

The quotient of 33,663,478,176 ÷ 5,248,800,000 yields 6 as the largest possible working number.   In testing the 6 one obtains the final difference, 0, which shows that the original number 222,620,278,176 is an exact fifth power.

1	900	324,000	58,320,000	5,248,800,000	33,663,478,176	6
	6	5,436	1,976,616	361,779,696	33,663,478,176	
1	906	329,436	60,296,616	5,610,579,696	0	

Accordingly, $\sqrt[5]{222,620,278,176} = 186$.

If the number is rather small, say less than 1,000, one may find its square root and cube root in various available handbooks such as that of the Chemical Rubber Publishing Company.   One may also obtain roots of any order by use of logarithm tables to as many digits as there are digits in the entries in the logarithm tables; the first few digits may also be obtained by use of the slide rule.   These methods will be presented in Lesson 16.   Modern computing machines can determine as many digits as one may desire for any root within a matter of seconds.

∽ PROBLEMS [CONCLUDED] ∽

11.23.   Compute the indicated roots to the best three digits.

   a. $\sqrt[5]{418,195,493}$

   b. $\sqrt[7]{268,435,456}$

    c. $\sqrt[6]{4.763}$

    d. Compute the cube root of the square root of 4.763 to the best three digits. How should this result compare with that of (*c*)? (Refer to Evolution of Surds in Section 11.4.)

11.24. The rate of interest, compounded annually, that is required to double an original principal in *n* years is equal to the *n*th root of 2 diminished by 1. For money to double itself in 7 years, the rate must be $\sqrt[7]{2} - 1$, compounded annually, or 1.104,1 . . . − 1, or 0.104,1 . . . , or 10.41 percent. What rate of interest, compounded annually, will double an original principal in 5 years? Give result to nearest 0.1 percent.

11.25. By computing a series of square roots determine the rate of interest, compounded annually, that will double a sum of money in 16 years.

11.26. Compute $\sqrt[6]{481,890,304}$ by (*a*) computing the cube root of the square root of this number; (*b*) computing the square root of the cube root of this number.

Note 1 ∽ *The use of the binomial theorem for obtaining rational approximations for surds.*

The binomial theorem expresses any power of the sum of two numbers as a sum of multiples of products descending powers of one of the two numbers by the ascending powers of the other number. Symbolically it appears thus:

$$(a + b)^n = a^n + na^{n-1}b + \frac{(n)(n-1)}{1 \times 2} a^{n-2}b^2 + \frac{(n)(n-1)(n-2)}{1 \times 2 \times 3} a^{n-3}b^3$$
$$+ \frac{(n)(n-1)(n-2)(n-3)}{1 \times 2 \times 3 \times 4} a^{n-4}b^4 + \frac{(n)(n-1)(n-2)(n-3)(n-4)}{1 \times 2 \times 3 \times 4 \times 5} a^{n-5}b^5 + \cdots$$

This remarkable formula was discovered by Isaac Newton and is often called "Newton's theorem." Newton derived it in response to a request from his friend John Wallis who futilely thought it would enable him to solve the problem of squaring the circle, i.e., to construct with compasses and straightedge a square that has the same area as that of a given circle. This problem has since been shown to be unsolvable with compasses and straightedge.

    If *n* is a unit fraction and if *a* is larger than *b* in absolute value, $(a + b)^n$ is approximately equal to $a^n + na^{n-1}b$, the sum of the remaining terms being altogether small as compared to the sum of the first two terms that have been retained. Hence to compute a rational approximation for the *n*th root of any natural number, let *a* be the integral *n*th power that is nearest to *a* + *b*. To compute $\sqrt[5]{40}$, write $\sqrt[5]{40}$ as

$$(32 + 8)^{\frac{1}{5}} = 2 + \frac{8}{5 \times 2^4} = 2 + \tfrac{1}{10} \text{ or } 2.1$$

And quite generally, if $a + b$ is the number whose nth root is required, and if A^n is the nearest exact nth power to $a + b$, then, using the first two terms of the binomial theorem, one has

$$(A^n + b)^{1/n} = (A^n)^{1/n} + \frac{1}{n}(A^n)^{1/n-1}b \qquad \text{which reduces to}$$

$$(A^n + b)^{1/n} = A + \frac{b}{A^{n-1}n}$$

as the required approximation formula for the nth root of $a + b$. Thus $\sqrt{17} = (16 + 1)^{\frac{1}{2}} = 4 + \dfrac{1}{2 \times 4} = 4.125$, whereas the more accurate decimal form for $\sqrt{17}$ is 4.123,106 . . . , so that the error in 4.125 is less than 0.002. Again,

$$\sqrt[3]{67} = \sqrt[3]{64 + 3} = 4 + \frac{3}{3 \times 4^2} = 4.062,5$$

whereas $\sqrt[3]{67} = 4.061,548, \ldots$, so that the error in 4.062,5 is less than 0.001.

Note 2 ⤳ Algebraic numbers versus transcendental numbers.

The complete set of all rational numbers may be visualized by positions, or "points," on any straight line of unlimited extent. Indeed, once the positions on the line are selected to represent the positions of the two numbers 0 and 1, the position of any other rational number may be located geometrically; i.e., the position may be determined concisely by the use of a straightedge and a pair of compasses (Section 5.7). Positions or points on the line that are not assigned to the rational numbers are said to represent *irrational numbers*. Such irrational numbers and all rational numbers constitute the complete set of *real numbers*. Until the complex numbers are introduced in Lesson 17, the word *number* means *real number*, rational or irrational, to which a position on the number line has been assigned.

Any decimal fraction that terminates or ultimately repeats periodically is a rational number; any decimal fraction that does not terminate or that does not sooner or later become periodic must be an irrational number. It has been shown (Section 5.7) that $\sqrt{2}$ is not a rational number; furthermore, $\sqrt[n]{p/q}$ cannot be a rational number unless p/q is the nth power of some rational number; i.e., $\sqrt[n]{p/q}$ is a rational number if and only if $p/q = (a/b)^n$. For, if $\sqrt[n]{p/q} = a/b$, then $p/q = (a/b)^n$ so that if a/b were rational, so also must p/q

be equal to the nth power of the rational number a/b, and therefore p/q must be rational since the nth power of any rational number must also be rational. Accordingly, if p/q is not the nth power of a rational number, then $\sqrt[n]{p/q}$ must be an irrational number. Such irrational numbers are called surd numbers.

All numbers hitherto encountered, except the actual number π itself, are called *algebraic numbers*. The *approximations* that are used for π, such as $\frac{22}{7}$, 3.141,6, and $\frac{355}{113}$, are *rational* numbers.

Definition. If A_1, A_2, A_3, . . . , A_n represent any set of integers, not all of them zeros, and if n and N represent any natural numbers, then ? represents an algebraic number. Actually ? represents any one of n algebraic numbers.

$$A_1 \times ?^n + A_2 \times ?^{n-1} + A_3 \times ?^{n-2} + \cdots + A_n \times ? = N$$

Particularly if $n = 1$ and $A_1 = 1$, then ? must represent a *natural number*. Again, if $n = 1$ and if $A_1 = +1$ or -1, then ? must represent an *integer*. If $n = 1$ and if A_1 is an integer, then ? represents the *rational number* N/A_1. If A_1 is a positive rational number and if $A_2 = A_3 = \cdots = A_n = 0$, then ? must represent the surd $\sqrt[n]{N/A_1}$, or the rational number a/b, provided $N/A_1 = (a/b)^n$; if A_1 is a negative rational number, n must presently be an odd natural number.

Moreover, if A_1, A_2, A_3, . . . , A_n are known integers and N a known natural number and if ? represents any rational number, the value of ?, if rational, can readily be determined by a limited number of trials; if ? is an irrational real number, its decimal fractional approximation may be obtained to any degree of accuracy by the algorithm that employed the successive series of working numbers, as successive digits of the decimal approximation of surds, the A_1, A_2, A_3, . . . , A_n serving as the first line of numbers.

Finally, the ? may or may not be equal to any combination of surds, but if ? represents a real number, ? may be assigned its unique position on the number line.

Quite generally, the expression $A_1 \times ?^n + A_2 \times ?^{n-1} + \cdots + A_n \times ? = N$ is called an algebraic equation, in which the A's and N represent integers, and n represents a natural number, and ?, a *root* or *solution* of the equation, is called an *algebraic* number. If the root is rational, or expressible by any specific combinations of radicals, it can be obtained by methods developed in algebra. Otherwise the roots may be obtained approximately in the form of decimal fractions to any desired degree of accuracy, but not with complete accuracy. Moreover, the natural number n is called the *degree* of the algebraic equation and indicates the exact number of roots the equation has or the number of numbers the ? can represent. Finally, if $A_1 = 1$, the ? represents numbers that are called *algebraic integers*. In contrast to algebraic integers, the integers of arithmetic, $0, +1, -1, +2, -2, +3, -3, \ldots$, are often called *rational* integers.

To illustrate, obtain the algebraic integer represented by ? in the equation $?^3 + 3(?) = 2$. Using the algorithm of successive working numbers, the successive digits of ? may be found as follows.

1	0	3	2		0.5
	0.5	0.25	1.625		
1	0.5	3.25	0.375		
	0.5	0.50			
1	1.0	3.75			
	0.5				
1	1.5				

The first working number cannot exceed the first digit of the decimal fractional form 2 ÷ 3 = 0.66 . . . . But 0.6 is found to be too large. Then *0.5* is found to be the correct working number.

1	1.5	3.75	0.375		0.09
	0.09	0.143,1	0.350,379		
1	1.59	3.893,1	0.024,621		
	0.09	0.151,2			
1	1.68	4.044,3			
	0.09				
1	1.77				

1	1.770	4.044,3	0.024,621,000		0.006
	0.006	0.010,656	0.024,329,736		
1	1.776	4.054,956	0.000,291,264		
	0.006	0.010,692			
1	1.782	4.065,648			
	0.006				
1	1.788				

1	1.788,00	4.065,648,000,0	0.000,291,264,000,000		0.000,07
	0.000,07	0.000,125,164,9	0.000,284,604,121,543		
1	1.788,07	4.065,773,164,9	0.000,006,659,878,457		
	0.000,07	0.000,125,169,8			
1	1.788,14	4.065,898,334,7			

As indicated in Section 11.8, ensuing digits of the required root may be obtained by dividing the 0.000,006,659,87 . . . by the 4.065,898 . . . , so that the required root is 0.596,071,39 . . . . However, if the degree is less than 5, the root, if irrational, may be expressed exactly in terms of radicals. For any degree greater than 4, the roots may be expressed in terms of radicals only in special situations. Thus the foregoing root may be expressed exactly as $\sqrt[3]{\sqrt{2} + 1} -$ $\sqrt[3]{\sqrt{2} - 1}$. It would be interesting to verify this fact by evaluating the radical expression to obtain the foregoing rational approximation for the root, namely, 0.596,071,3 . . . .

Any number that cannot serve as the root of an algebraic equation is called a transcendental number. The existence of transcendental numbers may be established by showing that: (1) The class of all algebraic numbers has the same cardinal number as the cardinal number of the set of natural numbers, namely, $\aleph_0$. (2) The class of all real numbers has a larger cardinal number than $\aleph_0$.

To prove that the cardinal number of the set of all algebraic numbers is $\aleph_0$, one must demonstrate that all algebraic numbers can be tabulated so that they may be paired off with the natural numbers. This may be done as follows.

The A's and the N are called the *coefficients* of the algebraic equation

$$A_1 \times ?^n + A_2 \times ?^{n-1} + A_3 \times ?^{n-2} + \cdots + A_n \times ? = N$$

The sum of n, the degree of the equation, and the absolute values of all the coefficients is called the *height* of the equation. There is no equation of height 1, as the sum of n and $|A_1|$ exceeds 1. There are two equations of height 2, namely, $+1 \times ? = 0$, $-1 \times ? = 0$ (each having the single root 0). There are eight equations of height 3, namely, $+1 \times ?^2 = 0$, $-1 \times ?^2 = 0$, $+2 \times ? = 0$, $-2 \times ? = 0$ (each having 0 as root); $+1 \times ? = +1$, $-1 \times ? = -1$ (each having $+1$ as root); $-1 \times ? = +1$, $+1 \times ? = -1$ (each having -1 as root). Now imagine that all roots of all equations are tabulated according to the heights of the equations, beginning with height 2, and omitting from the list any root that has occurred earlier in the list. As the number of roots of all equations of the same height is finite, each algebraic number will sooner or later occur in the list. Finally, pair off these algebraic numbers in the list with the consecutive natural numbers. The very possibility of pairing off the algebraic numbers in a one-to-one correspondence with the natural numbers is sufficient to prove that the set of all algebraic numbers has the same cardinal number as that of the set of natural numbers, namely, $\aleph_0$. The fact that the cardinal number of all irrational numbers is greater than $\aleph_0$ is established in Note 3.

After points, or positions, on the number line have been assigned to all the irrational *algebraic* numbers, there are infinitely many unassigned points on the number line. The unassigned points, or positions, on the number line represent the *transcendental* numbers. The French mathematician Charles Hermite proved in 1873 that the number e (2.712,281 . . .) is a transcendental number. The number e occurs prominently on many occasions in mathematical analysis; it is usually encountered first as the base of the system of natural, or Naperian, logarithms. In 1822 the German mathematician Ferdinand Lindemann proved that the important number π (3.141,592, . . .) is also transcendental. The important number π also occurs prominently in many situations of mathematical analysis; it is usually first encountered as the quotient of the numbers that represent the lengths of the circumference and the diameter of every Euclidean circle, or as the length of the circumference of the circle whose diameter is one unit of length.[1]

Note 3 ⟿ Positions for the irrational numbers on the number line. The cardinal number of the set of irrational numbers, Aleph-sub-one, $\aleph_1$.

Using the methods of elementary geometry (i.e., by use of unmarked straightedge and compasses), one may locate positions on the number line for $\sqrt[n]{R}$ if R represents any rational number and if n is any integral power of 2, namely, 2, 4, 8, 16, 32, . . . , as follows.

Draw a line through 0, perpendicular to the number line, and mark off on this perpendicular line the point P a unit's distance above 0; i.e., make the length from 0 to P equal to the distance on the number line from 0 to 1. Next, on the perpendicular line point Q below 0, mark off a distance equal to the rational number R. The two points P and Q are now regarded as the ends of a diameter of a circle which should be drawn with its center at the point midway between points P and Q so that its circumference passes through points P and Q. This circle also cuts the number line at points representing the numbers $+R^{n/2}$ and $-R^{n/2}$ to the right and to the left of 0, respectively. If $n = 2$, these two points on the number line are positions for $+\sqrt{R}$ and $-\sqrt{R}$. If n is larger than 2, that is, if $n = 2^k$, the previously described construction must be repeated k times. In each successive repetition the length laid off on the perpendicular line below 0 is equal to the length on the number line from 0 to the intersection points on the number line made by the circle most recently drawn. It is impossible to locate *geometrically* on the number line the appropriate positions for any other surds than the surds whose indices are integral powers of 2, namely, 2, 4, 8, 16, 32, ... This remarkable fact is established in advanced algebra or in college algebra.

The correct position for any irrational number whatever may be determined theoretically as follows. Let the irrational number be expressed decimally; i.e., in its nonperiodic decimal fractional form. The ensuing discussion is applied to the irrational number π whose decimal fractional expression can be exhibited to as many places as desired, as 3.141,592,653,793,238,462,643,38 . . . . The same treatment accorded to π applies to any other irrational number.

It is to be noted that two decimal fractions, whether rational or irrational, represent the same number if the decimal expressions are alike throughout. Moreover, if the decimal expressions are identical for a certain number of

[1] R. C. Archibald, "Klein's Famous Problems of Elementary Geometry," G. E. Stechert Company, New York, 1930.

digits, counting from the left ends of the two expressions, but differ in their next corresponding digit, the decimal expression that has the larger digit where the disagreement first occurs must represent the larger of the two numbers.   However, if the first digits to disagree are n and $n + 1$, and if all digits following the n are 9s, and all digits following the $n + 1$ are 0s, the two decimal expressions represent the same number. For example, $0.749,99 \ldots = 0.750,00 \ldots$, since $0.749,99 \ldots = 0.74 + 0.009,99 \ldots = 0.74 + \frac{9}{900} = 0.74 + 0.01 = 0.75$, while $0.750,00 \ldots$ is also equal to 0.75.

Consider now the following pairs of rational numbers:

3	4	3.141,592	3.141,593
3.1	3.2	3.141,592,6	3.141,592,7
3.14	3.15	3.414,592,65	3.141,592,66
3.141	3.142	3.141,592,653	3.141,592,654
3.141,5	3.141,6	. . . .
3.141,59	3.141,60		

The first number in each pair consists of the left end digits of the decimal expression for π, each ensuing such number containing one more digit than the first number of the preceding pair of numbers. The second number of each pair is obtained by adding one unit to the last digit of the first number of that same pair.

It is to be noted that: (1) The irrational number π lies between the two numbers of each of these pairs of numbers. (2) The position for π ought to lie on the number line between the positions of the two rational numbers of each of these pairs of rational numbers. (3) The distance between the two points representing any number pair is one-tenth as large as the distance on the number line between the two points representing the two numbers of the preceding number pair. (4) There can be only one point on the number line that lies between points representing the two numbers of each number pair, as the list of number pairs is extended indefinitely. For, if there were two such points marked as P and Q on the number line lying between all pairs of points representing the pairs of numbers in the number pairs, the distance between points representing the two numbers of number pairs eventually becomes smaller than the distance between the two alleged points marked P and Q, so that both P and Q could not lie between the points representing ensuing numbers of the number pairs. There can be only one point on the number line lying between points representing the numbers of each number pair. This point must represent π, as π always lies between the two numbers of each of these number pairs.

Contrariwise, every point, or position, on the number line must represent one number, rational or irrational, which may be determined as follows. Let the position of the point be called P. Now consider pairs of rational numbers of one digit, two digits, three digits, four digits, etc., whose representative positions on the number line are closest to P. For example, such a situation may occur as the following:

7	P	8	
7.4	P	7.5	
7.42	P	7.43	
7.429	P	7.430	
7.429,8	P	7.429,9	
7.429,81	P	7.429,82	

If the position on the number line representing any one of these rational numbers should coincide with P, then the position of P is to be identified with that rational number. If, however, no rational number in the extended pairs of rational numbers has its representing point on the number line to coincide with P, then P is identified with a rational number if the numbers in the number pairs become periodic, otherwise P represents an irrational number whose decimal fractional form is developed in the numbers of the number pairs that enclose P. Every real number, whether irrational or rational, has its unique position on the number line, so that there is a one-to-one correspondence between the set of real numbers and the set of points, or positions, on the number line.

The ensuing demonstration proves that the cardinal number of the set of real numbers is greater than the cardinal number of the set of natural numbers, namely, $\aleph_0$. The cardinal number of the set of rational numbers is also $\aleph_0$ (see Section 5.10). The proof rests upon the fact that any alleged one-to-one correspondence between the natural numbers and the real numbers always leaves out infinitely many real numbers from the alleged matching of natural numbers with real numbers.

Let it be supposed that a one-to-one correspondence has been established between the natural numbers and the real numbers, and that the real numbers are represented symbolically by $A_k(a_k b_k c_k d_k \ . \ . \ .)$ in which the subscript k indicates that that real number is to be paired off with the natural number k. The A_k represents the integral portion of that real number; the a_k, b_k, c_k, d_k, etc., represent the individual digits of that real number which occur to the right of the decimal point. If the real number is a terminating decimal fraction, the digits eventually become 0s.

Natural number	Real number
1	$A_1(a_1 b_1 c_1 d_1 \ . \ . \ .)$
2	$A_2(a_2 b_2 c_2 d_2 \ . \ . \ .)$
3	$A_3(a_3 b_3 c_3 d_3 \ . \ . \ .)$
. . .	. . . .
k	$A_k(a_k b_k c_k d_k \ . \ . \ .)$
. . .	. . . .

If the alleged pairing off of real numbers with natural numbers is correct, every real number must appear in the list. It is clear that every natural number appears in the list, for any natural number one may specify will sooner or later occur in the first column.

Now form a number whose integral portion is different from A_1, its first digit to the right of the decimal point different from a_1, its second digit to the right of the decimal point different from b_2, its third digit different from c_3, etc. It is clear that there are nine digits to choose for each new digit in forming this new number. The new number so formed cannot ever appear in the above list of real numbers, as it is different from the first number in its integral portion and differs from the kth real number in its kth digit to the right of the decimal point. Ergo, this new number cannot appear in the array of real numbers that is alleged to provide the one-to-one correspondence between the natural numbers and the real numbers. Since no alleged correspondence is ever possible between the set of real numbers and the set of natural numbers, many real numbers must of necessity be omitted from the alleged pairing. Hence the cardinal number of the set of real numbers must exceed the cardinal number of the set of natural numbers, $\aleph_0$. By general agreement, the cardinal number of the set of real numbers is represented by the symbol $\aleph_1$, which is pronounced as "aleph-one."

To prove that the cardinal number of the set of irrational numbers also exceeds $\aleph_0$, the demonstration just presented may be repeated word for word except that the word *real* must be replaced with the word *irrational*. Then, to prove that the cardinal number of the set of irrational numbers is also $\aleph_1$, one must set up a one-to-one correspondence between the set of all real numbers and the set of irrational real numbers. This may be done in many different ways, but only one way is sufficient, such as the following suggested way of pairing off all real numbers with all irrational numbers. For convenience, let all real numbers be expressed as nonterminating decimal fractions, supplying 0s after all terminating decimal fractions which are rational numbers; the 0 is now considered to be the period of a single digit. Now let e represent the right end digit of the period of a repeating decimal fraction and f the next larger digit in the cycle of digits, 0 1 2 3 4 5 6 7 8 9 0 1 2 . . .

In setting up a one-to-one correspondence between the set of real numbers and the set of irrational numbers, let the irrational number that is to be paired off with a rational number contain all the digits of the rational decimal form in precisely the same order but with these modifications: Insert between the first and second complete periods the digit f; insert between the second and third complete periods the two digits ff; insert between the third and fourth complete periods the three digits fff; continue this procedure, inserting an ever-increasing number of f's between the ensuing pairs of periods. This new number so formed cannot be a rational number as it is not periodic. For example, the periodic (rational) number 34.583,263,263,263 . . . is made to correspond to the irrational number 34.853,267,326,773,267,773,267,777,326,777,77 . . . . Again, the integer 5 = 5.000,000,000 . . . is paired off with the irrational number 5.010,110,111,011,110,111,110,111,111 . . . .

Let all other irrational numbers not so paired off with the rational numbers be paired off with themselves. Thus 3.141,592,653, . . . is paired off with itself.   Every real number, rational or irrational, is paired off with an irrational number, so that the cardinal number of the set of real numbers, specified as Aleph-one, must be the same cardinal number of the set of irrational numbers.

↬ CHALLENGES

1. Show that the set of irrational algebraic numbers has the cardinal number Aleph-zero.

2. Show that there are infinitely more transcendental numbers than algebraic numbers.

3. Prove that the sum of a rational number and an irrational number must be an irrational number.   Prove this proposition after replacing the word sum by (*a*) product, (*b*) difference, (*c*) quotient.

4. Show by examples that the sum of two irrational numbers may be a rational number.

5. Re-solve Challenge 4 after replacing the word *sum* by (*a*) product, (*b*) difference, (*c*) quotient.

↬ SUPPLEMENTARY PROBLEMS ↬

> *"A slow sort of country!"* said the Queen. *"Now, here, you see, it takes all the running you can do, to keep in the same place.   If you want to get somewhere else, you must run at least twice as fast as that!"*
>
> —*Through the Looking-Glass, II.*

S11.1.   Obtain the indicated positive root by inspection or by a few simple trials:

a. $\sqrt{196}$	*f.* $\sqrt{576}$	*k.* $\sqrt{81}$	*p.* $\sqrt{5\frac{4}{9}}$
b. $\sqrt{289}$	*g.* $\sqrt{676}$	*l.* $\sqrt[3]{729}$	*q.* $\sqrt{7\frac{1}{9}}$
c. $\sqrt{361}$	*h.* $\sqrt{784}$	*m.* $\sqrt[3]{343}$	*r.* $\sqrt{5\frac{19}{25}}$
d. $\sqrt{484}$	*i.* $\sqrt{841}$	*n.* $\sqrt[3]{216}$	*s.* $\sqrt{204\frac{4}{49}}$
e. $\sqrt{529}$	*j.* $\sqrt{2,025}$	*o.* $\sqrt[5]{32}$	*t.* $\sqrt[3]{37\frac{1}{27}}$

S11.2.   Perform the indicated operations:

a. $2\sqrt{3} + 5\sqrt{3} - 4\sqrt{3}$

b. $4\sqrt{7} - 7\sqrt{7} + 5\sqrt{7}$

c. $15\sqrt{5} - 5\sqrt{5} - 8\sqrt{7}$

    d. $3\sqrt{2} + 5\sqrt{2} + 9\sqrt{2}$

    e. $\frac{1}{2}\sqrt{2} + \frac{1}{4}\sqrt{2} - \frac{1}{3}\sqrt{2}$

    f. $(1\frac{1}{2})\sqrt{3} + (3\frac{1}{3})\sqrt{3} + (5\frac{5}{6})\sqrt{3}$

    g. $0.14\sqrt{2} + 0.28\sqrt{2} + 0.57\sqrt{2} + 0.01\sqrt{2}$

    h. $0.428\sqrt{3} + 0.571\sqrt{3} + 1.001\sqrt{3}$

    i. $0.12\frac{1}{2}\sqrt{7} + 0.37\frac{1}{2}\sqrt{7} + \frac{1}{2}\sqrt{7}$

    j. $2\sqrt[3]{2} + 3\sqrt{3} + 5\sqrt{3} + 3\sqrt[3]{2}$

S11.3. Perform the indicated operations:

    a. $5\sqrt{2} \times 3\sqrt{8} + 2\sqrt{4}$ *f.* $1000\sqrt[3]{243} \div 125\sqrt[3]{9}$

    b. $6\sqrt{8} \times 8\sqrt{72} \div 12\sqrt{6}$ *g.* $24\frac{2}{7}\sqrt{27} \div 85\frac{5}{7}\sqrt{3}$

    c. $12\sqrt{3} \div \sqrt{3} \div 2\sqrt{3}$ *h.* $\frac{5}{8}\sqrt{14} \div 3\frac{1}{5}\sqrt{7}$

    d. $119\sqrt[3]{15} \div 17\sqrt[3]{5}$ *i.* $62\frac{1}{2}\sqrt{5} \times 0.001\frac{3}{5}$

    e. $\sqrt[5]{133} \div \sqrt[5]{19}$ *j.* $4.28\frac{4}{7}\sqrt{2} \div 714\frac{2}{7}$

S11.4. Evaluate as a decimal fractional expression with error less than 0.001.

    a. $\sqrt{133}$ *f.* $\sqrt{11}$ *k.* $\sqrt{39.37}$ *p.* $\sqrt{0.00\frac{7}{8}}$

    b. $\sqrt{5\frac{3}{4}}$ *g.* $\sqrt{83\frac{1}{3}}$ *l.* $\sqrt{0.003}$ *q.* $\sqrt{0.0\frac{7}{8}}$

    c. $\sqrt{\frac{2}{3}}$ *h.* $\sqrt{125}$ *m.* $\sqrt{0.03}$ *r.* $\sqrt{0.\frac{7}{8}}$

    d. $\sqrt{\frac{7}{8}}$ *i.* $\sqrt{17}$ *n.* $\sqrt{0.3}$ *s.* $\sqrt{\frac{7}{8}}$

    e. $\sqrt{7\frac{7}{9}}$ *j.* $\sqrt{80}$ *o.* $\sqrt{0.33}$ *t.* $\sqrt{8\frac{3}{4}}$

S11.5. By reversing the operation of multiplication, simplify the radicand. Thus, $5\sqrt{3} = \sqrt{25} \times \sqrt{3} = \sqrt{75}$. Simplifying $\sqrt{75}$, one has $\sqrt{75} = \sqrt{25} \times \sqrt{3} = 5\sqrt{3}$.

    a. $\sqrt{12}$ *f.* $\sqrt[3]{16}$ *k.* $\sqrt[3]{3\frac{3}{8}}$ *p.* $\sqrt{\frac{1}{2}}$

    b. $\sqrt{18}$ *g.* $\sqrt[3]{54}$ *l.* $\sqrt[3]{\frac{324}{27}}$ *q.* $\sqrt{\frac{2}{3}}$

    c. $\sqrt{24}$ *h.* $\sqrt[3]{250}$ *m.* $\sqrt[3]{5,000}$ *r.* $\sqrt{\frac{5}{6}}$

    d. $\sqrt{20}$ *i.* $\sqrt[3]{81}$ *n.* $\sqrt[4]{64}$ *s.* $\sqrt{\frac{7}{12}}$

    e. $\sqrt{125}$ *j.* $\sqrt[3]{2,000}$ *o.* $\sqrt{\frac{1}{3}}$

One should not leave a fraction under any radical, $\sqrt{\frac{4}{5}} = \sqrt{\frac{20}{25}} = 0.8\sqrt{5}$, since one generally has a table of roots of integers but not of fractions. Thus, to evaluate in decimal fractional form, $\sqrt{\frac{5}{6}} = \frac{1}{6}\sqrt{30} = \frac{5.477,226}{6}$, which is quickly reducible to 0.912,871.

S11.6. Express the product of the following surds as a single surd:

    a. $\sqrt[3]{2}; \sqrt{3}$ *c.* $\sqrt{2}; \sqrt[3]{3}; \sqrt[6]{5}$ *e.* $\sqrt[4]{5}; \sqrt[3]{2}; \sqrt{125}$

    b. $\sqrt{3}; \sqrt[3]{4}$ *d.* $\sqrt{2}; \sqrt[3]{4}; \sqrt[6]{8}$ *f.* $\sqrt{2}; \sqrt[3]{2}; \sqrt[4]{2}$

S11.7. Compute the indicated roots to the nearest 0.001:

    a. $\sqrt[3]{377}$ *d.* $\sqrt[3]{4372}$ *g.* $\sqrt[3]{4.372}$

    b. $\sqrt[3]{37.7}$ *e.* $\sqrt[3]{437.2}$ *h.* $\sqrt[3]{0.372}$

    c. $\sqrt[3]{3.77}$ *f.* $\sqrt[3]{43.72}$ *i.* $\sqrt[3]{0.037,2}$

S11.8. Write by inspection the cube roots of the following perfect cubes:

a.	2,197	*f.*	54.872	*k.*	238,328	*p.*	571,787
b.	4,913	*g.*	103,823	*l.*	287,496	*q.*	658,503
c.	9,261	*h.*	132,651	*m.*	328,509	*r.*	778,688
d.	13,824	*i.*	157,464	*n.*	421,875	*s.*	884,736
e.	24,389	*j.*	175,616	*o.*	456,533	*t.*	970,299

S11.9. Compute by two different methods:

    a. $\sqrt[4]{71,639,296}$ *c.* $\sqrt[8]{43,046,721}$

    b. $\sqrt[6]{601,692,057}$ *d.* $\sqrt[9]{40,353,607}$

S11.10. Calculate the areas of the circles having the given radii: (*a*) $r = 3$, (*b*) $r = 4$, (*c*) $r = 5$. Observe that the largest circle has an area equal to the sum of those of the other two circles. Use any convenient expression for π.

S11.11. Calculate the radius of a circle whose area is equal to the sum of the two circles having radii 8 inches and 15 inches, respectively.

S11.12. Two circles having radii 24 and 25 inches are drawn about the same point as their common center. Calculate the area of the ring bounded by their two circumferences. Now compute the radius of the circle that has the same area as this ring.

S11.13. Re-solve Problem S11.12 if the radii of the two given circles are 55 and 48 feet.

S11.14. Given three circles of radii 12, 70, and 84 centimeters, calculate the radius of the circle whose area is equal to the combined areas of the three given circles.

S11.15. Calculate the radius of the circle whose area is equal to the sum of the areas of the circles whose radii are $6\frac{1}{2}$, $7\frac{4}{5}$, $10\frac{2}{5}$, and 13 inches. Does the result depend upon the value one uses for π?

S11.16. In the foregoing problems, S11.10 to 15 inclusive, replace the word *ring* by *flat ring having the same center as the two spheres.* Replace also the words *circle* and *circles* by *sphere* and *spheres*, respectively. Then write immediately the correct answers.

S11.17. Calculate the radius of the sphere whose volume is equal to the combined volumes of the spheres of radii 3, 4, and 5 inches. Does the result depend upon the value used for π?

S11.18. Compute to the nearest 0.001 inch the radius of the sphere whose volume is exactly equal to the sum of the volumes of the two spheres of radii 1 and 2 feet.

S11.19. The volume of fluid of depth h inches inside a hollow sphere of inside radius r inches is given by the formula:

$$V = \frac{\pi h^2(3r - h)}{3}$$

(Use $\pi = 3.141,6$.)

How many gallons of fluid are there inside a hollow ball of inside radius 3 feet if the depth of the fluid is 5 inches? (231 cubic inches = 1 gallon.)

S11.20. How many small balls of 1 inch diameter would be as heavy as one large ball of 1 foot diameter? Compute the weight of the large ball if each small ball weighs 1 ounce. (16 ounces = 1 pound.)

S11.21. Which has the larger volume and by how many cubic feet: one sphere of diameter $2\frac{3}{4}$ feet and another sphere of diameter $2\frac{2}{5}$ feet?

S11.22. The *magnitude* of a star is the measure of its brightness. The faintest stars visible to the unaided eye on a clear moonless night are of magnitude 6. If B represents the brightness of a star of magnitude 6, kB the brightness of a star of magnitude 5, k^2B of magnitude 4, etc., a star of any magnitude being k times as bright as a star of the next fainter magnitude, then k^5B represents the brightness of a star of magnitude 1, the average brightness of the 20 brightest stars in the skies. Further, 100 stars of magnitude 6 appear to be together as bright as a single star of magnitude 1. Hence $k^5B = 100B$, or $k^5 = 100$, or $k = \sqrt[5]{100}$. Compute the magnitude factor k to the nearest 0.001.

S11.23. Kepler's third law of the motions of the planets which he announced in 1618 as appearing to relate the average distance from the sun to the time of one complete revolution about the sun of any of the planets is $d = \sqrt[3]{P^2}$, in which d equals the distance in *astronomical units* and P the time in *years*. One astronomical unit equals 93,000,000 miles, the approximate average distance from the earth to the sun. The value of P may be obtained by patiently watching the movement of a planet from night to night. Use this formula to compute the average distance from the sun to the planets whose period of revolution is given:

Mercury $P = 88$ days (convert to decimal fractional part of a year)
Earth $P = 1$ year
Mars   687 days
Jupiter   11.86 years
Saturn   29.46 years
Pluto   247.7 years

S11.24. Evaluate $(2 + \sqrt{3})^2$ in two ways to the nearest 0.001. (a) Expand, or multiply, by use of the distributive law $(2 + \sqrt{3})(2 + \sqrt{3})$; *then* replace $\sqrt{3}$ by its approximate decimal value. (b) Replace $\sqrt{3}$ by its approximate decimal expression; add to it 2, *then* square the result.

S11.25. Convert $\sqrt{2}$ to its continued fractional form, using its approximate value as 1.414,214, or the fraction $\frac{1,414,214}{1,000,000}$. Note the periodic form of the continued fraction; i.e., the repetition of the 2 as successive quotients.

S11.26. Compute in two ways the decimal approximations to nearest 0.000,001: $(\sqrt{2} - 1)$, $(\sqrt{2} - 1)^2$, $(\sqrt{2} - 1)^3$, $(\sqrt{2} - 1)^4$, $(\sqrt{2} - 1)^5$. Why must these successive higher powers diminish in value?

S11.27. Explain how the quotient is affected if one divides the dividend and divisor by a common divisor, or if one multiplies the dividend and the divisor by a common multiplier.   *Hint:* If ma and mb represent the dividend and divisor, respectively, express the indicated division in fractional form.

S11.28.   By reference to the form of Euclid's algorithm used in Problem S11.25 verify the development in the following form:

$$
\begin{array}{c|c|c}
1 & \sqrt{2} & 1 \\
& 1 & \\
\hline
\sqrt{2}-1 & \quad 1 \quad & 2 \\
& 2 \quad \sqrt{2}-2 & \\
\hline
-2\sqrt{2}+3 & \sqrt{2}-1 & \\
\end{array}
$$

or

$$
\begin{array}{c|c|}
\sqrt{2}-1 & \quad 1 \quad \\
\end{array}
$$

Note that $1(\sqrt{2}-1) = \sqrt{2}-1$ and $(\sqrt{2}-1)(\sqrt{2}-1) = -2\sqrt{2}+3$; thus the ensuing quotients must continue to be 2s without alteration.

S11.29.   Recalling Problem S7.41, compute the first 10 convergents of $\sqrt{2}$.   Note how easily each is formed from the preceding one.

S11.30.   By using the decimal fractional approximation for the irrational numbers, obtain the periodic continued fractional form and the first five convergents for the following: (*a*) $\sqrt{5}$, (*b*) $\sqrt{10}$, (*c*) $\sqrt{26}$, (*d*) $\sqrt{27}$, (*e*) $\sqrt{37}$.

S11.31.   Using the procedure presented in Problem S11.28, show that the continued fractions obtained in the preceding problem are indeed periodic with the indicated period.

S11.32.   Show that what occurred in Problem S11.30 is necessary for any natural number a in $\sqrt{a^2+1}$.   Use the procedure in Problem S11.28 to establish this fact.

S11.33.   It can be demonstrated that the continued fractional form for $\dfrac{a+\sqrt{b}}{c}$ is always periodic if a, b, c represent any natural numbers whatever.   Obtain the period for $\dfrac{3+\sqrt{15}}{3}$.   Verify this periodic form by the method of Problem S11.28.   Obtain the first five convergents for $\dfrac{3+\sqrt{15}}{3}$.

S11.34.   Contrariwise, any periodic continued fraction is equal to a binomial surd of the form $\dfrac{a+\sqrt{b}}{c}$ in which a, b, c represent natural numbers.   For example, if

$$
x = 3 + \cfrac{1}{4 + \cfrac{1}{1 + \cfrac{1}{3 + \cfrac{1}{\cdots}}}}
\qquad \text{Period: 3, 4, 1}
$$

then $x = 3 + \cfrac{1}{4 + \cfrac{1}{1 + \cfrac{1}{x}}}$ which yields $x = \dfrac{6 + \sqrt{101}}{5}$

a. By using decimal approximations, obtain this periodic continued fraction.

b. By the method of Problem S11.28 show that this continued fraction is indeed periodic.

c. Obtain the first six convergents of $\dfrac{6 + \sqrt{101}}{5}$. By how much does the sixth convergent differ from $\dfrac{6 + \sqrt{101}}{5}$?

S11.35. Obtain the simplest common fraction (i.e., the earliest convergent) that differs by less than 0.000,001 from the following surds: (a) $\sqrt{7}$, (b) $\sqrt{13}$, (c) $\sqrt{19}$, (d) $\dfrac{5 + \sqrt{6}}{7}$.

S11.36. Solve the preceding problem for the transcendental number π.

LESSON 12 ❧ TESTS FOR CORRECTNESS OF RESULTS ❧ CASTING NINES AND ELEVENS ❧ CONGRUENT NUMBERS

"I am a dangerous man to fall foul of! See here." He stepped swiftly forward, seized the poker, and bent it into a curve with his huge brown hands. "See that you keep yourself out of my grip," he snarled, and hurling the twisted poker into the fireplace he strode out of the room.

"He seems a very amiable person," said Sherlock Holmes, laughing. As he spoke he picked up the steel poker and, with a sudden effort, straightened it out again.

—Sir Arthur Conan Doyle, *The Adventure of the Speckled Band*, by permission of the estate of Sir Arthur Conan Doyle.

12·1 ～ Checking the results of arithmetical operations

The possibility of committing errors in performing numerical calculations introduces some degree of uncertainty in the correctness of results. One should always check the work for possibility of incorrect results. This can be done by performing the corresponding inverse operation or by performing the operation suggested by the commutative laws. Such checks are illustrated as follows.

		Check by repeated		
Add:		*subtractions:*		

Check by reversing order of adding:

Add:				
2364	24311	or	24311
6089	7547		2364
8311	16764		21947
7547	8311		6089
24311	8453		15858
	6089		8311
	2364		7547

$7 + 1 = 8;\ 8 + 9 = 17;\ 17 + 4 = 21$
$4 + 9 = 13;\ 13 + 1 = 14;\ 14 + 7 = 21$
$4 + 1 = 5;\ 5 + 8 = 13;\ 13 + 6 + 2 = 21$
$2 + 6 + 8 = 16;\ 16 + 1 = 17;\ 17 + 4 = 21$
$5 + 3 = 8;\ 8 + 0 = 8;\ 8 + 3 + 2 = 13$
$2 + 3 + 0 = 5;\ 5 + 3 = 8;\ 8 + 5 = 13$
$7 + 8 = 15;\ 15 + 6 = 21;\ 21 + 2 + 1 = 24$
$1 + 2 + 6 = 9;\ 9 + 8 = 17;\ 17 + 7 = 24$

Subtract:	*Check by addition:*	*Check by subtracting difference from minuend to obtain subtrahend:*
1248405	273767	1248405
974638	974638	273767
273767	1248405	974638

Multiply:
```
   357
   628
  2856
   714
  2142
224196
```

Check by division:
```
          628                  357
357 224196          628 224196
    2142                 1884
    ────                 ────
     999                 3579
     714                 3140
    ────                 ────
    2856                 4396
    2856                 4396
```

*Check by
commuting order:*
```
   628
   357
  4396
  3140
  1884
224196
```

Divide:
```
       216
143 30985
    286
    ───
    238
    143
    ───
     955
     858
     ───
      97
```

Check by multiplication:
```
   143        216
   216        143
   ───        ───
   858        648
   143        864
   286        216
  ─────      ─────
  30888      30888
     97         97
  ─────      ─────
  30985      30985
```

*Check by
commuting order:*
```
       143
216 30985
    216
    ───
    938
    864
    ───
    745
    648
    ───
     97
```

*Compute by 37^3
involution:*
```
    37
    37
   259
   111
  1369
    37
  9583
  4107
 50653
```

Check by divisions:
```
        1369           37                         37
  37 50653      37 1369      or      1369 50653
     37            111                     4107
    ───           ───                      ────
    136           259                      9583
    111           259                      9583
    ───           ───
    255
    222
    ───
    333
    333
```

Check by evolution: $\sqrt[3]{50653} = ?$

```
1    00    000    50653 | 30
     30    900    27000
─────────────────
1    30    900    23653
     30   1800
─────────────────
1    60   2700
     30
─────────────────
1    90
─────────────────
```

```
1    90   2700   23653        | 7
      7    679   23653
──────────────────────
1    97   3379    0 (exact)
```

Therefore, $\sqrt[3]{50633} = 37$

By evolution, compute to four digits $\sqrt[3]{2}$ using the *conventional* method (the alternative method of root extraction is less liable to error).

		Check by
	2.000000000	1.259	*involution:*

3	2.000000000 $\mid$ *1.259*	*Check by involution:*
6	1	1.259
4	1000	1.259
364 × 2 = 728	728	11331
	272000	6295
432		2518
180		1259
25		1.585081
45025 × 5 =	225125	1.259
	46875000	14265729
		7925405
46875		3170162
3375		1585081
81		1.995616979
4721331 × 9 =	42491979	4383021
	4383021	2.000000000

Note that in checking inexact divisions (and inexact evolution), the remainder must be added to the multiplication (and to the involution) to complete the check.

The foregoing checks do certify conclusively the perfect accuracy of the corresponding arithmetical operations. However, these checks are quite inconvenient to apply, inasmuch as they involve lengthy arithmetical work and are just as likely to contain errors as the results they are designed to check. A desirable check should be one that is very easy to apply and that involves very little arithmetical calculation, thus reducing the possibility of errors.

12·2   Simple checks by casting out nines and elevens

To cast out 9 or 11 from a given natural number is to replace the natural number by the remainder obtained when the number is divided by 9 or by 11. In the case of 9s, the remainder is precisely the same as the remainder obtained by dividing the *sum of the digits* of the given natural number by 9. Dividing 8,147 by 9, one obtains the remainder 2; dividing the sum of the digits, $8 + 1 + 4 + 7$, or 20, by 9, the remainder is seen to be 2 also. However, this remainder is most easily obtained by ignoring the $8 + 1$, since its sum is 9; the sum then of $4 + 7$ is 11; then the sum of the digits of 11, namely, $1 + 1 = 2$, is the desired remainder.

To cast out 11s from a given natural number, one subtracts the sum of *alternate* digits of the given number, beginning with the tens digit, from the sum of the other set of alternate digits, beginning with the units digit, increasing the latter sum or diminishing the former sum by an appropriate sum of 11s to yield a *positive* result. This final positive result is the remainder if the original given natural number were to be divided by 11. Dividing 8,174 by 11, one obtains the remainder 1. (Check this statement.) This remainder 1 is also obtained by subtracting the sum $7 + 8$, or 15, from the sum $4 + 1$, or 5; diminishing the former sum 15 by 11, one obtains 4. Now $5 - 4 = 1$, the desired remainder. The correctness of these methods of obtaining remainders for divisions by 9 and 11 is demonstrated later in the lesson by use of congruent number relationships.

The method of checking by casting 9s or 11s consists in replacing the given numbers by these remainders, then performing upon these remainders the prescribed arithmetical operations, casting out 9s or 11s from the results and comparing them with the answer for the problem after casting out 9s or 11s from it. The two checks are exhibited for the illustrative examples provided above. Results of casting 9s and 11s are in the parentheses. To check addition:

	Nines		*Elevens*	
2364	(6)		$(4 + 3) - (6 + 2) = 7 - 8$, or $(7 + 11) - 8 =$	(10)
6089	(5)		$(9 + 0) - (8 + 6) = 9 - 14$, or $9 - 3 =$	(6)
8311	(4)		$(1 + 3) - (1 + 8) = (4 + 11) - (9) =$	(6)
7547	(5)		$(7 + 5) - (4 + 7) = 12 - 11 =$	(1)
24311	(2), (20)	or (2)	Adding these results:	(23)
			or $3 - 2 = 1$	

Now examine answer $(1 + 3 + 2) - (1 + 4) = (1)$; both tests reveal no error in the work of addition.

Subtraction is most simply checked by adding the difference to the subtrahend and noting that this result is the same as the minuend. To check multiplication:

	Nines			*Elevens*
357	(6)	Note that $(6) \times (7) = 42$,		$(10) - (5) = 5$
628	(7)	which yields 6. If an		$(14) - (2) = 1$
2856	(3)	error is detected, it may be		$5 \times 1 = 5$
714	(3)	located by testing the par-		Now examine the
2142	(0)	tial products.		answer, $224{,}196 =$
224196	(6)			$(6 + 1 + 2) -$
				$(9 + 4 + 2) =$
				$(9) - (4) = 5$ also

To check division, replace the divisor, dividend, quotient, and remainder by the results after casting out 9s and 11s.

Nines	*Elevens*
(0)	(7)
(8)|(7)	(0)|(9)

Remainder: $\overline{(7)}$ · Remainder: $\overline{(9)}$

Remainder: $\overline{(7)}$
Note that $(0) \times (8) + (7) = (7)$,
the dividend

Remainder: $\overline{(9)}$
Note that $(7) \times (0) + (9) = (9)$,
the dividend

To check involution: $37^3 = 50{,}653$

Nines	*Elevens*
$1^3 = 1$; casting 9s from 50,653, one also obtains 1	$4^3 = 64$; casting 11s from 64, one obtains 9. Casting 11s from 50,653, one also obtains $(3 + 6 + 5) - (5 + 0) = 9$

To check evolution: $\sqrt[3]{2} = 1.259 \ldots$. Ignore the decimal points in applying tests, that is, prove that $1259^3 + 4383021$ yields the same result as 2.

Nines	*Elevens*
$8^3 = 512$ yields (8); 4383021 yields (3). Now, $(8) + (3) = (11)$, or (2)	$(9 + 2) - (5 + 1) = (5)$; $5^3 = 125$. $(5 + 1) - (2) = (4)$. $(1 + 0 + 8 + 4) - (2 + 3 + 3) = (5)$. $2{,}000{,}000{,}000 = (11) - (2) = (9)$. Now, $(5) + (4) = (9)$

One must observe that the application of these checks, especially casting 9s, is very simple and quick; however, the check by casting 9s does not detect an error of inversion, that is, writing two consecutive digits in the wrong order, such as writing 23 for 32. Testing by casting 11s will detect this error. Likewise, the test by casting 11s may not detect certain peculiar errors. However, both checks together will detect errors in *almost* every instance, in about 99 cases in 100.

∾ PROBLEMS ∾

12.1. Cast out 9s and 11s from the following numbers. Then test the correctness of your results by performing the actual divisions by 9 and 11, respectively.

    a. 1,000,117   *c.* 12,348   *e.* 1,000,000,000
    b. 14,641   *d.* 77,707   *f.* 8,000,700,003

12.2. Three persons perform the multiplication, and obtain the three different results: (a) $587 \times 569 = 343{,}003$; (b) $587 \times 569 = 333{,}013$; (c) $587 \times 569 = 304{,}303$. Apply the checks of casting 9s and 11s to determine which products cannot be correct.   Then perform the multiplication to determine the correct product.

12.3. Perform the indicated operations and test all results by casting out 9s and 11s.   If a check indicates presence of error in a result, reexamine the work to obtain absolutely correct results.

  a. Obtain the sum of 4,793, 8,862, 6,203, and 4,196.

  b. Multiply 87,932 by 125.

  c. Divide 189,624 by 739.

  d. Compute the square root of 23 to nearest 0.001.   Check the result to 0.000,1 before rounding off.

  e. Compute the cube root of 31 to nearest 0.01.   Check the result to 0.001 before rounding off.

  f. Compute the fifth root of 300 to nearest 0.01.

12.4. A baseball diamond is a square having 90 feet on each side.   How far is the second base from home plate?   (That is, compute the length of a diagonal of the square.)   Give the result to the nearest inch.

12.5. The length of the diagonals of a rectangular block is equal to the square root of the sum of the squares of the lengths of the three edges.

  a. If the lengths of the three edges are 29, 116, and 412 feet, respectively, compute the length of the diagonals.

  b. If the edges are 3, 5, and 5 feet, respectively, give the result to the nearest 0.001 foot.   Results must be absolutely correct, as application of the tests by casting 9s and 11s should show.

12·3 ∾ Congruent numbers

Imagine the set of integers set forth in correct array from left to right with the 0 at some intermediate position, thus,

```
. . . −12 −11 −10 −9 −8 −7 −6 −5 −4 −3 −2 −1  0  1  2  3
. . .  *3  *4  *0 *1 *2 *3 *4 *0 *1 *2 *3 *4 *0 *1 *2 *3
    4   5   6   7  8  9 10 11 12 13 14 15 16 17 18 19 20 21 22 . . .
   *4  *0  *1  *2 *3 *4 *0 *1 *2 *3 *4 *0 *1 *2 *3 *4 *0 *1 *2 . . .
```

Now select a natural number called the *modulus*, or "measuring number," such as 5.   Then count off to the right repeatedly *five* numbers, indicating the counting by *.   Then repeat the counting backward to the left for the negative integers, as shown in the above array.   All integers that are matched with the same asterisked counting number are said to be *congruent to one another, with* *reference to the modulus 5.*   The symbol for congruence is ≡.   The phrase "with reference to" or "according to" the modulus is expressed by (mod.) wherein mod. is the abbreviation for the Latin equivalent, namely, *modulo*.   Thus, $17 \equiv 12$ (mod. 5); $22 \equiv -8$ (mod. 5).   A different modulus would determine a different set of congruent numbers.   Thus, using the modulus 7, one would have the integers marked off as follows:

. . .	−12	−11	−10	−9	−8	−7	−6	−5	−4	−3	−2	−1	0	1	2
		*2	*3	*4	*5	*6	*0	*1	*2	*3	*4	*5	*6	*0	*1	*2
3	4	5	6	7	8	9	10	11	12	13	14	15	16	17	18
*3	*4	*5	*6	*0	*1	*2	*3	*4	*5	*6	*0	*1	*2	*3	*4
19	20	21	22	23	24	25	26	27	28	29	30	31	32	33 . . .	
*5	*6	*0	*1	*2	*3	*4	*5	*6	*0	*1	*2	*3	*4	*5 . . .	

Note that the asterisked number represents the positive remainder for its associated number when divided by the modulus.   Thus $19 \div 5$ yields a remainder 4, as indicated by *4; $12 \div 7$ leaves a remainder 5, as indicated by *5.   To make this statement correct in all instances, one should add the modulus to a negative remainder.   Thus, $-14 \div 5 = -2$, with a remainder -4; or one could say a quotient of -3 and a remainder of $(-4 + 5)$ or *1, as shown in the chart.   Again, the quotient of dividing -12 by 7 would be -2 with a remainder of *2 (which is equivalent to a quotient of -1 and a remainder of -5).   The asterisked integers are called the "smallest positive residues for the modulus, as indicated."

12·4 ∾ Products and differences of congruent numbers

In general for any two integers, A and B, and modulus M, if $A \equiv a$ (mod. M), then $A = kM + a$; if also $B \equiv b$ (mod. M), then $B = hM + b$, wherein h and k represent integers.   Then AB should be equal to $(kM + a)(hM + b)$.   Multiplying out this latter product, using the distributive law of multiplication, one has, first, $(kM + a)hM + (kM + a)b$; then reapplying the distributive law, $kM \cdot hM + hM \cdot a + kM \cdot b + ab$, or by reversing the distributive law on the first three terms, one has $(kMh + ha + kb)M$, or, representing the value of the expression $(kMh + ha + kb)$ by N, one has $AB = NM + ab$, or in the symbols of congruence, $AB \equiv ab$ (mod. M).   Thus, it appears that the *products of two congruent numbers would be congruent numbers.*   To repeat, if $A \equiv a$ (mod. M) and $B \equiv b$ (mod. M), then $AB \equiv ab$ (mod. M).

It should be quite clear also that the difference between any two congruent numbers must be exactly divisible by the modulus.   Thus $17 \equiv 3$ (mod. 7) is correct, since $17 - 3$, or 14, is exactly divisible by the modulus, 7.   Again,

$25 \equiv 9 \pmod{5}$ is *not* correct, since the difference, $25 - 9$, or 16, is not exactly divisible by 5.   (See Note 1.)

12.5 ~ VALIDITY OF THE CHECKS BY CASTING NINES AND ELEVENS

Understanding these basic principles about congruent numbers, one should be ready to prove the correctness of the procedures of testing the results of arithmetical computations by casting out 9s or 11s.   In any addition or multiplication, the numbers may be replaced by their smallest positive residues for a specific modulus, then the product, or sum, must be congruent to the product or sum of the smallest positive residues of the original numbers.   Casting out 9s and 11s is easily done because the smallest positive residues of numbers with these two moduli (plural of modulus) are easily found.

With reference to modulus 9, any natural number is congruent to the number that is the sum of the digits of the given natural number.   Thus, 1,346,973,123 has for sum of digits 39, while 39 has for sum of digits 12, and finally 12 has for sum of digits 3.   Thus, 3 is the smallest positive residue of 1,346,973,223, modulo 9.   To prove that this is always true, let the natural number N have for its digits *g, fed, cba*, which means that $N = a + 10b + 100c + 1,000d + 10,000e + 100,000f + 1,000,000g$.

Now evidently, $10 \equiv 1 \pmod{9}$; multiplying 10 by 10 and 1 by 1, one obtains $100 \equiv 1 \pmod{9}$; again multiplying the numbers of these two congruences, one obtains $1,000 \equiv 1 \pmod{9}$.   Repetition of multiplications shows that $10^n \equiv 1 \pmod{9}$.   Multiplying the numbers in the successive congruences by $a, b, c, d, \ldots$, one obtains $a \equiv a \pmod{9}$, $10b \equiv b \pmod{9}$, $100c \equiv c \pmod{9}$, $1,000d \equiv d \pmod{9}$, $10,000e \equiv e \pmod{9} \ldots$.   Adding, $a + 10b + 100c + 1,000d + \cdots \equiv a + b + c + d + \cdots \pmod{9}$.   Thus it appears that if any positive integer whatever is divided by 9, one obtains the same remainder that results when dividing the sum of the digits of the natural number by 9.

Now to prove that the same remainder is obtained by dividing a natural number by 11, as arises by dividing the difference of the sums of the two sets of alternate digits by 11, the minuend set containing the units digit, one notes the congruence relationships.   Again let $N = a + 10b + 100c + 1,000d + 10,000e + \cdots$; note that $1 \equiv 1 \pmod{11}$ and that $10 \equiv -1 \pmod{11}$, since $10 - (-1) = 11$, exactly divisible by modulus 11.   Likewise, $100 \equiv 1 \pmod{11}$ and $1,000 \equiv -1 \pmod{11}$, $10,000 \equiv 1 \pmod{11}$ and, in general, $10^n \equiv +1 \pmod{11}$, if n is *even*, and $10^n \equiv -1 \pmod{11}$, if n is *odd*.   Multiplying these congruences, respectively, by $a, b, c, d, e, f, \ldots$, one has $a \equiv a \pmod{11}$, $10b \equiv -b \pmod{11}$; $100c \equiv c \pmod{11}$; $1,000d \equiv -d \pmod{11}$; $10,000e \equiv e \pmod{11} \ldots$.   Adding these congruences, one obtains $a + 10b + 100c + 1,000d + 10,000e + \cdots = N \equiv a - b + c - d + e \cdots \pmod{11}$.   Or $N \equiv (a + c + e + \cdots) - (b + d + f + \cdots) \pmod{11}$.

12·6 ∾ Cube roots of perfect cubes less than 1 billion
DETERMINED BY INSPECTION

Since the cubes of the one-digit natural numbers, namely, 1, 8, 27, 64, 125, 216, 343, 512, 729 have all their units digits different, it was shown how to mentally obtain the cube root of a perfect cube number that does not exceed 1 million. Now, since the residues of these nine cubes also are different, *modulo 11*, namely, 1, 8, 5, 9, 4, 7, 2, 6, 3, one may obtain the cube root of any perfect cube of not more than nine digits. To illustrate, obtain $\sqrt[3]{410,172,407} = (100a + 10b + c)^3$. Since $7^3 = 343$, and $8^3 = 512$, a must be 7; likewise $c = 3$, since the cube ends in 7. Thus the digits of the required cube root are $7b\,3$, whose smallest positive residue is $10 - b$. But the residue of the radicand is $23 - 4$, or 7. Hence $(10 - b)^3 \equiv 7$, whence, since $7 \equiv 216$ (mod. 11), $10 - b \equiv 6$, or $b = 4$, the middle digit of the required cube root. Therefore, $\sqrt[3]{410,172,407} = 743$. (See Problem 11.15, page 270.)

∾ Problems [CONCLUDED] ∾

12.6. Obtain by inspection the cube roots of the following perfect cube numbers:

a. 2,000,376	*d.* 69,934,528	*g.* 340,068,392
b. 7,189,057	*e.* 107,850,176	*h.* 469,097,433
c. 56,623,104	*f.* 163,667,323	*i.* 994,011,992

12.7. The formula for the sum of the fifth powers of the first n natural numbers is:

$$S = n^2(2n^4 + 6n^3 + 5n^2 - 1) \div 12$$

Use this formula to calculate the sum of the first nine fifth powers; i.e., for $n = 9$, the sum would be equal to $9^2(2 \times 9^4 + 6 \times 9^3 + 5 \times 9^2 - 1) \div 12$. Verify the result by obtaining the first nine fifth powers, then obtaining their sum. To avoid errors check each operation.

12.8. When Karl Friedrich Gauss (1777–1855) was a very young pupil he astonished his teacher by solving immediately and mentally the problem of calculating the sum of the first 100 natural numbers. The sum of the first n natural numbers is given by formula

$$S = n(n + 1) \div 2$$
$$\text{i.e., } (1 + 2 + 3 + 4 + \cdots + n) = n(n + 1) \div 2$$

Use this formula to compute the sum of the first 100 natural numbers. Since the sum of the first n cube numbers is equal to the square of the sum of the first n natural numbers, compute the sum of the first 100 cube numbers.   To avoid errors check all operations.

12.9.   The sum of the squares of the first n natural numbers is equal to $\dfrac{n(n+1)(2n+1)}{6}$.   Thus, $1 + 4 + \cdots + 10{,}000 = \dfrac{100(101)}{2} \dfrac{201}{3}$ $= 5{,}050 \times 67$.   Obtain mentally the sum of the first 100 square numbers.

12.10.   Since $(1 + 2 + 3 + \cdots + n)^2 = 1^3 + 2^3 + 3^3 + \cdots + n^3$, obtain now mentally the sum of the first 1000 cube numbers.

12.11.   Compute the sum of the first million natural numbers.   Compute the sum of the squares of these million natural numbers; also compute the sum of their cubes.

Note 1 ↭ *Equivalence of the two definitions of congruent numbers.*

It is desirable to show that the two definitions of congruent numbers are equivalent: The natural numbers A and B are congruent, modulo m, if, (*a*) when divided by m, A and B yield the same positive remainders that are less than m; and when (*b*) the difference, $A - B$, is exactly divisible by the modulus.

PROOF ↭

If (*a*) is true, then (*b*) must also be true.

$$A \div m = Q, \text{ with remainder } r, \text{ or } A = Qm + r$$
$$B \div m = Q', \text{ with remainder } r, \text{ or } B = Q'm + r$$
$$\text{Subtracting, obtain } A - B = (Q - Q')m$$

which means that $A - B$ is exactly divisible by m, yielding quotient $Q - Q'$.

If (*b*) is true, then (*a*) must also be true.   Now $A - B = mr$, since (*b*) is assumed to be true.   Let $A = hm + s$ and $B = km + t$; s and t are both less than m, and are positive numbers.

Then $A - B = (h - k)m + s - t$, wherein $s - t$ must be less than m in absolute value.   Therefore, $s - t$ must be equal to zero, since $A - B$ is exactly divisible by m.   Accordingly, $s = t$, which means that (*a*) is true.

$\mathcal{N}$*ote 2 ∽ Validity of the test*
of divisibility by seven.[1]

Proof of the test for divisibility by 7, namely, if the given number N is of form $10H + a$, and N is a natural number. The test is: If $H - 2a$ is divisible by 7, the number itself must be divisible by 7. Proof of correctness of the test:

$H - 2a \equiv 0$ (mod. 7)	Because $H - 2a$ is exactly divisible by 7
$49H + 7a \equiv 0$ (mod. 7)	For clearly $49H + 7a$ is divisible by 7

Adding: $\overline{50H + 5a \equiv 0}$ (mod. 7)   Next, dividing by 5, one obtains
$10H + a = N \equiv 0$ (mod. 7)   That is, N is also divisible by 7

Contrariwise, $H - 2a$ is *not* divisible by 7, which is expressed by $H - 2a \not\equiv 0$ (mod. 7). Again, $49H + 7a \equiv 0$ (mod. 7). Adding these two statements, one obtains $50H + 5a \not\equiv 0$ (mod. 7). Now dividing by 5, one obtains the statement that $10H + a = N \not\equiv 0$ (mod. 7); that is, the number N is *not* divisible by 7. Here are two illustrations.

Is 301 exactly divisible by 7? Remove the units digit, 1, and double it, obtaining 2. Subtract this 2 from the remaining portion of the number, 30, obtaining $30 - 2 = 28$. Now 28 is clearly seen to be divisible by 7. Therefore, 301 is divisible by 7.

Is 473 exactly divisible by 7? Double the units digit, $2 \times 3 = 6$. Now, $47 - 6 = 41$, which is clearly seen to be *not* divisible by 7. Therefore, 473 is *not* exactly divisible by 7.

$\mathcal{N}$*ote 3 ∽ Divisibility tests*
for any prime number.

Similar tests for divisibility of a natural number by primes 7, 13, 17, 19, 23, . . . , may be devised and may be expressed quite generally as follows: The special multiplier t is used for each specific test. For the primes 7, 13, 17, 19, 23, t has the specific values, respectively, 2, 9, 5, -2, -7. Multiply the units digit by t. Subtract this product from the remaining portion of the number. If the result so obtained is divisible by the specific prime, the original number is so divisible. Here are two examples.

Is 969 exactly divisible by 17? For 17 the value of t is 5. The units digit, 9, is multiplied by 5, yielding 45; $96 - 45 = 51$, which is clearly seen to be divisible by 17. Therefore, 969 is exactly divisible by 17.

Is 2134 exactly divisible by 23? For $p = 23$, $t = -7$; $4 \times (-7) = -28$; $213 - (-28) = 241$. One may here note that 241 is not divisible by 23. Or one may repeat the procedure upon 241: $1 \times (-7) = -7$; $24 - (-7) = 31$, which clearly is not divisible by 23. Therefore, 2134 is not divisible by 23.

[1] Refer to Section 6.6(4).

One may devise such tests for divisibility for *any prime number* and verify its correctness by congruence relationships. Thus, to devise the test for divisibility by 29, select a multiple of 29 which has 1 for the units digit, such as $9 \times 29 = 261$. Now the question is: What multiple of the units digit, 1, when combined with 26 (the other portion of the original number) yields 29, or any multiple of 29? Clearly $26 + 3 = 29$, or $26 - (-3) = 29$. Hence, for the prime number 29, t is equal to -3. To prove that this test is always valid, let a given number $N = 10H + a$. Suppose that $H - (-3)a$ is exactly divisible by 29; one must then show that N itself must be divisible by 29. Thus, $H - (-3)a$ or $H + 3a \equiv 0$ (mod. 29). Since $11 \times 29 = 319$, it is clear that $319H + 29a \equiv 0$ (mod. 29). Adding these two congruences gives $320H + 32a \equiv 0$ (mod. 29). Dividing by 32, one obtains $10H + a \equiv 0$ (mod. 29), which states that $N = 10H + a$ is exactly divisible by 29.

*N*ote 4 ∽ *"Right-end" long division.*

The *simplest* test for divisibility by *any integer* having as its units digit 1, 3, 7, or 9, is actual division by that integer, working the division *from the right*, as illustrated by the examples for prime 13. Observe that all primes except 2 and 5 have 1, or 3, or 7, or 9 as a unit digit.

8996	(692	7381	(337
26		91	
897		729	
117		39	
78		69	
78		39	
0	Remainder is 0; therefore, 8996 is exactly divisible by 13, yielding quotient 692	3	That is, final remainder 3000; therefore, 337 is not exactly divisible by 13

∽ S UPPLEMENTARY PROBLEMS ∽

These problems are designed simply for pleasure. As the sun eclipses the stars in brilliancy, so the wise man also eclipses the fame of others if he proposes problems, and still more if he solves them.

—Brahmagupta (*c.* 625 A.D.).

S12.1. Perform the indicated additions and check by casting 9s and 11s.

a.	3,480,511	*c.*	28,646,320,056	*e.*	365,299	*g.*	4,622,371
	8,886,315		74,236,887,231		112,233		4,680,876
	9,908,010		55,533,377,799		634,701		4,352,698
	5,632,563		70,011,562,211		765,432		5,319,124
	7,722,885		71,353,679,944		234,568		5,647,302
b.	3,456,789	*d.*	15,379	*f.*	4,019,652		
	7,531,975		84,621		5,980,348		
	2,468,102		98,721		5,766,224		
	3,142,536		24,387		4,233,776		
	9,080,706		75,613		7,778,888		

Problems (*d*), (*e*), (*f*), (*g*) suggest an addition curio: Mr. *A* supplies three of the addends, Mr. *B* supplies the other two, and immediately writes down the complete sum. Can you discover how this is possible?

S12.2. Perform the subtractions and check the results by casting out 9s and 11s. State two reasons why the check by adding difference to subtrahend to obtain the minuend is to be preferred to the tests of casting out the 9s or 11s.

a.	347,521	*b.*	679,532	*c.*	100,000	*d.*	102,030,408
	179,477		523,421		54,277		30,508,050

S12.3. Perform the indicated multiplications and check the products by casting out 9s and 11s and by performing the multiplications with the multiplier and multiplicand being interchanged.

a.	36,507	*b.*	10,031	*c.*	775,599	*d.*	3,572,468
	248		7,356		40,012		8,642,753

S12.4. Perform the multiplications by dividing the multiplicand with supplied 0s, as suggested by the relationships: $5 = \frac{10}{2}$; $25 = \frac{100}{4}$; $125 = \frac{1,000}{8}$. Check products by appropriate tests.

a.	354,987	*b.*	197	*c.*	3,578	*d.*	14,266	*e.*	401,123
	5		5		25		125		125

S12.5. Perform the divisions and check the results by casting out 9s and 11s.

    a. 6,743,547 ÷ 56,771   *d.* 3,005,001 ÷ 732

    b. 1,000,000 ÷ 15,625   *e.* 2,354,711 ÷ 9,731

    c. 453,288 ÷ 77,882   *f.* 7,000,000 ÷ 2,601

S12.6. Perform the indicated divisions by multiplying the dividend appropriately and inserting the decimal point, as suggested by the relationships given in Problem S12.4 and $\frac{10,000}{16} = 625$; $\frac{100,000}{32} = 3,125$; $\frac{1,000,000}{15,625} = 64$; $\frac{10,000,000}{78,125} = 128$.

     a. $47,000,000 \div 625$ *d.* $42,625 \div 3,125$

     b. $354,783 \div 125$ *e.* $35,117 \div 25$

     c. $436,771 \div 25$ *f.* $11,223,101 \div 78,125$

S12.7. Perform the indicated evolutions with best results to nearest 0.001; check all results by casting out 9s and 11s:

     a. $\sqrt{5,772}$ *d.* $\sqrt[5]{2}$ *g.* $\sqrt[8]{43,046,721}$

     b. $\sqrt[3]{2,415}$ *e.* $\sqrt[6]{4,773}$ *h.* $\sqrt[9]{134,217,728}$

     c. $\sqrt[4]{28,301}$ *f.* $\sqrt[8]{65,536}$ *i.* $\sqrt[8]{123,456,789}$

S12.8. Perform the exact evolutions mentally, checking all results:

     a. $\sqrt{169}$ *d.* $\sqrt[3]{389,017}$ *g.* $\sqrt[3]{5,832,000}$

     b. $\sqrt{961}$ *e.* $\sqrt[3]{614,125}$ *h.* $\sqrt[3]{35,287,552}$

     c. $\sqrt{441}$ *f.* $\sqrt[3]{39,304}$ *i.* $\sqrt[3]{251,239,591}$

S12.9. Which of the following congruences are correct?

     a. $16 \equiv 4 \pmod{6}$ *d.* $29 \equiv 51 \pmod{11}$

     b. $16 \equiv 4 \pmod{9}$ *e.* $92 \equiv 52 \pmod{11}$

     c. $16 \equiv 4 \pmod{3}$ *f.* $6902 \equiv 5 \pmod{11}$

S12.10. Verify the correctness of the congruences: (*a*) $31 \equiv 13 \pmod{9}$; (*b*) $7 \equiv 16 \pmod{9}$. Then is it necessarily true that $31 + 7 \equiv 13 + 16 \pmod{9}$? State and prove the general relationship suggested by this example.

S12.11. From S12.10*a* and *b* does it necessarily follow that $31 \times 7 \equiv 13 \times 16 \pmod{9}$? State and prove the general relationship suggested by this example.

S12.12. From S12.10*a* and *b* does it necessarily follow that $31 - 7 \equiv 13 - 16 \pmod{9}$? State and prove the general relationship suggested by this example.

S12.13. Is it true that $210 \equiv 30 \pmod{9}$? Then is it necessarily true that (*a*) $210 \div 5 \equiv 30 \div 5 \pmod{9}$? (*b*) $210 \div 3 \equiv 30 \div 3 \pmod{9}$? State and prove the general relationship suggested by these examples.

S12.14. Express the following natural numbers in their prime factor forms, using the tests for divisibility for various prime factors less than the square root of the given natural number:

     a.   355   *e.*   803   *i.*   1,211   *m.*   1,727

     b.   561   *f.*   893   *j.*   1,503   *n.*   1,932

     c.   721   *g.*   767   *k.*   1,441   *o.*   1,959

     d.   801   *h.*   987   *l.*   1,672

S12.15. Perform the following exact divisions by right-end division:

     a. $197,169 \div 123$ *c.* $557,151 \div 617$

     b. $3,998,203 \div 1,903$ *d.* $15,803,685 \div 447$

S12.16. Evaluate the sum $\dfrac{n^3}{3} + \dfrac{n^2}{2} + \dfrac{n}{6}$ for consecutive values of the natural numbers until you recognize the character of the sums. *Hint:* Compute the differences of consecutive sums so obtained.

S12.17. Compute the number of cubical blocks each 1 foot in each dimension that would be needed to erect a pyramid 200 feet high if each square layer of blocks is 1 foot shorter than the layer just below it. *Hint:* Use the result of the previous problem.

S12.18. Solve Problem S12.16 using $\dfrac{n^5}{5} + \dfrac{n^4}{2} + \dfrac{n^3}{3} - \dfrac{n}{30}$. *Hint:* Add the given fractions with common denominator.

S12.19. Obtain the least positive residues (Section 12.4) of consecutive squares 1, 4, 9, 16, etc., for the modulus 3, 5, 7, 11, 13. Note that these moduli are prime. Such least positive residues of squared integers are called *quadratic residues*.

    a. How many least quadratic residues are there for any prime modulus p?

    b. What curious feature have they?

    c. Are the quadratic residues of consecutive squares 1, 2^2, 3^2, . . . palindromic for a composite modulus?

S12.20. The other natural numbers less than p are called nonresidues. By considering various products complete the statements:

    a. The product of two residues is a ———————.

    b. The product of two nonresidues is a ———————.

    c. The product of a residue and a nonresidue is a ———————.

S12.21. Verify the statements made in the previous problem for modulus 23.

S12.22. *a.* Prove the statements of Problem S12.20 for any modulus that is a prime number.

    b. Attempt to discover corresponding relationships for composite moduli, as 15, 21, 35, ...

LESSON 13 ❧ PERCENT RELATIONSHIPS ❧ BASE, RATE, PERCENTAGE ❧ AMBIGUITIES

"Ah well," thought he, "one thing I've learned,
  Nor shall I soon forget;
Whatever frightens me again:
  I'll march straight up to it."

—"Harry and the Guidepost," *McGuffey's Third Eclectic Reader, 1879.*

13·1 ∼ Meaning of Percent and its Fractional Equivalences

Situations described in the language of percentages are readily understandable if one realizes that the term *percent* means merely "by the hundred," and that some item or quantity in the discussion, referred to as the *base*, denotes 100 percent. Accordingly, 1 percent denotes the fraction $\frac{1}{100}$, 2 percent denotes $\frac{2}{100}$, and in general, n percent means $\frac{n}{100}$, wherein n represents any number whatever.

Many problems involving the percent symbol may be made easy to understand by replacing the symbol $\%$ by the fraction $\frac{1}{100}$; then 8% means $8 \times \frac{1}{100}$, or $\frac{8}{100}$. For example, a student spent 60% of his money for books, 20% of the remainder for lunch, 25% of the remainder for transportation, and laid aside $5.50 for school fees. How much did he have left from an original amount of $24? Note that 60% means $\frac{60}{100}$ or $\frac{3}{5}$; 20% means $\frac{20}{100}$, or $\frac{1}{5}$; 25% means $\frac{25}{100}$, or $\frac{1}{4}$. Thus he spent for books $\frac{3}{5}$ of $24.00, or $14.40, having $9.60 left. He spent for lunch $\frac{1}{5}$ of $9.60, or $1.92, having left $9.60 − $1.92, or $7.68. He spent for transportation $\frac{1}{4}$ of $7.68, or $1.92, leaving $5.76. Laying aside $5.50 for school fees, he had left from the day's transactions 26 cents.

To work with such percentage expressions it is desirable to be able to change them readily to common, or decimal, fractions, and vice versa. The rule for changing $n\%$ to a fraction is to replace the percent symbol by $\frac{1}{100}$, or to multiply the expression by $\frac{1}{100}$. Thus $62\frac{1}{2}\% = 62\frac{1}{2} \times \frac{1}{100}$, or $\frac{125}{2} \times \frac{1}{100}$ or $\frac{125}{200}$, or $\frac{5}{8}$ in lowest terms.

To convert a common fraction, or decimal fraction, to the equivalent percent expression, one reverses the foregoing rule; thus, multiply the expression by 100 and affix the percent sign, since multiplying by 1 makes no change in value and $1 = 100\%$. Thus $\frac{1}{8} = \frac{1}{8} \times 100\%$, or $\frac{100}{8}\%$, or $12\frac{1}{2}\%$.

To convert decimal fractions to corresponding decimal percentage expressions, one moves the decimal point two places to the *right* and supplies the percent sign. To reverse this operation, i.e., to convert decimal percentage expressions to the corresponding decimal fractions, one moves the decimal point two places to the *left* and removes the percent sign. Thus, $0.062,5 = 6.25\%$; $0.75\% = 0.007,5$.

ᕈ PROBLEMS ᕈ

13.1. Express the following common fractions to the equivalent form with percent sign. Do not use the decimal point; use mixed numbers if necessary.

a. $\frac{3}{4}$ *e.* $\frac{3}{10}$ *i.* $\frac{13}{17}$ *m.* $\frac{5}{2}$

b. $\frac{7}{8}$ *f.* $\frac{3}{8}$ *j.* $\frac{2}{3}$ *n.* $\frac{10}{3}$

c. $\frac{19}{25}$ *g.* $\frac{5}{7}$ *k.* $\frac{5}{6}$ *o.* $\frac{15}{16}$

d. $\frac{4}{5}$ *h.* $\frac{5}{12}$ *l.* $\frac{4}{3}$

13.2. Express the following common fractions to exactly equivalent decimal forms with the percent symbol.

a. $\frac{3}{16}$ *d.* $\frac{19}{20}$ *g.* $\frac{19}{32}$

b. $\frac{23}{40}$ *e.* $\frac{119}{125}$ *h.* $\frac{121}{200}$

c. $\frac{49}{64}$ *f.* $\frac{18}{24}$ *i.* $\frac{28}{35}$

13.3. Express in best equivalent decimal form, with error less than 0.01%:

a. $\frac{5}{7}$ *d.* $\frac{5}{13}$ *g.* $\frac{17}{23}$ *j.* $\frac{53}{119}$

b. $\frac{1}{3}$ *e.* $\frac{5}{9}$ *h.* $\frac{23}{29}$ *k.* $\frac{428,571}{714,285}$

c. $\frac{7}{11}$ *f.* $\frac{14}{17}$ *i.* $\frac{355}{113}$ *l.* $\frac{44,444}{77,777}$

13.4. Express as common fractions with the percent sign:

a. 35% *d.* $57\frac{1}{7}\%$ *g.* $37\frac{1}{2}\%$ *j.* 40%

b. $12\frac{1}{2}\%$ *e.* $6\frac{1}{4}\%$ *h.* $87\frac{1}{2}\%$ *k.* $16\frac{2}{3}\%$

c. $66\frac{2}{3}\%$ *f.* $8\frac{1}{3}\%$ *i.* 75% *l.* $83\frac{1}{3}\%$

13.5. Express as common fractions without the percent sign:

a. $3.333 \ldots \%$ *c.* 0.03% *e.* $9.090,9 \ldots \%$

b. $3.636,3 \ldots \%$ *d.* 10.24% *f.* $55.55 \ldots \%$

13.6. An automobile costing \$4800 depreciated (declined in value) 40% of its cost during the first year following its purchase.

a. What was its value 1 year after its purchase?

b. During the second year it depreciated 30% of this latter value. What was its value at the end of this second year?

c. During each ensuing year it depreciated 20% of its value at the beginning of that particular year. What was its value at the end of the fourth year?

13.7. A debtor, wishing to pay a number of obligations, applies for a loan of $1,200.00 from a loan company. The company charges 2% of the loan for commission for making the loan, $\frac{1}{2}$% of the loan for insurance, and $8\frac{1}{3}$% for interest on the loan of $1,200.00. All these charges are deducted from the $1,200 when the loan is granted. The borrower agrees to repay the loan in 12 monthly installments of $100. How much cash does he carry from the loan office?

13.8. Mr. *A* spent 50% of his capital of $200.00 on Monday, 20% of the *remainder* on Tuesday, 10% of the new remainder on Wednesday, and 5% of the final remainder on Thursday.

   a. How much money did he then have?

   b. Solve this problem again with these expenditures in reverse order, namely, 5%, 10%, 20%, and finally 50%.

   c. To explain the surprising agreement of these two results, solve (*a*) and (*b*) again by computing the amounts immediately remaining after each daily expenditure. Thus for (*a*): These results would be 0.50×200; $0.80 \times (0.50 \times 200)$; $0.90 \times (0.80 \times 0.50 \times 200)$; $0.95 \times (0.90 \times 0.80 \times 0.50 \times 200)$; or finally, $0.95 \times 0.90 \times 0.80 \times 0.50 \times 200$. And for (*b*): 0.95×200; $0.90 \times (0.95 \times 200)$; $0.80 \times (0.90 \times 0.95 \times 200)$; $0.50 \times (0.80 \times 0.90 \times 0.95 \times 200)$; or finally, $0.50 \times 0.80 \times 0.90 \times 0.95 \times 200$. Hence the two results must be the same, by the validity of the commutative law of multiplication; i.e., the *order* of expenditures does not affect the final *result*.

13.9. Water expands $9\frac{1}{11}$% of its volume as it freezes into ice. How many cubic feet of ice can be formed by freezing 55 cubic feet of water?

13.10. Ice shrinks $8\frac{1}{3}$% of its volume in melting to form water. How many cubic feet of water are obtained by melting 120 cubic feet of ice?

13·2 ∽ Percentage situations simplified by base-rate-percentage relationships

More complicated problems involving percentage relations may be solved more readily by observing the following features:

1. A certain totality, or "whole amount," which is made to represent 100 percent; this particular quantity is called the *base*.

2. A certain fractional (proper or improper) number expressed with the percent sign is called the *rate*.

3. The corresponding fractional portion of the base is called the *percentage*.

In the following illustrative example these three items are to be noted: A farmer sells 40% of his wheat crop of 24,000 bushels. How many bushels did he sell? Here 24,000 bushels of wheat represents the *base;* 40% represents the *rate;* the number of bushels sold represents the *percentage.* Observe that the *base* and the *percentage* always denote the same kind of material or substance, whether bushels, dollars, miles, feet, persons, etc.

The rate, 40%, is equal to $\frac{2}{5}$ as a fraction. The problem now is to compute two-fifths of 24,000 bushels. Now one-fifth of 24,000 bushels is calculated by dividing 24,000 by 5, which is found to be 4,800 bushels. If one-fifth of the crop is 4,800 bushels, then two-fifths should be just twice as much as one-fifth; hence two-fifths of the crop should be $2 \times 4,800$ bushels, or 9,600 bushels. Clearly, this result is found directly by multiplying 24,000 by two-fifths, since this operation requires the division of the 5 into the 24,000 and the subsequent multiplication by 2. Hence we have two rules:

If the base *and the* rate *are known, the* percentage *is found by multiplying them; i.e.,* base $\times$ rate = percentage. *Expressing this multiplication in its two inverse forms, one obtains:* percentage $\div$ base = rate *and* percentage $\div$ rate = base. *These two relationships present the other rule of operation in percentage relationships.*

If the percentage is known, the missing item (base or rate) is obtained by dividing the percentage by the other known item.

In the previous example, 24,000 (base) corresponds to 100%; 9,600 (percentage) corresponds to 40%. Furthermore, $33\frac{1}{3}$% of 24,000 bushels is 8,000 bushels. Forty-three percent of 24,000 bushels is $0.43 \times 24,000 = 10,320$ bushels. Three percent of 24,000 bushels is $\frac{3}{100} \times 24,000$, or $0.03 \times 24,000 = 720$ bushels. In these instances 40% (rate) corresponds to 9,600 bushels (percentage):

$33\frac{1}{3}$% (rate) corresponds to   8,000 bushels (percentage)
  75% (rate) corresponds to 18,000 bushels (percentage)
  43% (rate) corresponds to 10,320 bushels (percentage)
   3% (rate) corresponds to   720 bushels (percentage)
100% corresponds to 24,000 (base)

Note that the base can be computed from *any of the five previous correspondences of rate and percentage.* For example, 8,000 (percentage) $\div$ $33\frac{1}{3}$% (rate) = 8,000 $\div$ $\frac{1}{3}$ = 8,000 $\times$ $\frac{3}{1}$ = 24,000 bushels. Only one such correspondence is needed to yield the base. Again, to solve the problem, "What percent of 24,000 bushels of wheat are 10,320 bushels of wheat?" one knows the *percentage*, 10,320 bushels of wheat, and the base, 24,000 bushels of wheat. To find the missing item, the rate, one must divide the percentage by the base, thus,

$$10,320 \div 24,000 \quad \text{or} \quad \frac{10,320}{24,000} = \frac{43}{100} \quad \text{or} \quad 43\%$$

Again, to find what percent of 24,000 are 7,000 bushels, one finds the result expressible as $\frac{7000}{24,000}$ or $\frac{7}{24}$ or $\frac{700}{24}\%$ or $29\frac{1}{6}\%$. One may henceforth solve all percentage problems by the use of these two rules, for they will suffice in every instance.

∾ Problems [concluded] ∾

13.11. There are 88 keys altogether on a standard piano keyboard. Of these keys $40\frac{10}{11}\%$ are black. How many keys are black?

13.12. A merchant's net profits in one particular month were $840. He devoted $16\frac{2}{3}\%$ to business purposes, $71\frac{3}{7}\%$ for domestic purposes, and saved the remainder. (*a*) How much cash did he save? (*b*) What percent of his net profits did he save?

13.13. A farmer devotes 40% of his 120-acre ranch to the cultivation of sugar beets, 25% to corn, 15% to beans, and the remainder to potatoes. How many acres does he devote to each crop?

13.14. A student spends 75% of his leisure time in reading. (*a*) If he spends 15 hours each week in reading, how much leisure time does he have? (*b*) What percent of the entire week of 168 hours does he enjoy as leisure time? (*c*) What percent of the entire week does he spend in reading?

13.15. A merchant sold a set of furniture for $156, gaining 30% as based upon the retail price. (*a*) Compute the gain in the transaction. (*b*) Compute the wholesale price.

13.16. A merchant sold an article at a profit of $24.00. If the wholesale price was $60, compute his percent of profit if he based his profit upon (*a*) the wholesale cost, (*b*) the retail price? Observe that the *percent of profit* is ambiguous; its base must be designated either as the *cost price* or the *sales price*.

13.17. A merchant sold an article at a loss of $24.00. If the wholesale price was $60, compute his percent of loss if he based his loss upon (*a*) the wholesale cost, (*b*) the retail price.

13.18. A contractor loses 19 days through bad weather during 14 weeks of 5 working days each. What percent of the working days was lost? Give the exact answer by use of correct fractional expression; also give the best decimal approximation to the nearest 0.01%.

13.19. In a certain college class five students received grade A, fifteen students received grade B, twenty-five students C, three students D, and two students F. Give the percent distribution. Check results by appropriate addition.

13.20. Two men, Mr. *A* and Mr. *B*, are employed simultaneously under the specified terms: Mr. *A* has a beginning monthly salary of $440.00, with a guaranteed increase in monthly salary of 1% per month; Mr. *B* also has a beginning monthly salary of $440.00, but with a guaranteed increase in monthly salary of 10% at the end of each period of six months. Let each successive increase in salary be taken to the nearest cent. (*a*) Which man has the larger annual salary for the first year of employment? (*b*) Which man has the larger annual salary for the second year of employment?

13.21. Each of four speculators has an initial capital of $10,000 and engages in two transactions, employing his entire current capital in each transaction.

    a. Compute the net gain or loss of each speculator, if the transactions are:

        Mr. *X* has a loss of 40%, followed by a gain of 65%
        Mr. *Y* has a gain of 75%, followed by a loss of 45%
        Mr. *Z* has a gain of 60%, followed by a loss of 35%
        Mr. *W* has a gain of 5%, followed by a loss of 5%

    b. How would the results be affected if the gains and losses were made in reverse order? (Refer to Problem 13.8*c*.)

    c. Compute the combined net gain or loss of all four men.

    d. What would have been the combined (net) gain or loss if these four men had combined their capital into a single sum of $40,000, then engaged in the eight transactions with the resulting current capital in each ensuing transaction?

13.22. What percentage of its games did a baseball team win if it won 19 of the 31 games it played? (*a*) Express the result to the nearest 0.1%. (*b*) Express this result as a decimal fraction without the % sign.

13.23. The following 10 teams, *A, B, C, . . . , J*, of a baseball league, have the following records: *A* won 32 games, lost 26 games; *B* won 4, lost 59; *C* won 27, lost 35; *D* won 42, lost 17; *E* won 46, lost 10; *F* won 21, lost 40; *G* won 19, lost 39; *H* won 49, lost 14; *I* won 28, lost 32; *J* won 32, lost 28. Arrange these 10 teams in a vertical column according to the percent of games won, exhibiting as customary the number of games won and lost and the rate to the nearest 0.001, without use of the % symbol.

13.24. A merchant reduces a bill by three successive discounts of 15%, 10%, and 5%.

    a. What single discount would be equivalent to these three successive discounts?

    b. Which is the more advantageous offer to a customer? Three successive discounts of 10%, or a single discount of 28%.

13.25. Obtain the missing items in the following:

    a. Twenty horses are what percent of 150 horses?

    b. Twenty percent of 150 horses equals what?

    c. One hundred fifty horses are 20% of how many horses?

13.26. A merchant sold an item for $36 and made a profit of 20% as based on the *wholesale price*. (*Hint:* 100% = *wholesale* price; since profit of 20% is based on this wholesale price, the retail price must be 100% + 20% or 120% of the wholesale price, which denotes the *rate*, corresponding to the *percentage*, $36.) Compute the wholesale price.

13.27. Solve the previous problem if the profit of 20% had been based on the retail price.

13.28. A merchant sells an article for $48, on which he suffers a loss of 25%.

    a. Calculate his loss on the transaction if the 25% is based on the selling price of $48.

    b. Calculate his loss if the 25% is *based on his wholesale price*. (*Hint:* Here the base must be the *wholesale price*, as specified, and must be represented by 100%; the 25% (loss) is based on this 100%; hence the sales price may be represented by 100% − 25% = 75%, which corresponds to the $48 selling price. Therefore, using these two items for corresponding rate and percentage, the base can be obtained.)

13.29. Seventy-two and one-tenth is 3% greater than a certain number. Obtain the number. (Problems such as this one are often improperly stated, as the *base* is not specified. Improperly stated problems may have a mischievous effect upon an earnest student—possibly raising doubts of his own mental ability. Note that the phrase "of a certain number" should follow 3% and the latter *a* should be *the;* correctly stated: Seventy-two and one-tenth is 3% of a certain number greater than the number. Obtain the number.)

13.30. What number, increased by 25% of itself, amounts to 2,125?

13.31. What number, diminished by 10% of itself, amounts to $\frac{3}{8}$?

13.32. An automobile was sold for $5,120, which was 25% of the cost above the cost. Compute the cost.

13.33. An automobile was sold for $5,120, which was declared to be 8% of the original price below the original price. What must have been the original price, to the nearest cent?

13.34. A bookseller purchases books from the publisher at 20% off the list price, then sells them at the list price. What was his rate of profit (*a*) based on the list price? (*b*) based on wholesale price?

13.35. A shoe merchant bought five cases of boots, containing twelve pairs each, for $90 a case, at 5% discount for cash. He retailed them at $8.50 a pair. (*a*) Compute his cash profit. (*b*) What was his rate of profit based on his cost price? (*c*) What was his rate of profit based on his retail price?

13.36. A customer bought an item, paying $492.18, which included 4% sales tax. Compute the amount of the tax.

13.37. What was the sales price of a new automobile if the 4% sales tax amounted to $158.64?

13.38. A merchant paid $960 on a bill of goods on which he had been given successive discounts of 25%, 20%, 20%. What was the original bill?

$\mathcal{N}$ote 1 ∾ *Percent versus percentage.*

The terms *percent* and *percentage* are two distinct entities and must be clearly distinguished in problems involving these expressions. Percent represents a *rate*, and is always an abstract number with the percent sign. Percentage represents the corresponding portion of a designated quantity of material or persons which corresponds to 100%. Thus, if 25% of 500 bushels of corn is 125 bushels of corn, then 25% denotes the *percent*, 125 bushels of corn denotes the *percentage*, and the 500 bushels of corn, corresponding to 100%, denotes the *base*. Observe that the *percentage* and the *base* denote the *same kind of material*, here, *bushels of corn*.

$\mathcal{N}$ote 2 ∾ *Percentage may exceed base—* *rate may exceed 100 percent.*

The *percentage* is not necessarily smaller than the *base;* it is clearly larger than the base if the percent, or rate, is greater than 100%.

As an illustration, suppose that a person bought a lot for $200 and sold it for $1,500, what would be the percent of profit? The *percentage*, or cash profit, is $1,300. If the percent of profit is to be *based upon the cost*, then the percent of profit (rate) = percentage (gain) ÷ cost (base), or $1,300 ÷ 200 = 6\frac{1}{2}$ times the cost, or $6\frac{1}{2} \times 100\%$, or 650% of the cost. Here the percent is greater than 100%, because the percentage (profit) is greater than the cost (base). If the percent of profit were *based upon the selling price*, the percent of profit would be $1,300 ÷ 1,500$, or $\frac{13}{15}$ times the selling price, or $\frac{13}{15} \times 100\%$, or $86\frac{2}{3}\%$.

*N*ote 3 ∽ *Ambiguity in percentage relationships.*

Success in solving problems involving percentage relationships depends upon clear recognition of the items that denote the base, the percent (rate), and the percentage. (Ambiguity is present in certain problems in which the base is not specified; *ambiguity* connotes susceptibility of *two* interpretations.) To illustrate, a man sold an article for $60 and gained $20. What was his percent of profit? Here the cost of the article must have been $40. Since the base is not specified, one may assume that it is the cost ($40) *or* the selling price ($60). Hence the problem is improperly stated and is ambiguous as it has *two* possible solutions: (1) If cost is the base, $\frac{20}{40} = \frac{1}{2}$, or 50% as the percent of profit. (2) If sales price is base, $\frac{20}{60} = \frac{1}{3}$, or $33\frac{1}{3}\%$ as percent of profit.

The ensuing analysis proves that the percent gain is greater when based upon cost price, and the percent loss is greater when based on sales price.

Let C = cost price
             S = sales price
Then $S - C$ = gain if S is greater than C

Therefore $(S - C)/C$ is greater than $(S - C)/S$ for the larger fraction has the smaller denominator if their positive denominators are equal, i.e., if rate of gain, based on cost, is greater than rate of gain based on sales price. Contrariwise, if C is greater than S, then $S - C$ = loss. Then, $(S - C)/S$ is greater than $(S - C)/C$. Accordingly, a merchant may make his gain appear least by expressing it percentwise as based on sales price; he may make his loss appear greatest by expressing it percentwise as based on sales price.

*N*ote 4 ∽ *Ambiguity not present if rate exceeds 100 percent.*

In a buying-selling transaction the gain G or loss L is the difference between the purchase price C and the sales price S. Thus, $C - S = L$, as C is greater than S; $S - C = G$, as S is greater than C. There are four situations to be considered:

1. Percent of *loss* as based on cost = $(C - S)/C \times 100\% = (1 - S/C) \times 100\%$, which must be less than 100% as S/C is a proper fraction.

2. Percent of *loss* as based on sales price = $(C - S)/S \times 100\% = (C/S - 1) \times 100\%$, which may be greater than or less than 100% as the improper fraction C/S may exceed 2.

3. Percent of *gain* as based on cost = $(S - C)/C \times 100\% = (C/S - 1) \times 100\%$, which may be greater than or less than 100% as the improper fraction may or may not exceed 2.

4. Percent of *gain* as based on sales price = $(S - C)/S \times 100\% = (1 - C/S) \times 100\%$, which must be less than 100% as C/S is a proper fraction.

Accordingly, if the percent of loss is greater than 100%, the *base* must be the sales price; taking the cost for the base would lead to absurdity. Likewise if the percent of gain is greater than 100%, the base must be the cost price; taking the sales price for base would lead to absurdity. Here are two illustrations:

A merchant lost 120% on an article that cost \$38.50. Compute his cash loss. Clearly, the base cannot be the cost, for 120% of \$38.50 is \$46.20, which is greater than the cost of the article and is absurd. Hence, the *base must be the sales price.* Thus 100% = sales price; 100% + 120%, the percent (rate) that represents the cost price, \$38.50 (percentage). Then, the base = percentage ÷ rate = \$38.50 ÷ $\frac{220}{100}$ = \$17.50, the sales price. Therefore, his cash loss = \$38.50 − \$17.50 = \$21.00.

A merchant gains 120% on an article that cost him \$40. Compute the sales price. Here the sales price cannot be the base, for if 100% (base) represents the sales price, the cost would be represented by 100% − 120%, or a negative number, which is absurd. Hence, the *base must be the cost price.* But if the base is the cost price, the gain would be 120% of \$40, or 1.20 × 40 = \$48, which yields the sales price as \$40 + \$48 = \$88.

ᴥ SUPPLEMENTARY PROBLEMS ᴥ

The active key stays new and bright,
Unused, it gathers rust and blight.

S13.1. Express the following percentages as common fractions in lowest terms:

a. 10%	h. 60%	n. 96%	t. $18\frac{3}{4}\%$
b. 15%	i. 75%	o. 99%	u. $7\frac{1}{7}\%$
c. 20%	j. 80%	p. $6\frac{1}{4}\%$	v. $33\frac{1}{3}\%$
d. 25%	k. 85%	q. $8\frac{1}{3}\%$	w. $37\frac{1}{2}\%$
e. 30%	l. 90%	r. $12\frac{1}{2}\%$	x. $62\frac{1}{2}\%$
f. 40%	m. 95%	s. $16\frac{2}{3}\%$	y. $87\frac{1}{2}\%$
g. 50%			

S13.2. Express these fractions with percent signs to nearest 0.01%:

a. $\frac{2}{3}$	h. $\frac{4}{11}$	n. $\frac{9}{13}$	t. $\frac{2}{15}$
b. $\frac{5}{6}$	i. $\frac{5}{11}$	o. $\frac{12}{13}$	u. $\frac{4}{15}$
c. $\frac{3}{7}$	j. $\frac{7}{11}$	p. $\frac{1}{12}$	v. $\frac{8}{15}$
d. $\frac{5}{7}$	k. $\frac{2}{13}$	q. $\frac{5}{12}$	w. $\frac{11}{15}$
e. $\frac{2}{9}$	l. $\frac{3}{13}$	r. $\frac{7}{12}$	x. $\frac{13}{15}$
f. $\frac{8}{9}$	m. $\frac{7}{13}$	s. $\frac{11}{12}$	y. $\frac{14}{15}$
g. $\frac{3}{11}$			

S13.3. Identify the base, rate, and percentage; obtain the missing one.

a. Obtain 2% of 150 sheep.

b. What percent of 37 is 8?

c. 70 is 25% of what number?

d. 5% of $14.40 equals how much?

e. $14.40 is 5% of what amount?

f. $12\frac{1}{2}$% of 640 acres equals what?

g. $37\frac{1}{2}$% of what number is 24?

h. $16\frac{2}{3}$% of 24 men are how many men?

i. 35 is 28% of what number?

j. What is $14\frac{2}{7}$% of 56?

k. What percent of 42 is $42\frac{6}{7}$?

l. 28 is $28\frac{2}{7}$% of what?

m. $\frac{1}{2}$% of 8,000 is what?

n. $3\frac{1}{3}$% of what is 90?

o. What percent of 75 is $18\frac{3}{4}$?

p. 99.44% of what is 1 pound?

S13.4. Compute the rate of sales tax on an article listed at $12.50 for which the buyer had to pay $13.25.

S13.5. Compute the total cost of an automobile listed at $4,995.00 if the buyer had to pay 10% federal tax, 5% state sales tax, and 2% city sales tax.

S13.6. Before the "truth in lending" legislation was considered, a customer purchased a new automobile under an "all-inclusive economy deal" comprising these terms: The customer pays at purchase date only the sales tax of 5% and agrees to pay 36 equal monthly payments beginning 1 month from date of sale.   The added charges are based upon and added to the list price of $4,000 as follows: interest and carrying charge, $3 \times 8\frac{1}{3}$% for the 3 years; complete repair charges for 3 years, 25%; insurance and public liability for 3 years, 15%; license plates for 3 years, 5%.   Calculate the amount of the buyer's monthly payment.

S13.7. Observe that in the ensuing examples the usable rate must be formed by an addition to 100% or by a subtraction from 100%.   The base is equivalent to 100%, the percentage is equivalent to the rate.

a. 1,463 is greater than what number by 6% of that number?

b. 68 is less than what number by 66% of that number?

c. What number, increased by $33\frac{1}{3}$% of itself, is equal to 812?

d. George spent 25% of his savings to buy a bicycle.   His remaining savings account amounted to $192.   What was the original amount of his savings? What did he spend for the bicycle?

e. A butcher sold meat for $1.12 a pound, which was 40% of the wholesale price more than the wholesale price.   How much did he pay for it? Compute his profit on 1,000 pounds of meat if no meat was lost in handling it.

S13.8. A creditor paid $225 on a note of $600.   (a)   What percent of the note did he pay?   (b)   After making a second payment of $225, what percent of the original note remained unpaid?

S13.9. During one year a sheepherder's flock increased to 2,214 sheep.   If this includes an increase of 35% of his flock 1 year ago, how many sheep did he have 1 year ago?

S13.10. The current annual salary of salesmen of a certain company was increased or diminished by 10% of itself as determined by the salesman's sales record. Compute the total salary over a 2 year period for a salesman whose previous annual salary of $10,000 was affected as follows: (*a*) increase of 10%, decrease of 10%; (*b*) decrease of 10%, increase of 10%.

S13.11. Solve Problem S13.10 if (*a*) the decreases were 5% and the increases were 15%; (*b*) the decreases were 15% and the increases were 5%.

S13.12. In 1966 the population of the United States was estimated as follows:

Under 18 years of age	70,665,000
18 to 65 years of age	106,736,000
65 years of age and over	18,457,000

What percent of the total population was in each of these three groups?

S13.13. Compute the percent of the population of California for the three groups: 6,608,000; 10,599,000; and 1,611,000. What percent of the total population of the United States were living in California in 1966 according to these estimated data?

S13.14. A real estate agent charges 5% of the sales price of real estate for which he negotiates the sale. Compute his monthly income from the following sales:
Three lots, selling for $750, $11,580, and $975, respectively
One drug store and stock for $135,000
Two residences, for $23,750 and $18,500
One tract of land of 300 acres at $250 an acre

S13.15. An auctioneer received $2,300 for selling paintings that were sold for $92,000. Calculate his percent of commission based upon the sales price of the paintings.

S13.16. A trial lawyer's charges are $33\frac{1}{3}\%$ of the damages paid to his client if settled out of court and 50% if settled in court. If, by settling a claim for insurance damages out of court, the client saved $1,200 in lawyer's fees, what was the amount of the settlement, and what was the lawyer's fee?

S13.17. If a lawyer received $1,500 for settling a damage claim for his client out of court, how much did the client receive?

S13.18. After a senior citizen pays $50 for doctor's services during 1 calendar year, Medicare pays 80% of the remainder.
 a. If the citizen's total bills during 1 year amounted to $175, how much of this amount did Medicare pay for him?
 b. During the ensuing year Medicare paid $256 for this citizen. Compute his total doctor's bills for this year.
 c. How much did Medicare save him for each of these 2 years, if his monthly premium for Medicare is $4?

S13.19. Compute the ordinary, or simple, interest on the following amounts:
 a. $5,000 for 3 years at 6% per year
 b. $6,250 for 10 years at $5\frac{1}{2}\%$ per year
 c. $3,000 for 3 months at 6% per year
 d. $3,000 for 10 months at 1% per month

S13.20. *a.* Teacher *A* borrows $3,000 on July 1 for summer expenses, paying 6% of $3,000 immediately for the loan, and pays off this loan in 10 monthly installments beginning on October 1 of the same year. He pays also as interest 1% of the unpaid balance with each monthly installment. Compute the entire amount of interest he pays for this loan.

   b. Teacher B deposits $300 on the first of each month for 10 months, beginning on October 1. These deposits earn $\frac{1}{2}$% interest per month. On August 1 and on September 1 of the ensuing year he withdraws $1,500. How much has he on deposit just before making his next monthly deposit of $300 on October 1?

   c. If these two teachers receive the same annual salary, would it be correct to state that Mr. *B*'s economic providence yields him a net annual income of $450 more than Mr. *A*?

The next two problems deal with compound interest. In calculating ordinary, or simple, interest for 1 year, one readily identifies the principal with the *base*, the rate of interest with the *rate*, and the computed interest with the *percentage*. Thus, the interest on $750 for 1 year at 6% is equal to $750 × 0.06 = $45.00. Further, the interest earned for *n* years must be *n* × $45. Hence, for 8 years the interest on $750 at 6% must be 8 × $45 = $360. The sum of the original principal and the earned interest is called the *amount*. Thus, the amount on $750 for 8 years at simple interest at 6% must be $750 + $360 = $1,110. Quite generally, if *P* represents the original principal, *A* the accumulated amount, *r* the rate of interest, *n* the number of years the account is active, and *I* the earned simple interest:

$$I = Prn$$
$$A = P + Prn \quad \text{or} \quad P(1 + rn)$$

However, if the interest is united to the principal at the end of each year to form the principal for the ensuing year, the total interest is called compound interest. Thus, for an initial principal of *P*, a specified (nominal) rate *r* at the end of 1 year is $A = P + I = P(1 + r)$. The interest earned during the *second* year is equal to $P(1 + r)r$, so that the amount at the end of the second year must be $P(1 + r) + P(1 + r)r$, which, by the distributive law, may be expressed as $A = P(1 + r)(1 + r)$, or $P(1 + r)^2$. Using this amount for the principal in the third year, the interest earned during the third year must be equal to $P(1 + r)^2 r$, whence the amount at the end of the third year must be $P(1 + r)^2 + P(1 + r)^2 r$. By use of the distributive law this expression may be reduced to the form $A = P(1 + r)^3$. By repeated applications, one is led to the formula for the *amount at compound interest*, namely, $A = P(1 + r)^n$, in which *P* represents the initial principal, *r* the nominal stated rate of interest for 1 year, and *n* the number of conversions.

S13.21. Compute the amount accumulated at simple and compound interest on $250 for 3 years at 6%. Note that for simple interest, $A = P(1 + rn)$, whereas for compound interest $A = P(1 + r)^n$. These two formulas are identical except for the position of the *n*.

S13.22. Compute the amount on $400 for 2 years at compound interest at a nominal yearly rate of 6%, but compounded semiannually. Accordingly, the formula is modified to become $A = P(1 + r/2)^{2n}$, and, quite generally, if the interest is compounded *m* times each year, at a nominal annual rate of interest *r*, $A = P(1 + r/m)^{mn}$.

The remaining problems deal with involution. The calculation of $(1 + r)^n$ is rather tedious by the repeated multiplication by $1 + r$. These involutions are facilitated by use of Pascal's triangle, a triangular array of natural numbers having 1s at the left and right sides; each other number is equal to the sum of the two numbers above it and nearest to it. The Pascal's triangle appears as follows:

```
                    1
                1       1
            1       2       1
        1       3       3       1
      1     4       6       4       1
    1     5     10      10      5       1
  1     6    15      20      15      6       1
. . . . . . . . . . . . . . . . . . . .
```

These successive rows of numbers are coefficients arising for the successive terms of the developed involution $(a + b)^n$. Thus,

$$(a + b)^1 = 1a + 1b$$
$$(a + b)^2 = 1a^2 + 2ab + 1b^2$$
$$(a + b)^3 = 1a^3 + 3a^2b + 3ab^2 + 1b^3$$
$$(a + b)^4 = 1a^4 + 4a^3b + 6a^2b^2 + 4ab^3 + 1b^4$$
. . . .

Accordingly, $(1 + r)^n$ is equal to the sum of the products of the successive powers of r by the coefficients of the n row in Pascal's triangle. For examples:

$$(1 + 0.03)^4 = 1 + 4(0.03) + 6(0.03)^2 + 4(0.03)^3 + 1(0.03)^4$$
$$= 1 + 0.12 + 0.0054 + 0.000108 + 0.00000081$$
$$= 1.125,508,81$$
$$1.06^5 = 1 + 5(0.06) + 10(0.06)^2 + 10(0.06)^3 + 5(0.06)^4 + 0.06^5$$
$$= 1 + 0.30 + 0.036 + 0.00216 + 0.0000648 + 0.0000007776$$
$$= 1.338,225,577$$

S13.23. Verify the preceding involutions, 1.03^4 and 1.06^5 by actual continued multiplications.

S13.24. Extend Pascal's triangle as far as the sixteenth row of numbers.

S13.25. Calculate the amount on $10,000 at compound interest (state results to nearest cent):

    a. For 5 years at a nominal interest of 4%.

    b. For 7 years at 8%.

    c. For 7 years at a nominal rate of 4%, compounded semiannually (i.e., compute 1.02^{14}).

    d. For 16 years at 6% compounded annually.

    e. Compute the amounts of (*a*) to (*d*) at simple interest at the corresponding nominal annual rates of interest.

S13.26. In 1950 Mr. Doe's annual salary was $6,000. For each ensuing odd-numbered year his salary was increased by 11% of his previous annual salary, but for each ensuing even-numbered year his salary was decreased by 10% of his previous annual salary.

    a. Calculate his annual salary for 1960.

    b. Identify and state his maximum and minimum annual salaries.

    c. Calculate his average annual salary for these eleven years.

S13.27. If Mr. Doe was employed before 1940 under these same salary adjustments, what must have been his annual salary for 1940?

S13.28. Compute the sums of the numbers occurring in each row of Pascal's triangle. What kind of numbers are they?

S13.29. In Pascal's triangle draw the following parallel lines:

    a. Join left 1 in row three with right 1 in row two.

    b. Join left 1 in row four with 2 in row three.

    c. Join left 1 in row five with left 3 in row four and 1 in row three.

    d. Join left 1 in row six with left 4 in row five and right 3 in row four; continue until 8 such parallel lines are drawn.

Draw also two upper parallel lines through the two unused 1s in the top two rows, exhibiting 10 parallel lines altogether. Now obtain the sums of the numbers on each parallel line. What kind of numbers are they?

S13.30. List in a vertical column the first 10 Fibonacci numbers, namely, 1, 1, 2, 3, etc. List in adjoining columns the squares of these numbers, namely 1, 1, 4, 9, etc., and the sums of these squares beginning with the first square, namely, 1, 2, 6, 15, etc. Finally discover the relationship between these sums and pairs of consecutive Fibonacci numbers.

LESSON 14 ❧ SIGNIFICANT DIGITS ❧ SIGNIFICANCE COMPUTATIONS

Now Periander of Corinth, who was a very close friend of Thrasybulus of Miletus, was informed of the response of the oracle of Delphi. Accordingly, Periander instantly dispatched a messenger to his friend to make him aware of the circumstances, so that he might adjust his operations appropriately.

—Herodotus, *History, I,* 20.

14·1 ∼ Exact numbers versus approximate numbers

The numbers used in arithmetical calculations are either *exact* or *approximate*. The number of cubic inches in a gallon, 231, or the number of inches in a meter, 39.37, are exact and are so defined by legal statute. However, such numbers as π or the square root of 2, when they are expressed in decimal form, cannot be exact as no exact decimal forms for such numbers exist. For such numbers only *approximate* decimal forms can be used. Numbers expressing the value of coins in a purse or the number of students in a particular room may be obtained as exact by careful counting. Such numbers as those representing the population of a large city or the bacteria in a certain culture are generally only approximate, since the actual number of individuals present changes during the counting process. In measuring the length of a field or a plank of wood, the result of measurements depends upon the accuracy of the tape (which may shrink or expand through change of temperature or stretch by stresses upon it) and upon the ability of the measurer's eye to read accurately the graduation markings or to estimate the small portions between them on the measuring tape. Accordingly, *all measurements* depend for their accuracy upon the efficiency, or reliability, of the instruments used, such as yardsticks, clocks, scales, etc., and upon the skill of the observer's nerves and muscular reaction in eye, ear, hand, etc. In all such situations he must be content with *approximate* data, whose accuracy is indicated in the language of "significant digits."

14·2 ∼ Significant digits

Definition. Any digit, excepting left end zero digits, is called a significant digit in a decimal number if it represents with complete accuracy that which it purports to measure, and if, in the right end digit, the error it involves is not greater than half of one unit of its position. Thus the number 3.14, when used as an approximation for π, contains three significant digits, since the error involved, 3.141,59 . . . $-$ 3.14 = 0.001,59 . . . , is less than 0.005. Again, 3.142 has *four* significant digits, as the error involved is less than 0.000,5. When a correct number is rounded off properly to fewer than known significant digits, the resulting digits (except for possible left end zeros) are all significant. A zero on the right end of a decimal number is generally to be regarded as significant, unless known to be nonsignificant. Thus the number of centimeters in 1 inch, namely, 2.540, has *four* significant digits, since the more accurate expression of this number is 2.540,005,07 . . . . Again, 2.540,0 has five significant digits, 2.540,01 has six significant digits, 2.540,005 has seven significant digits, but 0.000,254 has only *three* significant digits, since left end zeros are not significant, being used merely to put the decimal point in the desired position. Such a statement as "the average distance between the centers of earth and sun is approximately 93,000,000 miles" is quite unsatisfactory, as the extent of inaccuracy is not indicated. Research has shown that this measurement cannot be in error by more than 10,000 miles; hence a more precise expression for this distance should be 93,000,000 $\pm$ 10,000 miles. Accordingly, the number of significant digits in this estimate, 93,000,000, is only three. In the remaining pages of this text it is to be assumed that all digits of given measured numbers are significant (except for left end zeros).

14·3 ∾ Reliability of calculations that are based upon data of known inaccuracy

The results of calculations based upon inaccurate numbers must also be subject to inaccuracy. Such results, to be satisfactory, must also indicate their significant digits or the possible size of error present.

For example, if the edge of a square is measured as $10\frac{5}{16}$ inches, the error in measurement is known to be less than $\frac{1}{32}$ of 1 inch or $\frac{1}{2}$ of $\frac{1}{16}$ of 1 inch, as the graduated scale is read to the *nearest sixteenth* of an inch. Now, the area of the square as obtained as $10\frac{5}{16} \times 10\frac{5}{16} = 106\frac{89}{256}$ may not be assumed to be perfectly correct. The extent of uncertainty in such a computed result is estimated as follows: $(10\frac{5}{16} + \frac{1}{32})^2 = 106\frac{1,017}{1,024}$ square inches, largest possible area; $(10\frac{5}{16} - \frac{1}{32})^2 = 105\frac{721}{1,024}$ square inches, smallest possible area. Thus, the computed area, $106\frac{356}{1,024}$, is subject to error by as much as $\frac{661}{1,024}$ square inches. Its true value may be expressed as $106\frac{357}{1,024} \pm \frac{660}{1,024}$ square inches. Expressed decimally, the uncertainty to three, two, or one digit, the area of the square would appear, respectively, as 106.348 $\pm$ 0.645 square inches, 106.35 $\pm$ 0.64 square inches, or 106.3 $\pm$ 0.6 square inches.

To repeat, to obtain *reliable* results of calculations based upon *unreliable* data (whose range of uncertainty is known), one should perform *two* calculations employing extreme sets of data. The true result must lie between these two calculated results.

14·4 ~ SIGNIFICANCE COMPUTATION—MULTIPLICATION

To facilitate the tedious arithmetical calculations that are necessary, one uses "significance computations" which lessen the labor of the arithmetical operations. These matters are explained in the following illustrative problems.

Obtain the product of the measured numbers of *four* significant digits, i.e., correct to the nearest 0.005: 14.38 and 56.72. Let the digits of the multiplier be used from the *left*, instead of from the right as customary. The * denotes *unknown* digits that would be used for greater accuracy of measurement. In the partial and complete products these *'s continue to represent unknown digits.

```
14.38   *   *   *   *   *   *   . . .
56.72   *   *   *   *   *   *   . . .
_____
7190    *   *   *   *   *   *
8628        *   *   *   *   *
10066           *   *   *   *
2876                *   *   *
_____
815.6
```

The decimal point is placed in the product from these considerations: Using the nearest left digit by roundoffs, one has $10 \times 60 = 600$. Pointing off the answer to the nearest 600, one uses 815. Note that in the product only three digits are known with certainty, the 6 might have been as large as 9 by using neglected carryovers from the unknown numbers represented by the asterisks. Thus all work indicated in the columns containing an * is useless, and may be omitted, as follows:

```
14.38
56.72
_____
7190    Multiplying 1438 by 5
863     Multiplying 143 by 6, using carryover of 6 × 8 = 48, nearest
        carryover is 5
100     Multiplying 14 by 7, using carryover of 7 × 3 = 21, nearest carry-
        over is 2
3       Multiplying 2 × 1, using nearest carryover of 2 × 4 = 8, or 1
_____
815.6
```

This single multiplication does not reveal the number of significant digits in the product. This is revealed by making two separate multiplications using the largest possible five-digit numbers, then using smallest possible five-digit numbers. The correct product is between them.

In all products of *measured* numbers one must perform the two multiplications, using an extra digit 5 at the right end of the two numbers; this yields a product that must be *greater* than or equal to the correct product. Then the two measured numbers are adjusted to indicate the *smallest* values they might represent; this is done by diminishing the right end digit by 1, then supplying an extra right end digit 5. The product of these minimal numbers then must be less than or equal to the correct product. To perform the significance multiplication judiciously, one may *underline* the digits already used in the multiplier and those dropped from the multiplicand. This is illustrated in the two multiplications, in successive steps:

Maximum	*Minimum*
values	*values*
14.385	14.375
56.725	56.715
71925	71825

Multiply the multiplicand by the left end digit, 5, of the multiplier. Now underline the used digit of the multiplier and the right end digit of the multiplicand.

14.385	14.375
56.725	56.715
71925	71825
8631	8625

Multiply the four remaining digits of the multiplicand by the 6, the present left end digit of multiplier. The carryover of 6 × 5 (of multiplicand) is 3 of the 30. Now underline the used digit of the multiplier, 6, and the used right end digit of the multiplicand, 8, in the maximum and 7 in the minimum multiplicands.

14.385	14.375
56.725	56.715
71925	71825
8631	8625
1007	1006

Multiply the three remaining digits of multiplicands by 7, the current left end digit of the multipliers. Note the carryovers, 6 for the maximum, 5 for the minimum. Now underline the 3 in the multiplicand and the 7 in the multipliers. Then multiply the remaining digits of multiplicands by the new left end digit of the multipliers.

14.385	14.375
56.725	56.715
71925	71875
8631	8625
1007	1006
29	14

For maximum, multiply 14 by 2, note the carryover of 1, for $2 \times 3 = 6$, which is nearer to 10 than 0; for the minimum multiplication, multiply 14 by 1, noting carryover is 0, as $1 \times 3 = 3$, which is nearer to 0 than 10. Now underline 4 and 2 in the maximum array and 4 and 1 in the minimum. Then multiply the single remaining digit of the multiplicands by the single remaining digit of the multiplier, the carryover being 2 in each case, for $5 \times 4 = 20$ in each situation. Then add the partial products.

14.385	14.375
56.725	56.715
71925	71875
8631	8625
1007	1006
29	14
7	7
815.99	815.27

These products agree in only three digits; hence the product of the four-digit numbers, in this case, yields only three certain digits of product. Indeed, there are only *two significant digits* of the product, since roundings off to three digits yield 816 and 815, respectively. A convenient way to express the product with possible inaccuracy is to express the number midway between the foregoing two extremes and the difference between this mean and one of the extremes. Thus $\frac{1}{2}(815.99 + 815.27) = 815.63$; then $815.63 - 815.27 = 0.36$. The desired form of the product is 815.63 ± 0.36, or more simply, but less concisely, 815.6 ± 0.4, which shows the extent of possible error in the computed product.

Note that the product of two measured numbers cannot have more significant digits than the given number of fewer significant digits. The foregoing two given numbers show *four* significant digits each, but their product cannot be forecast but actually depends upon the actual digits themselves in the given numbers. Thus, no concise general rules can be given about the exact number of significant digits in the product of two measured numbers. However, there are at least as many significant digits in the product as two less than the number of significant digits in the given number of fewer significant digits.

A somewhat shorter method of obtaining the product of two measured numbers (approximately given numbers with known range of possible inexactness) is evident from the following considerations. Let the two numbers be represented by $A \pm a$ and $B \pm b$, in which A and B denote the exact values of the two numbers and the a and b their maximum possible errors arising from faulty measurements. The distributive law of multiplication shows the product to be $(A \pm a)(B \pm b) = AB \pm Ab \pm aB + ab$. Now for measured numbers the a and b are both 5 with the appropriate number of 0s to the left. Hence this product is $AB \pm a(A + B) + a^2$. To exhibit this method with the same two numbers previously used, 14.38 × 56.72,

14.38	14.38
56.72	56.72
7190	71.10
863	×0.005
100	±.355,5 or ±0.4, by rounding off
3	
815.6	

The extent of uncertainty of result: $0.005 \pm (14.38 + 56.72) + 0.005^2$. $0.005 \times 0.005 = 0.000,025$ (too small for consideration)

Hence the desired product form is 815.6 ± 0.4.

Following is an alternate scheme of multiplying two decimal forms. Justification for its validity appears by noting that it merely uses the distributive law of multiplication. The entire product of 14.38 and 56.72 is obtained; the unneeded digits of the product are noted and need not have been obtained. The successive partial products so obtained are doubly underlined.

14.38

56.72

5467716

268862

815.633,6

$5 \times 1 = 5$

$5 \times 4 + 6 \times 1 = 26$

$5 \times 3 + 6 \times 4 + 7 \times 1 = 46$

$5 \times 8 + 6 \times 3 + 7 \times 4 + 2 \times 1 = 88$

$6 \times 8 + 7 \times 3 + 2 \times 4 = 77$

$7 \times 8 + 2 \times 3 = 62$

$2 \times 8 = 16$

Note that these successive partial products are placed in position under the given numbers, with each new units digit one place further to the right. This process could have stopped after four digits of the complete product were provided for, since the product could not contain more than four significant digits. The range of possible error is found as above, ±0.4. If one of the given numbers or both of them are exact numbers, there is no occasion to consider possible presence of errors in them. To compute the circumference of a circle having a measured diameter 24.5 inches by formula, circumference = π × diameter, it would be useless to use the decimal form for π to more than three places, since the diameter is given only to three significant digits.

3.14	Possible error = $0.05 \times 3.14 = 0.157$
24.5	
6272	Thus the circumference = 76.93 ± 0.157 inches and is known to
1421	two significant digits only, as it may range from 77.087 to 76.773; or
76.93	more concisely, but less accurately, 76.9 ± 0.2 inches

Re-solving the foregoing problem by maximum-minimum values and noting the value of π is known exactly so far as desired, one uses the fifth digit of π only for the carryover in the first multiplication by 2.

Maximum	*Minimum*	*Average of extremes*	
3.1416 . . .	3.1416 . . .	77.12	
24.55	24.45	76.81	
6283	6283	2⎜153.93	
1256	1256	76.965	Mean
157	126	76.81	Minimum
16	16	0.155	Possible error
77.12	76.81		

The length of circumference is 76.965 ± 0.155, or less accurately, 76.9 ± 0.2 inches.

One may feel more secure in the carryovers by extending the extreme values by an extra digit 0.   Thus,

14.3850	14.3750
56.7250	56.7150
719250	718750
86310	86250
10070	10062
287	144
72	71
815.989	815.277
815.277	
2⎜1631.266	
815.633	
815.277	
.356	

I.e., 815.633 ± 0.356 or 815.6 ± 0.4

☙ PROBLEMS ☙

14.1.   Exhibit the product of the following pairs of measured numbers with possible errors given to one significant digit.   To check the work use both procedures as previously presented.

    a.   14.508 × 35.314   *c.*   0.005,72 × 680.5   *e.*   2.718,28 × 1.414,28
    b.   2.47 × 345.97   *d.*   1.44 × 5.9   *f.*   2.540,0 × 0.007,66

14.2.   Compute the volume of the cube whose measured edges are each 4.235 centimeters.

14·5 ~ Significance computation—division and evolution

To obtain the quotient of two measured numbers, one performs the two extreme divisions, using for maximum quotient the *minimum divisor* and the *maximum dividend*. To obtain the minimum quotient, one uses the *maximum divisor* with the *minimum dividend*.

Obtain the quotient of the measured numbers, 18.46 ÷ 5.73. In performing the two long divisions all useless digits are omitted. In each ensuing multiplication of the divisor its next right end digit is dropped, except for the carryover in the multiplication.

Maximum possible quotient	*Minimum possible quotient*
3.225	3.218
5.725|18.465	5.735|18.455
17175	17205
1290	1250
1145	1147
145	103
114	57
31	46
29	46
2	0

3.225	Maximum	3.2215	Mean
3.218	Minimum	3.218	Minimum
2|6.443		0.0035	Possible error
3.2215	Mean		

The quotient is 3.221,5 ± 0.003,5, or 3.222 ± 0.004, to one significant digit in uncertainty of the quotient. Thus the quotient is known to only two significant digits.

Similarly, root extractions of approximate numbers may be made. For example, compute as accurately as possible $\sqrt{14.3}$.

	Maximum possible root			Minimum possible root	
	14.35	(3.788		14.25	(3.775
	9			9	
67	535		67	525	
7	469		7	469	
748	66		747	56	
8	60		7	52	
	6			4	
	6			4	

3.788	3.7815
3.775	3.775
2⟌7.563	0.0065 Range of
3.7815	uncertainty

The desired root is 3.782 ± 0.007.

Thus the number 14.3 contains *three* significant digits, whereas $\sqrt{14.3}$ contains only *two* significant digits, 3.8. No general rule exists for the precise number of significant digits in the result of computations that have been performed upon numbers of known significant digits.

∽ PROBLEMS [CONCLUDED] ∽

14.3. Obtain the quotients, indicating possible uncertainty to one digit.

    a.   498.35 ÷ 598.3   *c.* π ÷ 0.056,2

    b.   1,020.8 ÷ 345.9   *d.*   37.29 ÷ π

14.4. Compute as accurately as possible the number of gallons of fluid a rectangular tank may contain, if its inside measured dimensions are 35.62 inches, 18.35 inches, and 10.27 inches. (231 cubic inches = 1 gallon *exactly*.)

14.5. Calculate the most accurate sum of the measured numbers 157.38, 91.20, 46.76, 79.48, and 77.92. Specify the uncertainty of the result.

14.6. Calculate the length of the diagonal of a rectangle whose measured length is 156.9 feet and width is 83.4 feet. State the result appropriately.

14.7. A farmer sets out fence posts along one boundary of a field that is exactly 3 miles long. He places these posts, one by one, 8 feet apart. If he measures each successive distance his measurements are subject to an error of as much as 0.1 inch. Compute the possible number of posts he uses. How many posts would be used if his measurements were exact? How could he plan his work to use this exact number and place the posts correctly?

Note 1 *A pretaste of trigonometry.*

Draw a circle with center at point zero and radius equal to *one* (foot or inch or centimeter, etc.). Draw also the horizontal and vertical diameters, having the right and top ends at points *M* and *N* respectively. Next draw the vertical and horizontal tangents touching the circle at these points *M* and *N*. Finally draw a line from *O* that cuts the circle at point *Q*, the vertical tangent line at point *R*, and the horizontal tangent line at point *S*. The angular space, taken clockwise, between the line segments *OM* and *OQ* is called the angle *A*. In the four indicated situations the angle *A* is said to be in the first, second, third, and fourth quadrants, respectively. (See Figure 14.1.)

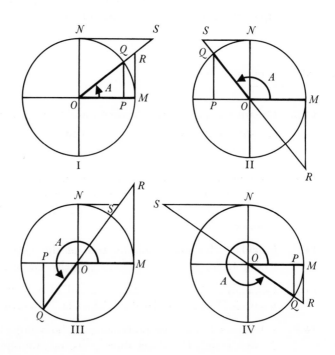

FIGURE 14.1

Six line segments have *lengths* that are of fundamental importance. They are the following with their customary names:

PQ = sine of A, abbreviated to sin A
OP = cosine of A, abbreviated to cos A
MR = tangent of A, abbreviated to tan A
NS = cotangent of A, abbreviated to cot A
OR = secant of A, abbreviated to sec A
OS = cosecant of A, abbreviated to csc A

Sines and tangents are regarded as *positive* if they lie *above* the horizontal diameter of the circle, negative if they lie below it. Cosines and cotangents are *positive* if they lie to the right of the vertical diameter of the circle, *negative* if they lie to the left of it. The secant is positive if points Q and R are on the same side of point O; the secant is negative if point O is between points Q and R. The cosecant is positive if points Q and S are on the same side of point O; the cosecant is negative if point O is between points Q and S.

	Quadrant I from 0° to 90°	Quadrant II 90° to 180°	Quadrant III 180° to 270°	Quadrant IV 270° to 360°
sin A = PQ	+	+	−	−
cos A = OP	+	−	−	+
tan A = MR	+	−	+	−
cot A = NS	+	−	+	−
sec A = OR	+	−	−	+
csc A = OS	+	+	−	−

The numerical values of the six trigonometrical quantities, called *functions* of the angle A, *apart from* + *or* − *signs*, are related by the rule:

The angle A *may be replaced by* A − *180° or 180°* − A, *or 360°* − A, *without changing the corresponding numerical value, apart from the sign, of the same trigonometric function.*

The sign of the function depends on the quadrant in which angle A lies. Thus sin 300° = − sin 60°, as 360° − 300° = 60°. Furthermore, if A lies in quadrant I, sin A = cos (90° − A), cos A = sin (90° − A), tan A = cot (90° − A), cot A = tan (90° − A), sec A = csc (90° − A), and csc A = sec (90° − A).

Accordingly one need have the numerical values of the six functions for angles from 0° to 45°, from which all others may be immediately obtained.

In the table on the front endpaper of this book, the degree readings on the left margin are associated with the function written above the respective column; the degree readings on the right of the table correspond with the functions listed below the columns.

*N*ote 2 ∿ *The three Pythagorean trigonometric identities.*

Observe that the triangles *OPQ*, *OMR*, and *OMS* are right triangles, so that $OP^2 + PQ^2 = OQ^2$, $OM^2 + MR^2 = OR^2$, and $ON^2 + NS^2 = OS^2$, respectively, or in the language of the trigonometric functions, $(\cos A)^2 + (\sin A)^2 = 1$, $1 + (\tan A)^2 = (\sec A)^2$, and $1 + (\cot A)^2 = (\csc A)^2$. These relationships are generally written as $\cos^2 A + \sin^2 A = 1$, $1 + \tan^2 A = \sec^2 A$, and $1 + \cot^2 A + \csc^2 A$.

∿ CHALLENGE

Verify these three relationships for several angles in the tables, such as for $A = 38°$, namely, $7780^2 + 0.6157^2 = 1, 1 + 0.7813^2 = 1.269^2$, and $1 + 1.280^2 = 1.624^2$. As the entries in the tables are correct only to the given five significant digits, these verifications will show such significance.

*N*ote 3 ∿ *The meaning of the names of the six trigonometric functions.*

Each of the names *sine*, *tangent*, and *secant* expresses a characteristic feature of the trigonometric function it represents.

Sine. The Latin equivalent for sine is *sinus* connoting an indentation, or gulf or bay. It appears on many medieval maps, as for example, the names *Sinus Tarentinus* and *Sinus Ligustigus* in southeastern and northwestern Italy. One may observe that the line *PQ* in Figure 14.1, **I**, representing sin *A*, marks off the *indentation MPQ* of the circle.

Tangent. This word is the root form of the Latin participle connoting "touching." The Latin verb *tango*, "I touch," has for its present participle *tangens, tangentis;* its perfect passive participle, *tactus*, supplies the root for our con*tact*. One may observe that the line *MR touches* the circle at *M* for all four quadrants.

Secant. The present participle of the Latin word *seco*, "I cut," is *secans, secantis*, whose root form is secant, connoting cutting. One may observe that the line *OR cuts* the circumference of the circle for each quadrant's position.

The prefix *co* in the words cosine, cotangent, and cosecant, is an abbreviation for *complement of*. The word *complement* (not compliment) connotes a *completion*, or *filling up*. Particularly, the complement of an acute angle is the additional angle needed to fill out the right angle. Thus,

The complement of angle 85° is 5°, since 85° + 5° = 90°
The complement of angle 60° is 30°, since 60° + 30° = 90°

Or quite generally the complement of angle *A* is the angle 90° − *A*.

∽ CHALLENGES

1. Sketch carefully Figure 14.1, I.

2. Draw a horizontal line through *Q*, cutting the line *ON* at *T*.

3. Mentally rotate this figure through 180° about the line *ON* as axis.

4. Sketch the figure that results from this operation.

5. Turn your sketch clockwise 90° about *O*, so that points *O*, *T*, *N*, are a horizontal line. Mark the angle *NOQ* by the letter *B*. Note that angle *B* is the complement of angle *A*.

6. Finally, from this sketch, show that:
   a. Cosine of *A* = sine of *B*, sine of *A* = cosine of *B*
   b. Cotangent of *A* = tangent of *B*, tangent of *A* = cotangent of *B*
   c. Cosecant of *A* = secant of *B*, secant of *A* = cosecant of *B*
   Or, comprehensively, any trigonometric function of any acute angle is equal to the co-named function of its complement.

∽ SUPPLEMENTARY PROBLEMS ∽

Indolent fellow—look at the ant!
Examine her ways and be wise.
She works on her own—entirely alone
And gains by her toil PARADISE.

—Proverbs 6:7,8.

Every calculated result should show its possible range of inaccuracy; the most satisfactory results indicate the smallest range of inaccuracy.

S14.1. Calculate the area of the following rectangles having the given measured dimensions:
   a. Length 2.48 inches, width 1.79 inches
   b. Length 453.47 feet, width 197.33 feet

    c.   Length 19.3 millimeters, width 5.8 millimeters

    d.   Length 7,352.72 feet, width 3,770.02 feet

    e.   Length 762.7 miles, 607.9 miles

S14.2. Compute the length of the diagonals and the perimeters of the rectangles in Problem S14.1.

S14.3. How many gallons of water are required to fill a rectangular pool whose measured dimensions are length 75 feet 6 inches, width 12 feet 8 inches, and depth 11 feet 9 inches? These measurements are subject to possible errors not exceeding one-half inch (1 gallon contains exactly 231 cubic inches).

S14.4. Compute the volume and area of a sphere of diameter 14.7 ± 0.05 inches.

S14.5. Obtain the value of a lump of solid gold valued at exactly $32 an ounce, if its measured weight is 53.62 ounces and if the weighing is subject to an inaccuracy of 2.3 percent as determined by experimentation.

S14.6. If a rectangular barge 24 feet long and 9 feet wide sank into the water 10 additional inches when an elephant was led onto it, what was the weight of the elephant if the water upon which the barge was floating weighed 62.5 pounds per cubic foot? Show the possible range of uncertainty in your calculated result if each measured dimension is subject to an inaccuracy of not more than $\frac{1}{2}$ inch and the weight of 1 cubic foot of water may be as much as $\frac{1}{2}$ ounce in error.

S14.7. Re-solve Problem S14.6 after replacing the numbers 24, 9, 10, 62.5, $\frac{1}{2}$, 1, and $\frac{1}{2}$, respectively, by 20, 8, 12, 65, 1, 1, and 1.

S14.8. Compute the weight of a medicine ball whose measured data comprise these significant digits: radius 5 feet, 9 ± 0.5 inches; weight of material in the ball 13 pounds, 13 ± 1 ounces per cubic foot.

S14.9. The dimensions of a rectangle are *exactly* $\sqrt[3]{9}$, $\sqrt[3]{12}$, and $\sqrt[3]{16}$. Compute these cube roots to the nearest 0.001. From these approximate values compute the volume of the rectangle, indicating the possible inaccuracy of the result. Then calculate the exact volume using the given *exact* dimensions, thus corroborating the validity of the computed volume.

S14.10. A *ton* of candy is to be packed into 1 pound boxes. If the packing is subject to maximum error of 0.2 ounce per box, how many boxes of candy may be expected from the packing? The *ton* is subject to an error of 8 pounds.

S14.11. One meter has been defined by federal statute to be exactly 39.37 inches in length. If 100 centimeters are equivalent to 1 meter, compute to one significant digit the error that is frequently made in stating that 1 inch = 2.54 centimeters exactly (as in Reader's Digest *Almanac* for 1969, page 715). Compute the number of inches in 1 billion centimeters using the relationships (*a*) 39.37 inches = 1 meter; (*b*) 1 inch = 2.54 centimeters. Compute the number of centimeters in 1 billion inches by using these same two relationships.

S14.12. In calculating the percent of error, the exact value is used as the base, and the actual error is used as the percentage. Compute to two significant digits the percent of error in these statements:

a.   1 foot = 0.304,8 meters (exactly)

b.   1 acre = 43,560 square feet (640 acres = 1 square mile)

c.   1 cubic foot = 7.49 gallons

d.   1 cubic foot = $7\frac{1}{2}$ gallons

S14.13. What should be the value of a spherical ball of pure gold, of measured diameter 3.47 centimeters, if 1 cubic centimeter of gold has been weighed and found to weigh 19.3 grams, and 1 gram of gold is worth exactly $1?

S14.14. How many cubical blocks of (measured) dimensions of edge 3.27 inches long would be equivalent in volume to 250 cubical blocks of edge 7.59 inches?

S14.15. What should be the weight of a hemispherical shell whose inner and outer diameters are measured as 47.3 and 49.7 inches, respectively, and if the material of which it is constructed has been weighed as 0.977 ounces per cubic inch? How many gallons of water can this hemisphere hold? Compute the weight of this water 64.83 pounds per cubic foot.

LESSON 15 MENSURATION EXACT AND APPROXIMATE EQUIVALENCES OF VARIOUS UNITS OF MEASURE

. . . *The flying or floating island is exactly circular; its diameter is 7,837 yards, or about four miles and a half, and consequently contains ten thousand acres.* . . .

—Jonathan Swift, *Gulliver's Travels*, Laputa.

15·1 ∾ THE USE OF VARIOUS UNITS TO PROVIDE MEASUREMENTS

The measure or *size* of a given object is the *number of times*, integral or fractional, that a certain standard *unit of measurement* could be taken in order to be exactly equivalent to the given object. The length of a straight line would be expressed in terms of a standard unit of length, as inch, foot, centimeter, miles, etc. A small length would generally be expressed in terms of a small unit of length, as millimeter, inch, etc.; a large length in terms of a large unit of length, as the mile, the light year, or the parsec. A given area would be measured in terms of a standard unit of area, as square foot, square yard, acre, square mile, etc. A square foot is an area 1 foot long and 1 foot wide. A volume would be expressed in terms of a unit of volume, as cubic foot, gallon, cord, perch, etc. A cubic foot is a volume 1 foot long, 1 foot wide, and 1 foot high. A gallon is *exactly* equivalent to 231 cubic inches, a cord of wood is rectangular pile 8 feet long, 4 feet high, and 4 feet wide. A perch of masonry is 1 rod long, 1 foot high, and $1\frac{1}{2}$ feet thick. Measurements of lengths, areas, and volumes are usually made *indirectly;* i.e., by measuring directly only certain lengths or angles. By special exact relationships between the measured quantities and the quantities desired measured, one calculates the measure of the quantity in question. It must be remembered that, although mathematical reasoning obtains *exact* relationships between the quantities that are measured and the quantities to be computed from these measurements, and these are expressed by certain *exact formulas*, the actual measurements made by a human being with his fabricated instruments for measuring are always subject to inaccuracy. This inaccuracy must be taken into consideration when estimating the result of calculations, as was indicated in the preceding lesson.

15·2 ∾ VARIOUS SYSTEMS OF MEASUREMENT

Exact relationships between units of measure are established by law. Some of these laws are given here.

Units of Length. The equivalence between the units of two systems, the English and the French, is established by federal statute by the *exact* equivalence: 1 meter = 39.37 inches. It was intended by the French revolutionists that 1 meter should equal 0.000,000,1 of the distance from the earth's equator to the North Pole; the English yard was said to equal the length of Henry VIII's arm.

ENGLISH SYSTEM	FRENCH, OR METRIC, SYSTEM
12 inches (in.) = 1 foot (ft)	10 millimeters (mm) = 1 centimeter (cm)
3 ft = 1 yard (yd)	10 cm = 1 decimeter (dm)
$5\frac{1}{2}$ yd or $16\frac{1}{2}$ ft = 1 rod (rd)	10 dm = 1 meter (m)
40 rd = 1 furlong (fur)	10 m = 1 decameter (dkm)
320 rd or 8 fur = 1 mile (mi)	10 dkm = 1 hectometer (htm)
3 leagues = 1 mile[1]	10 htm = 1 kilometer (km)

Certain other special units of length are used.

By mariners:	6 ft = 1 fathom
	120 fathoms = 1 cable length
	880 fathoms, or $7\frac{1}{3}$ cable lengths = 1 mi
By surveyors:	100 links = 1 chain
	80 chains = 1 mi
By cloth measurers:	$2\frac{1}{2}$ in. = 1 nail (na)
	4 na or 9 in. = 1 quarter (qr)
	4 qr = 1 yd
	1 ell Flemish = 3 qr or $\frac{3}{4}$ yd
	1 ell English = 5 qr or $1\frac{1}{4}$ yd
	1 ell French = 6 qr or $1\frac{1}{2}$ yd

Units of Area. The French system prefixes sq for square before each length unit; then one hundred of each area unit equal one next larger area unit. Thus, 100 sq mm = 1 sq cm, etc. The English system is as follows:

144 square inches (sq in.) = 1 square foot (sq ft)
9 sq ft = 1 square yard (sq yd)
$30\frac{1}{4}$ sq ft = 1 square rod (sq rd)
160 sq rd = 1 acre (A)
640 A = 1 square mile (sq mi)

Volume, or Solid, or Cubic Measurement. The cube of each length unit equals one higher volume unit, thus:

12^3, or 1728 cubic inches (cu in.) = 1 cubic foot (cu ft)
3^3, or 27 cu ft = 1 cubic yard (cu yd)

. . . .

Some special units are:

231 cu in. = 1 gallon (gal) (exact by federal statute)

[1] A league has had varying values from 2.4 to 4.6 miles at different times in different countries.

1 bushel = volume of cylinder of height 8 in. and diameter $18\frac{1}{2}$ in. (exact by federal statute)

1 bushel = 2,150.42 cu in. (approximate consequence of definition of bushel, with error less than 0.000,2 cu in.)

Special units for French system are:

10^3, or 1,000 cubic millimeters (cu mm) = 1 cubic centimeter (cu cm)
10^3, or 1,000 cu cm = 1 cubic decimeter (cu dm)
                        = 1 liter

. . . .

It appears that some measurements are *exact* by legal statute, while others derived from them are rounded off to approximate values; those involving π, as in the definition of a bushel, must be approximate, if expressed decimally.

15·3 ∾ Some important relationships of measurement with their mnemonic formulas

Rectangles.   In area units, the area of a rectangle is equal to the product of the numbers of width and length units, in the same corresponding units. If the length is 3 ft and width is 8 in., these measurements must be converted to the same length unit, e.g., inches or feet, etc.   Length = $12 \times 3 = 36$ in., width = 8 in.   Therefore the area is equal to $36 \times 8 = 288$ sq in.   Or length = 3 ft, width = 8 in. = $8 \div 12 = \frac{2}{3}$ ft.   Hence the area is equal to $3 \times \frac{2}{3} = 2$ sq ft.   Thus 2 sq ft are exactly equivalent to 288 sq in.

The formula for the area of a rectangle as expressed $A = l \times w$, is a brief mnemonic (memory help) for "the number of area units in a rectangle is equal to the product of the corresponding length units in the length and width, respectively."   The reasonableness of the formula is apparent from the following considerations (Figure 15.1).

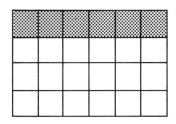

FIGURE 15.1

1. There are as many area units along the top edge, and in each lower strip, as there are length units in the top edge, since each such length unit is one edge of a corresponding area unit.

2. There are as many horizontal strips of area units as there are length units in the right, or left, vertical edge of the rectangle.

3. Hence, the total number of area units is equal to the product of the number of area units in each strip by the number of strips in the entire rectangle.

Parallelograms. The formula for the area of a parallelogram is given as $A = b \times h$, which is mnemonic for "the number of area units in a parallelogram is equal to the product of the *number* of length units in the base by the *number* of length units in the corresponding altitude." It may be recalled that a parallelogram is a flat four-sided figure whose opposite pair of straight edges are parallel. Either side may be regarded as a base, and the perpendicular distance between that side and the opposite side is the corresponding altitude.

The reasonableness of the formula appears from Figure 15.2. Observe that if the shaded triangle is removed from the right end and placed at the left end,

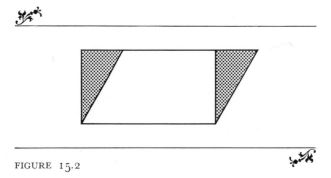

FIGURE 15.2

the parallelogram is converted into an equivalent rectangle with the same base. The area of the rectangle has already been determined to be equal to the product of the number of length units in the length of rectangle (or base of the parallelogram) by the number of length units in the width of the rectangle (or corresponding altitude of the parallelogram).

Triangles. The area of a triangle is given by the formula $A = \frac{1}{2}bh$, which is a mnemonic for "the number of area units in a triangle is equal to half the product of the numbers of length units in the base and corresponding altitude of the triangle."

Any side of the triangle may be used for the base; the corresponding altitude is the line drawn perpendicular to the base, extended if necessary, and extending to the opposite vertex. A parallelogram is formed by drawing lines through each of two vertices of the given triangle and parallel, respectively, to the opposite sides of the given triangle. These two lines so drawn and the third side of the original triangle form a new triangle, which is shaded in Figure 15.3.

It can be proved that the shaded triangle is exactly equivalent to the original (unshaded) triangle in every respect. Hence the area of the original triangle must be exactly half the area of the parallelogram. Now the parallelogram and the original triangle have the very same base and altitude; accordingly, as the area of the parallelogram is equal to the product of the number of common units of length in its base and its altitude, the area of the triangle must be equal to half this product. That is, $A = \frac{1}{2} bh$.

The ensuing formulas are presented with no attempt to show their reasonableness. One may be assured that they are proved to be completely correct in texts on plane and solid geometry. They are also mnemonics, for which all letters denoting lengths of lines are measured in length units, all letters representing areas are measured in the corresponding area units, and all letters representing volumes are to be measured in the corresponding volume units. Examples of corresponding length, area, and volume units are feet, square feet, and cubic feet, or cm, sq cm, and cu cm.

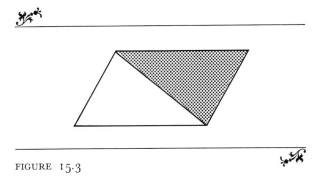

FIGURE 15.3

Circles. Area equals π times square of radius, or $A = \pi r^2$. Circumference equals π times diameter or $C = \pi d$, or $C = 2\pi r$.

Spheres. Area equals 4 times square of radius times π, or $A = 4\pi r^2$, or $A = \pi d^2$. Volume equals $\frac{1}{6}$ times π times cube of diameter, or $V = \frac{1}{6}\pi d^3$, or $V = \frac{4}{3}\pi r^3$.

Rectangular Solids. Volume equals product of lengths of three edges meeting at a corner, or V = length $\times$ width $\times$ height, or $V = lwh$.

Pyramids. Volume equals $\frac{1}{3}$ area of base times altitude, or $V = \frac{1}{3}bh$. The altitude of the pyramid is the perpendicular distance of the vertex above the base. If the edges of the base are equal to one another, and if the triangles forming the sides of the pyramid are all exactly alike, the pyramid is called a regular *pyramid*. The *slant height* of a regular pyramid is the length from the apex (top) of the pyramid to the midpoint of one of the edges of the base.   The total area of the triangles on the sides of the pyramid is called the lateral area of the pyramid.   The lateral area of a pyramid is equal to one-half the perimeter of the base multiplied by the slant height, $A = \frac{1}{2}pL$.

Cones.   The volume of any cone is equal to one-third the product of the area of the base by the altitude of the cone.   The altitude of any cone is the perpendicular distance from the vertex of the cone to the plane of the base.   That is, $V = \frac{1}{3}Bh$.   If the base of the cone is a circle and the vertex directly above the center of the circular base, the cone is called a *right circular cone*.

The lateral area of a right circular cone is equal to half the product of the circumference of the base by the slant height of the cone.   The slant height of a right circular cone is the length of a line drawn from any place in the circumference to the vertex of the cone, or $A = \frac{1}{2}CL$.

In the following 10 problems the measurements are assumed to be *exact*.

❦ Problems ❦

15.1.   Obtain the area of a rectangular field that is 1,210 ft long and 396 ft wide.   Express the result in number of (*a*) sq ft, (*b*) sq yd, (*c*) sq rd, (*d*) acres.

15.2.   A rectangular college campus is $\frac{1}{2}$ mile long and contains 80 acres.

    a.   Compute the width of the campus.

    b.   If 20 buildings, each 150 ft wide and 240 ft long, are to be placed on this campus, what percent of the total area will they cover?

15.3.   A sprinter can run 100 yd in 9.8 seconds.   (The world's record is 9.3 sec.)   How many miles could this sprinter run in one hour, if he could maintain this same speed of 100 yd per 9.8 sec?

15.4.   *a.*   Compute the total area of the walls and ceiling of a rectangular room 42 ft long, 30 ft wide, and 14 ft high, if no allowance is made for doors and windows.

    b.   Solve this problem if allowance is made for 2 doors 9 ft high and 4 ft wide, and 6 windows 8 ft high and $4\frac{1}{2}$ ft wide.

    c.   How many feet of molding would be needed to surround all windows, the tops and sides of the doors, and to extend along the edges between the adjoining walls and between the walls and the ceiling, if no allowance is made for fitting and cutting?

15.5.   *a.*   Compute the area of a path that is $3\frac{1}{2}$ ft wide and completely surrounds a rectangular flower bed that is 15 ft wide and 19 ft long.

    b. If 60 percent of the path is cement, 30 percent cinders, and the remainder brick, how many square feet of the path are brick?

    c. How many square yards of the bed are devoted to roses, if 25 percent of the bed is devoted to roses?

15.6. If one side of a parallelogram is 25 in. long, and the corresponding altitude is 18 in. in length:

    a. Compute its area.

    b. If another side of this same parallelogram is 45 in. long, what is the perpendicular distance between it and the other 45 in. side?

    c. Compute the perimeter of the parallelogram in feet.

15.7. The area of a parallelogram is 120 sq ft. The line joining a pair of opposite vertices is an altitude of the parallelogram and is 8 ft long. Calculate the perimeter of the parallelogram.

15.8. Compute in square feet the area of a triangle whose base is $\frac{2}{3}$ yd long and corresponding altitude is 15 in. Also obtain the result in square yards.

15.9. Compute the area and circumference of a circle whose radius is 28 in. if: (*a*) $\pi = 3\frac{1}{7}$; (*b*) $\pi = 3.141,6$. Express the difference in computed areas to nearest two significant digits; also difference in computed circumferences to nearest two significant digits.

15.10. Calculate the volume of a regular pyramid that has an altitude of 8 ft and perimeter of square base 48 ft. Also compute its lateral area.

15·4 ～ Heron's formula for the area of a triangle

If *a*, *b*, and *c* are the exact measurements of the three sides of a triangle, the area is given by the formula $A = \sqrt{s(s - a)(s - b)(s - c)}$, if $s = \frac{1}{2}(a + b + c)$. This remarkable formula is called Heron's formula, since its discovery is attributed to this Greek mathematician who flourished in Alexandria, Egypt, about 100 B.C.

To illustrate, let the sides of a triangle have dimensions *a* = 13 in., *b* = 14 in., *c* = 15 in.; then *s*, semiperimeter, $= \frac{1}{2}(13 + 14 + 15) = 21$ in., whence $s - a = 21 - 13 = 8$, $s - b = 21 - 14 = 7$, $s - c = 21 - 15 = 6$. Then $s(s - a)(s - b)(s - c) = 21 \times 8 \times 7 \times 6 = 7{,}056$; and finally, $\sqrt{7{,}056} = 84$ sq in. In this situation the area is an integer, as 7,056 is a *square number*. In general the product appearing under the radical is not a square number, and the resulting area is represented by an irrational number.

Triangles that have *integers* to represent the lengths of the sides and the area are called Heronic triangles, in honor of Heron. These triangles may be obtained by placing together two Pythagorean triangles having the two sides that are put into contact of equal lengths, while the other sides lie in a common base. The Heronic triangle having sides 13, 14, 15 is obtained by placing the Pythagorean triangles having sides 5, 12, 13 and 9, 12, 15 together so that the sides of length 12 coincide, and the bases 5 and 9 together make the base 5 + 9 = 14; thus the sides of the Heronic triangle are 13, 15, and base 14. The two Pythagorean triangles so used lie on opposite sides of their common side 12; if they were placed on the same side of the common side 12, one would obtain another Heronic triangle having sides 13, 15, and 9 − 5 = 4.

15·5 ～ Primitive heronic triangles

If the three sides of a Heronic triangle have no common divisor, the triangle is called a *primitive* Heronic triangle. By the prescribed method one may obtain 15 primitive Heronic triangles with sides less than 30, namely, those with sides:

(6, 5, 5)	(15, 13, 4)	(17, 17, 16)	(21, 20, 13)	(26, 25, 13)
(8, 5, 5)	(15, 14, 13)	(20, 13, 11)	(24, 13, 13)	(28, 25, 17)
(13, 13, 10)	(17, 10, 9)	(21, 17, 10)	(25, 17, 12)	(29, 25, 6)

Note that in each set of Heronic primitive numbers, one number is even, two numbers are odd.

15·6 ～ Rational features of heronic triangles

One may also verify that the three altitudes h_a, h_b, h_c to the three sides a, b, c, respectively, are $2A/a$, $2A/b$, $2A/c$, wherein A represents the area of the triangle.

The three altitudes of a triangle meet in a point called the *orthocenter* of the circle. The lengths of the portions of the altitudes between the orthocenter and the sides are, respectively,

$$\frac{a^4 - (b^2 - c^2)^2}{8aA} \qquad \frac{b^4 - (c^2 - a^2)^2}{8bA} \qquad \frac{c^4 - (a^2 - b^2)^2}{8cA}$$

These are *rational* numbers, since a, b, c, and A are integral numbers.

The radius of the *circumcircle* (circle whose circumference passes through the three vertices of the Heronic triangle) is given by the formula $r = \dfrac{abc}{4A}$.

The radius of the *incircle* (the circle that lies inside the triangle and is tangent to the three sides of the triangle) is given by the formula $r = \dfrac{A}{s}$, wherein $s = \frac{1}{2}(a + b + c)$, the semiperimeter of the triangle.

The radii of the *escribed circles* are also rational, and are, respectively, $\dfrac{A}{s-a}$, $\dfrac{A}{s-b}$, $\dfrac{A}{s-c}$. An escribed circle is a circle lying outside the triangle and is tangent to the three sides, extended when necessary. (See Figure 15.4.)

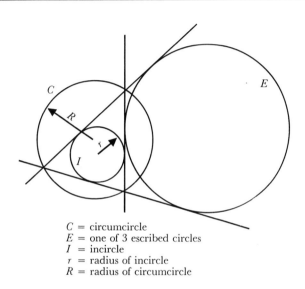

C = circumcircle
E = one of 3 escribed circles
I = incircle
r = radius of incircle
R = radius of circumcircle

FIGURE 15.4

Note that the sum of the reciprocals of the radii of the three escribed circles is equal to the reciprocal of the radius of the inscribed circle. The reciprocal of a number is the quotient of 1 divided by the number. The reciprocal of 3 is $\frac{1}{3}$; the reciprocal of $\frac{3}{4}$ is $\frac{4}{3}$.

◌ PROBLEMS [CONCLUDED] ◌

15.11. If the sides of a Heronic triangle are 17, 25, and 28 in., respectively, compute: (*a*) the area; (*b*) the three altitudes; (*c*) the radii of the incircle and escribed circles. (*d*) Verify the reciprocal relationship between these four radii.

15.12. Calculate the total area of the five-sided figure (pentagon) *ABCDE*, if the sides are of lengths: *AB* = 39 in., *BC* = 25 in., *CD* = 30 in., *DE* = 34 in., *EA* = 56 in., and the diagonals are *AC* = 40 in., *AD* = 50 in.

15.13. *a.* Compute the area of the parallelogram whose two adjoining sides are 41 and 52 ft in length, respectively, and having a diagonal 15 ft long.

    b. Compute the length of the two altitudes of this parallelogram.

15.14. The lengths of the edges of a thin triangular plate are 10, $6\frac{1}{4}$, and $9\frac{3}{4}$ ft, respectively. Through which of the three rectangular doors can it be moved if the thickness of the metal can be ignored?

    a. 3 ft wide, 4 ft high

    b. 2 ft wide, $5\frac{1}{2}$ ft high

    c. $4\frac{1}{2}$ ft wide, $4\frac{1}{2}$ ft high

15.15. Obtain the area of the triangle whose three sides are, respectively, 7 in., 8 in., and 9 in. (*a*) Obtain the result to the nearest 0.01 sq in.; (*b*) to the nearest sixty-fourth of a square inch.

15.16. Compute the number of cubic inches in a circular cylinder if the radius of the base is $3\frac{1}{2}$ in., and the height of the cylinder is 9 in. Give the result to the nearest 0.01 cu in. Refer to Section 10.5 for the appropriate value of π to be used.

15.17. *a.* Compute the approximate volume of the conical tent if the radius of the base is 4 ft and the height of the tent is 8 ft, using $3\frac{1}{7}$ for π.

    b. Compute the volume, using $\pi = 3.14$.

    c. Calculate the difference between the two foregoing results. As the true value of π lies between $3\frac{1}{7}$ and 3.14, the true value of the volume must lie between the two computed results in (*a*) and (*b*). Hence the inaccuracy in these computed results must be less than this difference.

15.18. How many cubic feet of sand are there in a conical pile of sand if the diameter of the base is 24 ft and the slant height of the pile is 13 ft? Give the result to the nearest 0.1 cu ft.

15.19. How many tons of material are there in a pyramid that is 25 ft high and whose base is a square whose side is 36 ft long? The material is estimated to weigh 245 pounds per cu ft (2,000 pounds = 1 ton).

15.20. Compute the (*a*) area and (*b*) volume of a wooden ball whose diameter is 10 in. in length. (*c*) Compute the weight of the ball to the nearest ounce, if the wood weighs 50 pounds per cu ft (16 oz = 1 lb).

15.21. Compute to the nearest cent the cost of gilding a metal sphere of radius $1\frac{1}{2}$ ft at a cost of 25 cents per sq ft.   Use appropriate value of π.

15.22. Compute to the nearest pound the weight of a cork ball of radius 3 ft, if the cork weighs 15 pounds per cu ft.

15.23. A rectangular piece of tin 16 by 24 in. is rolled to form the side of a cylinder cup.   What would be the volume of the cup so formed, if no allowance is made for joining the edges?   Give the results to the nearest 0.01 cu in.   Note that there are *two different solutions*.

15.24. A piece of tin in the form of a semicircle of radius 12 in. is rolled to form the lateral portion of a right circular cone.   Compute the volume of the cone so formed to the nearest 0.01 cu in., if no allowance is made for joining the edges of the tin.

15.25. The legal definition of a bushel in the United States is the volume of a circular cylinder whose inside diameter is $18\frac{1}{2}$ in. in length, and whose altitude is 8 in. in length.   However, in most printed tables it is stated that the legal bushel contains 2,150.42 cu in., with no hint that this is an approximation to the correct value.   Calculate to two nearest significant digits the error in this exhibition of value of a bushel.   (Use appropriate numbers of decimal places for π as given in Lesson 10.)

15.26. *a.* Calculate the number of acres in a circle of diameter 7,837 yd. (Refer to the excerpt from *Gulliver's Travels* on the first page of this chapter).

b. Compute the percent of error in this excerpt, as based upon the correct area.

Note 1 ∽ The determination of geometrical figures.

A geometrical figure, such as a triangle, circle, rectangle, etc., is said to *be determined* if one knows a minimum amount of information about it so that one may be able to obtain any desired information about it.   Thus a circle is determined by its radius, for if one knows the size of the radius one can then compute all other items pertaining to it, such as its diameter, circumference, area, etc.   A square is determined by a side; i.e., if one knows the length of a side of a square one can then obtain all other information about that square, such as the length of its diagonals, area, etc.   A triangle is determined by any one of the following sets of data: its three sides, two angles and any side, two sides and the angle between them.

Accordingly, a triangle is determined if one knows the value of any three of its three sides and three angles, if at least one of its known parts is a *side*.   The calculation of the numerical values of the other three parts (sides and angles) is called *solving the triangle*.

The triangle is of supreme importance in the various branches of scientific pursuit, such as geometry, physics, and astronomy, for all figures made up of straight lines may be divided up into triangles, which can then be studied individually.   A five-pointed star may be regarded as consisting of five triangles surrounding a pentagon (a five-sided polygon), then the pentagon may be divided up into three triangles by drawing two of its diagonals.   The subject of trigonometry was originally developed for the solution of all sorts of triangles.   The word *trigonometry* means "triangle measurement."

*N*ote 2 ∾ *Standard symbolism and formulas pertaining to the triangle.*

Associated with every ordinary (Euclidean) triangle are:

1.   Three sides whose lengths are generally represented by small letters, *a*, *b*, *c*, expressed in terms of some convenient unit of length, as inch, meter, etc.

2.   Three angles whose sizes are represented generally by capital letters, *A*, *B*, *C*, expressed in terms of some convenient unit, such as degrees, etc. Each capital letter marks the vertex that lies opposite the corresponding small letter, as indicated in the diagram in Figure 15.5.

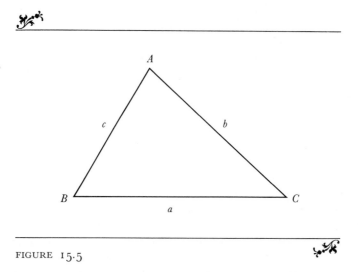

FIGURE 15.5

3.   The perimeter, *p*, which is equal to the sum of the lengths of the sides; i.e., $p = a + b + c$.   The semiperimeter $s = \frac{1}{2}p$.

4.   The area of the triangle, expressed in units of area that correspond to the unit of length that is used for the sides.   The area of the triangle is indicated by the letter *S* to avoid confusion with the angle *A*.   Formulas for

area are:

$$S = \sqrt{s(s-a)(s-b)(s-c)}, \text{ if the sides are known, } a, b, c$$

$$S = \tfrac{1}{2}ab \cdot \sin C, \text{ if two sides and included angle are known}$$

$$S = \frac{b^2 \cdot \sin A \cdot \sin C}{2 \cdot \sin (A + C)}, \text{ if any two angles and a side are known}$$

In every triangle $A + B + C = 180°$

5. The radius of circumcircle R is given by formulas:

$$R = \frac{abc}{4S} \qquad R = \frac{a}{2 \sin A} = \frac{b}{2 \sin B} = \frac{c}{2 \sin C}$$

(The circumference of the circumcircle passed through the three vertices.)

6. The radius of the incircle r is given by $r = S/s$, or

$$r = \sqrt{\frac{(s-a)(s-b)(s-c)}{s}}$$

Formulas that relate the sides and angles of a triangle are the following:

$$\frac{a}{\sin A} = \frac{b}{\sin B} = \frac{c}{\sin C} \qquad \text{(Law of sines)}$$

$$a^2 = b^2 + c^2 - 2bc \cdot \sin A \qquad \text{(Law of cosines)}$$
$$b^2 = c^2 + a^2 - 2ca \cdot \sin B$$
$$c^2 = a^2 + b^2 - 2ab \cdot \sin C$$

$$\tan \tfrac{1}{2}A = \frac{r}{s-a}, \tan \tfrac{1}{2}B = \frac{r}{s-b}, \tan \tfrac{1}{2}C = \frac{\cdot\, r}{s-c} \qquad \text{(Half-angle}$$

law of tangents)

$\mathcal{N}$*ote 3 ∾ Solution of triangle*
by use of trigonometry.

If the three sides of a triangle are known, the three angles may be obtained by use of the half-angle tangent laws. For example: If $a = 17$, $b = 25$, $c = 28$, then $r = 6$, whence $\tan \tfrac{1}{2}A = \tfrac{6}{18} = 0.333,3$, $\tan \tfrac{1}{2}B = \tfrac{6}{10} = 0.600,0$, $\tan \tfrac{1}{2}C = \tfrac{6}{7} = 0.857,1$. To the nearest $0.000,1$ the tables yield $\tfrac{1}{2}A = 18°$, $\tfrac{1}{2}B = 31°$, $\tfrac{1}{2}C = 41°$, with errors less than $\tfrac{1}{2}°$ in each angle. Therefore, $A = 36°, B = 62°$, $C = 82°$, with errors less than $1°$ in each angle.

The law of cosines will yield these three angles slightly more accurately with errors in angles themselves less than $\tfrac{1}{2}°$. Thus:

$$\cos A = \frac{b^2 + c^2 - a^2}{2bc} = \frac{625 + 784 - 289}{1400} = \frac{1120}{1400} = 0.800,0$$

$$\cos B = \frac{c^2 + a^2 - b^2}{2ca} = \frac{784 + 289 - 625}{952} = \frac{448}{952} = 0.470,6$$

$$\cos C = \frac{a^2 + b^2 - c^2}{2ac} = \frac{289 + 625 - 784}{850} = \frac{130}{150} = 0.152,9$$

Whence the tables yield $A = 36°$, $B = 63°$, $C = 81°$, with individual errors less than $\frac{1}{2}°$. The sum of the three angles of every flat triangle is 180°.

If two angles and a side are known, the law of sines will yield the unknown sides. The third angle is obtained from relationship $A + B + C = 180°$. For example, if $a = 12$, $A = 76°$, $B = 48°$. Then $C = 180° - 76° - 48° = 56°$. Now $\dfrac{b}{\sin B} = \dfrac{a}{\sin A}$ is equivalent to $b = \dfrac{a \times \sin B}{\sin A}$, whence $b = \dfrac{12 \times \sin 48°}{\sin 76°} = \dfrac{12 \times 0.7431}{0.9703} = 9.190$ to the nearest 0.001.

If two sides and the angle between them are known, the law of cosines will yield the third side. For example, if $a = 5$, $b = 8$, $C = 53°$, then

$$c^2 = a^2 + b^2 - 2ab \times \cos 53° = 25 + 64 - 80 \times (0.601{,}8) = 40.856{,}0$$

Therefore, $c = \sqrt{40.856{,}0} = 6.392$, to nearest 0.001.

❦ SUPPLEMENTARY PROBLEMS ❦

Measure your mind's height by the shadow it casts.

—Browning, *Paracelsus.*

S15.1. Calculate the area of the rectangles having the given dimensions:
 a. Length 17 ft, width 16 in.; obtain both forms of result.
 b. Length 375 yd, width 99 yd; give result in sq rd.
 c. Length 213 rd, width 93 rd; give result in acres.
 d. Length $\frac{1}{2}$ mi, width $\frac{3}{8}$ mi; give result in sq rd and in acres.
 e. Length 11 mi, width 7 mi; give result in acres.

S15.2. State the *exact* form of result in common or in decimal fractions:
 a. Rectangle of area 15 sq yd, length 25 ft; compute width in feet.
 b. Rectangle of area 25 sq ft, length 5 yd; compute width in feet.
 c. Obtain dimensions of rectangle in (a) in centimeters.
 d. Obtain area in (c) in square centimeters.

S15.3. A speed of 75 mi per hour would be equivalent to how many meters a second? State *exact* result, and the result in decimal form to nearest 0.01 m.

S15.4. Compute the area of a circle of diameter 1 m. State the result in square inches and in square centimeters to nearest 0.01 sq unit.

S15.5. Calculate the radius of the circle to nearest 0.01 in. if its area is (a) 1 sq ft, (b) 1 sq m, (c) 1 sq yd.

S15.6. Compute to the nearest 0.01 unit the volume of the sphere that has a radius of (a) 1 ft; (b) 1 m; (c) 1 yd. State results in cubic inches and in cubic centimeters.

S15.7. Obtain to the nearest 0.01 in. and nearest 0.01 cm the radius of the sphere of volume (a) 1 cu ft, (b) 1 cu m, (c) 1 cu yd.

S15.8. Compute in two different ways the number of cubic feet in the rectangular solid whose dimensions are, respectively, 9 yd, 15 yd, and 21 yd. How many cubic inches does this solid contain?

S15.9. Calculate to the nearest 0.01 sq in. the area of the triangle whose three sides are exactly 7 in., 11 in., and 14 in., respectively.

S15.10. Compute the three altitudes of the triangle whose three sides are 55 cm, 51 cm, and 26 cm, respectively. Also calculate the radii of the circumcircle and the inscribed circle.

S15.11. Obtain the area of the sphere whose measured diameter is 8.3 in. State the extent of accuracy of the result.

S15.12. Compute the volume of the sphere of the preceding problem.

S15.13. A thin plate in the form of a parallelogram weighing 73.12 gm is made of a substance that weighs 4.13 gm per cu cm, to the nearest 0.01 gm. The plate is 1 mm thick, to the nearest 0.01 mm. Compute: (*a*) the area of the parallelogram stating the extent of reliability of the computed result; (*b*) the perimeter of the parallelogram if the two measured altitudes are 14.37 cm and 19.56 cm, respectively. Indicate reliability of result.

S15.14. The measured dimensions of a regular pyramid with square base are 35.34 in. in height and 23.67 in. on one side of the square base. Compute: (*a*) the volume, indicating the reliability of the result; (*b*) the weight of 1 cu in. of this material, in ounces, as accurately as possible, if the entire pyramid is weighed as 142 pounds 3 ounces to the nearest ounce.

S15.15. Three solid silver and one ball of solid gold are recast into a single solid ball. If gold weighs 19.3 gm and silver weighs 10.5 gm per cu cm, to nearest 0.1 gm, and if the small balls measure 2.32 cm in diameter to nearest 0.01 cm, compute (*a*) the weight of the large ball, and (*b*) the diameter of the large ball. State the reliability of the results.

S15.16. A metal ball, consisting of equal amounts of gold and silver by weight, weighs $1,237.7 \pm 0.05$ gm. Compute its diameter, indicating accuracy of result.

S15.17. Using the formulas of trigonometry (Note 2, above) solve the triangles with given measured data: $a = 12.3$, $b = 7.9$, $c = 9.4$ inches, respectively.

S15.18. Solve the triangle if $C = 90°$, $c = 32.8$ cm, $A = 30°$.

S15.19. Solve the triangle if $A = 28°$, $b = 21.5$ in., $C = 62°$.

S15.20. If one neglects air resistance, the shape and motions of the earth, the range and maximum height a projectile attains depend upon the initial velocity and the angle of elevation of the projector. The range and height, in feet, are given by formulas $R = \dfrac{v^2 \sin 2A}{g}$ and $H = \dfrac{(v \sin A)^2}{2g}$, in which A = angle of elevation of the projector, v = ft per sec of initial velocity, and $g = 32.2$ ft per sec, the constant acceleration of gravity. Calculate H and R if $v = 500$ ft per sec, and $A = 30°$. How high would the projectile go if it were shot directly upward (with $A = 90°$)?

S15.21. Compute the time, in seconds, of the flights of the projectile in the preceding problem, if $t = \dfrac{2v \sin A}{g}$.

LESSON 16 ❧ THE USE OF LOGARITHMS AND THE SLIDE RULE IN ARITHMETIC

The invention of logarithms, by simplifying his lengthy calculations, has doubled the life of the astronomer.

—Pierre Simon, *Marquis de Laplace* (1749–1827).

16·1 ∿ THE USE OF LOGARITHMS GREATLY SIMPLIFIES ARITHMETICAL OPERATIONS. LAWS OF EXPONENTS

The use of logarithms enables one to perform the simpler arithmetical operations, addition, subtraction, multiplication, and division, respectively, instead of the more complicated ones, multiplication, division, involution, and evolution. Clearly, the operation of *division* by 3 is much simpler than the operation of *extraction of cube root*. The four simpler operations are performed upon *exponents*, subsequently to be identified with *logarithms*, and are to be noted in the correspondence of operation upon certain mathematical quantities with operations upon certain exponents as appears in the four *laws of exponents*, namely,

Law I	$a^m a^n = a^{m+n}$	Law III	$(a^m)^n = a^{mn}$
Law II	$a^m \div a^n = a^{m-n}$	Law IV	$(a^m)^{1/n} = a^{m/n}$

Observe that the original operations are simplified: multiplication by addition, division by subtraction, involution by multiplication, and evolution by division of exponents, respectively. Here is a résumé of exponents.

When the exponent is a *natural number:* a^n means $a \cdot a \cdot a \cdot a \cdots a$, taking a exactly n times as a factor. Thus, for example, 2^5 means $2 \times 2 \times 2 \times 2 \times 2$, or 32. The expression a^0 has the value for any value of a excepting $a = 0$. Thus, $3^0 = 1$, $1000^0 = 1$. The expression 0^0 is called an *indeterminate*, as 0^0 may represent any numerical value whatever (note S.21). Hence 0^0 is excluded from present considerations.

When the exponent is a negative integer, a^{-n} is equal to $\dfrac{1}{a^n}$. Thus $2^{-1} = \frac{1}{2}$, $3^{-4} = \dfrac{1}{3^4}$, or $\frac{1}{81}$.

When the exponent is a *unit fraction*, as $\frac{1}{2}, \frac{1}{3}, \frac{1}{4}, \ldots$, $a^{1/n}$ is equal to the nth root of a, expressed as $\sqrt[n]{a}$. Thus, $9^{\frac{1}{2}} = 3$; $25^{\frac{1}{2}} = 5$; $16^{\frac{1}{4}} = 2$.

353

When the exponent is any fraction, as $\frac{2}{3}$, $\frac{5}{8}$, $a^{p/q} = \sqrt[q]{a^p}$. Thus, $8^{\frac{2}{3}} = \sqrt[3]{8^2}$ or $\sqrt[3]{64} = 4$.

❧ PROBLEMS ❧

16.1. Evaluate the following expressions:

a. 2^5	*d.* 2^{-8}	*g.* $16^{\frac{1}{4}}$	*j.* $4^{\frac{3}{2}}$
b. 5^3	*e.* 17^0	*h.* $27^{\frac{1}{3}}$	*k.* $64^{\frac{2}{3}}$
c. 3^{-2}	*f.* $(-\frac{5}{8})^0$	*i.* $8^{\frac{2}{3}}$	*l.* $64^{\frac{5}{6}}$

16.2. Evaluate the following expressions in two different ways:

a. $2^3 \times 2^4 = 8 \times 16 = ?$ *h.* $3^{-4} \times 3^5$ *p.* $(8^2)^{\frac{1}{3}}$

or $2^{3+4} = 2^7 = ?$ *i.* $5^5 \times 5^{-5}$ *q.* $(27^{-\frac{1}{3}})^{-2}$

b. $3^3 \times 3$ *j.* $2^9 \times 2^{-10}$ *r.* $a^6 \div a^2$

c. $5^2 \times 5^3$ *k.* $2^{-2} \times 2^{-3}$ *s.* $a^6 \div a^3$

d. $2^3 \times 2^0$ *l.* $(2^2)^3$ *t.* $a^6 \div a^7$

e. $3^2 \times 3^0$ *m.* $(3^2)^3$ *u.* $a^{\frac{2}{3}} \div a^{\frac{1}{2}}$

f. $3^2 \times 3^4$ *n.* $(5^2)^{-2}$ *v.* $a^{-\frac{1}{3}} \div a^{-\frac{1}{4}}$

g. $2^{-2} \times 2^5$ *o.* $(8^{\frac{1}{3}})^2$

16.3. Reduce to a simpler form by use of the laws of exponents: (*a*) $a^3 \times a^4$, (*b*) $a^{-7} \times a^8$, (*c*) $(a^3)^4$, (*d*) $(a^{-1})^{-2}$, (*e*) $(a^5)^0$. Express with radicals: (*f*) $(a^2)^{\frac{1}{4}}$, (*g*) $a^{\frac{1}{5}}$, (*h*) $(a^{-\frac{1}{2}})^{-\frac{1}{3}}$, (*i*) $a^{\frac{3}{4}}$.

16·2 ❧ LOGARITHMS WITH THE BASE NUMBER TWO

Note the successive powers of 2: $2^{-4} = \frac{1}{16}$, $2^{-3} = \frac{1}{8}$, $2^{-2} = \frac{1}{4}$, $2^{-1} = \frac{1}{2}$, $2^0 = 1$, $2^1 = 2$, $2^2 = 4$, $2^3 = 8$, $2^4 = 16$, $2^5 = 32$, $2^6 = 64$, $2^7 = 128$, $2^8 = 256$, $2^9 = 512$, $2^{10} = 1,024$, $2^{11} = 2,048$, $2^{12} = 4,096$, $2^{13} = 8,192$, ...

It has been stated in Lesson 4 that $a^b = c$ may also be expressed as $b = \log_a c$. Accordingly, $2^c = N$ may be equivalently expressed as $\log_2 N = c$, which is read as "the logarithm of N to the base 2 is equal to c." Here one observes that the logarithm of any number N is the exponent c that the base 2 must have so that 2^c may be equal to the number N. Thus the foregoing powers of 2 may be recast to exhibit a table of logarithms of certain numbers from $\frac{1}{8}$, or 0.125, to 8192. The upper number represents a value of N; the number below is its logarithm for the base 2.

N	0.125	0.25	0.5	1	2	4	8	16	32	64	128	256	512	1,024	2,048	4,096	8,192
$c = \log_2 N$	−3	−2	−1	0	1	2	3	4	5	6	7	8	9	10	11	12	13

If the logarithm of N is c, then c is called the antilogarithm of N. That is, if log $N = c$, then $N =$ antilog c.

16·3 ∾ Laws of logarithms

To use the table of logarithms judiciously one should note that the laws of exponents may be recast into the form of logarithmic expressions. The following paragraphs illustrate this for the four laws of exponents.

Law I of Exponents. For the first law, $a^m a^n = a^{m+n}$. If $a^m = P$, then $m = \log_a P$; if $a^n = Q$, then $n = \log_a Q$; if $a^{m+n} = R$, then $m + n = \log_a R$. Hence the given expression $PQ = R$ gives rise to the new expression, since the sum of m and n is $m + n$, $\log_a P + \log_a Q = \log_a (PQ)$, which states:

The logarithm of the product of two numbers is equal to the sum of the logarithms of the factors of the product.

To perform a multiplication by logarithms, one obtains from the table of logarithms the logarithms of the multiplicand and of the multiplier; the sum of these two logarithms is the logarithm of the desired product. Apart from looking into the table for logarithms and finally finding the antilogarithm, i.e., the number corresponding to a certain logarithm, the arithmetical operation of multiplication is replaced by an addition. To illustrate, multiply (by logarithms) 64×128. From the foregoing table, we can add the logarithms as shown

$$
\begin{array}{r}
\log\ \ 64 = 6 \\
\log 128 = 7 \\
\hline
\log 64 \times 128 = 13
\end{array}
$$

That is, the logarithm of the product is equal to 13. Referring to the table, one notes that 13 is the logarithm of 8,192; therefore, the desired product is 8,192.

For another illustration obtain the product $0.125 \times 16 \times 256$. From the table, add the logarithms

$$
\begin{array}{r}
\log 0.125 = -3 \\
\log\ \ \ \ 16 = \ \ 4 \\
\log\ \ \ 256 = \ \ 8 \\
\hline
\log \text{ product} = \ \ 9
\end{array}
$$

Hence the product is 512, as the table indicates that 512 is the number whose logarithm is 9.

The table of logarithms used here is very restrictive as it shows only logarithms for 17 very special numbers. It is used merely to clarify the principles that one must master in order to use the more extensive tables. The table provided in the appendix supplies, to the nearest 0.000,1, the logarithms to base 10 for all numbers of *three* significant digits. Vega's tables provide logarithms of all numbers of five significant digits, in which the logarithms themselves are expressed to seven significant digits; i.e., to the nearest 0.000,000,1.

Law II of Exponents. For the law $a^m \div a^n = a^{m-n}$, if $a^m = P$, then $m = \log_a P$; and if $a^n = Q$, then $n = \log_a Q$. If $a^{m-n} = R$, then $m - n = \log_a R$. Since $P \div Q = R$, and since m less n equals $m - n$, one obtains the new expression, $\log_a P - \log_a Q = \log_a (P \div Q)$ which states:

The logarithm of the quotient of two numbers is equal to the logarithm of the dividend less the logarithm of the divisor.

To illustrate, compute $4096 \div 128$. From the table,

$$
\begin{aligned}
\log 4096 &= 12 \\
\text{Subtract } \log \quad 128 &= 7 \\
\hline
\text{Log of quotient} &= 5
\end{aligned}
$$

whence the tables yield the quotient 32. Again, apart from the three references to the table, the operation of arithmetical division is simplified by logarithms to the operation of arithmetical subtraction.

Law III of Exponents. For the third law, $(a^m)^n = a^{mn}$, if $a^m = P$ and $P^n = Q$, then $(a^m)^n = P^n = Q = a^{mn}$. If $a^m = P$, then $m = \log_a P$, and if $a^{mn} = Q$, then $mn = \log_a Q$; $n \times \log_a P = \log_a Q = \log_a P^n$, since $Q = P^n$. Or, more concisely, $\log_a P^n = n \times \log_a P$, which states:

The logarithm of the nth power of a number is equal to n times the logarithm of the number.

To illustrate, compute 16^3. From the table,

$$
\begin{aligned}
\log 16 &= 4 \\
\text{Multiply by the power} &\quad3 \\
\hline
\text{The logarithm of} \quad 16^4 &= 12
\end{aligned}
$$

Therefore, $16^4 = 4096$, as found in the table, as 4096 is the number whose logarithm is 12. Again, apart from two references to the table, the operation of raising a number to the third power is simplified by the simple arithmetical operation of multiplying by 3.

Law IV of Exponents. For the law $(a^m)^{1/n} = a^{m/n}$, let $a^m = P$; $P^{1/n} = Q$. Since $a^m = P$, $a^{m/n} = Q$, one has $m = \log_a P$, $m/n = \log_a Q$. That is, $1/n \log_a P =$

$m/n = \log_a Q = \log P^{1/n}$, or, more concisely, $\log_a P^{1/n} = 1/n \log_a P$; that is, $\log_a \sqrt[n]{P} = 1/n \log_a P$, which states:

The logarithm of the nth root of a number is equal to 1/nth of the logarithm of the number.

To illustrate, compute $\sqrt[4]{4,096}$.   From the table,

$$\log \quad 4,096 = 12$$
For fourth root $\div 4$
$$\text{Hence } \log \sqrt[4]{4,096} = 3 \qquad \text{Therefore}$$
$$\sqrt[4]{4,096} = 8 \qquad \text{From the table, since 8 is the number whose logarithm is 3}$$

Apart from two references to the logarithm table, the operation of extracting the *n*th root of a number is simplified to the arithmetical division of a logarithm by *n*.

To summarize, the four fundamental laws of operation with logarithms are (for any numbers *P*, *Q*, and *n*):

Law I $\log_a P + \log_a Q = \log_a PQ$ Law III $\log_a P^n = n \cdot \log_a P$
Law II $\log_a P - \log_a Q = \log_a P/Q$ Law IV $\log_a \sqrt[n]{P} = 1/n \log_a P$

To repeat, the foregoing table of 17 logarithms for base 2 was introduced only to exhibit the methods of using logarithms for performing the operations of arithmetical multiplication, division, involution, and extraction of roots.

16·4 ~ COMMON LOGARITHMS

The logarithms that are generally used for such calculations are logarithms having base 10 and are called *common logarithms*. It is clear that common logarithms of powers of 10 are integers; thus

log 0.001 = −3	log 100 = 2	log 10,000,000 = 7 . . .
log 0.01 = −2	log 1000 = 3	
log 0.1 = −1	log 10,000 = 4	Henceforth the base is not
log 1 = 0	log 100,000 = 5	indicated; thus log *A* means
log 10 = 1	log 1,000,000 = 6	$\log_{10} A$.

The calculation of common logarithms of numbers other than integral powers of 10 requires procedures that are developed in more advanced mathematics, namely, the calculus.

Zero has no logarithm for any usable base.   If $\log_a 0$ were equal to N, then a^N must be equal to 0.   But this is impossible, for if a and N are positive, then a^N

must be positive; if N is zero, then a^0 must equal 1; if N is negative, then a^{-P} equals the reciprocal, namely, $1/a^P$; in none of the three possibilities can a^N be equal to 0. Likewise, no negative number has a (real) logarithm. It should also be noted that only positive numbers other than 1 may serve for the base of the system of logarithms. Ten is the base of common logarithms used for computational purposes. In advanced mathematics logarithms having the base e, an irrational number having many important uses, namely, 2.718,28 . . . , are frequently used. Such logarithms are referred to as *natural logarithms*, or *Naperian* logarithms, in honor of John Napier (1550–1617), whose inventive genius led to the discovery and use of logarithms; however, Napier's tables of logarithms were quite different from our common logarithms or the natural logarithms.

∾ PROBLEMS [CONTINUED] ∾

16.4. By use of the four laws of operation with logarithms obtain the seven-digit logarithms for 4, 5, 6, 8, and 9, from the known three logarithms that are correct to the nearest 0.000,000,1: log 2 = 0.301,030,0, log 3 = 0.477,121,3, log 7 = 0.845,098,0.

16.5. From the three common logarithms given in the preceding problem and by use of the laws of logarithms, obtain the following logarithms: (*a*) log 35, (*b*) log 98, (*c*) log 144, (*d*) log 840, (*e*) log 56,000. Indicate the possible extent of inaccuracy of these logarithms.

16·5 ∾ TABLES OF COMMON LOGARITHMS—MANTISSA AND CHARACTERISTIC OF A COMMON LOGARITHM

Tables of common logarithms list all logarithms of numbers between 1 and 10 for various numbers of significant digits. The tables on the endpaper give such logarithms of numbers having three significant digits, and are listed to four significant digits; usually the *decimal point is omitted from the lists of logarithms and antilogarithms*. The three logarithms listed in Problem 16.4 are taken from Vega's tables which list seven-place logarithms for all numbers between 1 and 10 to five significant digits.

The tables presented on the back endpaper are *four-place* tables, as they provide to the nearest 0.000,1 the logarithms of numbers between 1 and 10. This four-place table yields logarithms for such numbers of three significant digits as follows.

The first one or two digits of the number appear under the N in the left-edge column; the next digit of the number (second or third), occurs in the top row of the table.   The required logarithm appears in the line of the leading digits and in the column under the final digit of the given number.   Thus, the logarithm of 2.37 is 0.3747, as this logarithm occurs in the horizontal row to the right of the first two significant digits, 2 and 3, and in the column headed by the third significant digit, 7.   Hence log 2.37 = 0.3747.   Similarly, log 4.79 = 0.6803, log 4.3 = 0.6335, log 2.1 = 0.3222, log 1.20 = 0.0792.   It is to be noted that all logarithms occurring in the first 10 rows of the table also occur in the column under 0.   The significance of this fact will become clear presently.

Law I of logarithms supplies the key to how the tables yield logarithms of any number greater than 10 of three significant digits.   Thus to find log 34.5 note that 34.5 = 10 × 3.45, whence logarithm of 34.5 = log 10 + log 3.45 = 1 + 0.5378 or 1.5378.   Again, log 345 = log 100 + log 3.45, since 100 × 3.45 = 345.   Hence the logarithm of 345 = 2 + 0.5378, or log 345 = 2.5378. Thus it may be noted that *the logarithm tables supply only the decimal fractional part of logarithms of numbers.*   Such fractional parts are called *mantissas* (mantissa is the Latin word for *extra portion*); the integral portion of a logarithm is called the *characteristic.*   Observe that the characteristic denotes the position of the decimal point of the number itself.   Thus

> log 3.45 = 0.5378   log 3,450 = 3.5378
> log 34.5 = 1.5378   log 34,500 = 4.5378
> log 345 = 2.5378

Accordingly, one may now obtain the logarithm of any number of three significant digits greater than 1 as follows.

Select the mantissa corresponding to the first three significant digits, ignoring the decimal point of the number.   Then supply for the characteristic the number that is one less than the number of digits on the left side of the decimal point of the given number.   For example, find the logarithm of 345,000.   The mantissa appears in the tables for the three significant digits 345, the 34 in the left column under N, the 5 in the top row of tables.   The 0.5378 appears in the same row as 34 and the same column as 5.   The integral portion of the complete logarithm, namely, the characteristic, is 5, since there are six digits in 345,000 left of its decimal point (if the point is not written, it is assumed to be at the right end of the number), and 5 is one less than 6.   Thus log 345,000 = 5.5378.

Recall that log 1 = 0, log 0.1 = −1, log 0.01 = −2, log 0.001 = −3, etc. Hence the logarithms of positive numbers between 0 and 1 are *negative.*   Note that   0.345 = 0.1 × 3.45;   0.0345 = 0.01 × 3.45;   0.00345 = 0.001 × 3.45. Hence log 0.345 = log 0.1 + log 3.45 = −1 + 0.5378; log 0.0345 = log 0.01 + log 3.45 = −2 + 0.5358; log 0.00345 = log 0.001 + log 3.45 = −3 + 0.5378.

The characteristics of logarithms of positive numbers less than 1 are nega- tive and are *one* greater (in absolute value) than the number of zeros appearing between the decimal point and the first significant digit of the number.   Since the *mantissas are always positive*, it would be awkward to compute with numbers partly negative (to left of decimal point) and partly positive (to right of decimal point).   Accordingly, it is the practice to add 10 to the negative characteristic and then subtract 10 from the entire combination, thus concentrating the negative portion of the logarithm in the -10.   Thus,

$$\log 0.345 = \log \frac{3.45}{10} = \log 3.45 - \log 10$$
$$= 0.5378 - 1$$
$$= 0.5378 + 9 - 10$$
$$= 9.5378 - 10$$
$$\log 0.00345 = \log \frac{3.45}{1000} = \log 3.45 - \log 1,000$$
$$= 0.5378 - 3$$
$$= 0.5378 + 7 - 10$$
$$= 7.5378 - 10$$

PROBLEMS [CONTINUED]

16.6. Obtain logarithms of the following numbers: (*a*)   5.37, (*b*)   876, (*c*)   20.3, (*d*)   72,000, (*e*)   1.77, (*f*)   0.000,571, (*g*)   0.667, (*h*)   0.012,5, (*i*)   0.001,06.

16.7. Obtain the value of the number N if log N equals the following: (*a*) 0.6355, (*b*) 1.9699, (*c*) 2.7050, (*d*) 3.9201, (*e*) 9.5514 − 10, (*f*) 7.6263 − 10, (*g*) 7.9685.

16.8. Perform by use of logarithms the following indicated operations: (*a*) 6.25 × 51.2, (*b*) 72,900 ÷ 225, (*c*) 30^6, (*d*) $\sqrt[9]{512}$.

16·6   IMPROVING ACCURACY IN LOGARITHMIC COMPUTATION—LARGER TABLES AND INTERPOLATION

The mantissas in a table of logarithms are generally irrational numbers and have been rounded off to the indicated number of places—four in our tables in the endpaper.   Hence there is the possibility of some error in the three digits considered to be significant in the result of a calculation with these logarithms. For example, to compute 2^{15}, one computes $15 \times \log 2 = 15 \times 0.3010 = 4.5150$, which yields 32,700, using the mantissa nearest to 0.5150; however,

$2^{15} = 32,768$, so that the best three digits, or to three significant digits, should be 32,800. More significant digits in the results of calculation by logarithms may be obtained by using tables with more significant digits in the mantissas. In general, the errors may be diminished by *interpolation* both for finding a logarithm of a number of more digits than the table immediately yields and for finding an additional digit in the computed antilogarithm. The size of error may be estimated by methods presented in Lesson 14.

16·7 ~ INTERPOLATION TO OBTAIN MANTISSA

It is to be noted that the mantissas increase with increasing antilogarithms and that the mantissas increase much more rapidly for small antilogarithms than for large antilogarithms. The difference between consecutive mantissas is called the *tabular difference* at that part of the table. The tabular difference for the consecutive mantissas 0000 and 0414 is 414; for 3617 and 3802 the tabular difference is 185; for mantissas 9899 and 9903, in the latter part of the table, the tabular difference has shrunk to 4. Thus the mantissas increase more slowly at the latter part of the logarithm table than at the beginning. Interpolation assumes that the rate of increase in a mantissa remains nearly constant throughout each particular tabular difference. The logarithms of 2.66 and 2.67 are, respectively, 4249 and 4265, with tabular difference 16, ignoring the point in the mantissa. For logarithms of numbers between 2.66 and 2.67 one computes the appropriate proportional part of the tabular difference and adds it to the smaller logarithm.

The logarithm of 2.665 is thus midway between 2.66 and 2.67; hence, $\frac{5}{10}$ of the tabular difference 16 is 8; adding 8 to the mantissa 4249, one obtains the desired result, log 2.665 = 0.4257. Again, to find the logarithm of 2.667, one computes $\frac{7}{10}$ of the tabular difference, or $0.7 \times 16 = 11.2$. Dropping 0.2 as less than 0.5, one adds the 11 to 4249, obtaining the result that log 2.667 = 0.4260. Once again, to obtain the logarithm of 46.672, one notes the mantissa for the first three significant digits, 466, which is 0.6684, with ensuing tabular difference 9; then $0.72 \times 9 = 7.38$. Dropping 0.38 as less than 0.5, one adds 7 to the mantissa: $6684 + 7 = 6691$, ignoring the decimal point before the mantissa so that, finally, log 46.672 = 1.6691. As a final illustration, obtain log 0.001,281,3. The mantissa for 128 is 1072 with tabular difference 34; then $0.13 \times 34 = 4.42$. Then $1072 + 4 = 1076$. Hence log 0.001,281,3 = 7.1076 − 10, which is most likely correct for the entire mantissa of four digits.

16·8 ~ INTERPOLATION FOR ONE ADDITIONAL DIGIT IN AN ANTILOGARITHM

Again the tabular difference yields a fourth significant digit, which may be reasonably assumed to be correct. Let log N = 2.2660. The mantissa 2660 does not occur in the table; the next smaller mantissa is 2648, which yields the three significants of the antilogarithm, namely, 184.   Then $2660 - 2648 = 12$, the portion of the tabular difference, 24, to yield the next digit of the antilogarithm, namely, $\frac{12}{24} = \frac{1}{2}$, of half the next digit's position, 0.5.   Thus $N = 184.5$ after pointing off according to the given characteristic 2.

Again, to obtain N, if $\log N = 8.8091 - 10$, one selects the largest mantissa in the tables that does not exceed 8091, namely, 8089, which yields digits for N, namely, 644.   The tabular difference here is 7 $(8096 - 8089)$.   Then $8089 - 8091 = 2$, whence $\frac{2}{7} = 2.857\ \ldots$, which yields the next significant digit, 3, for N, forming 6443.   The characteristic $8 - 10$, or -2, supplies the position of the decimal point.   Therefore $N = 0.06443$.

∾ PROBLEMS [CONCLUDED] ∾

Perform all necessary arithmetical operations by use of logarithms.   Interpolate for a fourth significant digit in all results.   This fourth digit is subject to uncertainty.

16.9.   Evaluate: (a) $3,576 \times 0.980,4$, (b) $1.342 \times 2.778 \times 0.124,5$, (c) 3.567^5, (d) $57.31 \div 1.684$, (e) $\sqrt[3]{32.56}$, (f) $7.32 \times 88.9 \div 230$.

16.10.   Compute the square root of 0.762.   (*Hint:* Write the characteristic in form $19.****-20$, rather than as $9.****-10$, to make the division by 2 yield a logarithm in standard form, $9.****-10$.)   The asterisks indicate digits of the mantissas.

16.11.   Compute the fifth root of 0.000,678,2.   Observe the preceding hint.

16.12.   If a sum of money A is put on deposit with a financial institution paying i percent interest, compounded each year, for n years, the total accumulated sum is given by the formula $S = A(1 + i)^n$.   What sum of money would $125 become, if invested for 50 years at 6 percent compounded yearly?   (*Hint:* Evaluate 125×1.06^{50}.)

16.13.   The volume of a sphere is given by formula $V = \frac{1}{6}\pi d^3$, which may be solved for d, yielding $d = \sqrt[3]{6 \times V/\pi}$.   Calculate the diameter of a sphere whose volume is 1,000 cubic feet.

16.14.   A freely falling body (neglecting air resistance), will fall S feet in t seconds, as given by the formula $S = \frac{1}{2}gt^2$, or $t = \sqrt{\dfrac{2S}{g}}.$ How long will it take a freely falling body to fall one mile if $g = 32.2$?

16.15. Suppose that 1 cent were invested 2,000 years ago at 6 percent compounded annually and continued to grow without interruption to the present time. Suppose now that the accumulated amount is invested in gold worth one-half million dollars per cubic foot. How large a ball of gold would this be? (To compute its diameter, use formulas in Problems 16.12 and 16.13.) Express result in miles.

16·9 ∿ CONSTRUCTION OF A SLIDE RULE.
ITS USE IN COMPUTATIONS

Mark off on two adjoining strips of suitable length as follows:

The L scale (L for log), having numbers at *exactly equal* intervals from 0 on the left end to 1 on the right end, the numbers so marked being 0 0.1 0.2 0.3 0.4 0.5 0.6 0.7 0.8 0.9 1. Let spaces between these graduation marks be subdivided into 10 equal subintervals, these subintervals to be subdivided into 10 smaller subintervals, etc.

The C scale (C for counterlog or antilog), having numbers from 1 at the left end to 10 at the right end, so situated on the scale that each number matches its common logarithm on the L scale. Thus, 1 matches 0, since log 1 = 0; 2 matches 0.3010, since log 2 = 0.3010; 3 matches 0.4771, since log 3 = 0.4771; 4 matches 0.6021, since log 4 = 0.6021; etc. Finally, 10 on the right end matches the 1 on the right end of the L scale, since log 10 = 1.

It will be noted that the numbers on the C scale are not at *equal* intervals, but are separated by their tabular differences indicated on the matching L scale. One recalls that tabular differences in the logarithm tables are greatest at the beginning of the table and gradually diminish to the minimum differences at the end of the table.

Ten subintervals on the C scale may now be marked off between the integers, to represent 1.1, 1.2, 1.3, 1.4, . . . , 1.9, 2.1, 2.2, 2.3, . . . , 9.9, each of these markings to match the marking on the L scale that represents its common logarithm. Thus 1.1 is opposite 0.0414, since log 1.1 = 0.0414; 1.2 is opposite 0.0792; . . . , 1.9 is opposite 0.2788, since log 1.9 = 0.2788; finally 9.9 is opposite 0.9956, since log 9.9 = 0.9956.

Now fasten these scales rigidly together so that their end markings coincide. Next construct an exact duplicate of this configuration, called L', D, respectively. The two scales L and L' in juxtaposition may be used to perform additions and subtractions, as was indicated in Lesson 2. Since these scales are logarithms of their numbers simultaneously carried along on the C and D scales, it will be noted that if a and b are the two numbers on L and L' scales that are added (or subtracted), their corresponding numbers A and B on the C and D scales are multiplied (or divided) since log A = a and log B = b. Hence one may ignore altogether the numbers on the L and L' scales and pretend to add the numbers represented on the C and D scales by sliding the C scale appropriately along the D scale of the slide rule; the number obtained as the sum is actually the product. To facilitate his understanding, the student should obtain any conventional slide rule.

The rules of procedure are: To multiply A by B, place the left end of the sliding C scale at A, on the immovable D scale. Then every number P of the C scale adjoins $P \times A$ on the D scale. Hence the number on the D scale matching B of the C scale is $A \times B$. The numbers used are *significant* digits, thus 2 represents 2 or 20 or 200 or 0.000,2. The proper place of the decimal point must be determined separately.

The left end of the D scale on most slide rules shows marking for *three* significant digits as far as 2; from 2 to 4 the third significant digit has a marking, if it is even; the positions of odd third significant digits must be estimated by the eye between the adjacent markings; between 4 and 10 the adjacent markings indicate the third significant digit if it is 5, otherwise the position for the third significant digit must be estimated by the eye.

To illustrate, multiply 17.6 by 2.68. Place the left end of the C scale at 176 on the D scale (at the sixth tiny graduation marking between the 7 and 8 which lie between large 1 and 2). Then move the hairline to 268 of the C scale. (The larger markings, generally unnumbered, indicate the second significant digit between 2 and 3; then the smallest intervals here represent two units of the third significant digit, so that the fourth smallest marking represents 268.) The hairline crosses the D scale between markings that represent the numbers of significant digits 47 and 48; the small space in which the hairline crosses seems to be cut slightly to the right of its lower marking, yielding about 1 for the third significant digit (space representing five units). Hence the product has 472 as its three significant digits.

To determine the position of the decimal point in the product, one obtains the product of numbers of one significant digit each obtained by rounding off the original numbers. Thus 17.6 rounds off to 20, 2.68 rounds off to 3. Now $20 \times 3 = 60$. Hence the decimal point must exhibit a product as near as possible to 60; that is, 47.2 is the required number, as 47.2 is nearer 60 than 4.72 or 472. Similarly, for all slide rule results, one performs mentally the indicated operations on numbers of one significant digit (obtained by rounding off the given number), then points off the resulting antilogarithm to yield the number nearest to this mentally computed result.

If the number on C extends beyond the D scale, one should place the right end of the C scale at the first of the given numbers to be multiplied. To multiply 75 by 36, or 36 by 75, this situation arises. The product yields the three significant digits 270. Since 40 (nearest multiple to the power of 10) times $80 = 2800$, the required product must be 2700.

Division is performed by reversing the foregoing rules. To divide 378 by 49 (one notes that the result must be near 7), place 49 of C scale above 378 of the D scale; the number that the left or right end of the C scale matches is the quotient, namely, about 771. Placing the point, one obtains as the quotient 7.71 $(400 \div 50 = 8)$.

One notes that the slide rule provides a very quick determination of products and quotients, although with limited accuracy and never beyond three significant digits, frequently only two. However, with this limited accuracy, the rule is invaluable in performing all operations that can be performed by logarithms.

If the reader wishes to pursue investigation of the capabilities of the various available slide rules, he should obtain a copy of *The Slide Rule*, by C. L. Johnston, published by Brown & Co., as most superb in scope and clarity of exposition and abundantly supplied with appropriate problems.

N*ote 1 ↔ Subdividing the degree,*
  the common unit of angle measure.

The unit of angle measurement, the degree, is subdivided into smaller units as follows: $1° = 60$ minutes, written as $60'$; $1' = 60$ seconds, written as $60''$. An angle of $1''$ is very small; in fact, the lines that form an angle of $1''$ separate so slowly that they are only 1 foot apart at a distance of approximately 39 miles from the vertex of the angle.

N*ote 2 ↔ The radian—a very useful*
  unit of angle measure.

Another unit of angular measurement, the *radian*, is very useful in many important situations. The angle at the center of a circle contains 1 radian if the arms (lines) of the angle contain a portion of the circumference having the same length as the radius of the circle. To clarify this definition, suppose that a radius of a circle is bent, without stretching or shrinking, so as to lie along the circumference of the circle. Then, if lines are drawn to the center of the circle from the ends of the radius (now lying along the circumference), they enclose an angle of 1 radian. The area enclosed by two radii and the arc of the circle from one radius to the other is called a *sector* of a circle. (See Figure 16.1*a*.)

Now since $C = 2\pi R$, it is clear that the radius could be bent and applied to the entire circumference exactly 2π times, so that there are 2π radians in the entire angular space around the center of the circle, $360°$. That is, 2π radians $= 360°$, or 1 radian $= \dfrac{360}{2\pi}$ degrees, or $57.295{,}779$ degrees, or $57° \ 17' \ 45''$ (to nearest second). Contrariwise, $1° = 0.017{,}453$ radian to nearest $0.000{,}001$ radian. There is no commonly used symbol for *radian*, as there is ° for degree. If a number denotes number of *radians*, the word radians should be supplied. However, the absence of a symbol for an angle measure usually connotes radians.

Thus $90° = \pi/4$ is to be read, "ninety degrees are equivalent to π-over-4 radians" (or 0.785,4 radian, to nearest 0.000,1 radian).

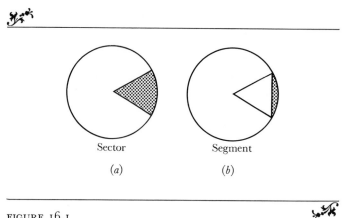

Sector   Segment

(*a*)   (*b*)

FIGURE 16.1

N*ote 3 ◌ Applications of radian measurement.*

The length of arc s of a sector is equal to the product of the number of radians A in its angle by the number of length units in the radius, $S = rA$.

The area of a sector S is equal to half the product of the square of the number of length units of the radius by the number of radians A in the angle, $S = \frac{1}{2}r^2A$.

A segment of a circle is the portion of the circle contained between an arc of a circle and the straight line that joins the ends of the arc.   Note Figure 16.1b; the shaded area is the segment.   The area of the segment Sg of a circle is given by the formula $Sg = \frac{1}{2}r^2 (A - \sin A)$, wherein r denotes the radius of the circle, and A the angle of the sector containing the segment.   (A must be measured in radians.)

To illustrate, let $A = 35°$ and $r = 8$ inches.   Since $1° = 0.017,453$ radian, then $35° = 35 \times 0.017,453 = 0.610,855$ . . . radian.

1.   The arc of the sector $= r \times A = 8 \times 0.610,855 = 4.886,84$ . . . inches.

2.   The area of the sector $= \frac{1}{2} \times 8^2 \times 0.610,855 = 19.547,36$ . . . square inches.

3.   The area of the segment $= \frac{1}{2} \times 8^2 \times (0.610,86 - 0.573,6) = 1.192$ . . . square inches, as tables in end paper are four-place only.

4.   The volume of fluid of depth d in a horizontal tank of radius r and length L wherein d, r, and L are given in the same length units and V is obtained in the corresponding volume units, namely, $V = \frac{1}{2}r^2 (A - \sin A)L$, where A is obtained from $\cos \frac{1}{2}A = (r - d)/r$, and is expressed in radians.

ᐇ CHALLENGE

About 250 B.C. the Greek mathematician Eratosthenes (also known for his sieve for finding prime numbers) measured the size of the earth, which he knew to be a sphere. He observed that at noon at the summer solstice, June 21, the sun shone down a well at Syene, Egypt. (This meant that the sun was in the zenith—directly overhead.) At the same time in Alexandria, 5,000 stadia to the north, the sun appeared to be $7\frac{1}{5}°$ south of the zenith. From these data Eratosthenes computed the circumference of the earth to be 250,000 stadia. How did he obtain this result?

The length of a stadium is uncertain. Columbus, who knew these details, interpreted it somewhat smaller than its more accurate size, namely, about one-tenth of a mile, and therefore Columbus thought the earth considerably smaller than its correct size. This accounts for his confidence in reaching Asia within a sailing's distance to the West.

ᐇ SUPPLEMENTARY PROBLEMS ᐇ

The best device for performing arithmetical operations is the one that requires the least time and effort and yields the most accurate result. The slide rule excels in ease and speed but yields results of very limited accuracy, that is, results of only a few significant digits. The accuracy of logarithm tables depends upon their extensiveness; a simple table that yields results of three significant digits may be presented in two pages; more extensive tables, such as those of Vega, containing seven digits in the mantissas and filling 184 pages, yield six significant digits. Modern electronic computers yield the maximum possible number of significant digits in the least possible time, frequently in a second or two, but these instruments are quite costly and are not available to everybody at all times. The logarithm table of four-digit mantissas, as provided in this text, is supplied to furnish the needed information and practice in the use of logarithms that one may require to use more elaborate tables. The mathematics student should have available a very comprehensive and inexpensive handbook such as the widely used Mathematical Tables from *Handbook of Chemistry and Physics*, published by the Chemical Rubber Publishing Company. The five-place tables, i.e., having five-digit mantissas, will facilitate the solving of the following problems involving the use of logarithms. However, the tables in this text are adequate for the solution of the following problems.

S16.1. Obtain the logarithms of the following numbers:

a.	243	*h.*	1.11	*n.*	3,020	*t.*	0.000,9
b.	4.71	*i.*	32.1	*o.*	75,000	*u.*	0.119
c.	77.3	*j.*	0.111	*p.*	98.5	*v.*	0.057
d.	101	*k.*	5,430	*q.*	5.51	*w.*	0.000,32
e.	500	*l.*	49,300	*r.*	0.662	*x.*	0.001,09
f.	70.9	*m.*	5,000	*s.*	0.035,2	*y.*	0.005,600,0
g.	960						

S16.2. Obtain the antilogarithms of the following logarithms:

a.	2.7924	*f.*	2.8325	*k.*	9.8698 − 10	*p.*	7.9542 − 10
b.	1.5539	*g.*	5.9912	*l.*	7.9400 − 10	*q.*	5.8633 − 10
c.	1.0128	*h.*	3.7110	*m.*	8.6138 − 10	*r.*	6.6117 − 10
d.	3.0043	*i.*	1.6684	*n.*	6.8904 − 10	*s.*	8.1335 − 10
e.	0.5999	*j.*	0.8000	*o.*	9.3010 − 10	*t.*	9.9996 − 10

S16.3. Obtain the logarithms of the following numbers. These require interpolation in a three-place table, such as that provided in this text. A three-place table requires no interpolation in yielding logarithms for three-digit numbers.

a.	6,115	*h.*	94,340	*n.*	70.67	*t.*	0.000,971,8
b.	1.985	*i.*	0.645,3	*o.*	695,800	*u.*	0.000,662,8
c.	40.73	*j.*	1.527	*p.*	6,147,000	*v.*	0.000,046,57
d.	4.331	*k.*	742.4	*q.*	2,755,000	*w.*	0.000,003,617
e.	472.3	*l.*	98,060	*r.*	0.099,86	*x.*	26,180,000
f.	7,554	*m.*	8.755	*s.*	0.006,723	*y.*	0.000,026,18
g.	78.16						

S16.4. Obtain the antilogarithms of the logarithms, interpolating for the fourth significant digit, in these numbers:

a.	2.7668	*f.*	3.9000	*k.*	2.3000	*p.*	9.7950 − 10
b.	3.6250	*g.*	5.7001	*l.*	1.3316	*q.*	7.9493 − 10
c.	1.7829	*h.*	4.5431	*m.*	3.6120	*r.*	8.8191 − 10
d.	0.5468	*i.*	0.2020	*n.*	5.5000	*s.*	9.0033 − 10
e.	1.8417	*j.*	3.4804	*o.*	3.3333	*t.*	7.0760 − 10

S16.5. Solve these problems by logarithms and give results to four significant digits:

a.	3.46×5.81	*f.*	$4,682 \div 941$	*k.*	2.134^2	*p.*	$\sqrt[3]{4,096}$
b.	$572 \times 0.006,77$	*g.*	$5,417 \div 8,113$	*l.*	35.76^3	*q.*	$\sqrt[6]{6,271}$
c.	917×309	*h.*	$56.91 \div 4.121$	*m.*	$0.085,41^2$	*r.*	$\sqrt[4]{1,296}$
d.	0.522×0.444	*i.*	$8,192 \div 1.024$	*n.*	1.062^4	*s.*	$\sqrt{7,131}$
e.	750×512	*j.*	$218.7 \div 36.05$	*o.*	0.03^7	*t.*	$\sqrt{0.145,7}$

Check these results by significance computations (Section 14.4 and 14.5).

S16.6. By use of logarithms compute the area of the triangle whose sides are of lengths 24.7 inches, 37.9 inches, and 50.2 inches, respectively. (*Hint:* First calculate s, $s - a$, $s - b$, and $s - c$ without using logarithms.)

S16.7. By use of logarithms calculate the radii of the inscribed and circumscribed circles of the triangle in Problem S16.6.

S16.8. By use of logarithms calculate the radius of the sphere whose volume is 64.76 cubic inches.

S16.9. Using logarithms and the formula $A = P(1 + i)^n$, compute the amount A from an original principal of $75.50, compounded annually for 10 years at the nominal rate of interest $i = 8$ percent. Verify the result by use of materials of Problems S13.22.

S16.10. By use of logarithms compute to three significant digits the difference $\frac{4 \cdot 181}{6 \cdot 765} - \frac{2 \cdot 584}{4 \cdot 181}$.

S16.11. Evaluate without logarithms and with logarithms as accurately as possible:

$a. \sqrt{\dfrac{2.34 \times 18.7 \times 976{,}000}{6.41^2 \times 78{,}900}}$ $b. \sqrt[3]{\dfrac{4.32 \times 76.9 \times 901 \times 53.1}{0.132 \times 67.5 \times 599 \times 0.003{,}33}}$

S16.12. Obtain the logarithms of base 3 to the nearest 0.0001 to complete the indicated table:

N	0.001,4	0.004,1	$\cdots$	0.333,3	$\cdots$	729
$\log_3 N$	-6	-5	$\cdots$	-1	$\cdots$	6

S16.13. Use the foregoing table of logarithms of base 3 to perform the following computations:

$a.$ $0.037,0 \times 243$ $c.$ 27^2 $e.$ $\sqrt{729}$

$b.$ $27 \div 729$ $d.$ $\sqrt[5]{243}$ $f.$ $\sqrt[3]{729}$

Now repeat these calculations with the common logarithms of the text.

S16.14. Follow through the proof that $\log_a b$ and $\log_b a$ are reciprocals; i.e., that $(\log_a b)(\log_b a) = 1$. Let $\log_b a = x$, then $b^x = a$. Whence $(b^x)^{1/x} = a^{1/x}$ or $b = a^{1/x}$, which is equivalent to the statement that $1/x = \log_a b$ or $x = 1/(\log_a b)$. Therefore, $\log_b a = 1/(\log_a b)$.

S16.15. Using the relationship obtained in the previous problem, calculate the logarithm of 10 for the bases (a) 2, (b) 3, (c) 5, (d) 7, (e) 10, (f) 100.

S16.16. Follow through the derivation of the remarkable relationship that $(\log_m a)/(\log_m b) = \log_b a$. Let $\log_m a = x$ and $\log_m b = y$; i.e., $(\log_m a)/(\log_m b) = x/y$, which are equivalent to $m^x = a$ and $m^y = b$. Whence $(m^x)^{1/x} = a^{1/x}$ and $(m^y)^{1/y} = b^{1/y}$, respectively, or $m = a^{1/x}$ and $m = b^{1/y}$, which yield $a^{1/x} = b^{1/y}$. Thus, $(a^{1/x})^x = (b^{1/y})^x$ or $a = b^{x/y}$, which is equivalent to $x/y = \log_b a$. Therefore, $\log_b a = (\log_m a)/(\log_m b)$. Incidentally, if $m = a$, then, as $\log_a a = 1$, one obtains the relation $\log_b a = 1/(\log_a b)$, as obtained in Problem S16.14. Thus, the four fundamental laws of logarithms (Section 16.3) may be increased by two other laws, namely,

Law V: $\log_b a = \dfrac{\log_m a}{\log_m b}$ Law VI: $\log_b a = \dfrac{1}{\log_a b}$

S16.17. By use of Law V (and by the table of common logarithms on the endpaper), compute the following logarithms of base 7:

N	2	3	5	9	12	15	16	144
$\log_7 N$								

How are the characteristics related to 7? Using this table, calculate (a) $\log_7 1{,}728$, (b) $\log_7 81$, (c) $\frac{144}{16}$.

S16.18. By use of Law V compute the following antilogarithms of base 7:

$\log_7 N$	1	0.7	0.49	0.343	1.2	1.24	1.248	0.6666
N								

S16.19. Obtain the indicated logarithms of base 7. Check the characteristics with reference to powers of 7:

N	1	10	100	1000	10,000	100,000	1,000,000
$\log_7 N$							

S16.20. Prove these generalizations of Law V:
a. $(\log_b a)(\log_c b)(\log_d c) = \log_d a$
b. $(\log_b a)(\log_d c)(\log_f e) = (\log_d a)(\log_f c)(\log_b e)$
c. $\log_b a^{\log_b a^{\log_b a}} = (\log_b a)^3$

S16.21. If P represents the period of a simple pendulum in seconds, i.e., the time for one complete swing back and forth, if L represents the length of the pendulum in feet, and if g represents the earth's gravitational constant of acceleration, then $P = 2\pi \sqrt{L/g}$ yields the period of the pendulum, with error less than 0.5 percent of the true period if the angle of a complete swing, the amplitude, is less than 15°. The value of g varies with the latitude on the earth's surface; thus, at the Canal Zone $g = 32.094,4$, in Greenland 32.235,3 feet per second², to six significant digits.
a. Compute to the nearest 0.01 sec the period of a pendulum of length 40 ft, exactly, if it swings through 5° of amplitude. The local value of g is 32.2. State the possible margin of error in P.
b. By peering through a telescope an observer counts 100 oscillations of a distant pendulum in 1 min 17 sec. If $g = 32.2$, compute the length of this pendulum.

S16.22. If the pendulum of Problem S16.21 subtends an angle A at the observer's eye, its distance from the observer is given by the formula $D = L/A$, in which the angle A must be expressed in radians and L and D in the same units of length. Using the value of L as found in Problem S16.21, calculate how far away it is from the observer, if angle A is measured to be $1.5''$. *Hints:* $60'' = 1'$; $60' = 1°$; $180°/\pi = 1$ radian.

S16.23. The *apparent* magnitude m of a star is a measure of its brightness as it appears to the observer; the *absolute* magnitude M is the measure of its brightness as it would appear to the observer if it were at a distance of 10 parsecs from the observer. A star's apparent magnitude m, its absolute magnitude M, and its distance D, are related by the formula:

$$M = m + 5 - 5 \log D \quad \text{or} \quad \log D = \frac{5 + m - M}{5}$$

in which D is measured in parsecs, and $\log D$ is a common logarithm, i.e., of base 10. A star's absolute magnitude may be determined by observing its spectrum, i.e., its appearance as viewed through a spectroscope; the star's apparent magnitude may be measured by a photometer. Compute in light years the distance from the observer of the following stars if their magnitudes have been determined as indicated. (1 parsec = 3.26 light years, as in Problem 3.19, to three significant digits.)

a.   Alpha Centauri (nearest star beyond the sun) $M = +4.1$; $m = -0.27$.

b.   Sirius (brightest star in our sky) $M = +1.5$; $m = -1.43$.

c.   Deneb (top star in the Northern Cross) $M = -4.8$; $m = 1.26$.

LESSON 17 ✥ THE IMAGINARY AND COMPLEX NUMBERS

17·1 ∾ Imaginary numbers.   Recapitulation of the real numbers

The so-called imaginary numbers supply solutions for such problems as $?^2 = -4$, $\log(-5) = ?$, $\sin ? = 2$, etc., which have no solution among the numbers hitherto considered.   As for $?^2 = -4$, it has been shown that the square of any number hitherto considered must be positive.   In the system of logarithms presented in the previous lesson, it was pointed out that only positive numbers have logarithms.   In the definition of $\sin A$, as the length of the segment PQ, it was evident that $\sin A$ must not exceed 1 in numerical value.   However, by enlarging the number system beyond the system of real numbers that fill up the real number line, and by extending the definitions of roots, logarithms, and the trigonometric functions, these three proposed problems have quite valid solutions.

To recapitulate, the numbers hitherto considered are the so-called *real* numbers, namely: (1) the integers that were assigned equally spaced positions on the number line; (2) the rational numbers whose positions on the number line were equally spaced between the positions of the integers—these rational numbers may be expressed as terminating or as cyclically repeating decimal fractions; (3) the irrational numbers that occupy positions on the number line that are unoccupied by the rational numbers—these irrational numbers may be expressed as unending decimal fractions which do not terminate nor repeat cyclically.   All positions on the number line are occupied by the real numbers; there is no room on the number line for further enlargement of the number system.

The imaginary and complex numbers are required in modern scientific investigations.   These numbers, it will be noted, include as special cases all numbers hitherto developed and constitute the complete number system of analysis.   In this final lesson their definition and some of their simpler properties are presented.

17·2 ∾ The four rational operations upon imaginary numbers

If a represents any real number, rational or irrational, the expression ai, or ia, is called a pure imaginary number or simply an imaginary number.   The name is misleading and reflects their dubious status when originally introduced into the number system. The four rational operations upon imaginary numbers are described by the four postulates:

Addition: $0 + i = i + 0 = i$, $1i = i$, $i + i = 2i$, $2i + i = 3i$, $ni + i = (n + 1)i$, and quite generally, $ai + bi = (a + b)i$, if n, a, b are any real numbers.

Subtraction: $ai - bi = (a - b)i$.

Multiplication: $0 \times i = i \times 0 = 0$, $a \times i = ai$, $i \times i = -1$, $a \times bi = abi$, $ai \times bi = -ab$.

Division: $0 \div i$ or $0/i = 0$, $1 \div i$ or $1/i = i/i^2 = i/-1 = -i$, $a/i = -ai$, $ai \div bi$ or $ai/bi = a/b$, $i \div 0$ is impossible.

17·3 ∞ COMPLEX NUMBERS. THE FOUR RATIONAL OPERATIONS UPON COMPLEX NUMBERS

If a and b are real numbers, the expression $a + bi$ is called a complex number; it comprises the sum of a real number a and an imaginary number, bi. The four rational operations upon complex numbers are described by the postulates:

Addition: $(a + bi) + (c + di) = (a + c) + (b + d)i$.

Subtraction: $(a + bi) - (c + di) = (a - c) + (b - d)i$.

Multiplication, as suggested by the distributive law: $(a + bi)(c + di) = a \times c + a \times di + bi \times c + bi \times di = ac + adi + bci - bd = (ac - bd) + (ad + bc)i$. The complex numbers $a + bi$ and $a - bi$ are called conjugate complex numbers. It is to be observed that their sum and product are *real* numbers. Thus $(a + bi) + (a - bi) = 2a$; $(a + bi)(a - bi) = a^2 + b^2$. Thus $\sqrt{a^2 + b^2}$ is also called the *absolute value* of $a + bi$; it is also the absolute value of $a - bi$.

Division: $(a + bi) \div (c + di)$, or

$$\frac{a + bi}{c + di} = \frac{(a + bi)(c - di)}{(c + di)(c - di)} = \frac{(ac + bd) + (bc - ad)}{c^2 + d^2}$$

or $\quad \dfrac{ac + bd}{c^2 + d^2} + \dfrac{bc - ad}{c^2 + d^2} i$.

Accordingly, the four rational operations upon complex numbers yield complex numbers as results. Again, division by 0 is impossible.

17·4 ∞ COMPREHENSIVE CHARACTER OF COMPLEX NUMBERS

The complex number $a + bi$ includes all kinds of numbers hitherto considered. Thus $a + 0i = a$, wherein a may represent in turn all natural numbers, all integers, all rational numbers, or all real numbers. Again, $a + bi$ represents all imaginary numbers if $a = 0$. Thus $0 + bi = bi$, wherein b may represent in turn all natural numbers, integers, rational numbers, or all real numbers. Hence, $a + bi$ represents all complex numbers if a and b represent in turn all possible pairs of real numbers. If a and b represent integers, then $a + bi$ represents integral complex numbers; if a and b represent rational numbers, then $a + bi$ is called a rational complex number.

17·5 ↝ Graphical representation of the imaginary numbers

Positions for the imaginary numbers are on the imaginary number line, which is obtained by rotating an image of the real number line through 90° about the position of 0 as center of rotation. Now the position of any real number a on the real number line is rotated into the position for ai on the imaginary number

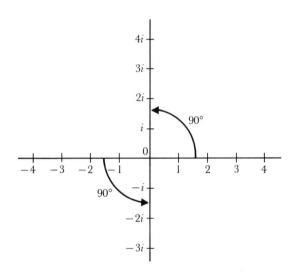

FIGURE 17.1

line. Thus, the perpendicular line of imaginary numbers contains positions for i, $2i$, $3i$, . . . , equally spaced above the 0 position of both lines; the positions for -1, $-2i$, $-3i$, . . . , are equally spaced below the 0 position. Since all positions of the real number line are occupied by real numbers, so are all positions on the imaginary line occupied by imaginary numbers, rational imaginary numbers as well as irrational imaginary numbers (note Figure 17.1).

17·6 GRAPHICAL REPRESENTATION OF COMPLEX NUMBERS

Positions for the complex numbers, $a + bi$, are available in the *plane* that contains the two number lines. This plane is called "the plane of the complete system of complex numbers," or "the plane of complex numbers," or simply, "the complex plane." The position for a specific complex number $a + bi$ is determined from the position of a on the real number line and the position of bi on the imaginary number line and may be precisely located geometrically as follows: Using a radius equal to the distance from 0 to bi and compass point at a, draw a complete circle; using a radius equal to the distance from 0 to a and with compass center at bi, draw the complete circle.

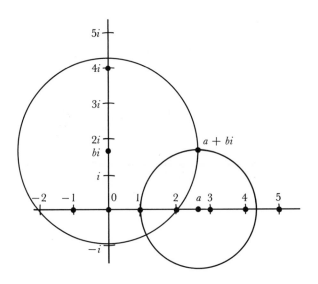

FIGURE 17.2

The intersection of these two circles that is directly above or below the position of a and directly to the left, or right, of the position of bi, represents the position for the complex number $a + bi$. Thus the position of any complex number $a + bi$ may be obtained geometrically if the positions of a and bi are known. (See Figure 17.2.)

17·7 ∞ GEOMETRICAL LOCATION OF THE RATIONAL COMPLEX NUMBERS IN THE COMPLEX PLANE

It is possible to locate in the complex plane *geometrically* any required position of the complex number, $a + bi$, if a and b represent specific *rational* numbers, and if two positions are selected to represent numbers 0 and 1. A *geometrical* construction, or solution, employs no other instruments than a pair of compasses and an *unmarked* straightedge, such as a foot rule or a meterstick if one ignores the markings on them.

To locate all real and imaginary integers, one first draws the line through the positions of 0 and 1. Such positions are called *points*. The line drawn through

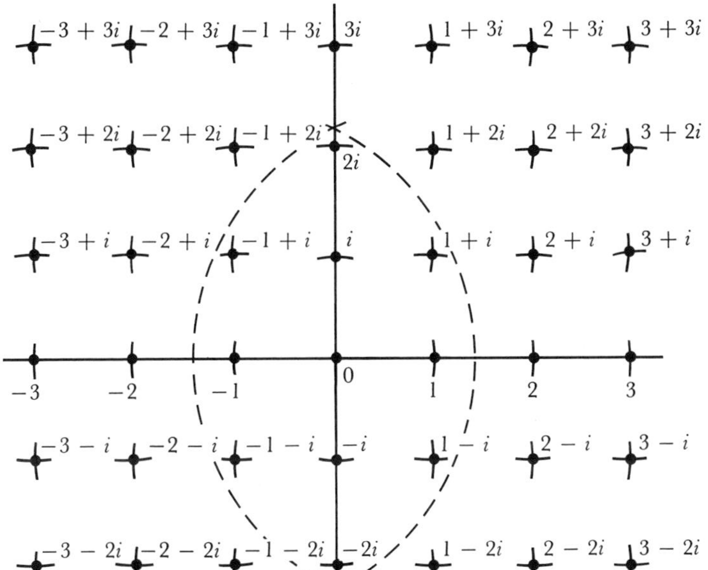

$$
\begin{array}{ccccccc}
-3+3i & -2+3i & -1+3i & 3i & 1+3i & 2+3i & 3+3i \\
-3+2i & -2+2i & -1+2i & 2i & 1+2i & 2+2i & 3+2i \\
-3+i & -2+i & -1+i & i & 1+i & 2+i & 3+i \\
-3 & -2 & -1 & 0 & 1 & 2 & 3 \\
-3-i & -2-i & -1-i & -i & 1-i & 2-i & 3-i \\
-3-2i & -2-2i & -1-2i & -2i & 1-2i & 2-2i & 3-2i \\
-3-3i & -2-3i & -1-3i & -3i & 1-3i & 2-3i & \\
\end{array}
$$

Locating images of complex numbers $a + bi$, in which a and b are integers, by intersecting arcs of *unit* circles. Compasses only suffice.

FIGURE 17.3

the points 0 and 1 represents the real number line. With the compass opening extending from point 0 to point 1, one may mark off points to represent the integers, the positive integers to the right of point 0 and the negative integers to the left of 0. The imaginary number line is located as follows: With any compass opening greater than the distance from 0 to 1 and with centers at points 1 and at −1, one draws circles that cut each other at points above and below point 0. Now with the straightedge one draws the line through these two circle intersections; this new line also passes through 0 and is the imaginary

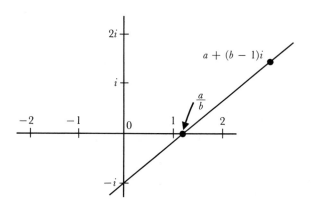

FIGURE 17.4

number line. With the compass opening equal to the distance from 0 to 1, one may mark off equal lengths on the imaginary number line, starting at 0; these new positions represent the imaginary numbers i, $2i$, $3i$, . . . , above the 0, and $-i$, $-2i$, $-3i$, . . . , below the 0. (See Figure 17.3.)

One next locates geometrically, as indicated in Figure 17.2, the points that represent the integral complex numbers, $a + bi$, in which a and b are integers, namely, $1 + i$, $1 + 2i$, $1 + 3i$, . . . , $1 - i$, $1 - 2i$, $1 - 3i$, . . . , $2 + i$, $2 + 2i$, $2 + 3i$, . . . , $-2 + i$, $-2 + 2i$, $-2 + 3i$, ... (See Figure 17.3.)

One may locate the real rational number a/b, geometrically, by drawing the line from the imaginary point $-i$ to the complex point $a + (b - 1)i$; this line crosses (intersects) the real number line at point a/b. (Note Figure 17.4.)

To locate the imaginary rational number p/qi geometrically, one draws the line from the real point -1 to the complex point $(p - 1) + qi$; this line intersects the imaginary number line at the point p/qi. (Note Figure 17.5.)

The correctness of these constructions is established by methods of plane geometry; their validity may be made apparent by locating, as described above, the points that represent such numbers as $\frac{2}{3}$, $-\frac{3}{4}$, $\frac{3}{2i}$, $-3\frac{1}{3i}$.

Finally, to locate the position in the complex plane for the *rational* complex number $a/b + (p/q)i$, one draws two circles, one circle with its center at the position of a/b and with radius the length from 0 to $(p/q)i$; the other circle with center at position of $(p/q)i$, and with radius the length from 0 to a/b. The

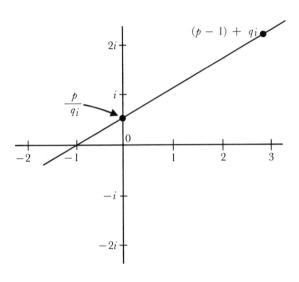

FIGURE 17.5

intersection of these circles which is above or below the position of a/b, and to the right or left of the position of $(p/q)i$ is the required position for the *rational* complex number $(a/b) + (p/q)i$.

17·8 ∾ Positions for irrational complex numbers that may be located geometrically

The only irrational complex numbers whose positions in the complex plane may be located geometrically (if positions of 1 and 0 are known) are those of the form $a\sqrt[m]{b} + c\sqrt[n]{d}\,i$, in which a, b, c, and d represent rational numbers, and m and n natural numbers that are powers of 2.   Thus, for example,

$$\tfrac{3}{4}\sqrt[8]{\tfrac{5}{7}} + \tfrac{2}{3}\sqrt[16]{1.37}$$

is so constructible (page 278, Note 3).

All other irrational complex numbers $h + ki$ may be located approximately by using rational approximations for h and k, if h and k are irrational; or for h or k, whichever is irrational.

৵ PROBLEMS ৵

17.1. Locate the positions for the numbers $2 + 3i$, $-5 + 6i$, $-7 - 3i$, and $6 - 7i$, in the complex number plane.   Join them in order by line segments to form a quadrilateral.

17.2. Solve Problem 17.1 after multiplying each of the four complex numbers by i.

17.3. Solve Problem 17.1 after multiplying each of the four numbers by i^2 or $-i$.

17.4. Solve Problem 17.1 after multiplying each of the four numbers by i^3 or $-i$.

17.5. By consideration of the results of Problems 17.2, 17.3, and 17.4, what effect is produced geometrically by multiplying a number by a power of i?

17.6. Solve Problem 17.1 after adding $-3 + 2i$ to each of the four numbers in the problem.   What geometrical effect is produced on a complex number by adding a complex number to it?

17.7. Draw the square whose vertices are at the points in the complex plane representing the numbers $1 + i$, $-1 + i$, $-1 - i$, and $1 - i$.

17.8. Solve Problem 17.7 after multiplying the four numbers in it by i. Explain the result geometrically.

17.9. The angle of a complex number is the angle between the right (positive) part of the real number line and the line drawn from 0 to the point representing the complex number.   Thus, the angle of i is 90°; the angle of $1 + i$ is 45°.   Solve Problem 17.7 after multiplying the four numbers in it by $1 + i$.   Explain the result geometrically.

17.10. The absolute value of the complex number $a + bi$ and of its conjugate $a - bi$ is $\sqrt{a^2 + b^2}$.   Compute the absolute value of the complex numbers $3 + 4i$, $1 + i$, $2 + 2i$.

17.11. The angle A of a complex number $A + bi$ is obtained from the relationships $\cos A = a/\sqrt{a^2 + b^2}$, $\sin A = b/\sqrt{a^2 + b^2}$. Calculate the sine and cosine of the angles of the three complex numbers in Problem 17.10. By reference to the trigonometry tables evaluate these angles to the nearest degree.

17.12. If $N = 3 + 4i$, compute N^2, N^3. Compute the absolute value and angle of N, N^2, and N^3. How are they related?

17.13. In the complex number system any number has n nth roots. By computing the cubes of $-\frac{1}{2} + \frac{\sqrt{3}}{2} i$ and of $-\frac{1}{2} - \frac{\sqrt{3}}{2} i$, verify that they are cube roots of 1. What is the other cube root of 1?

17.14. Show that the square of each of the two complex numbers in Problem 17.13 is equal to the other complex number.

17.15. Compute the absolute value and angle of each of the complex numbers in Problem 17.13.

*N*ote 1 ⟿ *The denumerable set of infinite, or transfinite, cardinal numbers,* $\aleph_0$, $\aleph_1$, $\aleph_2$, $\aleph_3$, $\aleph_4$, ...

One recalls that $\aleph_0$ represents the cardinal number of the set of natural numbers. The cardinal number of the set of rational numbers (all integers and all fractions) also has this same cardinal number $\aleph_0$, inasmuch as it is possible to establish a one-to-one correspondence between the natural numbers and the rational numbers. It has also been established that the set of all algebraic numbers (numbers that can be roots of algebraic equations) has this same cardinal number $\aleph_0$. Since the cardinal number of the set of real irrational numbers cannot be matched off in any one-to-one correspondence with the set of natural numbers, one must conclude that there must be irrational numbers that are not algebraic numbers. Such numbers are called *transcendental numbers*, the most famous of which are π and e.

To provide appropriate orientation for the ensuing discussion, one may regard the real irrational numbers as unending decimal fractions whose forms consist of all possible permutations (arrangements) of two or more of the digits 0, 1, 2, 3, 4, 5, 6, 7, 8, 9, and excluding those permutations that are periodic, as such forms represent rational numbers (Section 10.4).

To prove that the cardinal number of the set of real irrational numbers is greater than $\aleph_0$, one demonstrates that irrational numbers exist that are not included in any alleged one-to-one correspondence between the irrational numbers and the natural numbers. Let it be supposed that a one-to-one correspondence does exist between the irrational numbers and the natural numbers, and that it might appear thus:

Natural number	Corresponding irrational number
1	45.75091007 . . .
2	7.53908331 . . .
3	1830.02911648 . . .
4	.00000782 . . .
5	.75682409 . . .
. . .	. . . .

One may obtain an irrational number that does not occur anywhere in this list by forming its decimal portion as follows: Let each digit be the next digit of the cycle 1 2 3 4 5 6 7 8 9 0 of the corresponding digit of the successive irrational numbers in the alleged one-to-one correspondence, as underlined. This new irrational number would appear as .84013 . . . and hence differs from the nth irrational number in the list in its nth digit to the right of the decimal point, so it cannot possibly be in the list so arrayed. If, however, this newly constructed number is a periodic decimal fraction, and therefore, a *rational* number, one may revise the choice of new digits to obtain a new *irrational* number. Therefore, in any alleged one-to-one correspondence between the natural numbers and the real irrational numbers there must be other irrational numbers not included in the correspondence. Hence the cardinal number of the set of real irrational numbers must exceed $\aleph_0$, so it is represented by $\aleph_1$.

Next, consider a new set consisting of all possible unending permutations of two or more of the real irrational numbers. Let I with suitable subscripts represent the various irrational numbers; then a *permutation* of irrational numbers may be represented by P. Assume that a one-to-one correspondence could be set up between the irrational numbers and the permutations of the irrational numbers, thus:

Irrational number	Corresponding permutation of irrationals
I_1	$P_1 = I_{11}I_{12}I_{13}I_{14} \ldots$
I_2	$P_2 = I_{21}I_{22}I_{23}I_{24} \ldots$
I_3	$P_3 = I_{31}I_{32}I_{33}I_{34} \ldots$
I_4	$P_4 = I_{41}I_{42}I_{43}I_{44} \ldots$
. . .	. . . .

Now form a new permutation of irrational numbers from the irrationals in the list, namely, $P_0 = I'_{11}I'_{22}I'_{33}I'_{44} \ldots$ in which each I'_{kk} is formed from the corresponding I_{kk} by replacing the kth digit of I_{kk} by the next digit of the cycle 1 2 3 4 5 6 7 8 9 0 1, as was done in the preceding discussion. Thus, P_0 cannot be included in the alleged one-to-one correspondence because P_0 differs in at least one detail from every permutation alleged to be in the correspondence. Therefore the cardinal number of the set of permutations of the I's is greater than $\aleph_1$, and so is represented by $\aleph_2$, a larger infinite cardinal number than $\aleph_1$.

Next, consider the set of permutations of two or more of the P's of the previous discussion. Let such a permutation be represented by Q. By the same argument used in the previous discussion one may show that the cardinal number of the set of permutations Q must have a larger cardinal number than $\aleph_2$, so it is represented by $\aleph_3$. The same development may be continued indefinitely, each new set consisting of all possible permutations of two or more of the elements of the previous set. By the diagonal process, one constructs a new permutation that is not included in any alleged one-to-one correspondence between those elements and the permutations of those elements, and so must have an ever-larger infinite cardinal number. One is thus led to the existence of an unending list of infinite cardinal numbers, $\aleph_0$, $\aleph_1$, $\aleph_2$, $\aleph_3$, $\aleph_4$, ... As these cardinal numbers may be paired off with the natural numbers by their subscripts, this set of infinite cardinal numbers is itself denumerable (pages 112–113, Note 2).

Note 2 ↔ The sum of an infinite (unending) series of numbers; the number e.

Definition. The *sum* of an infinite series is defined as the number S, which the sum of the first n terms of the series approximates ever more closely as n increases indefinitely. To illustrate, consider the geometric series,

$$1 + \tfrac{1}{2} + \tfrac{1}{4} + \tfrac{1}{8} + \tfrac{1}{16} + \cdots$$

in which each term of the series is half the preceding term. If S_n represents the sum of the first n terms,

$$S_1 = 1$$
$$S_2 = 1 + \tfrac{1}{2} = \tfrac{3}{2} \qquad \text{that is} \qquad S_2 = 1\tfrac{1}{2}$$
$$S_3 = 1 + \tfrac{1}{2} + \tfrac{1}{4} = \tfrac{7}{4} \qquad \text{that is} \qquad S_3 = 1\tfrac{3}{4}$$
$$S_4 = 1 + \tfrac{1}{2} + \tfrac{1}{4} + \tfrac{1}{8} = \tfrac{15}{8} \qquad \text{that is} \qquad S_4 = 1\tfrac{7}{8}$$

S_n seems to be approximating ever closer to 2. To demonstrate that S is indeed equal to 2, one may obtain the sum of the geometric progression, consisting of n terms: $1 + \tfrac{1}{2} + (\tfrac{1}{2})^2 + (\tfrac{1}{2})^3 + \cdots + (\tfrac{1}{2})^n$. (See Problem S9.35.)

$$S_n + \frac{1 - (\tfrac{1}{2})^n}{1 - \tfrac{1}{2}} = 2 - (\tfrac{1}{2})^{n-1}$$

As n increases indefinitely $(\tfrac{1}{2})^{n-1}$ becomes indefinitely small, so that S_n approximates ever closer to 2. Therefore the sum of the unending series of numbers $1 + \tfrac{1}{2} + \tfrac{1}{4} + \tfrac{1}{8} + \cdots$ is *defined* as 2.

Again, the sum of the unending series of numbers $0.148 + 0.000,148 + 0.000,000,148 + 0.000,000,000,148 + \cdots$ is equal to the repeating decimal fraction $0.148,148,148, \ldots$, or $\frac{148}{999}$ or $\frac{4}{27}$.

The unending series of numbers $1 + 3 + 5 + 7 + \cdots$ does not have a sum, as $S_1 = 1$, $S_2 = 1 + 3$ or 4, $S_3 = 1 + 3 + 5 = 9$. Quite generally, $S_n = n^2$, so that as n continues to increase indefinitely, n^2 does not approximate any number S whatever but also continues to increase indefinitely.

Moreover, the series $1 + \frac{2}{3} + \frac{3}{9} + \frac{4}{27} + \frac{5}{81} + \cdots$ does have the sum $2\frac{1}{4}$, as one may test by adding various numbers of leading terms of the series. The ingenious student may devise a scheme to compute the precise sum S, as $2\frac{1}{4}$. (*Hint:* Each term of this series is the *product* of a term of an arithmetic and a term of a geometric progression. If the arithmetic series is $a + (a + d) + (a + 2d) + (a + 3d) + \cdots$, and the geometric series is $b + br + br^2 + br^3 + \cdots$, the sum of the first n terms of the product progression

$$S_n = \frac{ab(1 + r^{n+1})}{1 - r} + db \left(\frac{r - r^{n+1}}{(1 - r)^2} + \frac{nr^{n+1}}{1 - r} \right)$$

$$\therefore \ S = \frac{b}{(1 - r)^2} (a + dr - ar)$$

In the above series, $a = b = d = 1$; $r = \frac{1}{3}$.

The *harmonic series,* namely, $1 + \frac{1}{2} + \frac{1}{3} + \frac{1}{4} + \frac{1}{5} + \cdots$, does *not* have a sum, since S_n, the sum of the first n terms of the series, continues to increase indefinitely as n increases indefinitely. To clarify this situation, let successive terms of the series be grouped within pairs of parentheses so that the last terms enclosed by successive pairs of parentheses are the successive reciprocals of powers of 2. The series then appears as

$$(1 + \tfrac{1}{2}) + (\tfrac{1}{3} + \tfrac{1}{4}) + (\tfrac{1}{5} + \tfrac{1}{6} + \tfrac{1}{7} + \tfrac{1}{8}) + (\tfrac{1}{9} + \cdots + \tfrac{1}{16}) + \tfrac{1}{17} + \cdots$$

If $(\frac{1}{2})^k$ represents the last term within any pair of parentheses, there are 2^{k-1} terms within that pair of parentheses, all of which are larger than $(\frac{1}{2})^k$; hence the sum of all terms within the parentheses must exceed $2^{k-1} \times (\frac{1}{2})^k$, or $\frac{1}{2}$. Furthermore, as there are k pairs of parentheses as far as the term $(\frac{1}{2})^k$, the sum of all terms as far as $(\frac{1}{2})^k$ must exceed $k(\frac{1}{2}) + 1$, if k exceeds 1, as the first pair of parentheses contains a surplus 1. Accordingly, S_n must exceed $k(\frac{1}{2}) + 1$, if $n = k^2$. Hence S_n continues to increase indefinitely, and so cannot possibly approximate ever more closely to any particular number S.

As checks, one notes that $S_4 = 1 + \frac{1}{2} + \frac{1}{3} + \frac{1}{4} = 2\frac{1}{12}$, which exceeds $2(\frac{1}{2}) + 1$, or 2; $S_8 = 1 + \frac{1}{2} + \frac{1}{3} + \frac{1}{4} + \frac{1}{5} + \frac{1}{6} + \frac{1}{7} + \frac{1}{8} = 2\frac{599}{840}$, which exceeds $3(\frac{1}{2}) + 1$, or $2\frac{1}{2}$.

A very important number in mathematical analysis, represented by e, is the sum of the series

$$1 + \frac{1}{1} + \frac{1}{1 \times 2} + \frac{1}{1 \times 2 \times 3} + \frac{1}{1 \times 2 \times 3 \times 4} + \cdots$$

Let S_n represent the sum of the first n terms of the series, namely,

$$S_n = 1 + \frac{1}{1} + \frac{1}{1 \times 2} + \frac{1}{1 \times 2 \times 3} + \cdots + \frac{1}{1 \times 2 \cdots (n-1)}$$

It is next demonstrated that the sum of all terms following the first n terms have a sum that is smaller than the product of the nth term and $\frac{1}{n-1}$.

This sum (of all terms following the nth term) may be expressed as

$$\frac{1}{1 \times 2 \times 3 \cdots (n-1)} \left(\frac{1}{n} + \frac{1}{n(n+1)} + \frac{1}{n(n+1)(n+2)} \right.$$
$$\left. + \frac{1}{n(n+1)(n+2)(n+3)} + \cdots \right)$$

which is clearly smaller than

$$\frac{1}{1 \times 2 \times 3 \cdots (n-1)} \left(\frac{1}{n} + \frac{1}{nn} + \frac{1}{nnn} + \frac{1}{nnnn} + \cdots \right)$$

The terms within this pair of parentheses is a geometric series whose sum is $1/(n-1)$. Therefore, the sum of all terms of the original series following the nth term must be smaller than $\dfrac{1}{1 \times 2 \times 3 \cdots (n-1)(n-1)}$. Thus,

$$S_8 = 1 + \tfrac{1}{1} + \tfrac{1}{2} + \tfrac{1}{6} + \tfrac{1}{24} + \tfrac{1}{120} + \tfrac{1}{720} + \tfrac{1}{5049} = 2.718,253,9 \ldots$$

This represents the sum of the series to the nearest $0.000,05$, since

$$\frac{1}{1 \times 2 \times 3 \times 4 \times 5 \times 6 \times 7 \times 7} = 0.000,028$$

which exceeds the error involved by using S_8 instead of S, the sum of the entire series. The value of S, which is universally represented by the letter e, is $2.718,281,8$ to eight significant digits.

Logarithms that have the number e for base are called *natural*, or Naperian, logarithms. Since $\log_{10} e = 0.434,294,5 \ldots$, one may obtain the natural logarithm of any number from its common logarithm by multiplying the common logarithm by $\log_{10} e$, in accordance with Law V of logarithms (refer to Problem S16.16).

To simplify the notation, the symbol $n!$ is used to represent the product of all natural numbers from 1 to n; thus, $4! = 1 \times 2 \times 3 \times 4 = 24$, $7! = 1 \times 2 \times 3 \times 4 \times 5 \times 6 \times 7 = 5,040$. Thus

$$e = 1 + \frac{1}{1} + \frac{1}{2!} + \frac{1}{3!} + \frac{1}{4!} + \frac{1}{5!} + \cdots$$

In calculus one *defines* e^N for any number N, real or complex, as

$$e^N = 1 + \frac{N}{1} + \frac{N^2}{2!} + \frac{N^3}{3!} + \frac{N^4}{4!} + \frac{N^5}{5!} + \frac{N^6}{6!} + \cdots$$

Furthermore, for an angle of 1 radian,

$$\sin 1 = 1 - \frac{1}{3!} + \frac{1}{5!} - \frac{1}{7!} + \cdots \qquad \text{and}$$

$$\cos 1 = 1 - \frac{1}{2!} + \frac{1}{4!} - \frac{1}{6!} + \cdots$$

in which S_n differs from S by less than the $(n+1)$th term. Since 1 radian = 57.3°, approximately, the reader may verify that $\sin 57.3° = 1 - \frac{1}{6} + \frac{1}{120}$, with error less than $\frac{1}{5040}$, and $\cos 57.3 = 1 - \frac{1}{2} + \frac{1}{24}$, with error less than $\frac{1}{720}$.

It is also proved in calculus that if N represents any number whatever, real or complex, measured in radians if N is real,

$$\sin N = N - \frac{N^3}{3!} + \frac{N^5}{5!} - \frac{N^7}{7!} + \cdots$$

and

$$\cos N = 1 - \frac{N^2}{2!} + \frac{N^4}{4!} - \frac{N^6}{6!} + \cdots$$

Indeed, since these two infinite series do have unique sums for all values of N, real or complex, these series are generally taken as the definitions of the sine and the cosine, if N is not a real number less than 1 in absolute value.

These series reveal a remarkable relation between e and the sine and cosine, as follows. If N is replaced by iN in the series for e^N, one obtains

$$e^{iN} = 1 + \frac{(iN)}{1} + \frac{(iN)^2}{2!} + \frac{(iN)^3}{3!} + \frac{(iN)^4}{4!} + \frac{(iN)^5}{5!} + \frac{(iN)^6}{6!} + \frac{(iN)^7}{7!} + \cdots$$

Since $i^2 = -1$, $i^3 = -i$, and $i^4 = +1$, these numerators may be simplified, yielding

$$e^{iN} = 1 + \frac{iN}{1} - \frac{N^2}{2!} - \frac{iN^3}{3!} + \frac{N^4}{4!} + \frac{iN^5}{5!} - \frac{N^6}{6!} - \frac{iN^7}{7!} + \cdots$$

$$= \left(1 - \frac{N^2}{2!} + \frac{N^4}{4!} - \frac{N^6}{6!} + \cdots\right) + i\left(N - \frac{N^3}{3!} + \frac{N^5}{5!} - \frac{N^7}{7!} + \cdots\right)$$

$$= \cos N + i \sin N$$

Since π radians = 180° and 2π radians = 360°, $\cos \pi = -1$, $\cos 2\pi = +1$, $\sin \pi = 0$, $\sin 2\pi = 0$. Quite generally, for any even natural number n, $\cos n\pi = 1$; for any odd natural number n, $\cos n\pi = -1$ and for any natural number n, $\sin \pi n = 0$, one is led to the relationships

$$e^{\pi i} = e^{3\pi i} = e^{5\pi i} = e^{7\pi i} = -1;\ e^{2\pi i} = e^{4\pi i} = e^{6\pi i} = +1 = e^0$$

so that $\log_e 1$ has an unending number of values, namely, 0, $2\pi i$, $4\pi i$, . . . and $\log_e -1 = \pi i$, as well as $3\pi i$, $5\pi i$, ...

Quite generally, if complex numbers are available for use, any number, real or complex, has an unending set of logarithms. If N is a real positive number, $\log_e N$ has *one real* value and all other values are complex. The real logarithms appear in the tables of logarithms.

*N*ote 3 ⟿ *Résumé of the development of the system of natural numbers of primitive arithmetic into the complete number system and basic operations of modern analysis.*

The formidable structure of the complete number system of analysis rests firmly upon the basic notion of natural numbers which most persons learn to recite and use in their preschool days. These natural numbers constitute the fundamental undefinable elements of arithmetic, which are exhibited artificially by the use of digit symbols, usually by the Hindu-Arabic symbols 1, 2, 3, 4, 5, 6, 7, 8, 9, 0, which, alone (excepting the 0) or in all possible finite combinations with or without repetitions, represent all the natural numbers. Doubtless these symbols were developed from still more simple markings, possibly such as /, //, ///, ////, ⫰⫰⫰, ⫰⫰⫰ /, ...

Arranging the symbols for the natural numbers beginning with the first natural number and proceeding to some specified natural number is the first operation of arithmetic and is called *counting*. Thus, counting may be done mentally, orally, or in writing. From these two primitive concepts of natural numbers and of counting, the entire structure is developed. Thus, three basic operations upon natural numbers are:

Addition, or repeated counting, such as $3 + 8 = ?$ Here ? represents 11; or /// + ⫰⫰/// = ⫰⫰⫰ ⫰⫰⫰ /.

Multiplication, or repeated addition, such as $3 \times 5 = ?$ Here 3×5 means $5 + 5 + 5$, which yields 15.

Involution, or repeated multiplication, such as $3^5 = ?$ Here 3^5 means $3 \times 3 \times 3 \times 3 \times 3$, which yields 243.

These three operations are called the three *direct* operations of arithmetic, since they may always be performed directly upon any pair of the natural numbers and always yield just one natural number for the required result.

Four *inverse* operations are performed by reversing the direct operations. They are the following:

Subtraction, such as $8 + ? = 11$, or as $? + 3 = 11$, which may be written as $11 - 8 = ?$ and $11 - 3 = ?$, respectively. Thus, addition gives rise to just one inverse operation, since addition is commutative.

Division, such as $3 \times ? = 15$ and $? \times 5 = 15$, which may be written as $15 \div 3 = ?$ and $15 \div 5 = ?$, respectively. Thus, multiplication gives rise to just one inverse operation, since multiplication is commutative.

Evolution, such as $?^5 = 243$, which may be written as $\sqrt[5]{243} = ?$

Indexing, such as $3^? = 243$, which may be written as $\log_3 243 = ?$

The direct operation of involution gives rise to two different inverse operations, namely, *evolution* and *indexing*, since involution is not commutative.

Any direct operation upon any arbitrary natural numbers always yields one correct natural number for the required sum, product, or power. Then, any inverse operation upon *these same arbitrary numbers* and the associated sum, product, or power, also always yields one correct natural number for the required result.

The above examples are solvable, as they employ only the resulting numbers of the corresponding direct operations. Accordingly,

$11 - 3 = 8$, which is called the *difference*
$15 \div 3 = 5$, which is called the *quotient*
$\sqrt[5]{243} = 3$, which is called the *root*
$\log_3 243 = 5$, which is called the *logarithm*

Quite generally, any operation that may be performed upon any arbitrary numbers of a number system and which yields for its result a number of the same number system is said to be possible within the number system. Thus the three direct operations are always possible within the system of natural numbers. Otherwise expressed, "*the system of natural numbers is closed under the operations of addition, multiplication, and involution.*" However, the four inverse operations are not always possible within the system of natural numbers. These operations are possible within the system of natural numbers only under the indicated circumstances: Let a and b represent any two different natural numbers, or the same natural number. Then:

Subtraction, $a - b = ?$ is possible if and only if a exceeds b.

Division, $a \div b = ?$ is possible if and only if a is a multiple of b; i.e., if a occurs among the numbers a, $2a$, $3a$, $4a$, ...

Evolution, $\sqrt[a]{b} = ?$ is possible if and only if b occurs among the ath powers of the natural numbers; i.e., if b occurs among 1^a, 2^a, 3^a, ...

Indexing, $\log_b a = ?$ is possible if and only if a occurs among the powers of b, namely among b^1, b^2, b^3, b^4, ... Here if $b = 1$, a must also be 1, in which case *any natural number whatever* may serve as a correct logarithm.

It thus appears that the inverse operations are possible upon natural numbers only in certain quite special cases. The following inverse operations are evidently impossible within the system of natural numbers: $3 - 5 = ?$, $12 \div 5 = ?$ or $1 \div 2 = ?$, $\sqrt[3]{2} = ?$, $\log_2 5 = ?$ New types of numbers must be devised and included within the system of usable numbers to make operations such as the foregoing ones solvable. With such new kinds of numbers and with the revised, or enlarged, definition of each operation upon the natural numbers, these indicated operations are solvable.

Hence $3 - 5 = -2$, a negative integer; $12 \div 5 = \frac{12}{5}$ or $2\frac{2}{5}$, an improper fraction or mixed number, respectively; $1 \div 2 = \frac{1}{2}$, a proper fraction; $\sqrt[3]{2}$ is a surd number or a special kind of real algebraic irrational number, which may be represented approximately as a decimal fraction, 1.259,921, . . . ; $\log_2 5$ is a real transcendental number, which may be represented approximately by the decimal fraction 2.321,928, ... However, $\sqrt[3]{2}$ and $\log_2 5$ are themselves regarded as a surd number and a transcendental number, respectively.

The complete system of numbers of analysis arose from the program of enlarging the number system to provide numbers to represent the results of performing the inverse operations upon any arbitrary natural numbers, the enlargement of the definition of the three direct and four inverse operations so that they may be performed upon these new numbers, and the subsequent enlargement of the number system to provide numbers to serve as appropriate results of these seven operations upon these resulting new numbers. This program has led to the creation of:

1. Zero and the negative integers to permit subtraction upon any arbitrary natural numbers

2. Fractions to permit the division of any arbitrary natural numbers

3. Surd numbers (special real algebraic irrational numbers) to allow evolution upon any arbitrary natural numbers

4. Special real transcendental numbers to allow indexing of all natural numbers (however, in $\log_b a$, a must not be 1 if b is not 1; if $a = 1$ and $b = 1$, $\log_1 1$ has any numerical value whatever)

The application of basic operations upon these new types of numbers requires further enlargement of the usable number system and has led to the creation of:

5. Negative fractions, to permit subtraction of fractions in every situation

6. Imaginary numbers, to provide even roots of negative numbers, such as $\sqrt[2]{-4}$, which yields $2i$ for its required root. Moreover, $\log_e (-1) = \pi i$ in which e is the transcendental number 2.718,281,8 . . . .

7. Complex numbers as required to provide the root of an imaginary number. Thus $\sqrt{2i} = 1 + i$

Finally, with the introduction of the complex numbers or numbers of the form $a + bi$, in which a and b represent any real numbers whatever and i represents the number whose square is equal to -1, the number system of modern analysis is complete. Accordingly, the system of complex numbers is closed under the three direct operations of addition, multiplication, and involution, and the four inverse operations of subtraction, division, evolution, and indexing, *with just three specific impossibilities*, namely: division by zero, thus $a/0 = ?$ has no solution if a does not represent 0; indexing with base 1, thus $\log_1 a = ?$ has no solution if a does not represent 1; indexing with 0, thus $\log_b 0 = ?$ has no solution if b does not represent 0.

Accordingly, for any real numbers, a, b, c, d, subject to the three cited exceptions, one may perform the indicated operations:

Addition: $(a + bi) + (c + di) = ?$
Multiplication: $(a + bi)(c + di) = ?$
Involution: $(a + bi)^{c+di} = ?$
Subtraction: $(a + bi) - (c + di) = ?$
Division: $(a + bi) \div (c + di) = ?$
Evolution: $\sqrt[a+bi]{c + di} = ?$
Indexing: $\log_{a+bi}(c + di) = ?$

∾ CHALLENGES

1. Add $3 - 7i$ and $\frac{3}{4} + 19i$.

2. Subtract $\sqrt[3]{2} - \sqrt{3}i$ from $\sqrt{5} + \sqrt[3]{2}i$. (Give exact and approximate result.)

3. Multiply $5 + 12i$ by $5 + 12i$.

4. Divide $7 + 2i$ by $3 - i$. Divide 2 by $1 + i$.

5. Evaluate $(3 + 5i)^{1+i}$.

6. Evaluate $\sqrt[i]{2 + 3i}$.

7. Evaluate $\log_i i$. Evaluate $\log_{3+2i}(3 - 4i)$.

∾ SUPPLEMENTARY PROBLEMS ∾

Better the wise man than the strong,
For knowledge is stronger than bone and brawn.

S17.1. Obtain the sum of the following pairs of complex numbers:

    a. $A: 3 + 4i$, $B: 2 + 5i$ *e.* $A: -4 - 3i$, $B: 5 + 2i$
    b. $A: -5 + 6i$, $B: 4 - 2i$ *f.* $A: -2 - 3i$, $B: -3 - 2i$
    c. $A: 5 - 3i$, $B: 6 + 4i$ *g.* $A: 8 + 15i$, $B: 2 - 6i$
    d. $A: -1 - 3i$, $B: -3 - i$ *h.* $A: 1 - i$, $B: -1 - i$

S17.2. In Problem S17.1a to h represent by C, the sum. Then plot in the complex plane the points A, B, C, and 0: $0 + 0i$. Draw lines OA, OB, OC, AC, and BC. In each figure show why OC is a diagonal of a parallelogram.

S17.3. In each part of Problem S17.1 compute the two differences, $A - B$ and $B - A$, designating the differences as D and D'. Plot D and D' in each sketch of Problem S17.2. Identify the lines OD and OD' with the parallelogram in each individual sketch.

S17.4. Obtain the sum of the complex numbers, $A: 2 - 3i$, $B: 3 + i$, $C: 5 + 6i$, representing the sum by D. Plot these four points in the complex plane and the points representing the sums $A + B$, $A + C$, and $B + C$; draw the lines from 0 to each of these seven points. Finally draw the lines from points $A + B$, $A + C$, and $B + C$, to point D. From the diagram devise a graphical method of adding two or more complex numbers.

S17.5. Add graphically $A: -5 + 3i$, $B: 4 - 2i$, $C: 1 - 5i$, and $D: 2 - 7i$, plotting each successive sum, namely, $A + B$ as S_1, $S_1 + C = S_2$, $S_2 + D = S$. Repeat the addition in reverse order, as $D + C = S_1$, $S' + B = S_2'$, $S_2' + A = S$.

S17.6. Add graphically, as suggested in the previous problem, $A: 2 + i$; $B: -4 + i$; $C: 1 - 2i$; $D: 1 + 2i$.

S17.7. Obtain the product P for each pair A, B.

a. $A: 2 + i$, $B: 1 + 3i$ e. $A: 3 + 4i$, $B: 3 + 4i$

b. $A: 3 + 4i$, $B: 3i$ f. $A: 4 + 3i$, $B: 4 - 3i$

c. $A: 1 + 2i$, $B: -2 + 3i$ g. $A: 4 - 2i$, $B: 2 + i$

d. $A: -3 + 5i$, $B: 3 - i$ h. $A: -6 - 2i$, $B: -2 - 6i$

S17.8. The *absolute value* of a number is the actual distance from 0 to its location in the complex plane. Compute the absolute value of these numbers:

a. $3 + 4i$ e. $-15 - 8i$ i. $-8 + 15i$

b. -12 f. $+19$ j. $-23i$

c. $5i$ g. $2 + 3i$ k. $-2 + 5i$

d. $-5 + 12i$ h. $-39 - 52i$ l. $68 - 51i$

(Obtain decimal fractional approximations for the surds to the nearest 0.001.)

S17.9. In each part of Problem S17.7 calculate the absolute value of A, of B, and of P. How are these absolute values related in each set?

S17.10. If a, b, c, and d represent any four real numbers whatever then $a + bi$ and $c + di$ will represent any two complex numbers whatever. Recalling that the symbol for absolute value is a pair of vertical lines enclosing the number, prove that

$$|a + bi| \times |c + di| = |(a + bi)(c + di)|$$

Verify this relationship for:

a. $A: 3 + 4i$, $B: 5 - 12i$

b. $A: 4 + 5i$, $B: 10 - 8i$

c. $A: 3i$, $B: 4i$

d. $A: 13$, $B: 3i$

e. $A: 25$, $B: 35$

S17.11. The *angle* of a complex number is the angle, measured counterclockwise, from the line of positive real numbers to the line from 0 to the position of the complex number in the complex plane. Thus, the angle of the complex number $5 + 5i$ is $45°$, the angle of $3 - 3i$ is $315°$, the angle of all real positive numbers is $0°$, the angle of all real negative numbers is $180°$, the angle of all imaginary numbers ai is $90°$ if a is positive but $270°$ if a is negative. The angle of $7i$ is $90°$, the angle of $-7i$ is $270°$. Verify these statements from an actual sketch. Obtain the angle of the numbers: (*a*) $11 + 11i$, (*b*) $-7 + 7i$, (*c*) $19i$, (*d*) $-3 - 3i$.

S17.12. If r represents the absolute value of $a + bi$, sketch a figure and show that if A represents the angle of $a + bi$, then $\cos A = a/r$ and $\sin A = b/r$. Compute $\sin A$ and $\cos A$ for each of the following numbers, and by reference to the trigonometric tables, obtain as accurately as possible the angle of the numbers:

a.	$3 + 4i$	*d.*	$-12 - 5i$	*g.*	$24 + 7i$
b.	$-5 + 12i$	*e.*	$8 - 15i$	*h.*	$-24 + 7i$
c.	$4 + 3i$	*f.*	$8 + 15i$	*i.*	$-24 - 7i$

S17.13. Obtain the absolute value and angle of the following numbers. Then express the relationship that seems to exist between the angle of any number and the angle of a power of that number. Sketch the number and its powers in the complex plane.

a. A: $1 + 2i$, B: $(1 + 2i)^2$, C: $(1 + 2i)^3$, D: $(1 + 2i)^4$
b. A: $3 + 4i$, B: $(3 + 4i)^2$, C: $(3 + 4i)^3$, D: $(3 + 4i)^4$

S17.14. Compute the angles of the eight products of the eight pairs of complex numbers in Problem S17.7.

S17.15. Make a sketch indicating the position of two arbitrary numbers in the complex plane, marking them as A: $a + bi$ and B: $c + di$. Next draw a horizontal line through A and a vertical line through B, marking the intersection of these two lines as point C. It is to be noted that the length of the line segment AC is the absolute value of $a - c$; the length of BC is the absolute value of $b - d$. The distance between the points A and B may be computed by the Pythagorean theorem, as $\overline{AB}^2 = (a - b)^2 + (c - d)^2$.

a.   Calculate the distance between the eight pairs of points in Problem S17.1.
b.   Calculate the distance between the pairs of points in Problem S17.7.
Make the corresponding sketch for each of these 16 situations.

S17.16. In the complex plane sketch the points A: $2 + i$, B: $3 + 4i$, and their product P. Next draw the lines from 0 to each of these three points A, B, P. Also draw the line from 1 to A. The sketch should exhibit two triangles having vertices, or angles at 0, 1, A, and at 0, B, P. Compute the length of the three sides of each of these two triangles. Now compute the quotients of the lengths of pairs of corresponding sides, namely, OP/OA, $BP/1A$, $OB/O1$. If these three quotients are equal to one another the two triangles are *similar;* i.e., they are of same shape and have corresponding angles equal. Now compute the two corresponding angles at 0.

S17.17. Let A and B represent two points and point P their product in the complex plane. Draw the two triangles that have their vertices at 0, 1, A and 0, B, P. If numbers A, B, and P have absolute values a, b, r, then $ab = r$, or $b = r/a$, or $b/1 = r/a$. If A represents the number $p + iq$ and B represents

$s + it$, compute the distance from B to P, and the distance from 1 to A. Finally, show that $BP^2/1A^2 = b^2/1$, so that the triangles so formed must be similar for every arbitrary pair of numbers A and B and their product P. Therefore, the angle of the product of two numbers is equal to the *sum* of their angles.

S17.18. Verify the conclusion of the preceding problem with the 16 pairs of numbers listed in Problems S17.1 and S17.7 in this set of problems.

S17.19. Compute the absolute value and angle of i. Then write down immediately the values of i^2, i^3, and i^4. What is the angle of i^{13}?

S17.20. If r represents the absolute value of the number $a + bi$, then $r = \sqrt{a^2 + b^2}$, and $a + bi = r[a/r + (b/r)i] = r(\cos A + i \sin A)$, in which A represents the angle of $a + bi$. Therefore, $(a + bi)^n = r^n(\cos nA + i \sin nA)$. Now, by use of the trigonometric form of the following numbers obtain the indicated power; finally reconvert the required power back to the standard form, $a + bi$:

a. $(7 + 24i)^2$, $(7 + 24i)^3$, $(7 + 24i)^7$

b. $(1 + i)^n$, in which $n = 2, 3, 4, 5, 6, 7$, and 8, successively

c. $(1 + \frac{3}{2}i)^6$

d. $(3 + 4i)^n$, in which $n = 1, 2, 3, 4, 5$, and 6

S17.21. By reversing the rule for obtaining the nth power of a complex number, as stated in Problem S17.20, one may obtain an nth root of any complex number thus: Convert the number to its trigonometric form, then if $a + bi = r(\cos A + i \sin A)$, then $\sqrt[n]{a + bi} = \sqrt[n]{r}(\cos A/n + i \sin A/n)$. Since the sine and cosine of any angle are unchanged if the angle is increased by any multiples of 360°, the other $n - 1$ nth roots of $a + bi$ may be obtained by increasing the angle A/n by the $n - 1$ successive multiples of $360°/n$. Now obtain the n indicated roots of the complex numbers: (*a*) $\sqrt[3]{8i}$, (*b*) $\sqrt[3]{-1}$, (*c*) $\sqrt[4]{1}$, (*d*) $\sqrt[5]{1875 + 2500i}$.

S17.22. Since $\cos A + i \sin A = e^{iA}$ (Section 17.9), then $a + bi$ may also be written as re^{iA}, in which r is the absolute value and A is the angle of $a + bi$. The form re^{iA} is called the *exponential* form of $a + bi$. Express the numbers in exponential form: (*a*) $3 + 4i$, (*b*) $12 + 5i$, (*c*) $15 - 8i$, (*d*) $2 + 3i$, (*e*) i.

S17.23. Show that the number $e^{iA} = e^{i(A+2\pi)} = e^{i(A+2\pi n)}$ in which $n =$ any integer. (Recall that $360° = 2\pi$ rad.)

S17.24. Since $\cos A + i \sin A = e^{i(A+2\pi n)}$ then $\log_e (\cos A + i \sin A) = \log_e e^{i(A+2\pi n)} = i(A + 2\pi n) \times \log_e e = i(A + 2\pi n)$. Moreover, $\log_e (a + bi) = \log_e r(\cos A + i \sin A) = \log_e r + \log_e (\cos A + i \sin A) = \log_e r + i(A + 2\pi n)$. Obtain the natural logarithms (base e) of the numbers, indicating the unending set of logarithms of each: (*a*) $\log_e (4 + 3i)$, (*b*) $\log_e (-1)$, (*c*) $\log_e i$, (*d*) $\log_e 2$.

S17.25. Obtain the infinite set of common logarithms (base 10) of the following: (*a*) $\log 1$, (*b*) $\log 10$, (*c*) $\log (-3)$, (*d*) $\log \pi i$.

SUPPLEMENT ❦ SPECIAL TOPICS

HAMLET: There are more things in heaven and earth, Horatio, than are dreamt of in your philosophy. . . .

—Shakespeare, *Hamlet*, Act I, Scene 5.

S·1 ∽ A SUBTRACTION-ADDITION CURIO

Perform a subtraction by the following steps:

1. Write any three-digit natural number whose end digits are different.

2. Write the other three-digit number by reversing the order of the digits.

3. Subtract the smaller number from the larger number.

Without knowing the original number that was written, one may quote the *entire difference* if one knows only the *units digit* of the difference, for the middle digit is 9 and the sum of the end digits is also 9. To illustrate, select the three-digit number 724.

Step 1   724
Step 2   −427
Step 3   297   End digits $2 + 7 = 9$

To prove that this relationship is always present, let the digits of the larger number be a, b, c. To perform the subtraction, "borrowings" are necessary in the first two steps. For greater clarity the individual digits are enclosed in parentheses (). Recall that 1 in any digit's position is equal to 10 in the position to its right.

$(\ a - 1\ )$	$(10 + b - 1)$	$(\ 10 + c\ )$
$(\quad c\quad)$	$(\quad b\quad)$	$(\quad a\quad)$
$(a - 1 - c)$	$(\quad 9\quad)$	$(10 + c - a)$

Observe that the middle digit of the difference is 9 and that the sum of the end digits is also 9.

If no restriction is made on the digits of the original number and if the right digit of the difference is 0, all digits of the quotient are 0; if the right digit of the difference is 9, the entire difference is 99.

Perform an addition by the additional steps:

4. Now reverse the three digits of the difference obtained in Step 3. If the difference is 99, supply an initial 0 to make it 099.

5. Add the number obtained in Step 4 to the difference obtained in Step 3. The sum so obtained must always be 1,089 regardless of the original number selected. Continuing the illustrative example,

Step 3   297
Step 4   +792
Step 5   1089

Continuing the general proof, add

Difference, Step 3	$(a - 1 - c)$	(9)	$(10 + c - a)$
Reverse digits, Step 4	$(10 + c - a)$	(9)	$(a - 1 - c)$
	(9)	(18)	(9) = 1089

∽ CHALLENGES

1. Show that there are exactly 450 three-digit numbers that may be selected for minuend in Step 1; hence also 450 for subtrahend; only 9 may occur in Step 3; finally only one number occurs in the ultimate sum, namely, 1,089.

2. Adapt this subtraction-addition curio to numbers of base (*a*) 2, (*b*) 2, (*c*) 4, (*d*) 7, (*e*) 13. How many such numbers can occur in this subtraction-addition curio in Steps 1, 2, and 3?

3. Prove the curio for the arbitrary base (*b*).

4. Generalize this subtraction-addition curio by writing the two end digits so selected *m* times and the middle digit *n* times. Can you then tell the entire difference (and sum) if you know only the right end digit of the difference? For example, repeat *a* and *c* three times, *b* four times:

Step 1   5552222333
Step 2   −3332222555
Step 3   2219999778
Step 4   +8779999122
           10999998900

5. Re-solve Challenges 1, 2, 3 in light of the generalization in Challenge 4.

S·2 ∽ A LONG-DIVISION CURIO

Construct a divisor by the following steps:

1. Choose a three-digit natural number whose middle digit is 0 and whose end digits have a sum that is less than 10.

2. Multiply this three-digit number by 9.

Construct the corresponding dividend consisting of 11 digits as follows:

3. Let the two digits at the left end of the dividend be the same as the original left end digit selected in Step 1.

4. Let the two right end digits of the dividend be the same as the original right end digit selected in Step 1.

5. Let each of the seven middle digits of the dividend be the digit obtained by adding the end digits of Step 1.

Now perform without error the long division. The quotient so obtained must be 12345679, regardless of the numbers selected in Step 1. To illustrate these steps by an example:

Step 1   305
Step 2   2745
Step 3   33*********
Step 4   33*******55
Step 5   33888888855

```
              12345679
      2745 33888888855
           2745
            6438
            5490
             9488
             8235
            12538
            10980
             15588
             13725
              18638
              16470
               21685
               19215
                24705
                24705
```

Clarification of This Mystery: Note that $111{,}111{,}111 \div 9 = 12{,}345{,}679$. If the digits selected in Step 1 are a and b, and the sum $a + b = c$, then the dividend will be $9(a0b)$. Next consider the multiplication

$$\begin{array}{r} 111111111 \\ a0b \\ \hline bbbbbbbbb \\ aaaaaaaaa \\ \hline aacccccccbb \end{array}$$

which is equal to $(a0b) \times 9 \times 12345679$, since $9 \times 12345679 = 111111111$. Therefore, the required division, expressed in fraction form, becomes

$$\frac{aacccccccbb}{9 \times (a0b)} = \frac{(a0b) \times 9 \times 12345679}{9 \times (a0b)}$$

Cancelling the factors 9 and $a0b$, one obtains the quotient 12,345,679.

Challenges

1. Make a list of the 45 three-digit numbers that are possible for Step 1.
2. Generalize this long-division curio in the following way. Construct a *divisor* as follows:
   - *a.* Form a natural number consisting of $3 + 2n$ digits, whose end digits a and b have a sum c which is less than 10 and whose intermediate $1 + 2n$ digits are all 0s.
   - *b.* Multiply this $(3 + 2n)$-digit number, $a000 \cdots 0b$ by 9.
   - *c.* Construct the *dividend* as follows: Form an 11-digit number selected in Step 1, namely, a and b and their sum, c. Thus: *aa ccc cccc bb*. Now insert n zeros between these 10 pairs of consecutive digits. The *quotient* must then consist of n + one 1s, 2s, 3s, 4s, 5s, 6s, 7s, n 8s, and one 9. To illustrate, let $a = 3$, $b = 5$, $n = 2$; then $c = 8$.

     Divisor: $9 \times 3000005 = 27000045$
     Dividend: 3003008008008008008008008005005
     Quotient: 11122233344455566677789

     Verify this division.
3. Prove that this generalization is valid by applying the same reasoning as previously used. That is, begin by forming a natural number consisting of nine 1s with n zeros inserted between each pair of consecutive 1s; then divide this number by 9, etc.
4. Describe this curio and its generalization for each possible base less than 10 for expressing the natural numbers.

S·3 Obtaining mentally the kth powers of the natural numbers from 1 to n^k

This may be accomplished by performing $k - 1$ sets of mental additions.

1. Obtain the consecutive square numbers from 1 to n^2. For example, let $n = 13$; i.e., obtain 1, 4, 9, 16, as far as 13^2.

   a. Write the series of 26 consecutive natural numbers from 1 to 26.

        1 2 3 4 5 6 7 8 9 10 11 12 13 14 15 16 17 18 19 20 21 22
   23 24 25 26

   b. Strike out every second number, the multiples of 2. This may be indicated by underlining the alternate numbers in the foregoing series of natural numbers.

   c. Write the 13 sums of the remaining numbers consecutively, beginning with 1; thus

        $1, 1 + 3 = 4, 4 + 5 = 9, 9 + 7 = 16, 16 + 9 = 25, 25 + 11 = 36 \ldots$

   Thus

        1 4 9 16 25 36 49 64 81 100 121 144 169

   which is the required series of square numbers.

2. Obtain the consecutive cube numbers from 1 to n^3.

   a. Write the series of natural numbers from 1 to $3 \times n$.
   b. Cancel from this list every *third* number.
   c. Add consecutively the remaining numbers from 1, listing the sums in order.
   d. Cancel from this list every *second* number.
   e. Add consecutively the remaining numbers from 1. These are the required cube numbers.

   In the successive steps the number cancellations are indicated. Obtain the cubes from $1^3 = 1$ to 9^3. Write the series of natural numbers to 3×9, cancelling every third number:

        1 2 3 4 5 6 7 8 9 10 11 12 13 14 15 16 17 18 19 20 21 22
   23 24 25 26 27

   Adding consecutively, 1, $1 + 2 = 3$, $3 + 4 = 7$, . . . , and cancelling every second number, obtain:

        1 3 7 12 19 27 37 48 61 75 91 108 127 147 169 192 217 243

   Adding consecutively again, from 1; 1, $1 + 7 = 8$, $8 + 19 = 27$, . . . , one obtains:

        1 8 27 64 125 216 343 512 729

   These numbers are the required nine cube numbers.

3. To obtain the consecutive set of fourth powers of natural numbers from 1 to n^4, one sets forth the list of natural numbers from 1 to $4 \times n$:

   a. One cancels out every *fourth* number from the array of natural numbers.

   b. One adds consecutively from 1 the remaining numbers in the set.

   c. One then cancels out every *third* number from this latest set.

   d. One then adds consecutively from 1 the remaining numbers of the last set.

   e. One then cancels out every *second* number from the set.

   f. One then adds consecutively from 1 the remaining numbers in the set.

These sums are the desired fourth powers. Thus to obtain the first fourth powers of the natural numbers to 7^4:

> 1 2 3 ~~4~~ 5 6 7 ~~8~~ 9 10 11 ~~12~~ 13 14 15 ~~16~~ 17 18 19 ~~20~~ 21 22 23 ~~24~~ 25 26 27 ~~28~~
>
> 1 3 ~~6~~ 11 17 ~~24~~ 33 43 ~~54~~ 67 81 ~~99~~ 113 131 ~~150~~ 171 193 ~~216~~ 241 267 ~~294~~
>
> 1 ~~4~~ 15 ~~32~~ 65 ~~108~~ 175 ~~256~~ 369 ~~500~~ 671 ~~864~~ 1105 ~~1370~~
>
> 1   16   81   256   625   1296   2401

These seven numbers are the required fourth powers.

4. The general procedure should now be evident to obtain k consecutive nth powers of the natural numbers from 1 to k^n.

   a. One must set forth the series of nk natural numbers.

   b. One cancels out every kth number from the set beginning with k itself.

   c. One then adds consecutively from 1 the surviving numbers in the set.

   d. One then cancels out every $(k-1)$th number from the list of sums.

   e. One then adds consecutively from 1 the surviving numbers from the latest set.

   f. One then cancels out every $(k-2)d$ number from the list of sums.

Continuing with the alternating cancellations and additions, one finally obtains the set of required k^nth powers from 1 to k^n.

For a proof of the validity of this procedure for all powers of the natural numbers, the reader is referred to the author's proof in an article entitled "Ten Mathematical Refreshments," in *The Mathematics Teacher*, 63(2):102–108, 1965. This journal is available in university libraries.

❧ CHALLENGE

Obtain the seventh powers of the first five natural numbers by the foregoing procedure.

S·4 ～ Sₜₐₙᴅₐᵣᴅ ᴍᴀɢɪᴄ sϙᴜᴀʀᴇs ᴏғ ᴏʀᴅᴇʀ ᴛʜʀᴇᴇ

A magic square of order three is an arrangement of nine numbers represented by
$a, b, c, d, e, f, g, h, k$ in a square array, as

a	b	c
d	e	f
g	h	k

so that the three numbers in the rows, columns, and diagonals, yield the same
sum:

Rows	*Columns*	*Diagonals*
$a + b + c = S$	$a + d + g = S$	$a + e + k = S$
$d + e + f = S$	$b + e + h = S$	$c + e + g = S$
$g + h + k = S$	$e + f + k = S$	

If the nine numbers $a, b, c, d, e, f, g, h, k$ are the first nine natural numbers, the
square so formed is called a *standard magic square of order three*. Such a standard
magic square is easily constructed from the following considerations: (1) The
sum S must be 15; (2) the center number e must be 5; (3) the corner numbers
$a, c, g,$ and k must be *even* numbers. These three facts are proved as follows:

1. Note that the sum of all nine numbers is 45; i.e., $1 + 2 + 3 + 4 + 5 +$
   $6 + 7 + 8 + 9 = 45$. Note that the three rows contain all nine numbers:
   $(a + b + c) + (d + e + f) + (g + h + k)$, or $S + S + S = 45$, since
   each row has an individual sum of S. Thus, $3S = 45$, whence $S = 15$.

2. Selecting the middle column and the two diagonals, one has $(a + e + k) +$
   $(b + e + h) + (c + e + g) = S + S + S = 15 + 15 + 15 = 45$.
   Rearranging these nine numbers, one has $(a + b + c) + (g + h + k) +$
   $(e + e + e) = 45$, or $15 + 15 + 3e = 45$, or $30 + 3e = 45$, or $3e = 45 -$
   30, or $3e = 15$, or $e = 5$.

3. Since S must be 15, one should find all sets of three of these nine numbers
   that have this sum 15. They are found to be $(1 + 5 + 9)$, $(1 + 6 + 8)$,
   $(2 + 4 + 9)$, $(2 + 5 + 8)$, $(2 + 6 + 7)$, $(3 + 4 + 8)$, $(3 + 5 + 7)$,
   $(4 + 5 + 6)$.

Now the corner numbers, namely, $a, c, g,$ and k must occur in three of these
sets, since each corner number must be in one row, one column, and one
diagonal. Noting the eight listed sets of three numbers having a sum 15, one
observes that 5 occurs in *four* sets, as is necessary as the center number e lies in

both diagonals and in the middle row and the middle column. Furthermore, each of the even numbers 2, 4, 6, and 8 occurs in three of these eight sets; each of the odd numbers 1, 3, 7, and 9 occurs in only two sets each. Therefore, the *even* numbers must lie in the corners.

Alternately, after establishing the facts that the sum $S = 15$, and the center number of the square is 5, the placement of the other numbers may be easily determined as follows: If an *odd* number occurs in a corner, then the *opposite* corner must be odd. If a third corner is *odd*, then all other spaces must contain *odd* numbers (i.e., all nine consecutive natural numbers must be odd) which is impossible. If a third corner is *even*, then all other spaces must be *even* numbers (i.e., six of the natural numbers, 1 to 9 inclusive, must be even) which is also impossible.

If 0 and E indicate an odd and an even natural number, respectively, and the numbers 1, 2, 3, 4, 5, 6, 7, 8 indicate the order of consideration of the nature of the number (odd or even), since the sums must each be *odd*, 15, the two corresponding arrays would appear thus, as the center number 5 is *odd:*

01	05	03
06	0	07
04	08	02

01	E5	E3
E6	0	E7
E4	E8	02

Therefore, if a standard magic square of order three does exist, its corner numbers must be *even* natural numbers.

Indeed, these considerations do yield valid magic squares as follows: Place the 5 in the center of the square; place any even number in the upper left corner (this can be done in four different ways, using the 2 or 4 or 6 or 8). The lower left corner must be filled with the even number that makes the diagonal have the sum 15; it must be respectively 8 or 6 or 4 or 2. The other two corners, upper right and lower left, can now be filled in with the two remaining even numbers in either of two ways. Then the remaining empty squares may be filled in appropriately and uniquely with the other numbers. Thus, it is possible to make 4 × 2 standard magic squares of order three.

a.

2	9	4
7	5	3
6	1	8

b.

2	7	6
9	5	1
4	3	8

c.

8	3	4
1	5	9
6	7	2

d.

8	1	6
3	5	7
4	9	2

6	7	2
1	5	9
8	3	4

e.

6	1	8
7	5	3
2	9	4

f.

4	9	2
3	5	7
8	1	6

g.

4	3	8
9	5	1
2	7	6

h.

These eight standard magic squares are not really different; each one is merely the same as one particular one when turned into another position. Thus b, c, d, e, f, g, h are obtained, respectively, by turning a as follows:

Turn a about the diagonal $2 - 5 - 8$ to obtain b
Turn a about diagonal $4 - 5 - 6$ to obtain c
Turn a about the row $7 - 5 - 3$ to obtain f
Turn a about the column $9 - 5 - 1$ to obtain g
Rotate a clockwise through $90°$ to obtain e
Rotate a clockwise through $180°$ to obtain d
Rotate a clockwise through $270°$ to obtain h

Accordingly, there is only one essential, distinct standard magic square of order three, which may be represented by one of these eight squares.

S·5 ❧ Nonstandard magic squares of order three

If the nine symbols a, b, c, d, e, f, g, h, k do not necessarily represent the natural numbers 1, 2, 3, 4, 5, 6, 7, 8, 9, and if the square so formed from them has the same sum S for the three rows, three columns, and two diagonals, the square is still called a magic square. Such a square also has special relations among the various numbers comprising it, as noted in the following premises:

1. If $a + b + c + d + e + f + g + h + k = T$, then the common sum of the three numbers in the rows, columns, and diagonals, is $\frac{1}{3}T$, or S.

2. The number e in the center of the square is equal to $\frac{1}{3}S$.

3. The number e is equal to half the sum of the other two numbers in the same row, column, or diagonal.

4. Any corner number is equal to half the sum of the two numbers in the opposite row and column; thus, in the standard magic square, such as the first one marked by (a): $2 = \frac{1}{2}(1 + 3)$; $4 = \frac{1}{2}(7 + 1)$; $6 = \frac{1}{2}(9 + 3)$; $8 = \frac{1}{2}(7 + 9)$. Premises 1 and 2 are proved in the same way for nonstandard as for the standard magic square, by using $3S$ instead of $4S$.

To prove Premise 3, let p and q represent the other two numbers in the same row, column, or diagonal with the e. Then $e + p + q = S$; but $e = \frac{1}{3}S$.

Then $\frac{1}{3}S + (p + q) = S$, or $(p + q) = S - \frac{1}{3}S$, or $p + q = \frac{2}{3}S$. Thus, $e = \frac{1}{2}(p + q)$.

One proves that $a = \frac{1}{2}(h + f)$ as follows: Note that $2e = c + g$, shown in Premise 3 above. Since $S = 3e$, $g + h + k = 3e$ and $c + f + k = 3e$; then $6e = 2a + 2e + 2k$, twice the numbers in a diagonal. Adding, $(8e + c + g + 2k) + f + h = (8e + c + g + 2k) + 2a$, or $f + h = 2a$, or $a = \frac{1}{2}(f + h)$.

It can be shown that *any three numbers* may be inserted in any of the nine spaces of the magic suqare, subject only to Premises 3 and 4, and the magic squares can then be completed uniquely. To illustrate, let the numbers 3, 5, and 9 be inserted as follows:

	5	
3		
	9	

That is, $b = 5$, $d = 3$, and $h = 9$. Then $k = \frac{1}{2}(3 + 5) = 4$, $e = \frac{1}{2}(5 + 9) = 7$, and $S = 21$. Thus one has

	5	
3	7	
	9	4

Now the remaining missing numbers are readily and uniquely found:

$$a = 21 - (7 + 4) = 10$$
$$c = \frac{1}{2}(9 + 3) = 6$$
$$f = 21 - (6 + 4) = 11$$
$$g = \frac{1}{2}(5 + 11) = 8$$

yielding the square

10	5	6
3	7	11
8	9	4

To avoid fractions in completing a square from any three given number insertions, one should insert *even* integers in the corners and *odd* integers in the other five spaces, or vice versa, namely, *odd* numbers in the corners and *even* numbers in the other five spaces.

From three independent insertions (i.e., using numbers that do not violate Premises 3 and 4 above), one can finish the magic square uniquely. This statement is proved by the following considerations. Note the *eight* linear equations contain 10 unknowns, a, b, c, d, e, f, g, h, k, S.

Eq. (1) $a + b + c = S$ Eq. (4) $a + d + g = S$ Eq. (7) $a + e + k = S$
Eq. (2) $d + e + f = S$ Eq. (5) $b + e + h = S$ Eq. (8) $c + e + g = S$
Eq. (3) $g + h + k = S$ Eq. (6) $c + f + k = S$

Only five of the first six equations are independent; i.e., any one is a consequence of the other five. Thus the sum of the three equations in either set (1) (2) (3), or (4) (5) (6), diminished by the sum of any two equations of the other set, (4) (5) (6) or (1) (2) (3), respectively, yields the equation not used in the first six equations. For example, Equations $(1) + (2) + (3) - (4) - (5) = (6)$, which may readily be verified. That Equations (7) and (8) are entirely independent of the other equations follows from the fact that in the following square the diagonal numbers have different sums from the sum of row and column numbers

3	5	7
4	9	2
8	1	6

Observe that the sum of each of the rows and columns is 15, but the sum of the diagonals $7 + 9 + 8 = 24$ and $3 + 9 + 6 = 18$ is not 15.

Accordingly, one has *seven* independent linear equations involving 10 unknowns. To evaluate all 10 of them one must know any *three* of them, subject to Premises 3 and 4. Of course one may need fractional or negative numbers to complete a magic square from three given independent insertions made at random.

⟿ CHALLENGES

1. Complete the magic squares of order three.

2	3	
1		

3		1
		2

3	5	
4		

	−3	
	4	2

2.   Obtain the six independent magic squares of order three containing the numbers 8, 9, and having 12 as the sum of the rows, diagonals, and columns.

S·6 ∞ Standard magic squares of order four

It has been proved that there are 880 standard magic squares of order four; i.e., that none of these can be obtained from any others by rotating or turning about an axis.   However, 48 of these standard magic squares have quite fascinating properties, which are now presented.   Let $a, b, c, d, e, f, g, h, k, l, m, n, p, q, r, t$ represent the first 16 natural numbers, 1, 2, 3, 4, 5, 6, 7, 8, 9, 10, 11, 12, 13, 14, 15, 16, and let them be arranged in a square array

a	b	c	d
e	f	g	h
k	l	m	n
p	q	r	t

so that the four rows, the four columns, and the *eight* broken and straight diagonals have the same sum S.   Such an array is called a pandiagonal standard magic square of order four.   This sum S must be one-fourth the sum of all 16 natural numbers from 1 to 16, inclusive, which can readily be found to be 34.

	Row		*Columns*		*Diagonals*
1.	$a + b + c + d = S$	5.	$a + e + k + p = S$	9.	$a + f + m + t = S$
2.	$e + f + g + h = S$	6.	$b + f + l + q = S$	10.	$b + g + n + p = S$
3.	$k + l + m + n = S$	7.	$c + g + m + r = S$	11.	$c + h + k + q = S$
4.	$p + q + r + t = S$	8.	$d + h + n + t = S$	12.	$d + e + l + r = S$
				13.	$d + g + l + p = S$
				14.	$c + f + k + t = S$
				15.	$b + e + n + r = S$
				16.	$a + h + m + q = S$

Besides these 16 sets of four numbers totaling 34, there are many others:

Group 1:   Any set of four numbers forming a small square, as (a, b, e, f) or (g, h, m, n) yield the same sum, 34.   There are 16 such small squares.

Group 2:   The four corner numbers of three by three squares, as (a, c, k, m) or (f, h, q, t) yield this sum, 34.   There are four such sets.   Each pair of opposite corner numbers of these squares has a sum of 17.

Group 3: The four broken rows, as (a, b, m, n); the four broken rows, as (a, l, m, d).

Group 4: The four broken columns, as (a, e, m, r); the four broken columns, as (a, g, m, p).

These properties can be proved by combining judiciously some of the given 16 equations presented above to define the pandiagonal magic square. Thus Equations $(1) + (2) + (5) + (6) - (11) - (13)$ yield $2(a + b + e + f) = 2S$, or $a + b + e + f = S$. Similarly, all other sets of Group 1 can be proved.

Again, Equations $(1) + (3) + (5) + (7) - (13) - (15)$ yield $2(a + c + k + m) = 2S$, or $a + c + k + m = S$. The other three sets of Group 2 are similarly treated. Likewise $(a + f + m + t) + (a + h + m + q) - (f + h + q + t) = S$, which yields $2a + 2m = S$, or $a + m = \frac{1}{2}S$.

The ensuing illustration shows how five independent insertions in the magic square of order four may allow unique completion of the square. That is,

1	8	10	d
e	f	5	h
k	l	16	n
p	q	r	t

$a = 1$, $b = 8$, $c = 10$, $g = 5$, and $m = 16$. Since $a + m = \frac{1}{2}S$, then $\frac{1}{2}S = 1 + 16$; $S = 34$. Then $d = 34 - (1 + 8 + 10) = 15$; $k = 17 - 10 = 7$; $n = 17 - 8 = 9$; $l = 17 - 15 = 2$; $p = 17 - 5 = 12$. Then in the first column, $e = 34 - (1 + 7 + 12) = 14$; $f = 34 - (1 + 8 + 14) = 11$; $h = 34 - (14 + 11 + 5) = 4$; $q = 17 - 4 = 13$; $r = 17 - 14 = 3$; $t = 17 - 11 = 6$. Thus, the finished square appears as

1	8	10	15
14	11	5	4
7	2	16	9
12	13	3	6

It is clear that the square retains all its properties if the top row is placed under the other three rows, and this shift may be repeated so that any row can be shifted into any other row's position. Likewise the columns may be shifted, the left column placed at the right of the right column, repeatedly; these two shifts allow any number to be moved into any column and row at pleasure. Thus this square gives rise to 15 other fundamental (standard) pandiagonal magic squares of fourth order. Two other basic standard pandiagonal magic squares exist, which the reader is urged to complete. If done correctly, the natural numbers from 1 to 16 will appear in the result.

1	8		
	10	5	
		16	

1	8		
	10		
	5	16	

These three basic pandiagonal magic squares yield altogether 48 other ones by shifting their rows and columns appropriately. Besides these 48 pandiagonal standard magic squares of order four, there are 832 ordinary standard magic squares of order four (i.e., those whose *broken* diagonals do not yield the sum 34). As these are tedious to list and do not have the striking properties of the pandiagonal squares, they are omitted from discussion here.

ᕷ CHALLENGES

1. Complete the first two nonstandard pandiagonal magic squares of order four.

4	13		
	11	9	
		16	

	7	13	
25	16		
			10

12			6
	x	8	
		y	

2. Complete the third magic square, replacing x, y as follows:

   a. Let $x = 1, y = 16$

   b. Let $x = 1, y = 17$

   c. Let $x = 5, y = 23$

3. Make an accurate statement regarding the number of insertions required to determine uniquely a pandiagonal magic square of order four.

S·7 ~ PANDIAGONAL MAGIC SQUARES OF ORDER FIVE

There are 14,400 such magic squares of order five; i.e., squares whose five rows, five columns, and ten diagonals (straight and broken) yield the same sum, namely, $\frac{1}{5}(1 + 2 + 3 + 4 + 5 + 6 + 7 + 8 + 9 + 10 + 11 + 12 + 13 + 14 + 15 + 16 + 17 + 18 + 19 + 20 + 21 + 22 + 23 + 24 + 25)$, or 65. Such squares may be constructed quite easily as follows:

a	b	c	d	e
p	s	q	t	r
d	e	a	b	c
q	t	r	p	s
b	c	d	e	a
r	p	s	q	t
e	a	b	c	d
s	q	t	r	p
c	d	e	a	b
t	r	p	s	q

Write in correct order the letters a, b, c, d, e in top row. In each ensuing row write these letters in order beginning with a under c; when end of a row is reached, continue at the left end. Note that each row, each column, and each of the ten diagonals contains the five letters a, b, c, d, e. Write in correct order the letters p, q, r, s, t in the left column. In each ensuing column to the right, write these letters in order, beginning with p to the right of r. When the bottom of a column is reached, continue at the top. Note again that each row, each column, and each of the ten diagonals contains all five letters, p, q, r, s, t. Thus each of the twenty sets of five spaces, namely, the five rows, the five columns, and the ten diagonals contains the ten letters $a\ b\ c\ d\ e\ p\ q\ r\ s\ t$.

Furthermore, in the 25 spaces of the square there are 25 sets of small squares in each of the patterns

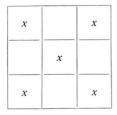

and

that contain all 10 of these letters. These two symmetric patterns may be small, involving adjoining spaces, or large, involving alternate spaces. An example of each of these four patterns includes, respectively, the spaces

occupied by

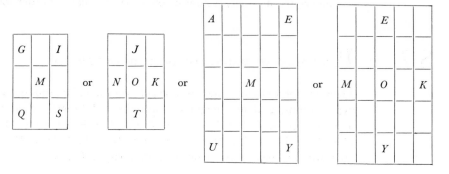

in the magic square represented by

A	B	C	D	E
F	G	H	I	J
K	L	M	N	O
P	Q	R	S	T
U	V	W	X	Y

To construct one of these amazing magic squares, one should assign the numbers 1, 2, 3, 4, 5 in any any one of the 120 different ways to the letters a, b, c, d, e; for example, one might let $a = 4, b = 3, c = 1, d = 2$, and $e = 5$. Next assign the five numbers 0, 5, 10, 15, and 20 in any one of the 120 possible ways to the letters p, q, r, s, and t. For example, one may let $p = 10, q = 20, r = 5, s = 15$, and $t = 0$. Thus in each of the 25 spaces of the large square, the number values of the letters are to be added. The upper-left space con-

taining the letters $\begin{array}{c} a \\ p \end{array}$ should be given the number 14, since $a = 4$ and $p = 10$;

likewise the next space at the top left containing the letters $\begin{array}{c} b \\ s \end{array}$ should be given

the number 18, since $b = 3$ and $s = 15$. Continuing throughout the large square one finally obtains the desired magic squares of order five.

14	18	21	2	10
22	5	9	13	16
8	11	17	25	4
20	24	3	6	12
1	7	15	19	23

As there are 120 different ways of assigning the five number values 1, 2, 3, 4, 5 to the letters a, b, c, d, e, and also 120 different ways of assigning the five numbers 0, 5, 10, 15, 20 to the letters p, q, r, s, t, there are altogether 120 × 120, or 14,400 different pandiagonal standard magic squares of order five. The pandiagonal squares obtained by shifting the rows from top to bottom, repeatedly, or the columns from left to right, repeatedly, are already included among the 14,400 basic squares so enumerated. To complete the set of numbers for a particular pattern of five numbers, say

	x	
x	x	x
	x	

or

	17	
24	3	6
	15	

(which has 65 for sum) or

	12	
19	23	1
	10	

where the pattern extends beyond the boundary of the magic square, one merely transfers the opposite row or column appropriately to make the completion possible. As there are twenty-five of each of these four basic patterns of five numbers having the sum 65, besides the five rows, five columns, and ten broken and straight diagonals, there are one hundred twenty such sets of five numbers in each pandiagonal standard magic square of order five. The number of standard (nonpandiagonal) magic squares is unknown at present, but it is at least 15,000,000. As their properties are not so striking as those of the pandiagonal squares, they are not considered here.

Nine independent random numbers inserted in nine spaces of the square determine completely and uniquely a pandiagonal magic square of order five. However, one must not fill in two different basic patterns to have different sums, for then the construction would not be possible. For example, one may fill in any two adjoining rows with the nine numbers, leaving one of them empty, and then by use of the smaller patterns such as 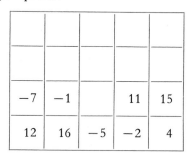 and

compute the numbers for the adjoining row, then the next row, and so on until the square is completed.

∾ CHALLENGES

1. Construct the pandiagonal magic square of order five by using the number values: $a = 5$, $b = 4$, $c = 3$, $d = 2$, $e = 1$, and $p = 0$, $q = 5$, $r = 10$, $s = 15$, $t = 20$.

2. Complete the following pandiagonal magic squares:

			22	14
7		11		18
19	6	25		2

	−7	−1		11	15
12	16	−5	−2	4	

S·8 ∾ A SECOND FUNDAMENTAL PROPERTY OF FRACTIONS

The fundamental property of fractions asserts that the value of a fraction remains unchanged if the numerator and denominator are multiplied or divided by the same number.   Now what happens to the value of a fraction if the numerator and denominator are positive integers and are increased or diminished by the same number?

A proper fraction increases in value if the same positive number is added to the numerator and to the denominator; an improper fraction is thereby decreased in value.   A proper fraction decreases in value if the same positive number is subtracted from the numerator and the denominator; an improper fraction is thereby increased in value.

Thus, $\dfrac{3 + 2}{7 + 2}$, or $\frac{5}{9}$, is larger than the original fraction, $\frac{3}{7}$; $\dfrac{7 + 3}{5 + 3}$, or $\frac{10}{8} = \frac{5}{4}$, is smaller than the original fraction $\frac{7}{5}$.

The reason for the foregoing situations is clear if one notes that adding the same number to the numerator and denominator is equivalent to the procedure of obtaining a fraction between the given fraction and 1, which may be written as $\frac{2}{2}$ or $\frac{3}{3}$ for the above two illustrations.

∾ CHALLENGES

1. Obtain an improper fraction smaller than $\frac{17}{16}$ having the denominator 20.

2. What can be stated about the successive differences of consecutive fractions in the sets?
   a. $\frac{3}{8}, \frac{4}{9}, \frac{5}{10}, \frac{6}{11}, \frac{7}{12}, \frac{8}{13} \cdots$
   b. $\frac{8}{3}, \frac{9}{4}, \frac{10}{5}, \frac{11}{6}, \frac{12}{7}, \frac{13}{8} \cdots$

S·9 ∾ THE DYADIC OR BINARY SYSTEM OF REPRESENTING NATURAL NUMBERS

This scheme of representing the natural numbers uses only *two* symbols, the 0 and the 1, for representing the natural numbers instead of the *ten* symbols 0, 1, 2, 3, 4, 5, 6, 7, 8, and 9 as used in the familiar decimal system. The "place value" property assigns specific values to the digit 1, according to its position in the expression for the particular natural number. The first 40 representations are listed:

1	1011	10101	11111
10	1100	10110	100000
11	1101	10111	100001
100	1110	11000	100010
101	1111	11001	100011
110	10000	11010	100100
111	10001	11011	100101
1000	10010	11100	100110
1001	10011	11101	100111
1010	10100	11110	101000

The 1s followed by 0s represent powers of 2: $10 = 2$, $100 = 2^2$, $1,000 = 2^3$, $10,000 = 2^4$, $100,000 = 2^5$, . . . , the *number* of 0s indicating the specific power of 2. Furthermore, the position of a 1 in a binary representation denotes the particular power of 2 so desired. For example, 10111010100 represents $2^{10} + 2^8 + 2^7 + 2^6 + 2^4 + 2^2 = 1,024 + 256 + 128 + 64 + 16 + 4 = 1,492$. Accordingly, to convert a number from the familiar decimal representation to the binary representation, one must obtain the necessary powers of 2 whose sum is equal to the number. This is done by repeatedly dividing by 2; the remainder at any stage denotes the power of 2 required for that stage. To convert the decimal from 1,492 to the binary form:

```
2 |1492
  2 |746      + 0 remainder
    2 |373    + 0 remainder
      2 |186  + 1 remainder, denoting 2²
        2 |93 + 0 remainder
          2 |46   + 1 remainder, denoting 2⁴
            2 |23 + 0 remainder
              2 |11   + 1 remainder, denoting 2⁶
                2 |5  + 1 remainder, denoting 2⁷
                  2 |2 + 1 remainder, denoting 2⁸
                    1  + 0 remainder
```

The final quotient, 1, denotes 2^{10}. The required binary form consists of the 1 of the final quotient, followed on the right by the series of remainders in the reverse order of obtaining them, namely here 10111010100.

To convert from a binary form to the corresponding decimal form one may add the specific powers of 2 that the positions of the 1s represent, or one may reverse the division procedure by repeatedly doubling and adding, beginning with the final 1. Thus, $2 \times 1 = 2$; $2 \times 2 = 4$, $4 + 1 = 5$; $2 \times 5 = 10$, $10 + 1 = 11$; $2 \times 11 = 22$, $22 + 1 = 23$; $2 \times 23 = 46$; $2 \times 46 = 92$, $92 + 1 = 93$; $2 \times 93 = 186$; $2 \times 186 = 392$, $392 + 1 = 393$; $2 \times 393 = 746$; $2 \times 746 = 1,492$.

∾ CHALLENGES

1. Convert the following decimal forms to binary forms of natural numbers:

   a. 63   *d.* 375   *g.* 1,588
   b. 64   *e.* 257   *h.* 1,967
   c. 65   *f.* 999   *i.* 4,096

2. Convert the binary form for the following memorable dates to decimal form:

   a. 11011110000   *c.* 10010111111
   b. 11001010100   *d.* 1011110001 (B.C.)

3. Show that $2^n + 1$ is never divisible by $2^m - 1$, if m and n are any natural numbers subject to the single restriction that m exceeds 2. (*Hint:* Express these two numbers in binary form; thus $2^n + 1 = 100 \cdots 001$, containing $n - 1$ 0s between the two 1s; for example, $2^3 + 1 = 1001$, noting two 0s. $2^m - 1 = 11 \cdots 11$, containing m 1s and no 0s; for example, $2^2 - 1 = 11$; $2^3 - 1 = 111$. Then attempt the long division of these binary forms and observe that the successive remainders, a single 1, prevent exact division.)

4. Using the same scheme as that suggested in the preceding challenge, show that $A^n + 1$ is never divisible by $A^m - 1$, if A denotes any natural number greater than 1 and m is greater than 2. (*Hint:* Express the numbers $A^n + 1$ and $A^m - 1$ in a system of base A. Let k denote the digit that represents the natural number $A - 1$.)

S·10 ∾ IDENTIFYING THE SECRET NUMBER

A	B	C	D	E	F
32	16	8	4	2	1
33	17	9	5	3	3
34	18	10	6	6	5
35	19	11	7	7	7
36	20	12	12	10	9
37	21	13	13	11	11
38	22	14	14	14	13
39	23	15	15	15	15
40	24	24	20	18	17
41	25	25	21	19	19
42	26	26	22	22	21
43	27	27	23	23	23
44	28	28	28	26	25
45	29	29	29	27	27
46	30	30	30	30	29
47	31	31	31	31	31
48	48	40	36	34	33
49	49	41	37	35	35
50	50	42	38	38	37
51	51	43	39	39	39
52	52	44	44	42	41
53	53	45	45	43	43
54	54	46	46	46	45
55	55	47	47	47	47
56	56	56	52	50	49
57	57	57	53	51	51
58	58	58	54	54	53
59	59	59	55	55	55
60	60	60	60	58	57
61	61	61	61	59	59
62	62	62	62	62	61
63	63	63	63	63	63

If one knows the columns that contain the secret number, one may identify it by adding the numbers at the top of those columns. Thus, if a person states that his age occurs in the columns headed by B, D, and F, one may tell him that his age is 21, as the sum of the top numbers in these columns, namely, 16, 4, and 1, is 21.

Such tables may be constructed as follows, by use of binary representation of the natural numbers, replacing each 1 in the representation by the natural number it denotes. For the first 7 numbers, keeping the digits in vertical columns, one would have:

```
        1           1
    1   0       2   0
    1   1       3   3
1   0   0   4   0   0
1   0   1   5   0   5
1   1   0   6   6   0
1   1   1   7   7   7
```

To make the table more compact one may omit the unnecessary 0s and move the remaining numbers upward as far as possible in the columns. Then one may mark the columns with letters A, B, C, etc., to identify them.

A	B	C
4	2	1
5	3	3
6	6	5
7	7	7

This small table enables one to identify any number from 1 to 7, inclusive, if one knows which columns contain it. The larger table with six columns enables one to identify numbers as far as 63.

CHALLENGES

1. Noting that the table will be completely rectangular, as in the two special tables appearing above, if the numbers extend as far as $2^n - 1$, how many columns and rows would be needed to enlarge the table as far as 255?

2. By examining the way the numbers proceed down the various columns can you quickly make such a table without referring to the binary numbers? Then extend quickly the larger table as far as 127.

S·11 THE RUSSIAN PEASANT'S METHOD OF MULTIPLYING NATURAL NUMBERS

This procedure enables one to perform the multiplication of natural numbers merely by repeatedly dividing by 2, by repeatedly multiplying by 2, and by an addition.

Placing the multiplier and the multiplicand on the same line, one repeatedly *divides the multiplier* and the ensuing quotients by 2, ignoring remainders of 1 that may occur, while repeatedly *multiplying the multiplicand* and the ensuing products by 2, keeping the successive quotients and products on the same line in parallel columns. Finally one adds those numbers in the multiplicand column that adjoin odd numbers in the multiplier column; the sum so obtained is the required product of the original multiplicand and multiplier. To illustrate, multiply 28 by 35, as follows:

Multiplier		*Multiplicand*
35	Odd	28*
17	Odd	56*
8		112
4		224
2		448
1	Odd	896*
		980

980   Sum of numbers marked by * which adjoin odd numbers in multiplier column

To demonstrate that this procedure must yield the correct product, one may observe that repeated division by 2 is the method of converting the multiplier to the binary form; even quotients produce 0s, odd quotients produce remainder 1, and consequently 1s in the binary form:

2 |35   Odd, yields remainder 1, which denotes 1 in units place

2 |17   Odd, yields remainder 1, denoting 2

2 |8   Even, yielding 0 remainder

2 |4   Even

2 |2   Even

1   Final quotient, denoting 2^5

Thus, the binary form for 35 is 100011, which denotes $2^5 + 2 + 1$. Hence the required product is obtained from $(2^5 + 2 + 1) \times 28 = 2^5 \times 28 + 2 \times 28 + 1 \times 28$, or $896 + 56 + 28 = 980$.

The commutative law of multiplication enables one to interchange the roles of the multiplicand and the divisor, thus

Doublings		*Halvings*	
35		28	
70		14	
140*		7	Odd
280*		3	Odd
560*		1	Odd
980			

980   Sum of the numbers marked by *

That is, the binary form of 28 is 11100, whence $35(2^4 + 2^3 + 2^2) = 35 \times 16 + 35 \times 8 + 35 \times 4 = 560 + 280 + 140 = 980$.

∾ CHALLENGES

1. Perform the indicated multiplications by the Russian peasant's method: (*a*) 64 × 127, (*b*) 75 × 57, (*c*) 150 × 148. Perform these three multiplications in reverse order. Check results by casting nines and elevens.

2. Modify the Russian peasant's method of multiplying natural numbers by a series of multiplications by 3, a series of divisions by 3, and an addition. Apply this scheme to the proposed multiplications: (*a*) 82 × 133, (*b*) 729 × 512, (*c*) 25 × 28. Apply the method in two ways, i.e., by commutative law of multiplication.

S·12 ∾ THE GAME OF NIM

Any convenient number of counters (coins, beans, matches, etc.) are placed into any desirable number of piles. The two players alternately remove any number of counters (at least one counter) from any one of the piles. The player who removes the final counter wins the game.

To illustrate, let *A* and *B* play with counters placed in three piles as indicated: in Pile 1 place 15 counters, in Pile 2 place 13 counters, and in Pile 3 place 10 counters. The game proceeds as follows:

	Pile 1	*Pile 2*	*Pile 3*
Original number of counters	15	13	10
A removes 8 from (1), leaving	7	13	10
B removes 5 from (2), leaving	7	8	10
A removes 5 from (1), leaving	2	8	10
B removes 7 from (3), leaving	2	8	3
A removes 7 from (2), leaving	2	1	3
B removes 3 from (3), leaving	2	1	0
A removes 1 from (1), leaving	1	1	0
B removes 1 from (1), leaving	0	1	0

Now that *A* removes the final counter from Pile 2, *B* loses the game, and *A* is the winner.

If *A* is familiar with binary numbers, while his opponent *B* is not, *A* can always win the game. A winning procedure is to express the number of counters in the various piles in binary form, arranging the digits of the binary numbers in vertical columns.   In the foregoing case *A* notes that in

Pile 1   15 = 1111
Pile 2   13 = 1101
Pile 3   10 = 1010
                ‾‾‾‾
                3222

A, playing first, removes a sufficient number of counters from the largest pile so that the resulting sums of digit columns will all be even numbers.   As they appear at the outset the sums are 3222, one column has an *odd* sum, namely, 3, the other columns are satisfactory, as they yield even sums, 222.   Hence *A* removes enough counters to make the upper left entry 1 change to 0; the 1 in 1111 denotes 2^3, or 8.   Therefore *A* removes 8 counters from Pile 1, making all sums even, as

Pile 1   0111
Pile 2   1101
Pile 3   1010
          ‾‾‾‾
          2222

Now, regardless of the number of counters *B* removes from a pile, *B* must convert at least one of these sums from an even to an odd number.   When *A* plays again, *A* restores the sums to even numbers again.   Thus *B*'s first play leaves the piles thus:

Pile 1   7 = 111
Pile 2   8 = 1000
Pile 3   10 = 1010
                ‾‾‾‾
           Sums 2121

A now converts the two 1s, which are odd, to 0s, which are even.   This he does by removing five counters from pile 1; 5 = 101, leaving

Pile 1   2 =   10
Pile 2   8 = 1000
Pile 3   10 = 1010
                ‾‾‾‾
                2020   All the sums are now even numbers

Thus the game proceeds, *B* making one or more of the sums odd, while *A* then restores all sums to even numbers, until finally *A* makes the columns have the smallest even sums, namely, zeros, which means that *A* removes the final counter or counters.

∾ CHALLENGE

If both *A* and *B* understand the application of binary numbers to the game of Nim, state the two conditions necessary for *A*, who plays first, to win.

S·13 ~ THE SIEVE OF ERATOSTHENES

This ancient algorithm for yielding the odd prime numbers, 3, 5, 7, 11, . . . , is performed as follows:

1. Write in order the list of consecutive odd integers beginning with 3.

2. Now remove from the list every *third* number *following* the 3; then remove every *fifth* number *following* the 5; remove every *seventh* number following the 7; remove every *eleventh* number following the 11. In general, remove every pth number following the p, wherein p is the smallest unused remaining number in the list. (One notes that p is a prime number.)

3. Now if at any stage of this algorithm one has just removed every qth number following the smallest surviving number q, which is necessarily prime, then all surviving numbers in the list as far as but not including q^2 are prime numbers.

Note that the *third, fifth,* and *seventh* numbers, respectively, have been removed from the list of odd numbers in the following array:

```
 3   5   7   9̸  11  13  1̸5̸  17  19  2̸1̸  23  2̸5̸  2̸7̸  29  31  3̸3̸  3̸5̸  37
3̸9̸  41  43  4̸5̸  47  4̸9̸  5̸1̸  53  5̸5̸  5̸7̸  59  61  6̸3̸  6̸5̸  67  6̸9̸  71  73
7̸5̸  7̸7̸  79  8̸1̸  83  8̸5̸  8̸7̸  89  9̸1̸  9̸3̸  9̸5̸  97  9̸9̸ 101 103 1̸0̸5̸ 107 109
1̸1̸1̸ 113 1̸1̸5̸ 1̸1̸7̸ 1̸1̸9̸ 121 1̸2̸3̸ 1̸2̸5̸ 127 1̸2̸9̸ 131 1̸3̸3̸ 1̸3̸5̸ 137 139 1̸4̸1̸ 143 1̸4̸5̸
1̸4̸7̸ 149 151 1̸5̸3̸ 1̸5̸5̸ 157 1̸5̸9̸ 1̸6̸1̸ 163 1̸6̸5̸ 167 169 . . .
```

Thus, all remaining numbers less than 121 are *prime numbers,* namely,

```
 3    5    7   11   13   17   19   23   29   31
37   41   43   47   53   59   61   67   71   73
79   83   89   97  101  103  107  109  113
```

In removing each eleventh number following the 11, the first number to be removed is 11×11, or 121, as all lower multiples of 11 have already been removed, such as 7×11, as this is 11×7 and has been removed with the seventh numbers following the seven. Only one remaining number other than 121 would be removed as far as 13^2, namely 143, or 11×13, so that the list of primes as far as 169 includes also the primes 127, 131, 137, 139, 149, 151, 157, 163, 167. Hence, including the only even prime, 2, there are four primes less than 3^2, nine primes less than 5^2, fifteen primes less than 7^2, thirty primes less than 11^2, thirty-nine primes less than 13^2.

Interesting Facts About Prime Numbers. The Sieve of Eratosthenes suggests some interesting facts about prime numbers. The prime numbers appear to become rarer as one passes to ever larger numbers; thus, all numbers between 113 and 127 are composite numbers (integers that are not prime numbers).

In fact, one can obtain as many consecutive composite numbers as desired. For example, to obtain 20 consecutive composite numbers one calculates the lowest common multiple of the 20 consecutive natural numbers, beginning with 2. This lowest common multiple is 232,792,560; then the 20 consecutive natural numbers starting with 232,792,560 + 2, or 232,792,562, are all composite. For, if K is the lowest common multiple of the n consecutive natural numbers beginning with 2, $K + 2$ is divisible by 2, $K + 3$ is divisible by 3, $K + 4$ is divisible by 4, and in general, if d does not exceed $n + 1$, $K + d$ is divisible by d; however, more than the n consecutive numbers so obtained may be composite. To obtain six consecutive composite numbers, note that the L.C.M. of the six natural numbers, 2, 3, 4, 5, 6, 7, is 420. Hence 420 + 2 is divisible by 2, 423 is divisible by 3, 424 is divisible by 4, 425 is divisible by 5, 426 is divisible by 6, 427 is divisible by 7. However, 428 is divisible by 2, 429 is divisible by 3, 430 is divisible by 2, but 431 is prime; since 421 is also prime, one obtains not merely six but *nine* consecutive composite numbers.

Prime numbers continue to occur in the list of natural numbers however one may proceed. An ancient proof of this fact occurs, and is known as *Euclid's Proof of the Infinitude of Prime Numbers*, because Euclid included it in his famous treatise on elementary mathematics (*The Elements of Euclid*, about 300 B.C.). The proof is as follows: Suppose that there were a last, or largest, prime number, which may be designated as p. Consider now the number obtained by multiplying together all prime numbers including the p; then add 1 to this product. Such a resulting number would appear as $N = 2 \times 3 \times 5 \times 7 \times 11 \times 13 \times \cdots \times p + 1$. Observe that this new number so obtained is not exactly divisible by any of the primes so used, as each division leaves the remainder 1. Therefore N must be a prime number different from all primes used to form it, or, if composite, must be divisible by a prime number different from the prime numbers so used. In either event, it appears that the list of primes as far as p does not include all prime numbers, so that it is impossible to reach a last prime number, as designated by p. To illustrate,

$2 \times 3 + 1 = 7$, a prime number larger than 3
$2 \times 3 \times 5 + 1 = 31$, a prime number larger than 5
$2 \times 3 \times 5 \times 7 + 1 = 211$, a prime number larger than 7
$2 \times 3 \times 5 \times 7 \times 11 + 1 = 2311$, a prime number larger than 11
$2 \times 3 \times 5 \times 7 \times 11 \times 13 + 1 = 30031$, a prime number larger than 13

but

$2 \times 3 \times 5 \times 7 \times 11 \times 13 \times 17 + 1 = 510,511$, a composite number whose prime factors are 19, 39, and 277, each of which is a prime number that is larger than 17

Many apparently true relationships involving prime numbers have resisted all attempts to prove or to disprove them, such as the following:

1. Two consecutive odd natural numbers that are prime numbers are called twin primes, such as (11, 13), (17, 19), (29, 31), (41, 43), etc. Do such twin primes continue to occur without end in the list of prime numbers? The answer is unknown.

2. Many prime numbers occur that are equal to 1 plus a square number, such as $2^2 + 1$, or 5; $6^2 + 1$ or 37; $16^2 + 1$ or 257, etc. Do such prime numbers continue to occur in the list of prime numbers? The answer is unknown.

3. At least one prime number seems to occur between consecutive square numbers. Is this always true for all pairs of consecutive square numbers? The answer is unknown.

4. It appears that every even number, beyond 2, can be expressed as the sum of two prime numbers. Thus $4 = 2 + 2$, $6 = 3 + 3$, $8 = 5 + 3$, $10 = 3 + 7$ or $5 + 5$, etc. Is this true for all such even numbers? The answer is unknown at this date.

S·14 ~ Fᴀᴄᴛᴏʀ ᴛᴀʙʟᴇꜱ

The Sieve of Eratosthenes provides a factor table, as well as a list of prime numbers. If one underlines every third number following 3, if one overlines every fifth number following 5, if one prefixes the * to every seventh number following 7, if one suffixes (places after) the * after every eleventh number following 11, if one prefixes the ′ before every thirteenth number following 13, one obtains a table of numbers as far as 289 which shows all factors of the composite numbers. The unmarked numbers are prime numbers. If one prefixes ″ before every seventeenth number following 17, the table may be extended as far as 361.

Notations:

a = divisible by 3	$\bar{a}$ = divisible by 5	*a = divisible by 7
a* = divisible by 11	′a = divisible by 13	″a = divisible by 17

3	′39	75	111	*147	183	219	″255	291	327
5	41	*77*	113	149	185	′221	257	293	*329
7	43	79	115	151	″187*	223	*259	295	331
9	45	81	′117	″153	*189	225	261	297*	333
11	47	83	″*119	155	191	227	263	′299	335
13	*49	″85	121*	157	193	229	265	*301	337

15	"51	87	123	159	'195	*231*	267	303	339
17	53	89	125	*161	197	233	269	305	341*
19	55*	*91	127	163	199	235	271	307	*343
*21	57	93	129	165*	201	237	*273	309	345
23	59	95	131	167	*203	239	275.*	311	347
25	61	97	*133	'169	205	241	277	313	349
27	*63	99*	135	171	207	243	279	*315	'351
29	'65	101	137	173	209*	*245	281	317	353
31	67	103	139	*175	211	'247	283	319*	355
33*	69	*105	141	177	213	249	285	321	*357
*35	71	107	'143*	179	215	251	*287	"323	359
37	73	109	145	181	*217	253*	"289	'325	361 = 19²

There are, accordingly, 72 prime numbers less than 361, including the 2.

Factor tables as far as 10,000,000 have been prepared by Professor D. N. Lehmer of the University of California (Berkeley) and published by the Carnegie Institute of Washington, D.C. These tables are available in all university libraries.

∽ CHALLENGES

1. By use of the factor table obtain the complete factorization of the numbers:

   a. 105 *c.* 273 *e.* 351 *g.* 277
   b. 279 *d.* 315 *f.* 323 *h.* 594 (even)

2. Extend the table as far as $29^2 = 841$.

3. List the number of twin primes that occur in the preceding table. There are 21 such pairs. There is one triple prime in the table. Why is this the only triple prime that can exist?

4. Find the six prime numbers in the table that have the form $a^2 + 1$.

S·15 ∽ EULER'S FORMULA FOR PRIME NUMBERS

A simple formula yielding only prime numbers does not exist. But certain formulas, for a limited number of integral values of n, namely, 0, 1, 2, 3, . . . , do yield only prime numbers. These formulas are $n^2 + n + A =$ a prime number from $n = 0$ to $n = A - 2$; for $n = A - 1$ the formula yields A^2. The three simplest formulas occur for $A = 11, 17$, and 41.   For $A = 41$, the formula $n^2 + n + 41$ is called Euler's Formula.

For $n = 0, 1, 2, 3, 4, 5, 6, 7, 8, 9, 10, 11$, the formula $n^2 + n + 11$ yields 11, 13, 17, 23, 31, 41, 53, 67, 83, 101, 121, all of which are prime numbers except the last one which is 11^2.   Again, for values of n from 0 to 16, the formula $n^2 + n + 17$ yields 17, 19, 23, 29, 37, 47, 59, 73, 89, 107, 127, 149, 173, 199, 227, 257, 289, all of which are prime except the last number, 289, which is 17^2.

Likewise, for $n = 0, 1, 2, 3, \ldots, 40$, Euler's Formula, $n^2 + n + 41$, yields the numbers 41, 43, 47, 53, 61, 71, 83, 97, 113, 131, 151, 173, 197, 223, 251, 281, 313, 347, 383, 421, 461, 503, 547, 593, 641, 691, 743, 797, 853, 911, 971, 1033, 1097, 1163, 1231, 1301, 1373, 1447, 1523, 1601, 1681.   All these numbers are prime except the last one, $1681 = 41^2$.

The preceding prime numbers are more readily obtained from these considerations: $n^2 + n$, or $n(n + 1)$, is called an oblong number, as it is the product of consecutive integers.   Accordingly, the oblong numbers are 2, 6, 12, 20, 30, 42, 56, ...   Observe that the successive differences between consecutive oblong numbers are the even integers, 2, 4, 6, 8, 10, 12, ...   The primes in the above lists may be obtained simply by adding the even numbers:

$$11, 11 + 2 = 13, 13 + 4 = 17, 17 + 6 = 23, 23 + 8 = 31, \ldots$$
$$17, 17 + 2 = 19, 19 + 4 = 23, 23 + 6 = 29, 29 + 8 = 37, \ldots$$
$$41, 41 + 2 = 43, 43 + 4 = 47, 47 + 6 = 53, 53 + 8 = 61, \ldots$$

Doubtless larger values of A await discovery so that $n^2 + n + A$ yields prime numbers for all integral values of n from 0 to $A - 1$, except the last one which is equal to A^2.   (*Caution:* The next larger value of A, if such valid value of A exists, must exceed 2,000.)

∾ CHALLENGES

1.   Examine the formula $n^2 + n + A$ for $A = 5$.   How many prime numbers does it yield?

2.   How many prime numbers occur that are less than 5^2 or 25?   How many of these does the formula yield?

3.   Verify the fact that the formula $A(A - 1) + \frac{1}{3}(A^3 - 3A^2 + 2A)$ yields the sum of all the $A - 1$ prime numbers that are obtained from the formula $n^2 + n + A$, for A having the values: (*a*) 5, (*b*) 11, (*c*) 17, 41.

4.   Simplify this formula to $A(A^2 - 1)/3$.

S·16 ∾ PYTHAGOREAN NUMBERS

Three natural numbers, a, b, and c, are called Pythagorean numbers if $a^2 + b^2 = c^2$; i.e., if the sum of the squares of two of them is equal to the square of the other one. Examples of such sets are (5, 12, 13) or (6, 8, 10), since 25 + 144 = 169, and 36 + 64 = 100, respectively. If the three numbers of a set do not have a common divisor, the set is called a *primitive set* of Pythagorean numbers. Thus the sets (3, 4, 5) and (5, 12, 13) are primitive; the set (6, 8, 10) is not primitive, since these numbers have a common divisor, namely 2. Removing the common factor, 2, one does obtain a primitive set (3, 4, 5) of Pythagorean numbers.

All primitive sets of Pythagorean numbers are given by the formulas $a = p^2 - q^2$, $b = 2pq$, $c = p^2 + a^2$, if p,q have no common factor *and if p is even and q is odd, or if p is odd and q is even.* There are 16 such primitive sets of Pythagorean numbers less than 100; they are obtained as indicated in the tabulation:

p	q	p^2	q^2	$a = p^2 - q^2$	$b = 2pq$	$c = p^2 + q^2$
2	1	4	1	3	4	5
3	2	9	4	5	12	13
4	1	16	1	15	8	17
4	3	16	9	7	24	25
5	2	25	4	21	20	29
5	4	25	16	9	40	41
6	1	36	1	35	12	37
6	5	36	25	11	60	61
7	2	49	4	45	28	53
7	4	49	16	33	56	65
7	6	49	36	13	84	85
8	1	64	1	63	16	65
8	3	64	9	55	48	73
8	5	64	25	39	80	89
9	2	81	4	77	36	85
9	4	81	16	65	72	97

Note that in each of these sets from the smallest (3, 4, 5) to the largest (65, 72, 97), some number of each set is divisible by 3, by 4, and by 5. Thus, 65 is divisible by 5, while 72 is divisible by 3 and by 4. In the set (63, 16, 65), 63 is divisible by 3, 16 is divisible by 4, and 65 is divisible by 5.

The foregoing formulas for *primitive sets of Pythagorean numbers* may be obtained as follows: $a^2 + b^2 = c^2$, $a = p^2 - q^2$, $b = 2pq$, $c = p^2 + q^2$, wherein p must be even, q odd, or p odd and q even. The numbers a and b cannot both be even, for then $a^2 + b^2$, or c^2, must also be even, whence c itself must be even, indicating that the set (a, b, c) has the common divisor 2. The numbers a and b cannot both be odd, for if $a = 2h + 1$ and $b = 2k + 1$, then $a^2 + b^2 = (2k + 1)^2 + (2k + 1)^2 = 4h^2 + 4h + 1 + 4k^2 + 4k + 1 = 4(h^2 + k^2 + h + k) + 2 = c^2$, showing that c must be even. But c^2 must then be divisible by 4, whereas the expression for c^2 is divisible by 2 but is not divisible by 4, showing an impossible situation. Therefore, of the a and b, one must be even, the other odd, and the c must also be odd. In the ensuing discussion let a be odd, b even, and c, necessarily, odd. Change the form $a^2 + b^2 = c^2$ into $b^2 = c^2 - a^2$.

Now $c^2 - a^2$ is equal to $(c + a)(c - a)$, which may be verified by multiplying out $(c + a)(c - a)$ by repeated use of the distributive law of multiplication. Since c and a are odd, $c + a$ and $c - a$ must be even numbers. Then let $(c + a)/2 = p$ and $(c - a)/2 = q$. By addition, $c = p + q$, and by subtraction $a = p - q$. Now p and q cannot have any common divisor other than 1, for if p,q did have a common factor, the distributive law applied to $p + q$ and to $p - q$ would show that c and a would also have that common factor, which is impossible as a, b, c is a primitive set. Now that $c + a = 2p$ and $c - a = 2q$, then $(c + a)(c - a)$, or b^2, must be equal to $2p \times 2q$, or $4pq$. But $4pq$ must be a square number; hence p and q, having no common factor, must themselves be square numbers and may be represented by p^2 and q^2, respectively. Hence $a = p^2 - q^2$; $b = 2pq$, since $b^2 = 4p^2q^2$; $c = p^2 + q^2$.

One may show that the numbers 3, 4, and 5 must always divide one of the numbers a, b, and c. Let a, b, c be a primitive set. Then one must have $a = p^2 - q^2$, $b = 2pq$, $c = p^2 + q^2$. Since p or q must be even, then $2pq$ must always be divisible by 4. This may be verified by reference to the sets already obtained less than 150.

Every natural number must be of form $3h$ or $3h + 1$ or $3h - 1$. Let $p = 3h$ or $3h \pm 1$ and $q = 3k$ or $3k \pm 1$. Now if p or q were equal to $3h$ or $3k$, respectively, then b, which is equal to $2pq$, would be divisible by 3. If, otherwise, p and q were of form $3h \pm 1$ and $3k \pm 1$, respectively, then $a = p^2 - q^2$ must be equal to $9h^2 \pm 6h - 9k^2 \pm 6k$, which is seen to be divisible by 3. Therefore a or b must always be exactly divisible by 3. (Check this in the foregoing solutions.)

Now every natural number must be of form $5h$, $5h \pm 1$, or $5h \pm 2$. Let $p = 5h$ or $5h \pm 1$ or $5h \pm 2$ and let q be of form $5k$ or $5k \pm 1$ or $5k \pm 2$. Now if p or q were of form $5h$ or $5k$, respectively, then b must be divisible by 5. If p and q were of form $5h \pm 1$, $5k \pm 1$, or $5h \pm 2$, $5k \pm 2$, respectively, then $p^2 - q^2$ would be of form $25h^2 \pm 10h - 25k^2 \pm 10k$, or $25h^2 \pm 20h - 25k^2 \pm 20k$, respectively, both of which are seen to be divisible by 5.

Finally, if $p = 5h \pm 1$, $q = 5k \pm 2$, or $5h \pm 2$, $5k \pm 1$, respectively, then $p^2 + q^2$ would have the form $25h^2 \pm 10h + 25k^2 \pm 20k + 5$, or $25h^2 \pm 20h + 25k^2 \pm 10k + 5$, respectively, both of which are seen to be divisible by 5. Thus the 4 must always divide b, the 3 must always divide a or b, the 5 may divide any one of the numbers a or b or c.

The Pythagorean numbers, primitive or nonprimitive, are the only integers that may serve to express simultaneously the length, width, and diagonal of a rectangle, when expressed in the same kind of units of length, such as inches, feet, centimeters, miles, etc.

⟳ Challenges

I. Extend the foregoing list of Pythagorean triples to include all such sets that do not exceed 150. There are eight such primitive sets.

2. Show that $(23 \times 37, \; 3 \times 4 \times 5 \times 7, \; 13 \times 73)$ is a primitive set of Pythagorean numbers. What are the values of p and q that produce these Pythagorean numbers?

S·17 ⟳ Generalized pythagorean numbers

Any set of more than three natural numbers, in which the square of one is equal to the sum of the squares of the others, are called *generalized Pythagorean numbers*. Thus the sets $(2,3,6,7)$ and $(1,4,8,12,15)$ are generalized Pythagorean numbers, since $2^2 + 3^2 + 6^2 = 4 + 9 + 36 = 49 = 7^2$, and $1^2 + 4^2 + 8^2 + 12^2 = 1 + 16 + 64 + 144 = 225 = 15^2$.

Observe that formulas for generalized Pythagorean numbers are natural extensions of the formulas for the Pythagorean numbers.

$$a^2 + b^2 = c^2 \qquad a^2 + b^2 + c^2 = d^2 \qquad a^2 + b^2 + c^2 + d^2 = e^2$$
$$\text{if} \qquad\qquad\qquad \text{if} \qquad\qquad\qquad\qquad \text{if}$$
$$a = p^2 - q^2 \qquad a = p^2 - q^2 - r^2 \qquad a = p^2 - q^2 - r^2 - s^2$$
$$b = 2pq \qquad\quad b = 2pq \qquad\qquad\quad b = 2pq$$
$$c = p^2 + q^2 \qquad c = 2pr \qquad\qquad\quad c = 2pr$$
$$\qquad\qquad\qquad d = p^2 + q^2 + r^2 \qquad d = 2ps$$
$$\qquad\qquad\qquad\qquad\qquad\qquad\qquad e = p^2 + q^2 + r^2 + s^2$$

The extension to sets of any number of numbers $a, b, c, d, e, f, \ldots$ is apparent. There are 85 sets of four numbers less than 100, such as $(1,2,2,3)$, $(2,3,6,7)$, $(4,4,7,9)$; two numbers in each set must be even, as the formulas show.[1] However, all primitive numbers of this extension cannot be obtained directly from the formulas. The set $(2,3,6,7)$ cannot be so obtained, since three square numbers cannot have the sum 7; however, if $p = 3$, $q = 2$, $r = 1$, the formulas yield $a = 4$, $b = 12$, $c = 6$, $d = 14$, yielding the set $(4,12,6,14)$, from which the common factor 2 may be removed from each number, yielding the primitive set $(2,6,3,7)$. Sets of four generalized Pythagorean numbers are the only integers that may represent simultaneously the measurement of length, width, height, and diagonal of a rectangular solid, using the same unit of measure for each dimension; for if a, b, c represent the length, width, and height of a rectangular solid, the length of its diagonal d is related to the three dimensions a, b, c by the formula $d^2 = a^2 + b^2 + c^2$.

[1] Proofs that these generalizations are correct are not supplied here as they are a bit too involved for this course. The author has supplied such proofs in the *National Mathematics Magazine*, vol. 10, no. 6, March, 1936.

ᴖ CHALLENGES

1. Obtain five primitive sets of generalized Pythagorean numbers for four numbers in each set; for five numbers in each set; for six numbers in each set. To facilitate the work, one should use numbers for $p, q, r, \ldots$ that have no common divisor, other than 1 of course.

2. Can you solve the author's proposed Problem No. 369 in *National Mathematics Magazine* for October 1940? The editors supplied solutions in the December issue, 1941 (vol. 16, no. 3). The problem appeared as follows:

   Let $a^2 + b^2 + c^2 = d^2$, in which a, b, c, d are integers having no common factor. (That is, a, b, c, d are a primitive set of generalized Pythagorean numbers.) Prove that:

   a. The integer d must be odd; of a, b, c, one is odd, two are even.
   b. Twelve is greatest number that divides $abcd$.
   c. If 3 divides d, 3 does not divide abc.
   d. If 3 does not divide d, 9 divides abc.
   e. If $d = 4k - 1$, 8 does not divide abc.
   f. If $d = 4k + 1$, 16 divides abc.

S·18 ᴖ PERFECT NUMBERS

A perfect number is a natural number that is equal to the sum of all its exact divisors excluding the number itself. The first three perfect numbers, 6, 28, and 496, are exhibited with their divisors; it is to be noted that the sum of the divisors is the number itself.

$$6 = 1 + 2 + 3 \qquad 28 = 1 + 2 + 4 + 7 + 14$$
$$496 = 1 + 2 + 4 + 8 + 16 + 31 + 62 + 124 + 248$$

Euclid's formula (*Euclid's Elements*, Book IX, Proposition 36) yields all *even* perfect numbers. No *odd* perfect number has ever been found, and nobody has proved that such a number cannot exist. Euclid's proposition states that if $2^n - 1$ is a prime number for any natural number n, then the product $(2^n - 1) \times 2^{n-1}$ is a perfect number.

To prove that $(2^n - 1)2^{n-1}$, represented by S, is a perfect number if n represents a natural number, and if $2^n - 1$ is a prime number, one computes the sum of all possible divisors of S. This sum, including S itself, is equal to

$$1 + 2 + 4 + 8 + \cdots + 2^{n-1} + (2^n - 1) + 2(2^n - 1) + 4(2^n - 1)$$
$$+ 8(2^n - 1) + \cdots + 2^{n-1}(2^n - 1)$$

which may be expressed as

$$(1 + 2 + 4 + 8 + \cdots + 2^{n-1})$$
$$+ (2^n - 1)(1 + 2 + 4 + 8 + \cdots + 2^{n-1})$$

or as

$$(1 + 2 + 4 + 8 + \cdots + 2^{n-1})(1 + 2^n - 1) \quad \text{or as} \quad \frac{2^n - 1}{2 - 1} \times 2^n$$

or $\quad (2^n - 1)2^n$

Deducting S to obtain the sum of all divisors of S which are less than S, one has

$$(2^n - 1)2^n - (2^n - 1)2^{n-1} \quad \text{or} \quad (2^n - 1)(2^n - 2^{n-1})$$
or $\quad (2^n - 1) \times 2^{n-1}(2 - 1) \quad$ or $\quad (2^n - 1)2^{n-1}$

which is the number S itself. Thus, one establishes the rule for obtaining even perfect numbers.

To show whether or not a number of the form $2^n - 1$ is a prime number is very tedious for large values of n. Consequently up to the year 1951 only 12 such primes were known, namely, those for $n = 2, 3, 5, 7, 13, 17, 19, 31, 61, 89,$ 102, 127. By that date the largest known prime number was $2^{127} - 1$, or

170,141,183,460,469,231,731,687,303,715,884,105,727

This number, multiplied by 2^{126}, yielded the largest then known perfect number. The use of electronic computers has since yielded five more prime numbers of the form $2^n - 1$, for $n = 521, 607, 1,279, 2,203,$ and $2,281$.

Seventeen perfect numbers are now known to exist (as of February, 1967), the largest perfect number arising from the use of $n = 2,281$, which produces the prime number $2^{2281} - 1$, which thus yields a natural number consisting of 687 digits. The corresponding largest known perfect number, accordingly, is $(2^{2281} - 1) \times 2^{2280}$, which yields a natural number consisting of 1,374 digits. Incidentally, $2^{2281} - 1$, consisting of 687 digits, is the *largest known prime number* as of this date.

⌘ CHALLENGES

1. Compute the five smallest perfect numbers. Verify that they are perfect by obtaining the sum of the exact divisors of each.

2. Obtain the sum of the exact divisors of $(2^4 - 1) \times 2^3$. Why is this number not a perfect number?

3. Verify that the sum of the factors of 3 is 4 or 2^2.
   Verify that the sum of the factors of 3×5 is 24 or $2^3 \times 3$.
   Verify that the sum of the factors of $3 \times 5 \times 7$ is 192 or $2^6 \times 3$.
   Verify that the sum of the factors of $3 \times 5 \times 7 \times 11$ is 2304 or $2^8 \times 3^2$.

4. If N_K is the product of the K smallest odd primes, i.e., $N_K = 3 \times 5 \times 7 \times 11 \times \cdots \times p_K$, wherein p_K is the Kth odd prime counting from 3, and if S_K is the sum of all the exact divisors (factors) or N_K, verify in the previous challenge that $S_{K+1} = S_K(1 + p_{K+1})$.

5. Prove that the relation in the previous challenge is true for N_K for all natural numbers K.

6. Calculate the length of tape that would be required to exhibit the decimal form of the prime number $2^{2281} - 1$, if the computer prints 10 digits in a length of 1 inch.

S·19 ~ THE FIBONACCI (NATURAL) NUMBERS

These numbers were seemingly devised in medieval times to tabulate the number of offspring in a progeny of guinea pigs. These numbers have many remarkable properties and still hold the interest of numerous professional and amateur arithmeticians who find pleasure in discovering hitherto unknown properties.[1]

The population growth of guinea pigs is associated with the series of Fibonacci numbers, as follows. Domesticated guinea pigs produce offspring at the age of 2 months. Let it be assumed that a first pair produces just one pair at the end of 2 months and at monthly intervals thereafter ad infinitum, and also that each new pair does likewise. If O represents a single pair present at the corresponding indicated monthly date, the population growth may be exhibited in a tree

[1] The *Fibonacci Quarterly* is the official journal of the Fibonacci Association and should be available at university libraries.

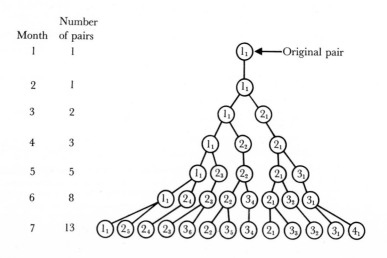

Month	Number of pairs
1	1
2	1
3	2
4	3
5	5
6	8
7	13

FIGURE S. I

diagram. One observes that each pair present at any specific date must be present also at the next ensuing date *and* that each pair present at the preceding date must provide a new pair at the next ensuing date; hence the total number of pairs present at any date is equal to the sum of the numbers of pairs present at the two preceding dates. Thus, the numbers of *pairs* present at successive monthly dates are precisely the Fibonacci numbers, as Figure S.1 clearly reveals.

The large number within each circle indicates the order of that pair by generation; thus 1 represents the original pair (first generation), the 2 represents an offspring of the original pair, or second-generation pair. The subscript indicates the rank by "primogeniture." Thus 3_2 and 3_5 are third-generation pairs, 3_2 has "priority" over 3_5 as 3_2 is the offspring of 2_1 whereas 3_5 is an offspring pair of 2_2, a younger pair than 2_1.

The series of Fibonacci numbers is unending toward the right and appears as follows:

$$1 \quad 1 \quad 2 \quad 3 \quad 5 \quad 8 \quad 13 \quad 21 \quad 34 \quad 55 \quad 87 \quad 144 \quad 233 \ldots$$

The leading two numbers are 1s; then each ensuing number is the sum of the two preceding numbers. The customary symbolism for these numbers is F_n, the n denoting the ordinal number of the particular Fibonacci number designated by F_n. The first 40 Fibonacci numbers are listed as follows:

$F_1 = 1$	$F_{11} = 89$	$F_{21} = 10{,}946$	$F_{31} = 1{,}346{,}269$
$F_2 = 1$	$F_{12} = 144$	$F_{22} = 17{,}711$	$F_{32} = 2{,}178{,}309$
$F_3 = 2$	$F_{13} = 233$	$F_{23} = 28{,}657$	$F_{33} = 3{,}524{,}578$
$F_4 = 3$	$F_{14} = 377$	$F_{24} = 46{,}368$	$F_{34} = 5{,}702{,}887$
$F_5 = 5$	$F_{15} = 610$	$F_{25} = 75{,}025$	$F_{35} = 9{,}227{,}465$
$F_6 = 8$	$F_{16} = 987$	$F_{26} = 121{,}393$	$F_{36} = 14{,}930{,}352$
$F_7 = 13$	$F_{17} = 1{,}597$	$F_{27} = 196{,}418$	$F_{37} = 24{,}157{,}817$
$F_8 = 21$	$F_{18} = 2{,}584$	$F_{28} = 317{,}811$	$F_{38} = 39{,}088{,}169$
$F_9 = 34$	$F_{19} = 4{,}181$	$F_{29} = 514{,}229$	$F_{39} = 63{,}245{,}986$
$F_{10} = 55$	$F_{20} = 6{,}765$	$F_{30} = 832{,}040$	$F_{40} = 102{,}334{,}155$

The following three special properties of the Fibonacci numbers may be verified in the foregoing limited list.

1. The sum of all Fibonacci numbers from F_1 to F_k, inclusive, is equal to $K_{k+2} - 1$. For example, the sum of the first seven Fibonacci numbers is one less than the ninth one: $1 + 1 + 2 + 3 + 5 + 8 + 13 = 33$, which is equal to $34 - 1$.

2. Each even-numbered Fibonacci number, as $F_2, F_4, \ldots, F_{2k}$, is equal to the *difference* of the squares of two alternate previous Fibonacci numbers. Each odd-numbered Fibonacci number, as $F_1, F_3, F_5, \ldots, F_{2k+1}$, is equal to the *sum* of the squares of two consecutive previous Fibonacci numbers.

(Let $F_0 = 0$ and $F_{-1} = 1$ to make this universally true.)   As examples,

$$13 = 3^2 + 2^2 \qquad \text{or} \qquad F_7 = F_4{}^2 + F_3{}^2$$
$$21 = 5^2 - 2^2 \qquad\qquad\qquad F_8 = F_5{}^2 - F_3{}^2$$
$$34 = 5^2 + 3^2 \qquad\qquad\qquad F_9 = F_5{}^2 + F_4{}^2$$
$$55 = 8^2 - 3^2 \qquad\qquad\qquad F_{10} = F_6{}^2 - F_4{}^2$$
$$89 = 8^2 + 5^2 \qquad\qquad\qquad F_{11} = F_6{}^2 + F_5{}^2$$
$$144 = 13^2 - 5^2 \qquad\qquad\quad F_{12} = F_7{}^2 - F_5{}^2$$

And, quite generally, $F_{2k} = (F_{k+1})^2 - (F_{k-1})^2$ and $F_{2k+1} = (F_{k+1})^2 + (F_k)^2$.

3.   If a is an exact divisor of k, then F_a is an exact divisor of F_k.   For example, 13 is an exact divisor of 26; therefore F_{13}, or 233, is an exact divisor of F_{26}, or 121,393.   This may be verified as $121{,}393 \div 233 = 521$.

That the three foregoing properties are valid in general may be proved as follows.

Property 1.   Note that $F_1 + F_2 = F_4 - 1$, since $1 + 1 = 3 - 1$, and that $F_1 + F_2 + F_3 = F_5 - 1$, since $1 + 1 + 2 = 5 - 1$.   Accordingly, the theorem is true for k terms, namely, $F_1 + F_2 + \cdots + F_k = F_{k+2} - 1$, if $k = 4$ or 5.   Now if the theorem is true for any specific value of k, it must also be true for the next higher value of k, as may be verified by adding the next higher F_{k+1} to both members of the equality.   Thus $F_1 + F_2 + \cdots + F_k + F_{k+1} = F_{k+1} + F_{k+2} - 1$.   But, on the right, one notes that $F_{k+1} + F_{k+2} = F_{k+3}$.   Therefore, $F_1 + F_2 + \cdots + F_{k+1} = F_{k+3} - 1$.   Thus, if the theorem is true for any number of Fibonacci numbers, the theorem must also be true for the next larger number of Fibonacci numbers.   Thus, the theorem is universally true, as it has already been tested for $k = 3$ and 4.   The test for $k = 2$ would have been sufficient, and $F_1 + F_2 = F_4 - 1$, as $1 + 1 = 3 - 1$.

This method of proof is called *mathematical induction* and is of frequent use in advanced courses of mathematics.   The method consists of testing a simple case for correctness, then showing that if the theorem is true for any specific case, it must necessarily hold for the next higher case.   If both Properties 1 and 2 are established, it is clear that the theorem must be true in *all* cases beyond the case tested in Property 1.

Property 2.   The two parts of this theorem are proved concurrently.   Thus, for values of k as far as $k = 5$, the formulas are valid:

$$F_{2k+1} = (F_{k+1})^2 + (F_k)^2 \qquad F_{2k} = (F_{k+1})^2 - (F_{k-1})^2$$

Now if these formulas are valid for a specific value of k, it is next demonstrated that they must both be true for the next larger value of k.   Adding the two equalities one obtains, since $F_{2k+1} + F_{2k} = F_{2k+2}$,

$$F_{2k+2} = (F_{k+1}{}^2 + 2F_{k+1}F_k + F_k{}^2) - (F_{k+1}{}^2 - 2F_{k+1}F_{k-1} + F_{k-1}{}^2)$$
$$+ 2F_{k+1}(F_{k+1} - F_k - F_{k-1}) = (F_{k+1} + F_k)^2 - (F_{k+1} - F_{k-1})^2 + 2F_{k+1} \times 0$$

Hence, $F_{2k+2} = F_{k+2}{}^2 - F_k{}^2$. Again, $F_{2k+1} = F_{k+1}{}^2 + F_k{}^2$. Accordingly, since $F_{2k+1} + F_{2k+2} = F_{2k+3}$, one obtains $F_{2k+3} = F_{k+2}{}^2 + F_{k+1}{}^2$. Thus the two statements are true also for $k + 1$. If the original two equalities are correct for a particular value of k, the previous discussion proves that the same equalities must necessarily be correct for the value $k + 1$. Hence the theorem is universally true.

Property 3. Proof that F_a is an exact divisor of F_k if a is an exact divisor of k is:

$$F_a = F_a$$
$$F_{a+1} = F_{a+1}$$

$$\overline{F_{a+2} = F_{a+1} + F_a} \qquad \text{Adding}$$
$$\overline{F_{a+3} = 2F_{a+1} + F_a} \qquad \text{Adding the two previous equalities}$$
$$\overline{F_{a+4} = 3F_{a+1} + 2F_a} \qquad \text{Adding the two previous equalities}$$
$$\overline{F_{a+5} = 5F_{a+1} + 3F_a} \qquad \text{Continuing to add the last two equalities}$$
$$\overline{F_{a+6} = 8F_{a+1} + 5F_a}$$

Thus it appears that for values of k from 2 to 6, inclusive, one has $F_{a+k} = F_k F_{a+1} + F_{k-1} F_a$. As this formula is true for *all* values of a, replace a by $a + 1$, namely,

$$
\begin{aligned}
F_{a+1+k} &= F_k F_{a+2} + F_{k-1} F_{a+1} \\
&= F_k(F_a + F_{a+1}) + (F_{k+1} - F_k)F_{a+1} \\
&= F_k F_a + F_k F_{a+1} + F_{k+1} F_{a+1} - F_k F_{a+1} \\
&= F_{k+1} F_{a+1} + F_k F_a \qquad \text{but} \qquad F_{a+1+k} = F_{a+(k+1)}
\end{aligned}
$$

Therefore the formula is true for $k + 1$, if it is true for k; hence the formula is true for all values of k as well as for all values of a. Now F_0 has been defined as having the value 0; then if a and k denote any natural numbers whatever, it is true that $F_{a+k} = F_k F_{a+1} + F_{k-1} F_a$. Now let $k = a$, so that one has $F_{a+a} = F_{2a} = F_a F_{a+1} + F_{a-1} F_a$. Thus, the distributive law shows that F_a is an exact divisor of F_{2a}. Next let $k = 2a$, so that one has $F_{a+2a} = F_{3a} = F_{2a} F_{a+1} + F_{2a-1} F_a$. Replacing F_{2a}, one has $F_{3a} = F_a F_{a+1} + F_{a-1} F_a + F_{2a-1} F_a$. Again, the distributive law shows that F_a is an exact divisor of F_{3a}.

Thus one observes that F_a is an exact divisor of F_{a+ka} if $k = 1$ or 2. Now, if the formula shows that F_a is a factor of F_{a+ka}, one must show that F_a is necessarily a factor of $F_{a+(k+1)a}$. Now $F_{a+(k+1)a} = F_{(k+1)a} F_{a+1} + F_{(k-1)a-1} F_a$.

But $F_{(k+1)a} = F_{a+ka}$, which is assumed to be divisible by F_a. Again, by the distributive law, F_a is a factor of the right member of this equality and, consequently, F_a is an exact divisor of $F_{a+(k+1)a}$, for all integral values of k greater than $k = 2$.

Finally, let $k = b - 1$ in the form F_{a+ka}, and one obtains the desired result—that $F_{a+(b-1)a} = F_{ab}$ is exactly divisible by F_a.

Thus the proofs of the three remarkable properties of the Fibonacci numbers are complete.

∾ CHALLENGES

1. By reference to the list of the Fibonacci numbers write immediately the sum of the first 30 Fibonacci numbers.

2. By a single subtraction obtain the sum of the Fibonacci numbers from F_{21} to F_{30} inclusive.

3. Obtain the sum of all 40 numbers listed above. (*Hint:* Extend the list to F_{42}.)

4. Factor completely the numbers (*a*) 317811, (*b*) 14,930,352.

5. Obtain two square numbers whose sum is (*a*) 4,181, (*b*) 1,346,269.

6. Since the relationship $F_{n+2} = F_{n+1} + F_n$ is equivalent to the relationship $F_n = F_{n+2} - F_{n+1}$, one may obtain the value of the Fibonacci number that lies immediately to the left of two consecutive Fibonacci numbers. Now use this latter formula to define and extend the Fibonacci series indefinitely to the left for negative and zero values of n in F_n, if n represents a natural number. State the relationship between F_{-n} and F_n.

7. If p/q represents a proper fraction, one may define F_n for proper fractional values of n, as follows: $F_{p/q} = p/q$; $F_{1+(p/q)} = 1$; as universally, $F_n + F_{n+1} = F_{n+2}$. Evaluate the following Fibonacci numbers: (*a*) $F_{\frac{2}{3}}$, (*b*) $F_{\frac{4}{5}}$, (*c*) $F_{\frac{7}{3}}$, (*d*) $F_{4\frac{3}{8}}$.

8. Defining *consecutive* Fibonacci numbers F_h and F_k as those for which $k - h = 1$, prove the correctness of the formula for the sum of n consecutive Fibonacci numbers beginning with $F_{p/q}$, if p/q is a proper fraction,

$$S = F_{n+1} + \frac{p}{q} \times F_n - 1.$$

9. Define F_n for (real) irrational values of n. (Refer to Challenge 7.) Then evaluate *exactly* (*a*) $F_{\sqrt{2}}$, (*b*) F_π, (*c*) $F_{(\sqrt{2}+\sqrt{3})}$. Give the best rational approximations of these three Fibonacci expressions to the nearest 0.000,1.

10. Extend the family tree of the progeny of guinea pigs for one additional month, inserting correct numbers within each new circle for the next 21 circles of the diagram. How many guinea pigs would be present at the end of 4 years?

11. Make a corresponding family tree of the 10 generations of descendants of Adam as catalogued by longevity and birthdates in the fifth chapter of the Old Testament book of Genesis. Note the extreme longevity, such as that of Adam, extending over 9 generations; however, none of these 10 patriarchs was drowned in the Great Flood, although only the tenth patriarch, Noah, entered his boat.

S·20 ⮜ The fundamental theorem of arithmetic

The *Fundamental Theorem of Arithmetic* asserts that a given natural number has only one prime factor form, such as those listed in Section 6.4. One obtains the prime factor form of a natural number by dividing it by any exact prime divisor, then dividing each ensuing quotient by an exact prime divisor, until a quotient finally occurs that is itself a prime number. The successive divisors and the final prime quotient constitute the factors of the required prime factor form.

Note the two sets of exact divisions that yield the prime factor form of the natural number 280.

2	280		5	280
2	140		2	56
2	70		7	28
5	35		2	4
	7			2

Thus $280 = 2 \times 2 \times 2 \times 5 \times 7 \qquad 280 = 5 \times 2 \times 7 \times 2 \times 2$
$\qquad\quad = 2^3 \times 5 \times 7 \qquad\qquad\qquad\quad = 2^3 \times 5 \times 7$

The two procedures yield the same prime factors, though in different orders; then the commutative law of multiplication permits the rearrangement of factors to yield identical results.

A proof of the correctness of the fundamental theorem of arithmetic appears in the *Disquisitiones Arithmeticae* of Gauss (1801). Subsequent translations from the original Latin into French and German and recently into English by Yale University Press are available in university libraries. The proof as given in this famous work rests upon three preliminary propositions.

Proposition 1. If each of two positive integers a and b is less than a particular prime number p, the product of the two integers is not divisible by p.

Proposition 2. If each of any two integers is not divisible by a prime number p, the product of the two integers cannot be divisible by the prime p.

Proposition 3. If each of a set of numbers a, b, c, d, . . . is not divisible by a prime number p, the product of the numbers, namely $a \cdot b \cdot c \cdot d \cdots$, cannot be divisible by the prime number p.

⮜ Challenges

1. Give a numerical example to illustrate the foregoing preliminary Propositions 1, 2, and 3.

2. Master the definitions of concepts relating to congruence relationships, as set forth in ensuing paragraphs (*a*) through (*d*).

   a. Two integers, *a* and *b*, are said to be congruent according to a modulus *m*, if they yield the same positive remainder when divided by *m;* or, equivalently stated, if their difference is exactly divisible by the modulus. In symbols, $a \equiv b$ (mod. *m*). Thus 17 is congruent to 9 according to the modulus 4, or $17 \equiv 9$ (mod. 4), because $17 - 9$, or 8, is exactly divisible by the modulus 4. However, $12 \equiv 7$ (mod. 2) is false, since $12 - 7$, or 5, is not exactly divisible by the modulus 2. Which two of the five alleged congruences are false?

   i. $23 \equiv 9$ (mod. 7)   iii. $15 \equiv 1$ (mod. 5)   v. $850 \equiv 58$ (mod. 6)
   ii. $19 \equiv -5$ (mod. 6)   iv. $222 \equiv 86$ (mod. 11)

   b. Two numbers that are congruent according to a particular modulus are each multiplied by the same number, or increased by the same number, or diminished by the same number. The resulting products, sums, or differences, respectively, are also congruent according to the same modulus. Thus it is true that $27 \equiv 12$ (mod. 5). Then $135 \equiv 60$ (mod. 5) is also correct (multiplying the two numbers by 5); also $34 \equiv 19$ (mod. 5) is correct (adding 7 to the two numbers); also $16 \equiv 1$ (mod. 5) is correct (subtracting 11 from the two numbers). Likewise, $9 \equiv 3$ (mod. 5) is correct (dividing the two numbers by 3). These four congruences should be tested for correctness.

   The congruences resulting from multiplication, addition, and subtraction are always correct with the same modulus in the resulting congruences. To obtain a correct result when the two numbers are divided by the same number, it may be necessary to divide the modulus by the highest common divisor of the modulus and the divisor. Thus $42 \equiv 6$ (mod. 12) remains true if the two numbers 42 and 6 are divided by 3, yielding $14 \equiv 2$ (mod. 12); however, if the two numbers 42 and 6 are divided by 2, the resulting congruence, $21 \equiv 3$ (mod. 12) is false, but the resulting congruence is true if the modulus also is divided by the 2, as $21 \equiv 3$ (mod. 6) is true.

   c. Two or more correct congruences may be added, subtracted, or multiplied, termwise, and will yield correct resulting congruences with the same modulus. To illustrate, test the given congruences for correctness and perform the indicated operations:

   i. Add: $7 \equiv 2$ (mod. 5)   ii. Multiply: $14 \equiv 3$ (mod. 11)
             $19 \equiv 4$ (mod. 5) $6 \equiv -5$ (mod. 11)
             $\overline{31 \equiv 16}$ (mod. 5) $\overline{84 \equiv -15}$ (mod. 11)
             $57 \equiv 22$ (mod. 5)   Note that $84 - (-15)$, or 99, is exactly divisible by 11

   In the remaining problems, perform the indicated operations and test the resulting congruences for correctness:

iii. Add: $19 \equiv 7$ (mod. 6)
$\phantom{\text{Add: }}-4 \equiv 20$ (mod. 6)
$\phantom{\text{Add: }}18 \equiv 0$ (mod. 6)
$\phantom{\text{Add: }}73 \equiv 37$ (mod. 6)

v. Subtract: $66123 \equiv 207$
$\phantom{\text{Subtract: 66123 }}$(mod. 9)
$\phantom{\text{Subtract: }}65430 \equiv 198$
$\phantom{\text{Subtract: 65430 }}$(mod. 9)

iv. Multiply: $19 = 10$ (mod. 3)
$\phantom{\text{Multiply: }}11 = 20$ (mod. 3)

vi. $2^3 \equiv 1$ (mod. 7)
$2^{12} \equiv 1$ (mod. 7) Obtained by raising 2^3 and 1 to fourth power

d. The residues of a given number, with reference to a particular modulus, are the numbers obtained by adding or subtracting multiples of the modulus to the given number. Thus for the modulus 7, the residues of 19 are $19 - 7$, or 12; $19 - 14$, or 5; $19 - 21$, or -2; $19 + 7$, or 26; etc. Arranged in a line they would appear as an endless array of numbers—endless in both directions:

$\dots -37, -30, -23, -16, -9, -2, 5, 12, 19, 26, 33, 40, 47, \dots$

Of these residues 5 is called the *least positive residue* of 19 (mod. 7). Note that all these residues are congruent to one another, according to the modulus 7. Hence, any true congruence remains true if either, or both, numbers in the congruence is replaced by any of its own residues, according to the indicated modulus.

3. Obtain the least positive residues of the numbers 37, 55, 900 for the modulus 11. If a number is exactly divisible by the modulus, its least positive residue may be taken as 0 or the modulus itself.

4. Replace the numbers in the following congruences by their least positive residues. Note that if the given congruence is true, the resulting congruence is also true.
    i. $107 \equiv 811$ (mod. 11)
    ii. $107 \equiv 81$ (mod. 13)
    iii. $3,000 \equiv 300$ (mod. 9)
    iv. $1,025 \equiv 521$ (mod. 9)

5. Justify the steps to prove that if $a \equiv b$ (mod. M), then $ka \equiv kb$ (mod. M):
    i. $a - b = nM$
    ii. $k(a - b) = knM$
    iii. $ka - kb = (kn)M$
    iv. $ka \equiv kb$ (mod. M)

6. Devise proofs for the other relationships given on congruences in the preceding paragraph *b*.

7. Gain an understanding mastery of Gauss' proof of the correctness of the fundamental theorem of arithmetic that follows.
    Proof of preliminary Proposition 1 (see above): Suppose that numbers $b, c, d, \dots$, all smaller than p, do exist so that $ab \equiv 0$, $ac \equiv 0$, $ad \equiv 0$, $\dots$, (mod. p), and that b is the smallest of the set of numbers $b, c, d, \dots$. Now b cannot be 1, for then $a \times 1 = a$, and a cannot be divisible by p

as a is smaller than p. Since p cannot be divisible by b, p must lie between the two nearest multiples of b, as seen when the multiples of b are marked off on the number line:

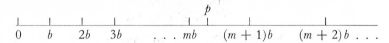

Since p is larger than mb, $p - mb$, which may be denoted by b', is positive. Since it is supposed that $ab \equiv 0$ (mod. p), multiplying by m must obtain a true congruence $mab \equiv 0$ (mod. p). Moreover, p is divisible by p, so that $p \equiv 0$ (mod. p), and $ap \equiv 0$ (mod. p). Then by subtraction

$$mp \equiv 0 \text{ (mod. } p)$$
$$amp \equiv 0 \text{ (mod. } p)$$
$$mp - amp \equiv 0 \text{ (mod. } p) \quad \text{or} \quad a(p - mb) \quad \text{or} \quad ab' \equiv 0 \text{ (mod. } p)$$

which means that b' is divisible by p. Thus b', which is included among the numbers $b, c, d, \ldots$, is smaller than b, while b is the smallest one of the set, which is clearly absurd. Therefore, if a is smaller than p, no other number smaller than p exists so that the product of a by it is divisible by p.

Proof of preliminary Proposition 2 (see above): Suppose that the numbers a and b are not divisible by p, the prime number; then their product cannot be divisible by p. Let the smallest positive residues of a and b (mod. p) be respectively, a' and b'. Then a' and b' must each be smaller than p. Now $a \equiv a'$ (mod. p) and $b \equiv b'$ (mod. p), then $ab \equiv a'b'$ (mod. p). If ab were divisible by p, $ab \equiv 0$ (mod. p); then also must $a'b' \equiv 0$ (mod. p). But this is impossible by Proposition 1. Therefore if each of two numbers is not divisible by the prime number p, their product cannot be divisible by the same prime number p.

Proof of preliminary Proposition 3 (see above): If no number in the set of numbers $a, b, c, d, \ldots$, is divisible by the prime number p, then their product $a \cdot b \cdot c \cdot d \cdots$ cannot be divisible by this prime number p. According to the preceding proposition, ab cannot be divisible by p. Then since ab and c are not divisible by p, the product of ab and c cannot be divisible by p; i.e., $(ab)c$, or abc, is not divisible by p. Continuing the same argument, since abc and d are each not divisible by p, neither can the product $(abc)d$, or $abcd$, be divisible by p. Continue the argument with each ensuing number after d until finally one obtains the product of all the numbers in the set as not being divisible by the prime number p. *Note:* Unless p denotes a *prime* number, the foregoing Propositions 1, 2, and 3 are not necessarily true. For in Proposition 1 the two numbers 8 and 9 are each smaller than 12; yet their product, 8×9, or 72, is divisible by 12. For Proposition 2 the numbers 8 and 9 are not divisible by 6; yet the product, 72, is divisible by 6. And for Proposition 3, the numbers 3 and 4 and 5 are each not divisible by 12; yet their product $3 \times 4 \times 5$, or 60, is divisible by 12.

Proof of the fundamental theorem of arithmetic: One may now prove that any natural number has a unique set of prime factors; i.e., that any two procedures used to obtain a prime factor form for N must yield the same set of prime factors.

Suppose that N is factored in two sets of prime factors, namely, $N = a^{a'}b^{b'}c^{c'}d^{d'}$ . . . , and $N = p^{p'}q^{q'}r^{r'}s^{s'}$ . . . , the exponents indicating how many times the prime number occurs over which the exponent is written. Thus in the first factorization the prime factor a occurs a' times, etc. One can now make the three following observations:

Every prime factor occurring in the first factorization, such as a, must also occur among the prime factors $p, q, r, s, \ldots$, of the second factorization. For if a did not occur among these latter primes, then, since none of the primes $p, q, r, s, \ldots$, is divisible by the prime a, then the product $p'q'r's' \cdots$, could not be divisible by a, which is an impossible situation as a does divide this product N as it is a factor of N.

By the same argument every prime factor occurring in the second factorization $p^{p'}q^{q'}r^{r'}s^{s'} \cdots$ must also occur among the factors $a, b, c, d, \ldots$ so that all prime factors in either set occur in the other set; i.e., the two factorizations contain the same prime factors.

Any prime number that occurs in both of these two factorizations must occur with the same frequency in each factorization. Let the exponent of a in the two factorizations be m and n respectively, and let m be greater than n. Then removing (dividing by) a^n in each of the factorizations, $N = a^m b^{b'} c^{c'} d^{d'} \cdots$, and $N = a^n b^{b''} c^{c''} d^{d''} \cdots$, and $N/a^n = a^{m-n} b^{b''} c^{c''} d^{d''}$ $\cdots$. Here the second factorization contains the prime factor a, which is lacking from the first factorization, for the number N/a^n, an impossible situation, as has just been demonstrated. Therefore every prime factor must occur in both factorizations and must have the same exponent also in each factorization, which means that the factorizations are exactly alike in every detail; i.e., the natural number has a unique factorization.

S·21 ∽ Some curious consequences of the fundamental theorem of arithmetic

Formula 1. The prime factor form of a natural number yields the *number of exact divisors* of the natural number. Let the natural number $N = a^{a'}b^{b'}c^{c'}d^{d'}$ $\cdots$. Then any exact divisor contains some, or all, of these prime factors with exponents not greater than the exponents in the prime factor form and may contain no other prime factor. Since each exponent k' has $k' + 1$ possibilities, namely, $0, 1, 2, 3, 4, \ldots, k'$, the total number of exact divisors must be the product of $(a' + 1)(b' + 1)(c' + 1)(d' + 1) \cdots$. For example, $12 = 2^2 \times 3^1$. The number of divisors of 12 is equal to $(2 + 1)(1 + 1)$, or 6, since the exponents are 2 and 1, respectively. The six divisors are 1, 2, 3, 4, 6, and 12. Again, there are $(4 + 1)$, or five, divisors of 16, or 2^4, namely, 1, 2, 4, 8, and 16.

Formula 2. The sum of all exact divisors, of $N = a^{a'}b^{b'}c^{c'}d^{d'} \cdots$ is equal to the product:

$$\frac{(a^{a'+1} - 1)(b^{b'+1} - 1)(c^{c'+1} - 1)(d^{d'+1} - 1) \cdots}{(a' - 1)(b' - 1)(c' - 1)(d' - 1) \cdots}$$

Thus, if $12 = 2^2 \times 3^1$, the sum of all the divisors of 12 is equal to

$$\frac{(2^3 - 1)(3^2 - 1)}{(2 - 1)(3 - 1)} \quad \text{or} \quad \frac{7 \times 8}{1 \times 2} = 28$$

Note that the sum of 1, 2, 3, 4, 6, and 12 is 28.

To verify the rule for obtaining the sum of the exact divisors of a natural number, one must first obtain the formula for the sum of all powers of a number a up to n. That is, obtain a simple formula for S in the expression: $S = 1 + a + a^2 + a^3 + a^4 + \cdots + a^{n-1} + a^n$. Now $aS = a + a^2 + a^3 + a^4 + \cdots + a^n + a^{n+1}$. Then, subtracting, $S - aS = 1 - a^{n+1}$. Or, using the distributive law, $S(1 - a) = 1 - a^{n+1}$, whence by dividing by $1 - a$, one obtains

$$S = \frac{1 - a^{n+1}}{1 - a}$$

or by multiplying numerator and denominator by -1, one obtains

$$S = \frac{a^{n+1} - 1}{a - 1}$$

the desired formula for the sum of the successive powers of a. Now, if $N = a^{a'}b^{b'}c^{c'}d^{d'} \cdots k^{k'}$, then the total product of

$$(1 + a + a^2 + a^3 + \cdots + a^{a'})$$
$$(1 + b + b^2 + b^3 + \cdots + b^{b'})$$
$$(1 + c + c^2 + c^3 + \cdots + c^{c'})$$
$$(1 + d + d^2 + d^3 + \cdots + d^{d'})$$
$$\cdots \cdots \cdots \cdots \cdots \cdots$$
$$(1 + k + k^2 + k^3 + \cdots + k^{k'})$$

will yield all possible products that can be formed by taking one number from within each of the parenthesis combinations; these products include all possible divisors of N. Therefore, the sum of all such products is

$$S = \frac{a^{a'+1} - 1}{a - 1} \frac{b^{b'+1} - 1}{b - 1} \frac{c^{c'+1} - 1}{c - 1} \frac{d^{d'+1} - 1}{d - 1} \cdots \frac{k^{k'+1} - 1}{k - 1}$$

Hence, if $N = 2^7 \times 3^5 \times 5^4$, or 19,440,000, N has exactly $8 \times 6 \times 5$, or 240, exact divisors; the sum of these 240 exact divisors is

$$\frac{(2^8 - 1)(3^6 - 1)(5^5 - 1)}{1 \times 2 \times 4} = 72{,}492{,}420$$

Formula 3. If the natural number N has the prime factor form $a^{a'} b^{b'} c^{c'} \dots k^{k'}$, then there are exactly $n \left(1 - \dfrac{1}{a}\right) \left(1 - \dfrac{1}{b}\right) \left(1 - \dfrac{1}{c}\right) \cdots \left(1 - \dfrac{1}{k}\right)$ numbers that are smaller than the natural number N that are relatively prime to N, i.e., that have no common factor with N other than 1.

Since $12 = 2^2 \times 3$, there are $12 \left(1 - \frac{1}{2}\right) \left(1 - \frac{1}{3}\right)$, or $12 \times \frac{1}{2} \times \frac{2}{3}$, or four such numbers, namely, 1, 5, 7, 11. Furthermore, the sum of such numbers is $\frac{1}{2} N^2 \left(1 - \dfrac{1}{a}\right) \left(1 - \dfrac{1}{b}\right) \left(1 - \dfrac{1}{c}\right) \cdots \left(1 - \dfrac{1}{k}\right)$. Note that the sum of 1, 5, 7, and 11 is 24, which is also obtained from $\dfrac{12^2}{2} \times \frac{1}{2} \times \frac{2}{3}$.

To establish these formulas, note that there are N/a multiples of a that do not exceed N, namely, $a, 2a, 3a, 4a, \dots, (N/a)a$. Thus there are N/a numbers not exceeding N that have the common factor a with N. Hence there are

$$N - \left(\frac{N}{a}\right) = N \left(1 - \frac{1}{a}\right)$$ numbers that do *not* have the factor a in common

with N. Next, there are N/b numbers not exceeding N that have the common factor b with N, namely, $b, 2b, 3b, \dots, (N/b)b$; but among these N/b multiples of b, there are $\left(\dfrac{N}{b}\right) \left(1 - \dfrac{1}{a}\right)$ numbers less than N that are multiples of b but are not at the same time multiples of a. Subtracting this number of multiples of a that are not multiples of b from $N \left(1 - \dfrac{1}{a}\right)$, one obtains $N \left(1 - \dfrac{1}{a}\right) - \left(\dfrac{N}{b}\right) \left(1 - \dfrac{1}{a}\right)$. By the distributive law, removing the common factor $N \left(1 - \dfrac{1}{a}\right)$, one obtains $N \left(1 - \dfrac{1}{a}\right) \left(1 - \dfrac{1}{b}\right)$. This formula yields the numbers less than N and relatively prime to a and b.

Next consider the multiples of c, namely, $c, 2c, 3c, \dots, (N/c)c$; of these multiples of c there are $\left(\dfrac{N}{c}\right) \left(1 - \dfrac{1}{a}\right) \left(1 - \dfrac{1}{b}\right)$ that are relatively prime to a and b. Subtracting this number from $N \left(1 - \dfrac{1}{a}\right) \left(1 - \dfrac{1}{b}\right)$, one obtains $N \left(1 - \dfrac{1}{a}\right) \left(1 - \dfrac{1}{b}\right) - \left(\dfrac{N}{c}\right) \left(1 - \dfrac{1}{a}\right) \left(1 - \dfrac{1}{b}\right)$, which by the distributive law again yields $N \left(1 - \dfrac{1}{a}\right) \left(1 - \dfrac{1}{b}\right) \left(1 - \dfrac{1}{c}\right)$. Continuing the process, one obtains the desired formula $N\left(1 - \dfrac{1}{a}\right)\left(1 - \dfrac{1}{b}\right)\left(1 - \dfrac{1}{c}\right) \cdots \left(1 - \dfrac{1}{k}\right)$ as giving the number of numbers less than N and having none of the common factors $a, b, c, \ldots, k$.

Furthermore, if a and N have no common factor, then $N - a$ and N have no common factor; for, by the distributive law, the common factor of N and $N - a$ must be a factor of the difference $(N - a) - N$, or of a; but N and a are relatively prime. Therefore $N - a$ and N are also relatively prime. Hence the numbers less than N and prime to N may be combined into pairs, a and $N - a$, whose sum is N; since there would be half as many pairs as there are such numbers their sum must then be half such a number times N.

To illustrate, there are 100 $(1 - \frac{1}{2})$ $(1 - \frac{1}{5})$, or $100 \times \frac{1}{2} \times \frac{4}{5}$, or 40 numbers less than 100 and relatively prime to 100, namely, 1,99, 3,97, 7,93, 9,91, 11,89, 13,87, 17,83, 19,81, 21,79, 23,77, 27,73, 29,71, 31,69, 33,67, 37,63, 39,61, 41,59, 43,57, 47,53, and 49,51, or 20 pairs, each pair having the sum 100 so that the sum of all 40 such numbers must be 20×100, or 2,000.

⁕ CHALLENGES

1. How many exact divisors has 100? Calculate the sum of these exact divisors. Verify these two answers by listing these factors and adding them.

2. If N is a power of a prime number p, namely, $N = p^n$, show that there are exactly $n + 1$ exact divisors of N, and that the sum of these divisors is $(p^{n+1} - 1)/(p - 1)$. Use the foregoing established formulas.

3. Obtain the formula that yields the sum of all the factors that are less than the number itself. This is obtained merely by deducting N from a foregoing expression. Now obtain the sum of all such divisors for the numbers (a) 6, (b) 28, (c) 17, (d) 496.

S·22 ⁕ CYCLICAL INTEGERS

An integer consisting of n digits is called a cyclical integer if the n products resulting by multiplying it by $1, 2, 3, \ldots, n$, respectively, exhibit the same digits in the same cyclical order. Thus, 142857 is a cyclical integer, since the six products

$$1 \times 142857 = 142857 \qquad 4 \times 142857 = 571428$$
$$2 \times 142857 = 285714 \qquad 5 \times 142857 = 714285$$
$$3 \times 142857 = 428571 \qquad 6 \times 142857 = 857142$$

all exhibit the same array of digits in all products.

Observe that these six products may be obtained from the original 142857 by transferring some of the digits from one of the numbers to the other end without disturbing the order; thus the second product is obtained by removing the 14 from the left end of 142857 to the right end, obtaining 285714; similarly, for the other five products, different sets of digits are so transferred.

The next larger cyclical integer is the 16-digit number 0,588,235,294,117,647, retaining the initial zero. Observe the first two of the sixteen products: $2 \times 0,588,235,294,117,647 = 1,176,470,588,235,294$, which may be obtained by moving the final six digits to the left end of the number;

$$3 \times 0,588,235,294,117,647 = 1,764,705,882,352,941$$

which may be obtained by moving the final five digits of the original number from the right end to the left end. The entire sixteen products may be written down after obtaining the final required two digits of the products.

By way of explanation, these cyclical integers are merely the periods of $p - 1$ digits of repeating decimal fractions obtained by converting the fraction $1/p$ to its decimal form, if p represents a prime number. Thus, $\frac{1}{7} = 0.142857\ 142857\ 142857 \ldots$ and $\frac{1}{17} = 0.0588235294117647\ 0588235294117647 \ldots$. Observe that only those prime numbers that yield a repeating decimal fraction for $1/p$ that has a period of $p - 1$ digits can produce a cyclical integer.

Since $\frac{1}{13} = 0.076923\ 076923 \ldots$ the prime number 13 does not yield a cyclical integer. In converting the fraction $1/p$ to its decimal fractional form by dividing $1.000 \ldots$ by p, the successive remainders must be less than p. Now there are only $p - 1$ integers less than p to serve as such remainders. As the period of $1/p$ is not delayed, repetition begins when the remainder 1 recurs. Now if the period consists of $p - 1$ digits, all integers from 1 to $p - 1$, inclusive, must occur among the successive remainders. Hence, for the period of fraction a/p, the period begins at the point where the a occurs as a remainder, showing that the period of a/p has the same recurring digits as the digits for the decimal form of $1/p$, which clarifies the mystery of cyclical integers.

To illustrate, observe the division scheme that yields the decimal form for $\frac{1}{7}$:

```
     0.142857
   _____
 7 1.00000000 . . .
   7
   __
    30                Remainder 3
    28
    __
     20               Remainder 2
     14
     __
      60              Remainder 6
      56
      __
       40             Remainder 4
       35
       __
        50            Remainder 5
        49
        __
         1            Original 1 as remainder; here period repeats
```

Continued division yields the same cycle of remainders, 1, 3, 2, 6, 4, 5.   Thus, for the decimal form for $\frac{3}{7}$, the first remainder is the numerator 3, which yields ensuing remainders exactly as previously in the cycle, 3, 2, 6, ...   Hence $\frac{3}{7} = 0.42857$ . . . or 3×0.142857 . . . .

The approximation for π, $\frac{355}{113}$, yields a cyclical integer of 112 digits.

∾ CHALLENGES

1.   Which of the prime numbers 11, 17, 19, 31, 37 yield cyclical integers?

2.   Show that the prime number 29 yields the cyclical integer

    0344827586206896551724137931

    Add the two 14-digit integers consisting of the first and last halves of this cyclical integer.

3.   Section off any cyclical integer into equal portions.   Now add these portions.   What astonishing array of digits do you obtain in the sum?   For example, the cyclical integer 142857 may be sectioned as follows:
    (a) $142 + 847$,   (b) $14 + 28 + 57$,   (c) $1 + 4 + 2 + 8 + 5 + 7$.

4.   The 28 digits of the cyclical integer arising from the prime number 29 may be sectioned off into sets of 14, 7, 4, 2, or 1 digit(s), respectively.   Add these five different sectionings.   Can you formulate a rule to describe the remarkable sums so obtained?

5.   Obtain the 112-digit cyclical integers that the prime number 113 yields. Since $112 = 2^4 \times 7$, there are $(4 + 1)(1 + 1)$, or 10 exact divisors of 112. However, there are only nine possible sectionings of the 112 digits of the cyclical integer.   Why not 10?   Test the sums of these various sections with the rule formulated in the preceding challenge.

6.   Describe the cyclical features of the periods of (a) $\frac{1}{13}$, (b) $\frac{2}{13}$, (c) $\frac{3}{13}$, (d) $\frac{4}{13}$ · · · ·

7.   Discover cyclical features of the periods of a/p if the period of $1/p$ contains fewer than $p - 1$ digits.   Note that the integers that may be used for the numerator a may be segregated into n distinct classes, wherein $n = \dfrac{p - 1}{d}$ and d represents the number of digits of the period of $1/p$.   *Hint:* Obtain the periods of $\frac{1}{31}, \frac{2}{31}, \frac{3}{31}, \cdots, \frac{1}{43}, \frac{2}{43}, \frac{3}{43}, \cdots, \frac{1}{53}, \frac{2}{53}, \frac{3}{53}, \cdots$ until the general cyclical situations become clear.

S·23 ∾ THE PERIOD OF THE DECIMAL FRACTIONAL FORM FOR $1/p$, FOR p AS PRIME

Two rather remarkable properties of the period of the decimal fractional form for $1/p$, if p is a prime number, are the following:

1.   The number of digits in the period is an *exact divisor of $p - 1$*.

2. If the period consists of an *even* number of digits, the two numbers formed by the two halves of the period have a sum consisting of 9s only.

To illustrate, $\frac{1}{13} = 0.076923\ 076923\ \ldots$. Note that 13 is a prime number, whence $p - 1 = 12$. The number of digits in the period, 6, is an exact divisor of 12. The two halves of the period, 076923, namely 076 and 923, have a sum 999, which consists of 9s entirely.

Again, the number of digits in the period of the decimal form for $\frac{1}{19}$ must be an exact divisor of 18, namely, 1 or 2 or 3 or 6 or 9, or 18. When half the period is obtained by division the remaining digits may be immediately obtained by subtracting from 9, one by one, the digits already found.

```
19|1.0000000000|0.052631578947368421
   95
  ──
    50
    38
    ──
   120
   114
   ───
     60
     57
     ──
      30
      19
      ──
     110
      95
     ───
     150
     133
     ───
     170
```

Repetition of digits begins as soon as the period is completed; since repetition does not begin with the second digit or *third* or *fourth* digits, repetition is impossible with fifth or sixth digits; as repetition does not begin with the seventh or ninth digit, one is certain that the period consists of 18 digits. After nine digits are obtained, the remaining digits may be noted to be: $9 - 0$, or 9; $9 - 5$, or 4; $9 - 2$, or 7, . . . , that is, deducting from 9 each of the digits already found.

To prove that the two properties hold for all such unit fractions, $1/p$ with prime denominator, it is advantageous to use a very important congruence relationship known as Fermat's theorem, namely: If a is not divisible by the prime number p, then $a^{p-1} \equiv 1 \pmod{p}$. This relationship is proved correct as follows.

Obtain the least positive residues of a, $2a$, $3a$, . . . , $(p - 1)a$; these residues will be positive numbers that are all less than p. No two of these residues can be equal, for if the residues of $ha = ka$, where h and k denote positive integers less than p, then if $h > k$, $ha \equiv ka \pmod{p}$, or $ha - ka \equiv 0 \pmod{p}$, or $(h - k)a \equiv 0 \pmod{p}$. Since both h and k are less than p, their difference,

$h - k$, must also be less than p and so $h - k$ cannot be a divided by p. Then, dividing the terms of the congruence by $h - k$, one obtains $a \equiv 0$ (mod. p), which is clearly impossible, since a is smaller than p. Therefore all the foregoing residues are different from one another; as there are $p - 1$ of them, they must be the entire set of positive integers 1, 2, 3, 4, . . . , $p - 1$. Expressing the congruences, one has

$$a \equiv R_1 \text{ (mod. } p)$$
$$2a \equiv R_2 \text{ (mod. } p)$$
$$3a \equiv R_3 \text{ (mod. } p)$$
$$\cdot \cdot \cdot \cdot \cdot \cdot \cdot \cdot \cdot$$
$$(p - 1)a \equiv R_{p-1} \text{ (mod. } p)$$

Here the R's, with subscript numbers to distinguish them from one another, are the complete set of numbers 1, 2, 3, 4, . . . , $(p - 1)$. Hence the product of these $p - 1$ congruences must be $a(2a)(3a) \cdot \cdot \cdot (p - 1)a \equiv 1 \times 2 \times 3 \times 4 \times \cdot \cdot \cdot \times (p - 1)$ (mod. p). Dividing both terms of this congruence by these numbers, 2, 3, 4, 5, . . . , $p - 1$, since each is less than p, one obtains $a^{p-1} \equiv 1$ (mod. p). One may now establish the correctness of the two original assertions:

For Property 1, the number of digits of the period of the decimal fractional form for $1/p$ must be an exact divisor of $p - 1$. Let d denote this number of digits of the period. Observe that in carrying out the division 1.00000 . . . $/p$ to obtain the period of the decimal fraction, each successive remainder is the residue of 10, 100 or 10^2, 1,000 or 10^3, 10,000 or 10^4, ... At the stage where the remainder 1 appears one has completed the period of the decimal fractional form for $1/p$. Then $10^d \equiv 1$ (mod. p), and d is the *smallest* integral power of 10 that is congruent to 1 for modulus p.

Now if d were not an exact divisor of $p - 1$, then $(p - 1) \div d$ would be a quotient q *and a remainder* r. That is, $p - 1 = qd + r$. Then $10^{p-1} = 10^{qd} \times 10^r$, while r is smaller than d. Since $10^d \equiv 1$ (mod. p), then $(10^d)^q \equiv 1$ (mod. p), therefore, replacing 10^{p-1} and 10^{qd} by their least positive residues, namely, 1, then $10^{p-1} \equiv 10^{qd} \times 10^r$ (mod. p), reduces to $1 \equiv 10^r$ (mod. p); but this last expression is impossible, since d is the smallest integral exponent 10 may have to yield such a congruence. Therefore r must be 0, which means that $p - 1$ must be exactly divisible by d.

For Property 2, if the period consists of an even number of digits, the sum of the two numbers consisting of the two halves of the period consists of 9s only. Let $d = 2k$ be the number of digits in the period of the decimal fraction. Then $10^{2k} \equiv 1$ (mod. p); taking the square roots of each term, one has $10^k \equiv 1$ (mod. p) or $10^k \equiv -1$ (mod. p). Since k is smaller than d, $10^k \equiv 1$ is impossible. Therefore $10^k \equiv -1$, or $p - 1$ (mod. p). Now k denotes the number of digits in the half-period of the decimal fraction. Let m denote any integer less than k. Then in the division that is to yield the period let the mth remainder be r and the next ensuing digit of the period be A. Thus, multiplying:

$$10^m \equiv r \ (\text{mod. } p)$$

$$\frac{10^k \equiv -1 \ (\text{mod. } p)}{10^{m+k} \equiv -r \equiv p - r \ (\text{mod. } p)}$$

$$
\begin{array}{r}
. \ . \ A \\
p\overline{\smash{)}1.00000} \\
\cdots \\
\cdots \\
r
\end{array}
$$

Accordingly, the mth remainder is r, and the $(m + k)$th remainder is $p - r$. Now let the digit in the quotient following the remainder $p - r$ be B. That is, adding:

$$\frac{10r}{p} = A + \frac{e}{p}$$

$$\frac{10(p - r)}{p} = B + \frac{f}{p}$$

$$\frac{10r + 10(p - r)}{p} = A + B + \frac{e}{p} + \frac{f}{p}$$

wherein e/p and f/p must be proper fractions, neither being equal to zero

Thus, $10 = A + B + (e/p) + (f/p)$; therefore $(e/p) + (f/p)$ must be integral and since $(e/p) + (f/p)$ must be less than 2, $(e/p) + (f/p)$ must equal 1. Therefore $A + B$ must be equal to 9. Since A and B represent any corresponding digits in the two half-periods, the sum of all such pairs must also be equal to 9.

⟋ CHALLENGES

1. Test the two foregoing properties for the periods of the decimal forms of $\frac{1}{11}$, $\frac{1}{17}$, $\frac{1}{37}$, $\frac{1}{29}$, $\frac{1}{3}$.

2. Separate the period of the decimal form for $\frac{1}{19}$ into three equal portions, then add the three 6-digit numbers. What peculiarity appears among the digits of the result?

3. Separate the period of the decimal form for $\frac{1}{17}$ into four equal portions, then add the four resulting four-digit numbers. What peculiarity do the digits of this result show?

4. Pursue the investigation suggested by the two preceding challenges with other periods that can be separated into equal portions, until you are convinced of your surmise of all such results.

5. State convincing reasons why the sum of the digits of the period of the decimal form for $1/p$, p being a prime number greater than 3, must be a multiple of 9.

6. Read understandingly each step of the proof of the generalization of the second proposition, namely, if the period of a decimal form for $1/p$, p being prime, is separated into any number of equal sections and the result-

ing numbers added, the sum will consist of digits such that the end digits add to 9, and all intervening digits are 9s. (The sections consist of at least two digits each.)

The universal correctness of the statement that the sum of numbers formed from the equal-digit sections of the period of the decimal form for $1/p$, if p is prime, follows the same pattern as that for the special case for the sum of the three-digit numbers formed from the eighteen-digit period of the decimal form for $\frac{1}{19}$. Observe how the division of 1.000 . . . by 19 is broken up into the six portions:

0.052	631	578	947	368	421
19|1.000	19|12000	19|11000	19|18000	19|7000	19|8000
95	114	95	171	57	76
50	60	150	90	130	40
38	57	133	76	114	38
12	30	170	140	160	20
	19	152	133	152	19
	11	18	7	8	1

Note that the residue of 1×1000 is 12 and that $1000 = 19 \times 052 + 12$; the residue of 12×1000 is 11 and $12000 = 19 \times 631 + 11$; of 11×1000 is 18 and $11000 = 19 \times 578 + 18$; of 18×1000 is 7 and $18000 = 19 \times 947 + 7$; of 7×1000 is 8 and $7000 = 19 \times 368 + 8$; of 8×1000 is 1 and $8000 = 19 \times 421 + 1$. Observe that each remainder, or residue, of the foregoing long divisions is the same multiple of 1000 in the ensuing dividend, and that the final remainder, 1, is the multiple of 1000 in the first of the dividends.

Add the following equalities, using the distributive law of addition in the sums:

$$1 \times 1000 = 19 \times 052 + 12$$
$$12 \times 1000 = 19 \times 631 + 11$$
$$11 \times 1000 = 19 \times 578 + 18$$
$$18 \times 1000 = 19 \times 947 + 7$$
$$7 \times 1000 = 19 \times 368 + 8$$
$$8 \times 1000 = 19 \times 421 + 1$$

$(1 + 12 + 11 + 18 + 7 + 8) \times 1000 = 19 \times$ (sum of three-digit sections) $+ (12 + 11 + 18 + 7 + 8 + 1)$. That is, $57 \times 1000 = 19 \times$ (the sum of the three-digit sections) $+ 57$.

Now, dividing both members of the equality by 19 and subtracting 3 from the results, one obtains $3000 - 3 =$ the sum of the three-digit sections of the period. But $3000 - 3 = 2997$, the sum of the end digits being 9 and the intermediate digits all 9s. Will this result always occur?

The proof of the general theorem follows the foregoing pattern. Let the period of the decimal form of $1/p$ contain d digits; let this period be separated into m sections of d/m, or q digits in each section. Accordingly, there will be m separate long divisions, having as remainders the least positive residues of 10^q, where q is successively 1, 2, 3, 4, . . . , d. Observe that if the first such residue is R, the ensuing residues must be R, $R \times 10^q$, $R \times 10^{2q}$, . . . , $R \times 10^{(m-1)q}$. The sum of these residues must be a multiple of p, as is thus proved. Note that $10^{mq} = 10^d \equiv 1 \pmod{p}$. Let the sum of the foregoing residues be S; i.e., $R(1 + 10^q + 10^{2q} + \cdots + 10^{(m-1)q}) \equiv S \pmod{p}$. Now $10 - 1$, or 9, cannot be a multiple of p if p is not 3. Now multiply both members of this congruence by $10 - 1$ and obtain

$$R \times (10 - 1)(10^{(m-1)q} + 10^{(m-2)q} + \cdots + 10^{2q} + 10^q + 1) \equiv 9S \pmod{p}$$

or $\quad R \times (10 - 1) \times \dfrac{(10^{mq} - 1)}{(10 - 1)} = R \times (10^{mq} - 1) \equiv 9S \pmod{p}$

but $10^{mq} \equiv 1$, whence $0 \equiv 9S$, or $S \equiv 0 \pmod{p}$. Therefore the sum of the foregoing remainders must be a multiple of p. Accordingly, adding the series of equalities,

$$10^q = p \times (\text{first set of digits in period}) + R$$
$$R \times 10^q = p \times (\text{second set of digits in period}) + R'$$
$$R' \times 10^q = p \times (\text{third set of digits in period}) + R''$$
$$\cdots \cdots \cdots \cdots \cdots \cdots \cdots \cdots \cdots \cdots \cdots$$
$$k \times p \times 10^q = p \times (\text{sum of the } q\text{-digit numbers formed from period}) + kp$$

That is, the sum of the q-digit numbers formed from the period $= k \times 10^q - k$ or $k(10^q - 1)$, or a multiple of a number consisting of q 9s.

∾ CHALLENGE

Prove Property 2 for an even number of digits by the pattern of proof used for the general situation. Thus,

First half of period	*Second half of period*
$p\overline{)\quad 10^{d/2}}$	$p\overline{)\quad R \times 10^{d/2}}$
$\cdots$	$\cdots$
$\cdots$	$\cdots$
$\cdots$	$\cdots$
R	1

Then, adding

$$1 \times 10^{d/2} = p \times \text{(first half of period)} + R$$
$$R \times 10^{d/2} = p \times \text{(second half of period)} + 1$$

$$\overline{(1 + R) \times 10^{d/2} = p \times \text{(sum of the two halves of period)} + (1 + R)}$$

Now $R^2 - 1 = (R - 1)(R + 1) \equiv 0$ (mod. p), dividing by $R - 1$ which, being less than p, cannot be a multiple of p. Then $R + 1$ must be a multiple of p, but R is less than p, therefore $R + 1$ must be exactly equal to p. Hence dividing out the p, one obtains $10^{d/2} - 1 = $ the sum of the two halves of the period. Note that 10 to any power diminished by 1 is a number consisting entirely of 9s.

S·24 ~ The concept of infinity

The expression "N equals infinity" or "N becomes infinite" or "N approaches infinity" simply means that there exists another number greater than any specified number. To state that the number of natural numbers is infinite means that there are more natural numbers than any stated number of them, or that there is a successor of every natural number. Thus, infinity is not a number but a term for a circumstance or state of affairs. In mathematical symbols one expresses the notion as lim $N = \infty$.

Again, $\lim_{N \to \infty} 1/N = 0$ means that the fraction $1/N$ may be made as near to 0 as one pleases by taking N sufficiently large. Thus, $1/N - 0$ is less than 0.001 if N is taken greater than 1,000.

Again, $\lim_{N \to 0} 1/N = \infty$ means that the fraction $1/N$ will become greater than any specified number whatever if one takes N sufficiently small. Thus, $1/N$ is greater than 250,000 if one takes N smaller than $\frac{1}{250,000}$ or 0.000,004.

Finally, $\lim_{N \to \infty} \dfrac{3N + 5}{7N + 2} = \frac{3}{7}$, because the fraction $\dfrac{3N + 5}{7N + 2}$ can be made to differ from $\frac{3}{7}$ by as small a number as one may desire by taking N sufficiently large. Thus, $\dfrac{3N + 5}{7N + 2} - \frac{3}{7} = \dfrac{29}{49N + 14}$, which is less than 0.001 whenever N is greater than $(29 \times 1000 - 14)/47$, or $591\frac{27}{49}$. Otherwise evaluated,

$$\lim_{N \to \infty} \frac{3N + 5}{7N + 2} = \lim_{N \to \infty} \frac{3 + (5/N)}{7 + (2/N)} = \frac{3}{7}$$

$$\text{since} \quad \lim_{N \to \infty} \frac{5}{N} = 0 \quad \lim_{N \to \infty} \frac{2}{N} = 0$$

Hence, whenever the term *infinity* is used, it implies a situation in which some numerical quantity is made to become larger than any prescribed number value.

Some useful mnemonics are: $\frac{1}{0} = \infty$, $\dfrac{1}{\infty} = 0$, $a \times \infty = \infty$ (if a is not zero).

S·25 ～ THE SEVEN INDETERMINATES

"Brothers and sisters, my pretty maid,
How many may you be?"
"How many? Seven, sir," she said,
And wondering looked at me.

—Wordsworth, *We Are Seven*

Seven expressions involving divisions, multiplication, subtraction, and involutions, namely, (1) $\frac{0}{0}$, (2) $\frac{\infty}{\infty}$, (3) $\infty \times 0$, (4) $\infty - \infty$, (5) 0^0, (6) ∞^0, (7) 1^∞, are called *indeterminates* inasmuch as each such expression may logically be given any numerical value whatever.

1. For the division $\frac{0}{0}$, the definition of division a/b expressly excludes the value of 0 for b. However, the fraction a/b may approach indefinitely near to some value, which is then assigned to $\frac{0}{0}$ in this instance. Thus, the fraction kN/N always has the value k for all values of N so long as $N \neq 0$. Accordingly, if N is assigned numerical values as near to zero as one may desire, but not zero itself, kN/N continues to have the value k. Therefore, $\lim\limits_{N \to 0} \frac{kN}{N} = \frac{0}{0} = k$, whence $\frac{0}{0}$ may be assigned any arbitrary value k.

   Consider $\lim\limits_{N \to 0} \frac{\pm N}{N^2} = \frac{0}{0}$, but if $N \neq 0$, $\frac{\pm N}{N^2} = \frac{\pm 1}{N}$, and $\lim\limits_{N \to 0} \frac{\pm 1}{N} = \pm \infty$.
   Thus $\frac{0}{0}$ may have any numerical value whatever, real or complex, and may also occur in situations leading to $\pm \infty$.

2. a. For the division $\frac{\infty}{\infty}$, let $k \neq 0$. Consider $\lim\limits_{N \to 0} \frac{k/N}{1/N} = \frac{\infty}{\infty}$. But $\frac{k/N}{1/N} = k$ for any value of N different from 0. Therefore, in this instance, $\frac{\infty}{\infty}$ has the value k which is assigned to it. Therefore, $\frac{\infty}{\infty}$ has the arbitrary value $k \neq 0$.

   b. Consider $\lim\limits_{N \to 0} \frac{1/N}{1/N^2} = \frac{\infty}{\infty}$, but if $N \neq 0$, $\frac{1/N}{1/N^2} = N$ and $\lim\limits_{N \to 0} N = 0$, so that in this instance $\frac{\infty}{\infty} = 0$. Therefore $\frac{\infty}{\infty}$ may have any numerical value assigned to it, including zero.

   c. Consider $\lim\limits_{N \to 0} \frac{\pm 1/N^2}{\pm 1/N} = \frac{\infty}{\infty}$. But if $N \neq 0$, $\frac{\pm 1/N^2}{\pm 1/N} = \pm \frac{1}{N}$ and

$\lim\limits_{N \to 0} \dfrac{\pm 1}{N} = \pm\infty$. Thus $\dfrac{\infty}{\infty}$ may have any numerical value whatever, real or complex, and may also occur in situations leading to $\pm\infty$.

3.   *a.*   For the multiplication $0 \times \infty$, let k and N be assigned any arbitrary value except 0. Then $\lim\limits_{N \to 0}\left(kN \times \dfrac{1}{N}\right) = 0 \times \infty$. But if $N \neq 0$, $\dfrac{1/N}{kN} = k$. Therefore, $0 \times \infty$ may have any arbitrary value except 0 in this instance.

    b.   Consider $\lim\limits_{N \to 0} N^2 \times \dfrac{1}{N} = 0 \times \infty$; but if $N \neq 0$, $N^2 \times \dfrac{1}{N} = N$ and $\lim\limits_{N \to 0} N = 0$. Therefore, $0 \times \infty$ may also have value 0.

    c.   Consider $\lim\limits_{N \to 0} \pm N \times \dfrac{1}{N^2} = 0 \times \infty$; but if $N \neq 0$, $N \times \dfrac{1}{N^2} = \pm\dfrac{1}{N}$ and $\lim\limits_{N \to 0} \dfrac{\pm 1}{N} = \pm\infty$. Thus $0 \times \infty$ may have any numerical value whatever, including $\pm\infty$.

4.   For the subtraction $\infty - \infty$, let a, N, k be assigned any arbitrary values, real or complex, except that N and k must not represent zero.

    a.   Consider $\lim\limits_{N \to 0}\left[\dfrac{a + kN}{N} - \dfrac{a}{N}\right] = \infty - \infty$; but if $N \neq 0$, $\dfrac{a + kN}{N} - \dfrac{a}{N} = k$ and $\lim\limits_{N \to 0} k = k$.

    b.   Consider $\lim\limits_{N \to 0}\left[\dfrac{a \pm N}{N^2} - \dfrac{a}{N^2}\right] = \infty - \infty$; but if $N \neq 0$, $\dfrac{a \pm N}{N^2} - \dfrac{a}{N^2} = \dfrac{\pm 1}{N}$ and $\lim\limits_{N \to 0} \dfrac{\pm 1}{N^2} = \pm\infty$. Thus $\infty - \infty$ may represent any numerical value whatever, including $\pm\infty$.

5.   *a.*   For the involution 0^0, let c represent any number, real or complex, whose absolute value is greater than 1, and let b represent any integer greater than 1. Then, if $a^b = c$, the absolute value of a must be greater than 1. (Let $N > 0$.) Consider $\lim\limits_{N \to 0}(a^{-b/N})^{-N} = 0^0$; but if $N \neq 0$ $(a^{-b/N})^{-N} = a^b = c$, for $|c| > 1$.

    b.   Let c represent any number whose absolute value is less than 1, and let b represent any negative integer smaller than -1; then if $a^b = c$, the absolute value of a must be greater than 1. If N remains positive, consider $\lim\limits_{N \to 0}(a^{b/N})^N = 0^0$; but then $(a^{b/N})^N = a^b = c$, for $|c| < 1$.

    c.   Let N represent any positive real numbers less than 1. Consider $\lim\limits_{N \to 0}(N)^0 = 0^0$; but for $N \neq 0$, $N^0 = 1$. Therefore, $0^0 = 1$.

d. Recalling that $e^{\pi i} = -1$, wherein $e = 2.718,281,8 \ldots$, consider $\lim_{N \to 0} (e^{1/N})^{\pi i N} = 0^0$, but $(e^{1/N})^{\pi i N} = e^{\pi i} = -1$.

e. Let a represent any real number greater than 1, N positive. Consider $\lim_{N \to 0} (a^{-1/N^2})^{-N} = 0^0$; but $(a^{-1/N^2})^{-N} = a^{1/N}$, and $\lim_{N \to 0} a^{1/N} = +\infty$.

f. Let a represent any real negative number less than -1 and restrict N to reciprocals of odd natural numbers. Consider $\lim_{N \to 0} (a^{-1/N^2})^{-N} = 0^0$; but $(a^{-1/N^2})^{-N} = a^N$ and $\lim_{N \to 0} a^N = -\infty$.

Thus 0^0 may have any numerical value, real or complex, including $\pm \infty$.

6. For the involution ∞^0, replace N and N^2 by $-N$ and $-N^2$, respectively, in the discussion for 0^0, except for c, where N is replaced by $1/N$. One is led to the required results that ∞^0 may have:

a. All numerical values of absolute value greater than 1
b. All numerical values of absolute value less than 1
c. The value $+1$
d. The value -1
e. The value $+\infty$
f. The value $-\infty$

7. a. For the involution 1^∞, let c represent any number, real or complex, except 0 or 1; let b represent a positive integer greater than 1 and let N be positive. Let $a^b = c$. Consider $\lim_{N \to 0} (a^N)^{b/N} = 1^\infty$; but $(a^N)^{b/N} = a^b = c$.

b. Consider $\lim_{N \to 0} (e^{2\pi N})^{1/N} = 1^\infty$; but $(e^{2\pi N})^{1/N} = e^{2\pi i} = 1$.

c. Let a be positive, real, and less than 1, and N positive. Consider $\lim_{N \to 0} (a^N)^{1/N^2} = 1^\infty$; but $(a^N)^{1/N^2} = a^{1/N}$ and $\lim_{N \to 0} a^{1/N} = 0$.

d. Let a be real and greater than 1, and N positive. Consider $\lim_{N \to 0} (a^N)^{1/N^2} = 1^\infty$; but $(a^N)^{1/N^2} = a^{1/N}$ and $\lim_{N \to 0} a^{1/N} = +\infty$.

e. Let N be restricted to the reciprocals of positive odd integers and a be real and greater than 1. Consider $\lim_{N \to 0} (-a^N)^{1/N^2} = 1^\infty$; but $(-a^N)^{1/N^2} = -a^{1/N}$ and $\lim_{N \to 0} -a^{1/N} = -\infty$.

Thus 1^∞ may represent any numerical value whatever, real or complex, and may also be equal to $\pm \infty$.

The foregoing discussions demonstrate that each of the seven indeterminates may be regarded as equal to any number whatever, real or complex, as well as being equal to $\pm \infty$. The actual occurrence of an indeterminate in any specific situation will suggest the appropriate numerical value it should have on that particular occasion. Thus, if $a \neq b$, $\dfrac{a^2 - b^2}{a - b} = a + b$, since $a^2 - b^2 =$

$(a - b)(a + b)$. Since $\lim\limits_{b \to a} \dfrac{a^2 - b^2}{a - b} = \frac{0}{0}$, and $\lim\limits_{b \to a} (a + b) = 2a$, it is proper to

evaluate the $\frac{0}{0}$ in this case as $2a$.

⤳ CHALLENGES

1. Evaluate, if $a = b$:

   a. $\dfrac{a - b}{a - b}$ d. $\dfrac{4x^2 - 36}{2x - 6}$ for $x = 3$

   b. $\dfrac{a^3 - b^3}{a - b}$ e. $\dfrac{3x^2 + 2x + 1}{x^2 - 2x + 3}$ for $x = \infty$

   c. $\dfrac{a^n - b^n}{a - b}$ f. $(2^{1/x})^{3x}$ for $x = 0$

2. Evaluate (a) $\log_0 1$, (b) $\log_1 0$, (c) $\log_0 0$.

3. If $f(x)$ and $g(x)$ are not identically zero and if $f(a) = 0$, $g(a) = 0$, and if $f(x)$ and $g(x)$ are repeatedly differentiable at $x = a$, show that $\lim\limits_{x \to a} f(x)^{g(x)}$, which assumes the form 0^0, always has the value 1 if it has any value at all. Such problems are generally listed in texts on the calculus as indeterminate. Is this really appropriate?

ANSWERS

L<small>ESSON</small> 1 ∞

The successor of any natural number designated as N may be represented symbolically by $N + 1$, the predecessor of N by $N - 1$.

1.1. *a.* 48; 46   *e.* 3,001; 2,999   *h.* 12,346; 12,344
    b. 61; 59   *f.* 65,100; 65,098   *i.* 67,891; 67,889
    c. 90; 88   *g.* 10,001; 9,999   *j.* 9,010; 9,008
    d. 272; 270

1.2. *a.* 52,180; fifty-two thousand, one hundred eighty
    b. 322,875,436,107; three hundred twenty-two billion, eight hundred seventy-five million, four hundred thirty-six thousand, one hundred seven
    c. 1,020,030,004,000,005; one quadrillion, twenty trillion, thirty billion, four million, five
    d. 7,853,800,742; seven billion, eight hundred fifty-three million, eight hundred thousand, seven hundred forty-two

1.3. *a.* 36,137,064,305   *d.* 186,230
    b. 56,000,893   *e.* 586,000,000,000,000
    c. 1,200,003

1.4.   23
       976
     7,000
    31,416
    98,738
   230,499
 1,020,300

1.5. 2,460
2,641
4,265
4,623
6,247
6,429

1.6. *a.* 26
b. (i) 50 (ii) 13 (iii) 7
c. 9
d. 6, namely, ABC, ACB, BAC, BCA, CAB, CBA

1.7. *a.* 49 *d.* (i) 7, 4 (ii) 11, 11
b. (i) 12 (ii) 11 (iii) 1, 1 (iv) 10, 12
c. 3

1.8. *a.* Twenty times: 9, 19, 29, 39, 49, 59, 69, 79, 89, 90, 91, 92, 93, 94, 95, 96, 97, 98, 99

b. Nine times: 10, 20, 30, 40, 50, 60, 70, 80, 90

c. Nine single-digit numbers, namely, 1 to 9, inclusive; ninety two-digit numbers, namely, 10 to 99, inclusive, or 180 digits; altogether 180 digits and 9 digits, or 189 digits

1.9. *a.* 9 single-digit numbers, namely, 1 to 9, inclusive

b. 90 two-digit numbers, namely, 10 to 99, inclusive

c. 900 three-digit numbers, namely, 100 to 999, inclusive

d. 9,000,000,000 ten-digit numbers, namely, 1,000,000,000 to 9,999,999,999 inclusive

1.10. *a.* (i) 90,998 (ii) 10,204 *b.* 10,198 *c.* 91,003
90,999   10,203   10,200   91,001
91,000   10,202   10,202   90,999
91,001   10,201   10,204   10,203
91,002   10,200   90,998   10,201
91,003   10,199   91,000   10,199
91,004   10,198   91,002
          91,004

1.11. . *a.* 1 dot *d.* 10 dots
. . *b.* 3 dots *e.* 1, 3, 6, 10, 15, 21, 28, 36, 45, 55
. . . *c.* 6 dots
. . . .

1.12. . *a.* 1 dot
. . . *b.* 4 dots
. . . . *c.* 9 dots
. . . . . . *d.* 16 dots
e. 1, 4, 9, 16, 25, 36, 49, 64, 81, 100

f. These numbers of dots may be arrayed into square configurations of equally spaced dots, thus:

etc.

1.13. *a.* ⋯   *b.* ⋯   *c.* ⋯

d. 2, 6, 12, 20, 30, 42, 56, 72, 90, 110

e. Observe the separation into triangular configurations.

1.14. *a.* 1 dot   *b.* 8 dots   *c.* 27 dots   *d.* 1, 8, 27, 64, 125

1.15. Fifteen rows contain only two trees in each row.

LESSON 2

2.1. *a.* 531   *b.* 855   *c.* 1,386

2.2. 167,810

2.3. 1,020,360,733,289,034

2.4. 586,036,194,451,431

2.5. 1,388,952

2.6. 26,665

2.7. 1,606,396,929,323,892

2.8. 199,970

2.9. 120,000

2.10. 9,512 ft

2.11. *a.* 40 books   *b.* 108 books

2.12. *a.* Los Angeles: 1,503,997
   b. Total in 1940: 3,006,131; total in 1960: 4,058,071
   c. Los Angeles: 2,479,015

2.13. $12,495

2.14. 62 hours

2.15. 50 chairs

2.16.   72 letters

2.17.   3,828,395

2.18. $330,041,758,709

2.19.   41

2.20.   657 cows

2.21.   *A*: $4,860, $6,300, $7,740; *B*: $4,800, $6,200, $7,600; *A*'s annual salary exceeds *B*'s annual salary by an amount that increases by $40 in each ensuing year.

2.22.   Grand total: 43,058

2.23.   1775

2.24.   101,500

2.25. $33,850

LESSON 3 ∾

3.1.
a.	24,192	*g.*	12,345,679
b.	436,755		24,691,358
c.	524,288		49,382,716
d.	111,111,111		61,728,395
e.	74,074,074		86,419,753
f.	37,037,037		98,765,432

All digits from 1 to 9, inclusive, occur in each of these six products except that digit which is obtained by subtracting the multiplier from 9.

3.2.   *a.*   8,225,819   *b.*   58,425,649   *c.*   670,592,745

3.3.   *a.*   960   *b.*   453,600   *c.*   97,000   *d.*   87,900   *e.*   77,000

3.4.   *a.*   149   *b.*   298   *c.*   400

3.5.
a.	2,197	*e.*	10,000,000,000
b.	676	*f.*	0
c.	6,561	*g.*	1
d.	512		

3.6.   2,025

3.7.   91,125

3.8.   1; 16; 81; 256; 625; 1,296

3.9.   *a.*   1   *b.*   4   *c.*   9   *d.*   16   *e.*   25   *f.*   36

Rule: The sum of any arbitrary number of consecutive odd numbers, beginning with 1, is equal to the square of the number of odd numbers so added.

3.10. *a.* 1   *a.* 1
        b. 3   *b.* 9
        c. 6   *c.* 36
        d. 10   *d.* 100
        e. 15   *e.* 225

Rule: The square of the sum of any arbitrary number of consecutive natural numbers, beginning with 1, is equal to the sum of the cubes of these same natural numbers.

3.11. 7,884 miles; cost $140.16

3.12. $76.08

3.13. 180 sq ft; 20 sq yd; 25,920 sq in

3.14. $39.96

3.15. $38,522,880

3.16. $80; $21

3.17. 270 cu ft; 16,740 lb

3.18. *a.* 2,835 cu ft   *b.* $40.95

3.19. 5,875,976,736,000 miles

3.20. $8,235.43; $8,736.12

3.21. *a.* 810 games   *b.* $108,000

3.22. 320 specimens

3.23. *a.* 2,561 miles   *b.* $61.07

3.24. 600 books; $2,850

3.25. *a.* 8   *b.* 27   *c.* 64   *d.* 125

Rule: The sum of *n* consecutive odd numbers from $(n^2 - n + 1)$ to $(n^2 + n - 1)$, inclusive, is equal to the cube of *n*, or n^3.

Lesson 4 ∾

4.1. *a.* 9   *b.* 8   *c.* 4   *d.* 7   *e.* 8   *f.* 9   *g.* 7

4.2. *a.* 98   *b.* 46   *c.* 52

4.3. *a.* 15   *b.* 14   *c.* 36   *d.* 21   *e.* 18 (277 − 173 = 104)

4.4. *a.* 181   *b.* 198   *c.* 301   *d.* 1,138

4.5. *a.* 743,610   *b.* 714,285   *c.* 998,766

4.6. *a.* 432,100,001   *b.* 4,308,643

4.7. *a.* −30   *e.* 285,714   *i.* +8   *m.* +7
        b. −506   *f.* −571,428   *j.* −17   *n.* +6
        c. −81,334   *g.* −15   *k.* +3   *o.* +6
        d. −2,579,765 *h.* −4   *l.* −6   *p.* −4

4.8.   −18

4.9.   −362,880

4.10.   *a.*   −36   *d.*   −23   *g.*   +2
          b.   145   *e.*   −131   *h.*   −7
          c.   75   *f.*   +55   *i.*   −7

4.11.   *a.*   −32   *d.*   −216   *g.*   −343
          b.   25   *e.*   −100,000   *h.*   −2,187
          c.   729   *f.*   1,000,000

4.12.   *a.*   250°C   *b.*   450°F   *c.*   250°K

4.13.   Day 1: $1,500.00   Day 7: −$25.05
          Day 2: $1,245.00   Day 8: $1,224.95
          Day 3: $1,410.75   Day 9: $1,109.55
          Day 4: $1,390.20   Day 10: $949.90
          Day 5: $954.95   Maximum day 1: $1,500.00
          Day 6: $974.95   Minimum day 7: overdrawn $25.05

4.14.   *a.*   Assassination of Caesar by 709 years   *b.*   45 years

4.15.   *a.* $910   *b.* $912

4.16. $754 and $793

Lesson 5 ❧

5.1.   *a.*   8   *f.*   7   *k.*   8   *p.*   9
          b.   7   *g.*   9   *l.*   6   *q.*   6
          c.   9   *h.*   8   *m.*   9   *r.*   5
          d.   8   *i.*   1   *n.*   6   *s.*   8
          e.   9   *j.*   7   *o.*   2   *t.*   8
          Sum is 140

5.2.   *a.*   7,282   *c.*   12,345,679   *e.*   3,145
          b.   274,232   *d.*   512   *f.*   12,345,679

5.3.   *a.*   −145   *d.*   +5,017   *g.*   +169
          b.   +435   *e.*   −20,068   *h.*   −6
          c.   −87   *f.*   0   *i.*   +103

5.4.   *a.*   102   *c.*   99   *e.*   19
          b.   94   *d.*   13

5.5.   253 books

5.6.   19 miles per gallon

5.7. $51.84

5.8.   7 days

5.9.   3 years

5.10. 10,816 sq ft

5.11. *a.* 10   *b.* $4.40

5.12. $64.45

5.13. 39 crates

5.14. 63,360 in.; 5,892,480,000,000 miles

5.15. *a.* $\frac{4}{9}$ *d.* $\frac{1}{3}$ *g.* $\frac{4}{7}$ *j.* $\frac{1}{3}$
 b. $\frac{4}{7}$ *e.* $\frac{2}{3}$ *h.* $\frac{2}{3}$ *k.* $\frac{1}{4}$
 c. $\frac{2}{5}$ *f.* $\frac{3}{11}$ *i.* $\frac{2}{3}$ *l.* $\frac{1}{3}$

5.16. *a.* $\frac{23}{4}$ *d.* $\frac{10}{3}$ *g.* $\frac{75}{8}$ *j.* $\frac{100}{7}$
 b. $\frac{25}{3}$ *e.* $\frac{100}{3}$ *h.* $\frac{477}{20}$ *k.* $\frac{10,000}{7}$
 c. $\frac{25}{4}$ *f.* $\frac{75}{2}$ *i.* $\frac{7,000}{9}$ *l.* $\frac{1,000,000}{7}$

5.17. *a.* $\frac{2}{3} < \frac{3}{4}$ *d.* $\frac{12}{5} < \frac{17}{7}$ *g.* $\frac{571,428}{857,142} = \frac{2}{3}$
 b. $\frac{7}{12} > \frac{11}{21}$ *e.* $\frac{7}{8} < \frac{8}{9}$ *h.* $\frac{428,571}{857,142} = \frac{1}{2}$
 c. $\frac{8}{11} < \frac{4}{5}$ *f.* $\frac{10}{17} > \frac{9}{16}$ *i.* $\frac{285,714}{857,142} > \frac{2}{7}$

5.18. $\frac{1}{6}$ $\frac{2}{5}$ $\frac{3}{7}$ $\frac{1}{2}$ $\frac{5}{9}$ $\frac{5}{8}$ $\frac{2}{3}$ $\frac{7}{10}$ $\frac{3}{4}$

5.19. *a.* $37\frac{32}{53}$ *d.* $21,319\frac{8}{47}$ *g.* $666,991\frac{52}{853}$
 b. $785\frac{4}{17}$ *e.* $227,207\frac{20}{71}$ *h.* $255,489\frac{3,079}{65,537}$
 c. $8,189\frac{20}{23}$ *f.* $377,703\frac{158}{367}$

5.20. 77 small blocks

5.21. 52

5.22. 6,480 lb

5.23. 6,912 gal

5.24. $3\frac{31}{48}$ in

5.25. $1,989\frac{127}{432}$ lb

LESSON 6 ⤙

6.1.

61 is prime	$75 = 3 \times 5^2$	$88 = 2^3 \times 11$
$62 = 2 \times 31$	$76 = 2^2 \times 19$	89 is prime
$63 = 3^2 \times 7$	$77 = 7 \times 11$	$90 = 2 \times 3^2 \times 5$
$64 = 2^6$	$78 = 2 \times 3 \times 13$	$91 = 7 \times 13$
$65 = 5 \times 13$	79 is prime	$92 = 4 \times 23$
$66 = 2 \times 3 \times 11$	$80 = 2^4 \times 5$	$93 = 3 \times 31$
67 is prime	$81 = 3^4$	$94 = 2 \times 47$
$68 = 2^2 \times 17$	$82 = 2 \times 41$	$95 = 5 \times 19$
$69 = 3 \times 23$	83 is prime	$96 = 2^5 \times 3$
$70 = 2 \times 5 \times 7$	$84 = 2^2 \times 3 \times 7$	97 is prime
71 is prime	$85 = 5 \times 17$	$98 = 2 \times 7^2$
$72 = 2^3 \times 3^2$	$86 = 2 \times 43$	$99 = 3^2 \times 11$
73 is prime	$87 = 3 \times 29$	$100 = 2^2 \times 5^2$
$74 = 2 \times 37$		

6.2. *a.* $2^2 \times 3^2 \times 7 = 252$ *d.* $2 \times 3^2 \times 7 = 126$
 b. $2^6 \times 3^3 = 1,728$ *e.* $2^5 \times 3^2 = 288$
 c. $2 \times 5^3 \times 11 = 2,750$ *f.* $2 \times 5 \times 7^3 = 3,430$

6.3. *a.* $2^3 \times 3 \times 7 = 168$ *f.* $2^9 \times 5^{15} \times 7^3$
$$= 5,359,375,000,000,000$$
 b. $2 \times 3^2 \times 5 \times 7^2 = 4,410$ *g.* $5 \times 13 = 65$
 c. $3^5 \times 5^4 = 151,875$ *h.* $2 \times 3 \times 5 = 30$
 d. $2^3 \times 3^2 \times 5^2 = 1,800$ *i.* $2^6 \times 3^4 \times 5^2 = 129,600$
 e. $2^8 \times 3^4 = 20,736$ *j.* $2 \times 3^2 \times 5^3 = 2,250$

6.4. *a.* 3×47 *d.* 29×31
 b. $7 \times 19 \times 43$ *e.* $2^{10} \times 3^2$
 c. $7 \times 11 \times 13$ *f.* $2 \times 3 \times 5 \times 7 \times 11 \times 13 \times 17$

6.5. *a.* $\frac{14}{17}$ *d.* $\frac{3}{4}$ *g.* $\frac{64}{91}$
 b. $\frac{3}{5}$ *e.* $\frac{2}{3}$ *h.* $\frac{2}{3}$
 c. $\frac{3}{5}$ *f.* $\frac{22}{29}$ *i.* $\frac{8}{143}$

6.6. *a.* $\frac{2}{3}$ *d.* $\frac{1}{3}$ *g.* $\frac{113}{355}$
 b. $\frac{3}{5}$ *e.* $\frac{7}{11}$ *h.* $\frac{2 \cdot 048}{6,561}$
 c. $\frac{101}{297}$ *f.* $\frac{5}{8}$ *i.* $\frac{3}{5}$

6.7. *a.* $1\frac{1}{8}$ *d.* $2\frac{3}{8}$ *g.* $145\frac{7}{10}$ *j.* $9\frac{49}{111}$
 b. $1\frac{1}{6}$ *e.* $43\frac{25}{44}$ *h.* $410\frac{11}{12}$ *k.* $\frac{73}{187}$
 c. $1\frac{7}{15}$ *f.* $101\frac{1}{6}$ *i.* $298\frac{71}{72}$ *l.* $\frac{1}{6}$

6.8. (*b*) is larger by $\frac{77}{160}$

6.9. $\frac{4}{5}$

6.10. 660 marbles

6.11. 12 rectangles

6.12. 216 blocks

6.13. 72 men

6.14. 256 lb

6.15. $720\frac{3}{4}$ ft

6.16. $1,074\frac{1}{4}$ ft; 1,088 ft

6.17. $18\frac{11}{12}$ lb

6.18. $\frac{1}{200}$ in. shorter

6.19. *a.* *B* heavier by $\frac{1}{400}$ lb   *b.* $\frac{351}{400}$ lb

6.20. *a.* $\frac{3}{20}$ of job   *b.* $\frac{1}{6}$ of job

6.21. *a.* 18 acres; 20 acres   *c.* $13\frac{1}{2}$ tons; 15 tons
 b. 45 mi; 50 mi   *d.* 9 mss.; 10 mss.

6.22. *a.* $12\frac{5}{16}$ ft   *b.* $2\frac{3}{16}$ ft

6.23. $\frac{11}{16}$ in.

6.24. $\frac{1}{16}$ of his money

6.25. $\frac{1}{60}$ of study time

6.26. $2.02\frac{3}{4}$

6.27. 40 tons

6.28. 4 hours, $8\frac{1}{2}$ minutes

6.29. Volume of box is $229\frac{11}{16}$ cu in.; too small by $1\frac{5}{16}$ cu in.

6.30. $\frac{1}{4}$, $-\frac{1}{25}$, $\frac{1}{144}$, $-\frac{1}{841}$; $\frac{99}{70}$, $\frac{239}{169}$
They are unit fractions with denominator equal to product of denominators.

6.31. *a.* $\frac{3}{8}$ *d.* $\frac{63}{100}$ *g.* $\frac{16}{81}$

     b. $\frac{35}{96}$ *e.* $\frac{1}{8}$ *h.* $\frac{1,001}{2,160}$

     c. $\frac{21}{32}$ *f.* $\frac{56}{135}$

6.32. *a.* pq/st *d.* q/ps^2 *g.* r/t

     b. q/t *e.* $p^2r^6t^6$ *h.* p^2q^2/s^2t^2

     c. pqr/st *f.* 1 *i.* p^2/q^2

6.33. *a.* pt/rs *c.* r^2/sq *e.* $p^2q^6r^{14}s^2t^3$

     b. p/t *d.* pr/q *f.* p^5/q^5

6.34. *a.* $\frac{5}{11}$ *c.* $52\frac{1}{2}$ *e.* $\frac{7}{26}$

     b. $\frac{5}{7}$ *d.* $\frac{11}{14}$ *f.* $9\frac{209}{324}$

6.35. *a.* $\frac{25}{432}$ *d.* $\frac{3}{8}$ *g.* $39\frac{3}{8}$ *j.* $20\frac{5}{12}$

     b. $\frac{1}{7}$ *e.* $\frac{1,024}{59,049}$ *h.* $\frac{90}{91}$ *k.* 600

     c. $\frac{1}{2}$ *f.* $\frac{105}{2,431}$ *i.* $10\frac{1}{3}$ *l.* $17\frac{13}{36}$

6.36. *a.* $\frac{3}{5}$ *d.* 2 *g.* $1\frac{1}{3}$ *j.* pq^2t^2/rs^3

     b. $\frac{6}{7}$ *e.* 8 *h.* st/q^2

     c. $1\frac{1}{3}$ *f.* $\frac{18}{49}$ *i.* q/s

6.37. $190\frac{1}{2}$ sq ft; $14.12\frac{7}{8}$

6.38. *a.* $6\frac{3}{8}$ sq ft   *b.* $11\frac{1}{2}$ ft

6.39. *a.* $617\frac{1}{7}$ gal   *b.* $5,156\frac{1}{4}$ lb

6.40. $85\frac{23}{24}$ cents; 86 cents

6.41. 31 boxes; $1\frac{1}{3}$ lb

6.42. $29\frac{1}{6}$ minutes

6.43. 63 dozen; 42 dozen

6.44. 16 books

6.45. $192.50

6.46. $(\frac{3}{4})^3$ is greater than $(\frac{5}{8})^2$ by $\frac{1}{32}$

6.47. $3,355.92\frac{23}{96}$

6.48. *a.* $36\frac{3}{5}$ lb   *b.*   400 lb

6.49. *a.* $\frac{1}{3}$ of job   *b.* $4\frac{4}{5}$ days

6.50. $1\frac{229}{275}$ days, 12 hours, 36 minutes

LESSON 7 ⤴

7.1. *a.* $\frac{4}{9}$ *d.* $-\frac{12}{19}$ *g.* $-\frac{2}{9}$ *j.* $-\frac{29}{30}$

   b. $\frac{2}{5}$ *e.* $\frac{2}{3}$ *h.* $\frac{8}{27}$ *k.* $-\frac{49}{51}$

   c. $-\frac{3}{4}$ *f.* $-\frac{3}{5}$ *i.* $-\frac{1}{2}$ *l.* $-\frac{127}{255}$

7.2. *a.* $-\frac{11}{24}$ *c.* $-\frac{1}{77}$ *e.* $1\frac{11}{48}$

   b. $-\frac{11}{20}$ *d.* $\frac{5}{132}$ *f.* $1\frac{1}{9}$

7.3. Same as in 7.2.

7.4. *a.* $6\frac{7}{12}$

   b. $4\frac{6}{7}$

   c. $-4\frac{9}{11}$

   d. $-14\frac{5}{13}$

   e. $-5\frac{5}{7}$

   f. $7\frac{2}{5}$

   g. $-1\frac{5}{8}$

   h. $5\frac{3}{8}$

   i. $8\frac{1}{7}$

   j. $-4\frac{1}{2}$

   k. $5\frac{5}{9}$

   l. $-\frac{1}{7}$

m. $-4\frac{11}{15}$

n. $-3\frac{2}{9}$

o. $3\frac{7}{10}$

p. $-9\frac{5}{8}$

7.5.   *a.* $3\frac{7}{8}$ *c.* $-4\frac{2}{3}$ *e.* 11

     b. $3,159$ *d.* $10\frac{3}{4}$ *f.* $14\frac{7}{18}$

7.6.   *a.* $\frac{5}{12}$ *c.* $-\frac{9}{20}$ *e.* $1\frac{1}{2}$ *g.* $-\frac{3}{5}$

     b. $-\frac{5}{21}$ *d.* $-16\frac{1}{4}$ *f.* -6 *h.* $-\frac{15}{256}$

7.7.   *a.* $-3\frac{3}{4}$ *c.* $\frac{210}{221}$

     b. $-22\frac{25}{32}$ *d.* $-\frac{27}{256}$

7.8.   *a.* 17 *c.* $2\frac{14}{15}$

     b. $-13\frac{19}{60}$ *d.* -5

7.9.   *a.* $58°, 64°, 67°, 63°, 56°, 66°, 58°, 63°, 59°$

     b. $67°$ maximum; $56°$ minimum

     c. $+1°$

7.10.   *a.* $62\frac{1}{2}°, 69\frac{4}{5}°, 64\frac{3}{10}°, 60\frac{9}{10}°, 65\frac{7}{10}°, 76\frac{9}{10}°, 76\frac{3}{5}°, 63\frac{1}{10}°, 71\frac{7}{10}°$

     b. $76\frac{9}{10}°$ maximum; $60\frac{9}{10}°$ minimum

     c. $9\frac{1}{5}°$

7.11.   *a.* $A:$ $+5\frac{3}{10}$, retained $C:$ $+10\frac{7}{10}$, promoted $E:$ $+1$, retained

     $B:$ $-5\frac{1}{2}$, dismissed $D:$ $+5\frac{1}{2}$, retained

     b. $+17$ points

7.12.   *a.* Fifth day, $103\frac{7}{20}$

     b. Second day, $97\frac{29}{40}$

     c. $-2\frac{1}{40}$, the net decline in the six days

7.13.   Same as the original position

7.14.   On June 21 the sun is $23\frac{1}{2}°$ north of the position of September 21

7.15.   *a.* 3 years, $333\frac{4}{7}$ days, to Mars and return, which is reduced by 1 day if a leap year occurs during the trip.

     b. 352 years $91\frac{3}{7}$ days, for years of 365 days each; however, 84 or 85 leap years must occur during this time according to our Gregorian calendar for which the century years, 2000, 2100, etc. are not leap years, unless divisible by 400. Accordingly, the trip must require 352 years, $6\frac{3}{7}$ or $5\frac{3}{7}$ days.

LESSON 8 ∽

8.1.   *a.*   1,994,374   *e.*   1,336,336
      b.   3,085   *f.*   1,024
      c.   4,873,431,264   *g.*   100
      d.   185,864,186,368,000

8.2.   *a.*   1,447   *e.*   12   *i.*   3
      b.   214,287   *f.*   11   *j.*   5
      c.   128   *g.*   5
      d.   501   *h.*   3

8.3.   *a.* $-3,105$ *d.*   23   *g.* $130\frac{13}{24}$
      b. $-48\frac{23}{40}$ *e.* $-38\frac{1}{4}$ *h.* $-8\frac{5}{6}$
      c. $-131,099$ *f.* $7\frac{13}{14}$

8.4.   *a.* $-1,288$ *d.*   260   *g.* $-2,520$
      b. $8\frac{1}{6}$ *e.*   0   *h.*   374
      c. $-39,375$ *f.* $-3\frac{3}{7}$

8.5.   *a.* $4\frac{6}{13}$ *e.*   0   *i.* $-\frac{2}{5}$
      b. $\frac{2}{5}$ *f.*   Impossible   *j.* $-\frac{1}{14}$
      c. $\frac{7}{12}$ *g.* $-\frac{1}{12}$
      d. $\frac{21}{80}$ *h.* $\frac{11}{111}$

8.6.   *a.*   729   *d.* $-\frac{1}{128}$ *g.*   64   *j.*   1
      b.   625   *e.* $-1,331$ *h.* $-100,000$ *k.* $\frac{4}{25}$
      c. $-4\frac{17}{27}$ *f.* $56\frac{1}{4}$ *i.* $6\frac{303}{512}$ *l.* $-\frac{27}{1,000}$

8.7.   *a.*   356   *b.* $13\frac{3}{4}$ *c.*   2   *d.* $5\frac{1}{3}$

8.8.   *a.* -113 *b.* $-12\frac{1}{2}$ *c.* $-12\frac{1}{12}$ *d.*   1   *e.* $1\frac{9}{16}$

8.9.   *a.*   28   *e.* $11\frac{5}{9}$ *i.*   3
      b.   26   *f.*   7   *j.*   115
      c.   14   *g.*   2
      d. $7\frac{11}{12}$ *h.*   3

8.10.   *a.*   5

       b. $2\frac{1}{8}$

       c. $\frac{7}{12}$

       d. -2

e. $-9\frac{5}{8}$

f. $\frac{1}{2}$

g. $1\frac{1}{2}$

h. 0

i. $-\frac{13}{24}$

j.

8.11. *a.* $5\frac{1}{12}$ *b.* 2

8.12. *a.* $3\frac{13}{24}$

b. $3\frac{13}{24}$

c. The sum of the arithmetic means obtained respectively from each pair of a set of pairs of numbers is equal to the arithmetic mean of the two sums consisting, respectively, of one number of each pair of the set of pairs of numbers.

d. The arithmetic means of the three pairs of numbers are, respectively, 6, -7, and -3, and yield the sum -4; the sum of the first number of each pair is $+6$, the sum of the other number of each pair is -14. The arithmetic mean of $+6$ and -14 is also equal to -4.

LESSON 9

9.1. *a.* $\frac{3}{4}$ *f.* $\frac{1}{4,000}$ *k.* $456\frac{9}{20}$ *p.* $99\frac{11}{25}$

b. $\frac{17}{20}$ *g.* $56\frac{1}{8}$ *l.* $\frac{19}{200}$ *q.* $6\frac{2}{5}$

c. $\frac{9}{16}$ *h.* $7\frac{5}{32}$ *m.* $\frac{51}{500}$ *r.* $7\frac{1}{25}$

d. $9\frac{7}{8}$ *i.* $3\frac{7}{10}$ *n.* $\frac{23}{250}$ *s.* $8\frac{1}{125}$

e. $\frac{1}{16}$ *j.* $\frac{7}{20}$ *o.* $5\frac{7}{100}$ *t.* $\frac{11}{200}$

9.2. *a.* 0.5625, 4 as $16 = 2^4$ *g.* 0.034375, 6 as $320 = 2^6 \times 5$

b. Denominator has factor 3 *h.* 1.8125, $\frac{87}{48} = \frac{29}{16}$, 4 as $16 = 2^4$

c. 0.056, 3 as $125 = 5^3$ *i.* Denominator has factor 13

d. 0.0592, 4 as $625 = 5^4$ *j.* Denominator has factor 7

e. Denominator has factor 3 *k.* 0.3046875, 7 as $128 = 2^7$

f. Denominator has factor 11 *l.* 0.256, 3 as $125 = 5^3$

9.3. *a.* 0.609375   *e.* 0.925
       b. 0.8125   *f.* 1.244
       c. 0.875   *g.* 0.0126953125
       d. 0.984   *h.* 0.76

9.4. *a.* $1\frac{1}{3}$ *f.* $\frac{1}{70}$ *k.* $78\frac{11}{80}$ *p.* $\frac{3}{1,700,000}$
       b. $\frac{2}{7}$ *g.* $\frac{1}{7}$ *l.* $\frac{5}{9}$ *q.* $\frac{1}{3,000,000,000}$
       c. $34\frac{17}{60}$ *h.* $1\frac{3}{7}$ *m.* $10\frac{1}{300}$ *r.* $\frac{1}{7}$
       d. $\frac{1}{15}$ *i.* $7\frac{3}{4}$ *n.* $\frac{1}{1,400}$
       e. $6\frac{2}{3}$ *j.* $8\frac{5}{8}$ *o.* $\frac{3}{700}$

9.5. *a.* 0.6154   *e.* 0.1739   *i.* 0.2727
       b. 0.9412   *f.* 0.4286   *j.* 0.6808
       c. 0.6316   *g.* 0.3793
       d. 0.2381   *h.* 0.7778

9.6. *a.* $0.\overline{351}\ldots$ *i.* $0.6\overline{3}\ldots$
       b. $0.\overline{714285}\ldots$ *j.* $0.\overline{4117647058823529}\ldots$
       c. $0.\overline{285714}\ldots$ *k.* $0.\overline{263157894736842105}\ldots$
       d. $0.\overline{7}\ldots$ *l.* $0.\overline{8260869565217391304347}\ldots$
       e. $0.\overline{5}\ldots$ *m.* $0.32\overline{142857}\ldots$
       f. $0.\overline{615384}\ldots$ *n.* $0.7\overline{083}\ldots$
       g. $0.\overline{076923}\ldots$ *o.* $0.70\overline{285714}\ldots$
       h. $0.\overline{153846}\ldots$ *p.* $0.8\overline{09523}\ldots$
       q. $0.\overline{755102040816326530612244897959183673469387}\ldots$
       r. $0.\overline{592}\ldots$ *t.* $0.4\overline{2}\ldots$
       s. $0.\overline{282051}\ldots$ *u.* $0.831168\ldots$

9.7. *a.* $0.21\overline{153846}\ldots$ *f.* $0.8\overline{3}\ldots$
       b. $0.25\overline{3}\ldots$ *g.* $0.1\overline{6}\ldots$
       c. $0.82\overline{142857}\ldots$ *h.* $0.79\overline{3}\ldots$
       d. $0.\overline{254132231404958677685950}\ldots$ *i.* $0.00\overline{90}\ldots$
       e. $0.4\overline{6}\ldots$ *j.* $0.06250\overline{0}\ldots$

9.8. Verifying for Problem 9.6:
       a. (i) 3 is a divisor of $37 - 1$, or 36, (ii) does not apply, as 3 is odd
       b. (i) 6 is a divisor of $7 - 1$, or 6, (ii) $714 + 285 = 999$
       c. Same as (*b*)
       d-e. Not applicable, as 9 is not prime
       f-h. (i) 6 is a divisor of $13 - 1$, or 12, (ii) $615 + 384 = 999$, $076 + 923 = 999$, $153 + 846 = 999$
       i. (i) 2 is a divisor of $11 - 1$, or 10, (ii) $6 + 3 = 9$

   j. (i) 16 is divisor of 17 − 1, or 16, (ii) 41,176,470 + 58,823,529 = 99,999,999

   k. (i) 18 is divisor of 19 − 1, or 18, (ii) 263,157,894 + 736,842,105 = 999,999,999

   l. (i) 22 is a divisor of 23 − 1, or 22, (ii) 82,608,695,652 + 17,391,304,347 = 99,999,999,999

m-o. Inapplicable, as denominators contain, respectively, the factors 2^2, 2^3, and 5^2

p-u. Not applicable, as the denominators contain more than a single prime factor, other than 2 or 5

Verifying for Problem 9.7:

   a. (i) 6 is an exact divisor of 13 − 1, or 12, (ii) 153 + 846 = 999

   b. (i) 1 is an exact divisor of 3 − 1, or 2, (ii) Inapplicable as the number of digits in the period is not an even number, namely 1

   c. (i) 6 is an exact divisor of 7 − 1, or 6, (ii) 142 + 857 = 999

   d. (i) 22 is not an exact divisor of 121 − 1, or 120, 121 is not prime (ii) However, 41,322,314,049 + 58,677,685,950 = 99,999,999,999

e-h. Denominator contains the single prime 3 apart from 2s and 5s, (i) period contains one digit, 1 is divisor of 3 − 1, or 2, (ii) Not applicable, as 1 is odd

i-j. Denominator contains no prime factor, other than 2s and 5s. Thus, decimal fraction is terminating, not periodic.

9.9. *a.* $\frac{1;174}{1;547}$ *b.* 0.7589   *c.* 0.7589

     d. $\frac{1;174}{1;547}$ is *exact*, and therefore more accurate than the approximation 0.7589, which agrees with it for these first four digits. The common fractional procedure is more laborious.

9.10. *a.* $\frac{1}{7} = 0.\overline{142857}$ . . . $\frac{3}{7} = 0.\overline{428571}$ . . . $\frac{5}{7} = 0.\overline{714285}$ . . .

        $\frac{2}{7} = 0.\overline{285714}$ . . . $\frac{4}{7} = 0.\overline{571428}$ . . . $\frac{6}{7} = 0.\overline{857142}$ . . .

     All of these periods contain the same six digits in the same cyclic order; this occurs because the periods contain the maximum number of digits, namely, 7 − 1, or 6. Hence, from the known period of $\frac{1}{7}$, one may write down immediately the others, in order of the size of the leading digit of the period, namely, 1, 2, 4, 5, 7, 8. Note that every possible remainder, 1, 2, 3, 4, 5, and 6, occurs in the division algorithm that yields the decimal form for each common fraction having the denominator 7.

     b. $\frac{1}{13} = 0.\overline{076923}$ . . . $\frac{2}{13} = 0.\overline{153846}$ . . .

     In the division algorithm for obtaining the decimal fractional form for $\frac{1}{13}$, six different remainders occur, namely, in order, 1, 10, 9, 12, 3, 4; six still different remainders occur for $\frac{2}{13}$, namely, in order, 2, 7, 5, 11, 6, 8. As these remainders exhaust all possible remainders in a division by 13, namely, 1, 2, 3, 4, 5, 6, 7, 8, 9, 10, 11, and 12, the two foregoing periods, 076923 and 153846, provide all possible cyclic sets of periods for all common proper fractions having denominator 13.   Listing them in order of size, one has

$\frac{1}{13} = 0.076923 \ldots$ $\qquad$ $\frac{7}{13} = 0.538461 \ldots$

$\frac{2}{13} = 0.153846 \ldots$ $\qquad$ $\frac{8}{13} = 0.615384 \ldots$

$\frac{3}{13} = 0.230769 \ldots$ $\qquad$ $\frac{9}{13} = 0.692307 \ldots$

$\frac{4}{13} = 0.307692 \ldots$ $\qquad$ $\frac{10}{13} = 0.769230 \ldots$

$\frac{5}{13} = 0.384615 \ldots$ $\qquad$ $\frac{11}{13} = 0.846153 \ldots$

$\frac{6}{13} = 0.461538 \ldots$ $\qquad$ $\frac{12}{13} = 0.923076 \ldots$

9.11. *a.* (i) Three four dot seven six five, (ii) Thirty-four *and* seven hundred sixty-five thousandths, (iii) Same as in (ii).

b. i. Two zero three zero four zero dot five zero six zero seven

ii. 203,040.50,607: two hundred three thousand, forty, *and* fifty thousand, six hundred seven hundred-thousandths

iii. 203,040.506,07: two hundred three thousand, forty *and* five hundred six thousandths, seven hundred-thousandths

c. i. Six five four seven seven zero nine zero dot one two three four five six seven eight

ii. 65,477,090.12,345,678: sixty-five million, four hundred seventy-seven thousand, ninety *and* twelve million, three hundred forty-five thousand, six hundred seventy-eight hundred-millionths

iii. 65,477,090.123,456,78: sixty-five million, four hundred seventy-seven thousand, ninety *and* one hundred twenty-three thousandths, four hundred fifty-six millionths, seventy-eight hundred-millionths

d. (i) Nine eight six six dot two and three-fifths, (ii) 9,866.2$\frac{3}{5}$: nine thousand, eight hundred sixty-six *and* two and three-fifths tenths, (iii) Same as in (ii).

e. (i) Three four dot five six and seven-eighths, (ii) 34.56$\frac{7}{8}$: thirty-four *and* fifty-six and seven-eighths hundredths, (iii) Same as in (ii).

f. (i) One nine zero dot three five eight and seven-twelfths, (ii) 190.358$\frac{7}{12}$: one hundred ninety *and* three hundred fifty-eight and seven-twelfths thousandths, (iii) Same as in (ii).

g. (i) Zero dot zero zero zero one and two-thirds, (ii) 0.0,001$\frac{2}{3}$: one and two-thirds ten-thousandths, (iii) 0.000,1$\frac{2}{3}$: one and two thirds ten-thousandths.

h. (i) Zero dot zero zero and four-fifths, (ii) 0.00$\frac{4}{5}$: four-fifths hundredths, (iii) Same as in (ii).

i. (i) Zero dot zero zero zero and five-sixths, (ii) 0.000$\frac{5}{6}$: five-sixths thousandths, (iii) Same as in (ii).

    j. (i) Zero dot zero zero zero zero and seven-eighths, (ii) 0.0,000$\frac{7}{8}$: seven-eighths ten-thousandths, (iii) 0.000,0$\frac{7}{8}$: seven-eighths ten-thousandths.

    k. (i) One zero zero two zero zero zero zero five zero dot zero five zero zero two zero one, (ii) 1,002,000,050.0,0500,201: one billion, two million, fifty, *and* five hundred thousand, two hundred one, ten-millionths, (iii) 1,002,000,050.050,020,1: one billion, two million, fifty *and* fifty thousandths, twenty millionths, one ten-millionth.

    l. (i) One dot four two zero and three-eighths, (ii) 1.420$\frac{3}{8}$: one *and* four hundred twenty and three-eighths millionths, (iii) Same as in (ii).

9.12. *a.* 1,036.63$\frac{2}{3}$ *d.* 3.141,6

      b. 1,000,000,200.026$\frac{1}{5}$ *e.* 1.414,214

      c. 36,000.000,035$\frac{2}{5}$ *f.* 0.142,85$\frac{1}{7}$

LESSON 10 ∾

10.1. *a.* 129.133,14   *b.* 7.135,1   *c.* 344.822,1   *d.* 481.090,34

10.2. *a.* 5.231   *c.* 4.097,67   *e.* −7.700,05

      b. 1.235,91   *d.* −3.991   *f.* −21,428.55

10.3. *a.* −3,633.307,4   *b.* 0   *c.* −1,111.111,1

10.4. *a.* 4.912,32   *c.* −2.012,01   *e.* 3.000,000,666,601

      b. 18.671,17   *d.* 556.937,5   *f.* 2.441,406,25

10.5. *a.* 5.2   *c.* 32,000   *e.* 0.000,021

      b. 30.3   *d.* −5.01   *f.* 0.06

10.6. *a.* 0.908   *c.* 0.006   *e.* 2.054

      b. 8.142   *d.* 0.035   *f.* 0.560

10.7. $\frac{21}{34}$ $\frac{76}{123}$ $\frac{55}{89}$ $\frac{34}{55}$, whose decimal fractional forms are, respectively, 0.617,6 . . . , 0.617,8 . . . , 0.617,9 . . . , 0.618, . . .

10.8. 4,320,000,000 years. This length of time is nearly equal to the currently generally accepted estimate of the age of the earth, 4$\frac{1}{2}$ billion years.

10.9. *a.* $\frac{3}{11}$ *c.* $\frac{13}{33}$ *e.* $\frac{29}{33}$ *g.* $\frac{1}{1375}$ *i.* $\frac{1}{90,000}$

      b. $\frac{367}{909}$ *d.* $\frac{5}{27}$ *f.* $\frac{1}{11}$ *h.* $\frac{7}{1,100}$

10.10. *a.* $\frac{3,441}{5,500}$ *c.* $\frac{4,683}{11,000}$ *e.* $\frac{478,751}{550,000}$

      b. $\frac{415,949}{499,500}$ *d.* $\frac{55,553}{450,000}$ *f.* $\frac{307}{825}$

10.11. $\pi = 3.141,592,653,$ . . . , correct to 10 digits.

      a. $\frac{22}{7} = 3.142,8$ . . . , correct to 3 digits; error is +0.001,2 . . .

b. $\frac{355}{113} = 3.141,592,920, \ldots$, correct to 7 digits; error is
   $+0.000,000,267$

c. $3.141,6$, correct to 5 digits; error is $+0.000,007,3 \ldots$
The ensuing answers for Problems 12 to 17, inclusive, assume that
$3.141,6$ is the exact value of π and yield results that are too large by
the product of the result by $0.000,007,3 \ldots$, since $3.141,6$ is larger
than the true value of π by $0.000,007,3 \ldots$. In Lesson 14 a
method for the determination of possible size of errors resulting from
inaccurate data is provided.

10.12. *a.* 615.753,6 sq in.   *b.* 3,848.46 sq ft   *c.* 4.908,75 sq yd

10.13. *a.* 87,964,8 in.   *b.* 219.912 ft   *c.* 7.854 yd

10.14. *a.* 452.390,4 sq ft   *b.* 58.088,184 sq in.   *c.* 15.260,686,425,6 sq cm

10.15. *a.* 904.780,8 cu ft   *b.* 41.629,865,2 cu in.
   c. 5.605,758,813,670,4 cc

10.16. 965.387,5 lb

10.17. *a.* 216 balls   *b.* 256.564 lb   *c.* 8 balls, 256.564 lb
   d. 1 ball, 256.564 lb

10.18. The exact weight is $\dfrac{245\pi}{3}$, or $256.563,400,043, \ldots$ to nearest
   $0.000,000,000,003$ lb

   a. $256\frac{2}{3}$ or $256.66 \ldots$

   b. $256\frac{191}{339}$ or $256.563,421,8 \ldots$ which is most nearly exact, involving an error less than $0.000,022$ lb

Lesson 11 ∾

11.1. *a.* 10   *e.* 12   *i.* $1\frac{1}{3}$ *m.* $\frac{2}{3}$
       b. 7   *f.* 21   *j.* 3   *n.* 0.09
       c. 13   *g.* $\frac{5}{7}$ *k.* 2   *o.* 0.2
       d. 31   *h.* $\frac{3}{4}$ *l.* 3   *p.* 0.1

11.2. *a.* $12\sqrt{3}$ *i.* $9\sqrt{7} + 12\sqrt[3]{3}$
       b. $(1\frac{5}{12})\sqrt[3]{5}$ *j.* $2\sqrt{3} + 12\sqrt[3]{3} + 3\sqrt[3]{4} + 5\sqrt[3]{6}$
       c. $0.49\sqrt{\frac{2}{3}}$ *k.* $2\sqrt{3} + 5\sqrt[3]{6} - 9\sqrt{7} + 3\sqrt[3]{4}$
       d. $0.375\sqrt{2}$ *l.* $6\sqrt[6]{72}$
       e. $400\sqrt[3]{30}$ *m.* 3
       f. $\sqrt{6}$ *n.* $\sqrt[6]{40}$
       g. $7\sqrt[3]{3}$ *o.* $\sqrt[6]{28}$
       h. 24   *p.* $\sqrt[6]{\frac{10}{7}}$

11.3. The indicated operations are to be performed upon the decimal approximations for the surds appearing in the problem; the result must then be compared with the following decimal approximation for the surd form of the answer. The two decimal fractions thus compared should be identical for the first five of six digits on their left ends.

a.	20.784,612	*g.*	10.095,750	*l.*	12.237,894
b.	2.422,466	*h.*	24	*m.*	3
c.	0.400,080,59	*i.*	41.118,759	*n.*	1.849,311
d.	0.530,330,25	*j.*	34.618,910	*o.*	1.742,581
e.	0.1,242.893,2	*k.*	−6.499,849	*p.*	1.061,248
f.	2.449,490				

11.4. *a.* Note that the square of each of these numbers is greater than the square of the preceding number and remains less than 2: 1.96; 1.9881; 1.999,396; 1.999,961,64; 1.999,989,924,1; 1.999,998,409, 369.

   b. Note that the square of each of these numbers is less than the square of the preceding number and remains greater than 2: 4; 2.25; 2.016,4; 2.002,225; 2.000,244,49; 2.000,018,208,4; 2.000,001,237, 796. Therefore $\sqrt{2}$ lies between any number of one of these series and all numbers of the other series. Thus, the successive numbers of each series are ever better approximations for the square root of two. However, the *best* rational decimal approximations to $\sqrt{2}$ for the number of digits used are the following: 1; 1.4; 1.414; 1.414,2; 1.414,21; 1.414,214.

11.5. $(\frac{3}{2})^2 = 2 + \frac{1}{4}$; $(\frac{7}{5})^2 = 2 - \frac{1}{25}$; $(\frac{17}{12})^2 = 2 + \frac{1}{144}$; $(\frac{41}{29})^2 = 2 - \frac{1}{841}$; $(\frac{99}{70})^2 = 2 + \frac{1}{4,900}$; $(\frac{239}{169})^2 = 2 - \frac{1}{28,561}$.

Thus the squares of these common fractions become ever nearer to 2, alternating above and below 2; the differences of these fractions are unit fractions whose denominators are the product of the consecutive fractions. Thus, $\frac{3}{2} - \frac{7}{5} = \frac{1}{10}$; $\frac{17}{12} - \frac{7}{5} = \frac{1}{60}$, . . . , $\frac{99}{70} - \frac{239}{169} = \frac{1}{11,830}$.

11.6. *a.* 963   *b.* 85.9   *c.* 14.76   *d.* 23.232   *e.* 256   *f.* 0.27

11.7. 1.732,051

11.8. *a.* 19.494   *c.* 31.411,99   *e.* 31,942.198,6
      b. 2.406,2   *d.* 2.236,068

11.9. *a.* 17 ft; 46 ft; 120 sq ft
      b. 89 yd; 238 yd; 3,120 sq yd
      c. 317 m; 766 m; 23,100 sq m
      d. 269 in.; 658 in.; 17,940 sq in.

11.10. 33 yd; 65 yd

11.11. 112 cm; 1,680 sq cm

11.12. 25 rd

11.13. 15 ft

11.14. $\sqrt{14} = 3.742$ in.

11.15. *a.* 26   *c.* 92   *e.* 44   *g.* 98   *i.* 89
      b. 63   *d.* 32   *f.* 61   *h.* 76   *j.* 59

11.16. *a.* 431   *c.* 649   *e.* 983   *g.* 5,862   *i.* 23,448
      b. 465   *d.* 781   *f.* 928   *h.* 2,968

11.17. *a.* 3.997   *c.* 0.405   *e.* 0.040
      b. 0.826   *d.* 0.146   *f.* 4,642.471

11.18. Volume = 4,913 cu in.   Volume = Area of face times length of edge; i.e., the *number* of cubic units of volume in the cube equals the *number* of square units of area in one face multiplied by the *number* of length units in one edge.

11.19. 14.088,8 cu in.

11.20. *a.* 2.5 in.   *b.* 19.635 sq in.

11.21. *a.* 2.5 in.   *b.* 65.45 cu in.

11.22. 26.035 . . . in., or $26\frac{2}{64}$, to the nearest sixty-fourth of an inch.

11.23. *a.* 53   *b.* 16   *c.* 1.30 (1.297 . . .)   *d.* Same as in (*c*)

11.24. 14.87% to nearest 0.01%

11.25. 4.42% to nearest 0.01%

11.26. *a.* 28   *b.* 28

LESSON 12 ∾

12.1. *a.* 1;8   *b.* 7;0   *c.* 0;6   *d.* 1;3   *e.* 1;10   *f.* 0;10

12.2. Checking by casting 11s shows (*a*) cannot be correct. Tests fail to indicate that (*a*) and (*b*) are also incorrect. The correct product is 334,003.

12.3. *a.* 24,054   *c.* $256\frac{440}{739}$ *e.* 3.14
      b. 10,991,500   *d.* 4.796   *f.* 3.13

12.4. 127.279 . . . ft; 127 ft, 3 in.

12.5. *a.* 429 ft   *b.* 7.681 ft

12.6. *a.* 126   *c.* 384   *e.* 476   *g.* 698   *i.* 998
      b. 193   *d.* 412   *f.* 547   *h.* 777

12.7. 120,825

12.8. 5,050; 25,502,500

12.9.   338,350

12.10. $(500,500)^2$ or   250,500,250,000

12.11.   500,000,500,000   333,333,833,333,500,000
250,000,500,000,250,000,000,000

LESSON 13 ∾

13.1.   *a.* 75%   *e.* 30%   *i.* $76\frac{8}{17}\%$ *m.* 250%
b. $87\frac{1}{2}\%$ *f.* $37\frac{1}{2}\%$ *j.* $66\frac{2}{3}\%$ *n.* $333\frac{1}{3}\%$
c. 76%   *g.* $71\frac{3}{7}\%$ *k.* $83\frac{1}{3}\%$ *o.* $93\frac{3}{4}\%$
d. 80%   *h.* $41\frac{2}{3}\%$ *l.* $133\frac{1}{3}\%$

13.2.   *a.* 18.75%   *d.* 95%   *g.* 59.375%
b. 57.5%   *e.* 95.2%   *h.* 60.5%
c. 76.562,5%   *f.* 75%   *i.* 80%

13.3.   *a.* 71.43%   *d.* 38.46%   *g.* 73.91%   *j.* 44.54%
b. 33.33%   *e.* 55.56%   *h.* 79.31%   *k.* 60%
c. 63.64%   *f.* 82.35%   *i.* 314.16%   *l.* 57.14%

13.4.   *a.* $\frac{7}{20}$ *d.* $\frac{4}{7}$ *g.* $\frac{3}{8}$ *j.* $\frac{2}{5}$
b. $\frac{1}{8}$ *e.* $\frac{1}{16}$ *h.* $\frac{7}{8}$ *k.* $\frac{1}{6}$
c. $\frac{2}{3}$ *f.* $\frac{1}{12}$ *i.* $\frac{3}{4}$ *l.* $\frac{5}{6}$

13.5.   *a.* $\frac{1}{30}$ *b.* $\frac{2}{55}$ *c.* $\frac{3}{10,000}$ *d.* $\frac{64}{625}$ *e.* $\frac{1}{11}$ *f.* $\frac{5}{9}$

13.6.   *a.* $2,880   *b.* $2,016   *c.* $1,290.24

13.7. $1,070

13.8.   *a.* $68.40   *b.* Same as in (*a*).

13.9.   60 cu ft of ice

13.10.   110 cu ft of water

13.11.   36 black keys

13.12.   *a.* $100.00   *b.* $11\frac{19}{21}\%$

13.13.   48 acres sugar beets; 30 acres corn; 18 acres beans; 24 acres potatoes

13.14.   *a.* 20 hours of leisure time   *b.* $11\frac{19}{21}\%$ *c.* $8\frac{13}{14}\%$

13.15.   *a.* Gain: $46.80   *b.* $109.20

13.16.   *a.* 40%   *b.* $28\frac{4}{7}\%$

13.17.   *a.* 40%   *b.* $66\frac{2}{3}\%$

13.18. $27\frac{1}{7}\%$; 27.14%

13.19.   *A*, 10%; *B*, 30%; *C*, 50%; *D*, 6%; *F*, 4%.   Sum is 100%.

13.20.   *a.* First annual salaries: *A*, $5,580.22; *B*, $5,544.   *A*'s salary is
larger by $36.22.

      b. Second year's salaries: *A*, \$6,287.95; *B*, \$6,708.24. *B*'s salary is larger by \$420.29.

13.21. *a.* *X*, loss \$100; *Y*, loss \$375; *Z*, gain \$400; *W*, loss \$25

      b. Results are same as in (*a*).

      c. Net loss, \$100

      d. Net loss, \$45.95

13.22. *a.* 61.3%   *b.* 0.613

13.23.

E	46	10	0.821	*I*	28	32	0.467
H	49	14	0.778	*C*	27	35	0.435
D	42	17	0.712	*F*	21	40	0.344
A	32	26	0.552	*G*	19	39	0.328
J	32	28	0.533	*B*	4	59	0.063

13.24. *a.* 27.325%

      b. Three successive discounts of 10% are equivalent to 27.1%, so a single discount of 28% is better to buyer by 0.9%.

13.25. *a.* $13\frac{1}{3}\%$ *b.* 30 horses   *c.* 750 horses

13.26. Wholesale price, \$30.00

13.27. Wholesale price, \$28.80

13.28. *a.* Loss, \$12   *b.* Loss, \$16

13.29. 70

13.30. 1,700

13.31. $\frac{5}{12}$

13.32. \$4,096

13.33. \$5,565.22

13.34. *a.* 20%   *b.* 25%

13.35. *a.* \$82.50   *b.* $19\frac{17}{57}\%$ *c.* $16\frac{3}{17}\%$

13.36. Sales tax, \$18.93

13.37. Sales price, \$3,966

13.38. \$2,000

Lesson 14 ∽

14.1. *a.* 512.335 ± 0.026; less concisely, 512.33 ± 0.03

      b. 854.546 ± 1.742, or 854.6 ± 1.8; less concisely, 855 ± 2

      c. 3.892,45 ± 0.003,69 or 3.892,5 ± 0.003,7; less concisely, 3.892 ± 0.004

      d. 8.496 ± 0.102 or 8.50 ± 0.10; less concisely, 8.5 ± 0.1

e. 3.844,408 ± 0.000,022; less concisely, 3.844,41 ± 0.000,02

f. 0.019,456,40 ± 0.000,013,09 or 0.019,456,4 ± 0.000,013,1; less concisely, 0.019,45 ± 0.000,02

14.2. 75.955,5 ± 0.027,2 cu in.; less concisely, 75.96 ± 0.02 cu in.

14.3. *a.* 0.832,94 ± 0.000,08

b. 2,951,2 ± 0.000,6

c. 55.90 ± 0.05

d. 11.869,8 ± 0.001,6; less concisely, 11.870 ± 0.002

14.4. 29.059 ± 0.027 gal; less concisely, 29.06 ± 0.03 gal

14.5. 452.740 ± 0.025; less concisely, 452.74 ± 0.03

14.6. 177.68 ± 0.07 ft

14.7. If measurements are exact, 1,981 posts would be used. Maximum number of posts, 1,983, with final interval 102.1 in. long. Minimum number of posts, 1,979, with final interval 90.3 in. long. (Assuming extreme errors, which are cumulative.) To set out the exact number of posts correctly, the farmer could halve the distance of 3 miles, then halve the two parts. Continuing to halve these new intervals until the entire 3 miles would be halved 11 times, he would obtain a theoretical distance of $92\frac{13}{16}$ in. for each of the intervals. Then he measures the correct distances from these subdivision points to the required exact positions of the 1,979 intervening posts; as there would be not more than one post in each of these intervals, the errors of measurement would not be cumulative.

LESSON 15 ∽

15.1. *a.* 479,160 sq ft   *c.* 1,760 sq rd

     b. 53,240 sq yd   *d.* 11 acres

15.2. *a.* $\frac{1}{4}$ mile or 80 rd   *b.* $20\frac{80}{121}\%$ or 20.66 . . . %

15.3. $20\frac{470}{539}$ mi per hr or 20.8719 . . . (nearly $20\frac{7}{8}$ mi per hr)

15.4. *a.* 3,276 sq ft   *b.* 2,988 sq ft   *c.* 394 ft

15.5. *a.* 287 sq ft   *b.* 28.7 sq ft (brick)   *c.* $7\frac{11}{12}$ sq yd

15.6. *a.* 450 sq in.   *b.* 10 in.   *c.* $11\frac{2}{3}$ ft

15.7. 64 ft

15.8. $1\frac{1}{4}$ sq ft; $\frac{5}{36}$ sq yd

15.9. Area: *a.* 2,464 sq in.   *b.* 176 in.

     Circumference: *a.* 2,463.014,4 sq in.   *b.* 175.929,6 in.

     Difference: *a.* 0.99 sq in.   *b.* 0.07 in.

15.10. 384 cu ft; 240 sq ft

15.11.   *a.* 210 sq in.   *c.* 6 in.; $11\frac{2}{3}$ in.; 21 in.; 30 in.
          b. $24\frac{12}{17}$ in.; $16\frac{4}{5}$ in.; 15 in.   *d.* $(\frac{1}{6} = \frac{3}{35} + \frac{1}{21} + \frac{1}{30})$

15.12.   1,908 sq in.

15.13.   *a.* 468 sq ft   *b.* 9 ft; $11\frac{17}{41}$ ft

15.14.   (*b*) and (*c*)

15.15.   *a.* 26.83 sq in.   *b.* $26\frac{53}{64}$ sq in.

15 16   346.36 cu in.

15.17.   *a.* 134.095 . . . cu ft   *b.* 133.973 . . . cu ft.   *c.* 0.122 cu ft

15.18.   754.0 cu ft

15.19.   1,323 tons

15.20.   *a.* 314.16 sq in.   *b.* 523.6 cu in.   *c.* 15 lb 2 oz

15.21. $7.07

15.22.   1,696 lb

15.23.   488.92 cu in. if $h = 24$ in.; 733.39 cu in. if $h = 16$ in.

15.24.   391.78 cu in.

15.25.   0.000,17 (use π to nearest 0.000,000,01)

15.26.   *a.* 9,966.53 . . . acres   *b.* 0335,8 . . . %

Lesson 16 ∾

16.1.   *a.* 32   *d.* $\frac{1}{256}$ *g.* 2   *j.* 8
        b. 125   *e.* 1   *h.* 3   *k.* 16
        c. $\frac{1}{9}$ *f.* 1   *i.* 4   *l.* 32

16.2.   *a.* 128   *g.* 8   *m.* 729   *s.* a^3
        b. 81   *h.* 3   *n.* $\frac{1}{625}$ *t.* a^{-1}
        c. 3,125   *i.* 1   *o.* 4   *u.* $\sqrt[6]{a}$
        d. 8   *j.* $\frac{1}{2}$ *p.* 4   *v.* $\sqrt[4]{a}$
        e. 9   *k.* $\frac{1}{32}$ *q.* 9
        f. 729   *l.* 64   *r.* a^4

16.3.   *a.* a^7 *d.* a^2 *g.* $a^{\frac{1}{5}}$ or $\sqrt[5]{a}$
        b. a *e.* a^0 or 1, if $a \neq 0$ *h.* $a^{\frac{1}{6}}$ or $\sqrt[6]{a}$
        c. a^{12} *f.* $a^{\frac{1}{2}}$ or $\sqrt{a}$ *i.* $a^{\frac{7}{8}}$ or $\sqrt[8]{a^7}$

16.4.   *a.* log 4 = 0.6020600   *d.* log 9 = 0.9542426
        b. log 8 = 0.9030900   *e.* log 6 = 0.7781513
        c. log 5 = 0.6989700

16.5.   *a.* 1.5440680   *c.* 2.1583626   *e.* 4.7481880
        b. 1.9912260   *d.* 2.9242793

16.6.   *a.*   0.7300   *d.*   4.8573   *g.* $9.8241 - 10$
        b.   2.9425   *e.*   0.2480   *h.* $8.0969 - 10$
        c.   1.3075   *f.* $6.7566 - 10$ *i.* $7.0253 - 10$

16.7.   *a.*   4.32   *c.*   507   *e.*   0.356   *g.*   93,000,000
        b.   93.3   *d.*   8320   *f.*   0.00423

16.8.   *a.*   320   *b.*   324   *c.*   729,000,000   *d.*   2

16.9.   *a.*   3,506   *c.*   577.4   *e.*   3.193
        b.   0.464,1   *d.*   34.04   *f.*   2.829

16.10.   0.873

16.11.   0.232,4

16.12. $2,301

16.13.   12.41 ft

16.14.   18.10 sec

16.15.   46,920,000,000 miles, using our four-place tables of logarithms; however, these tables yield only one significant digit, namely the initial digit, 4. Vega's seven-place tables of logarithms yield the result, 47,348,900,000, of which only the leading four digits are valid, or 47,350,000,000 miles. If the center of this golden sphere were placed, in imagination, at the center of the sun, the sphere would contain the orbits of all the planets.

L ESSON 17

17.1. $A(2 + 3i)$, $B(-5 + 6i)$, $C(-7 - 3i)$, $D(6 - 7i)$

17.2. $A(-3 + 2i)$, $B(-6 - 5i)$, $C(3 - 7i)$, $D(7 + 6i)$

17.3. $A(-2 - 3i)$, $B(5 - 6i)$, $C(7 + 3i)$, $D(-6 + 7i)$

17.4. $A(3 - 2i)$, $B(6 + 5i)$, $C(-3 + 7i)$, $D(-7 - 6i)$

17.5.   Multiplication by i effects a counterclockwise rotation about 0 through angle of 90°. Multiplication by $(i)^n$ (if n is a natural number) effects a counterclockwise rotation about 0 through an angle of $n \times 90°$.

17.6. $A(-1 + 5i)$, $B(-8 + 8i)$, $C(-10 - i)$, $D(3 - 5i)$. Adding a complex number $a + bi$ effects a translation, or movement, in the *direction* of angle of $a + bi$, and through a *distance* equal to the absolute value of $a + bi$, or $\sqrt{a^2 + b^2}$. In this instance angle A, of $-3 + 2i$, is given by

$$\cos A = \frac{-3}{\sqrt{13}} \text{ or } -0.8321; \sin A = \frac{2}{\sqrt{13}} \text{ or } 0.5547$$

Whence $A = 180° - 34°$, or 146° (to nearest degree); $\sqrt{a^2 + b^2} = \sqrt{9 + 4} = \sqrt{13} = 3.605551 \ldots$ or approximately 3.6.

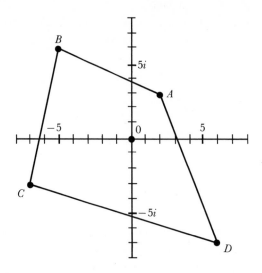

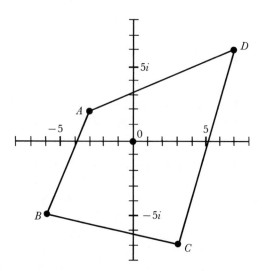

FIGURES A17.1 AND A17.2

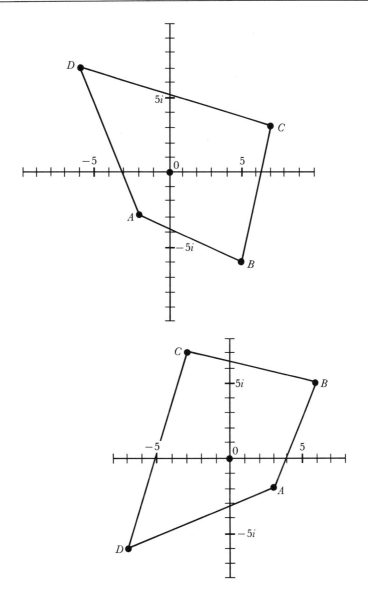

FIGURES AI7.3 AND AI7.4

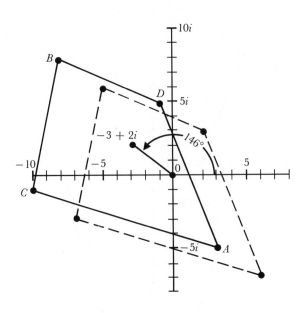

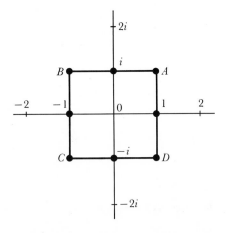

FIGURES A17.5 AND A17.6

17.7. $A(1 + i)$, $B(-1 + i)$, $C(-1 - i)$, $D(1 - i)$

17.8. $A(-1 + i)$, $B(-1 - i)$, $C(1 - i)$, $D(1 + i)$

Multiplying the numbers in Problem 17.7 by the number i rotates their positions in the plane counterclockwise about 0 through the angle of i, namely 90°. The distance of points A, B, C, D from 0 remains unchanged, since the absolute value of the multiplier i is equal to 1.

17.9. $A(2i)$, $B(-2)$, $C(-2i)$, $D(2)$. Multiplying a complex number $a + bi$ effects a counterclockwise rotation about 0 through the angle of $a + bi$; and a multiplication of all lengths by the absolute value of $a + bi$. Thus, the angle of $1 + i$ is 45°, and $|1 + i| = \sqrt{2}$, so that

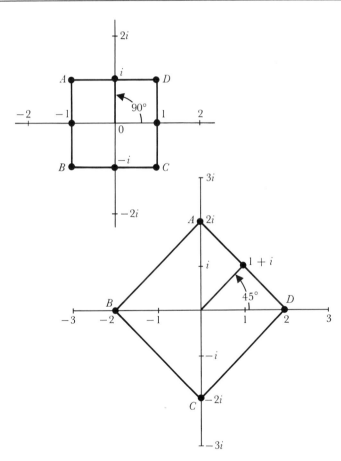

FIGURES A17.7 AND A17.8

the square in Problem 17.7 is *rotated* counterclockwise through 45°
and *expanded* by factor $\sqrt{2}$ to yield the square of Problem 17.9.

17.10.   *a.* $|3 + 4i| = \sqrt{9 + 16} = \sqrt{25} = 5$

b. $|1 + i| = \sqrt{1 + 1} = \sqrt{2}$ or approximately 1.414 . . .

c. $|2 + 2i| = \sqrt{4 + 4} = \sqrt{8} = 2\sqrt{2}$ or approximately 1.414

17.11.   *a.* $\cos A = \frac{3}{5} = 0.6000$; $\sin A = \frac{4}{5} = 0.8000$

Tables yield $A = 53°$ (to nearest degree)

b. $\cos A = \dfrac{1}{\sqrt{2}} = 0.7071$; $\sin A = \dfrac{1}{\sqrt{2}} = 0.7071$

Tables yield 45° (this angle is exact)

c. $\cos A = \dfrac{2}{\sqrt{2}} = 0.7071$; $\sin A = \dfrac{2}{\sqrt{2}} = 0.7071$

Same angle as given in (*b*).

17.12. $|N| = |3 + 4i| = 5$
$|N^2| = |-7 + 24i| = 25$
$|N^3| = |-117 + 44i| = 125$

Thus, the absolute values of successive *powers* of a complex number
appear to be the successive *powers* of its absolute value, in this instance,
5, 25, 125.

The angle of N is given by $\cos A = \frac{3}{5}$, or 0.6000, and $\sin A = \frac{4}{5}$, or
0.8000. Thus, A is in the first quadrant and contains 53°, to nearest
degree.

The angle of N^2 is given by $\cos A = \dfrac{-7}{25}$, or -0.2800, and $\sin A =$
$\frac{24}{25}$, or about 0.9600. Accordingly this angle A is in the second
quadrant and contains $180° - 74°$, or 106°, to nearest degree.

The angle of N^3 is given by $\cos A = \dfrac{-117}{125}$, or -0.9360, and
$\sin A = \frac{44}{125}$ or 0.3520. Accordingly this angle A is in the second
quadrant and contains $180° - 21° = 159°$ to the nearest degree.

Thus, it appears that the angles of the successive *powers* of a complex
number appear to be the successive *multiples* of the angle of the given
complex number, in this instance, 53°, 106°, 159°. (These features of
successive powers of any complex number are universally true.)

17.13.   The other cube root of 1 is 1.

17.14. $\left(-\frac{1}{2} + \dfrac{\sqrt{3}}{2}i\right)^2 = -\frac{1}{2} - \dfrac{\sqrt{3}}{2}i;$ $\left(-\frac{1}{2} - \dfrac{\sqrt{3}}{2}i\right)^2 = -\frac{1}{2} + \dfrac{\sqrt{3}}{2}i$

17.15. $\left|-\frac{1}{2} \pm \dfrac{\sqrt{3}}{2}\right| = \sqrt{\frac{1}{4} + \frac{3}{4}} = 1.$ For $-\frac{1}{2} + \dfrac{\sqrt{3}}{2}i$, the angle A is given by $\cos A = -\frac{1}{2} = -0.5000$, $\sin A = \dfrac{\sqrt{3}}{2} = 0.8660$. Whence A is in

the second quadrant and contains $180° - 60° = 120°$. For $-\frac{1}{2} -$

$\dfrac{\sqrt{3}}{2}\, i$, the angle A is given by $\cos A = -\frac{1}{2} = -0.5000$, $\sin A =$

$\dfrac{-\sqrt{3}}{2} = -0.8660$, whence A is in the third quadrant and contains

$180° + 60° = 240°$.

Thus, the three cube roots of 1, when plotted in the complex plane, are at vertices of a regular (equilateral) triangle. The four numbers listed in Problem 17.7 are the four fourth roots of -4. Observe that their positions in the complex plane are at the corners of a square. And, quite generally, it is proved in advanced algebra that the nth roots of any number, real or complex, have positions in the complex plane that mark the n vertices of a regular polygon, if the absolute value of the given number, real or complex, is equal to *one*. The vertices of the regular polygon are, successively, $A = \sqrt[n]{a + bi}$, A^2, A^3, A^4, . . . , $A_n = a + bi$ if $|a + bi| = \sqrt{a^2 + b^2} = 1$.

INDEX

Absolute magnitude of star, 370
Absolute value, of complex number, 374, 380, 391–392
  of integer, 80
Accuracy of measurements, 321
Acts of Apostles, 122
Addend, 15
Addition, xii, 15, 65
  associative law, 15, 65
  carryover in, 20
  of common fractions, 124
  commutative law of, 16
  Dick's trick problem in, 37
  horizontal and vertical, 34
  of integers, 77
  of meterstick slide rule, 26, 27
  of natural numbers, 15–17, 387
  of number-pairs of integers, 77
  of surds, 248
Addition-subtraction curio, 395, 396
Addition tables of single-digit numbers, 18
Aleph-one, 281
Aleph-zero, 24, 112, 113, 164
Alephs, denumerable set of, 381–383
Algebraic number, 275
Algebraic operations, rules of, 80, 81
Algebraic sum, 186

Algorithm, for change of base of number system, 189, 190
  Euclid's, 133, 142, 172
Alice in Wonderland, 166
Ambiguity in percentage relationships, 311, 313
Amount in compound interest, 317
Angstrom, 213
Antilogarithm, 358
Apparent magnitude of star, 370
Approximate numbers versus exact numbers, 321
Approximation, best decimal fractional, 204, 205
  common fractional for $\sqrt{2}$, 259
  for surds, as decimal fractions, 251
Arc, circular, length of, 366
Area, of circle, 231, 341
  of circular sector, 366
  of circular segment, 366
  lateral, of pyramid and cone, 342
  of parallelogram, 340
  of rectangle, 52, 339
  of triangle, 340, 341, 343, 348, 349
  of sphere, 352
Arithmetic, fundamental theorem of, 128, 435
Arithmetical mean, 186, 193

Arithmetical progression, 33, 191
Assemblage, 3
Associative law, of addition, 15, 65
    of multiplication, 40, 41, 65
Astronomical unit, 105

Basal fractions, terminating and
    repeating, 216
Base, for Arabic number system, 12
    conversion from one to another of
        number system, 189
    of logarithms, 67, 369
Base-rate-percentage relationships,
    307, 308
Binary numbers, 12, 119, 413–415
Brahmagupta, 300
Browning, Robert, 244
Bushel, legal definition of, 339

Caesar, Julius, 98
Calendar, Gregorian, 37
Captain Lindenburn's card trick, 215
Cardinal number, of finite sets, 7, 15
    infinite, or transfinite, 25, 381
    of set, of natural numbers, 24
        of rational numbers, 112–115
        of real numbers, 280, 281
Carroll, Lewis, 166, 219, 240, 282
Carryovers, in addition, 20
    in multiplication, 46
Casting out nines and elevens, 291–
    293, 296, 297
Centimeter, 25
Chambered Nautilus, The, by O. W.
    Holmes, 150
Checks of arithmetical operations,
    289–293
Circle, area of, 231, 341
    circumference of, 231, 341
Circular arc, length of, 366
Circular cylinder, volume of, 242
Circulating decimal fraction, 206

Circumcircle, 344
Circumference of circle, 231, 341
Coefficient, of algebraic equation, 277
    of friction, 139
    of surd, 248
Common fraction, conversion to
        equivalent decimal fraction, 200,
        202, 204
    generalization of, 151, 152
Commutative law, of addition of
        natural numbers, 16, 65
    of multiplication of natural num-
        bers, 39, 65
Commutative-multiplication curios,
    57
Complex numbers, 374
    absolute value of, 374, 380, 391–
        392
    angle of, 380, 390–392
    exponential form of, 393
    four rational operational opera-
        tions upon, 374, 383
    geometrical location of, 376, 379
    infinite set of logarithms of, 393
Compound interest, law of, 317, 318
Cone, volume of, 342
Congruent numbers, 294, 436
    equivalence of two definitions of,
        298, 299
    product and difference of, 295, 296
    theorems on, 436–438
Conjugate complex numbers, 380
Continued fractions, 168, 286–288
Convergents, of common fractions,
        171–176, 286, 287
    of continued fractions, 170, 171
Conversion of base of natural num-
        ber, 189
Correspondence, of rational numbers
        with natural numbers, 112, 115
    of real numbers and irrational
        numbers, 281, 282
Cosine, definition of, 331
Counting, 3, 7, 65

Crockett, David, 178
Cube number, 9
Cube root algorithms, 261–265
  of $\sqrt{2}$ to twelve digits, 268
  of unity, 381
Curio, addition-subtraction, 395, 396
  long division, 396–398
Cyclical integers, 442–444

Decimal fractions, addition of, 225
  advantages over common fractions, 199
  conversion to equivalent common fractions, 200
  definition and symbolism of, 199
  delayed repeating, 207, 208
  division of, 226
  multiplication of, 226
  nonterminating, 208
  period of, 206, 207, 444–450
  reading of, 211–212
  repeating or periodic, 206
  subtraction of, 226
Decimal nomenclature in England, 12
Decimal point, use of, 228
Decimal system, digit symbols of, 3
Decimeter, 25
Degree, subdivisions of, 365
Delayed decimal fractions, 207–209
Denumerable sets, 25, 113
Difference, definition of, 66
Digit symbols, ordered cycle of, 4
Direct operation, definition of, 159
  on natural numbers, 179
"Discimus agere agendo," 144
Distance, measured on number line, 186
  of a planet, 370
  of a star, 320
Distributive law, of multiplication and addition of natural numbers, 42, 65
  proof of, 42

Dividend, definition of, 66
Divisibility tests for prime numbers, 127, 128, 299, 300
Division, xii, 66, 160
  of common fractions, 131, 132
  of decimal fractions, 226
  exceptional situations in, 102
  of natural numbers, 388
  not associative, 102
  by prime-factor forms, 131
  as repeated subtractions, 99–103
  right-end, 300
  of surds, 249
Doyle, Arthur C., 288
Dyadic system of representing natural numbers, 413–415

$e (= 2.718,281,8 \ldots)$, infinite series for, 384, 385
  proved to be transcendental, 277
Edison, Thomas A., 90
English method of reading large natural numbers, 12
English system of weights and measures, 338
Equivalent sets, 24
Eratosthenes, on measurement of size of earth, 367
  sieve of, 420, 421
Escribed circle, 348
Euclid's algorithm, 133, 134, 142, 143
Euclid's Elements of Geometry, 234
Euclid's theorem on infinitude of prime numbers, 142
Euler's formula $(e^{iN} = \cos N + i \sin N)$, 386
Euler's polynomial yielding prime numbers $(n^2 + n + 41)$, 423, 424
Evolution, 160, 245, 388
Exact numbers versus approximate numbers, 321
Exponent, as integer, 182
  laws of, 130, 353–357

Exponent, as natural number, 49
  as unit fraction, 353
  as zero, 49

Factor tables, 422, 423
Factorial n, $(n!)$, 385
Fahrenheit-centigrade relationship, 83
Falling body, law of, 362
Fibonacci numbers (F_n), 35, 94, 95,
  319, 430–434
  as progeny of guinea pigs, 434
Figurate numbers, 195, 196
Friction, coefficient of, 139
Fundamental property of fractions,
  108, 109, 412, 413
Fundamental theorem of arithmetic,
  128
  consequences of, 439–442
  proof of, 435–439

Gallon, approximate value of, 148
  legal definition of, 337, 338
Game of NIM, 13, 418, 419
Gauss, 297
Generalized Pythagorean numbers,
  427, 428
Geometrical figure, determination of,
  348
Geometrical location, of rational
  points on number line, 107, 108
  of special surds on number line,
  278
  of special irrational complex numbers on number line, 379
Geometrical operation, of addition
  and subtraction, 140, 141
  of multiplication and division, 141,
  142
Geometrical progression, 169, 193, 194
Gibbon, Edward, 32
Gold atom, diameter of nucleus of,
  213

Goodrich, S. C., 116
Great Flood, 434
Greater than, less than, symbols for,
  110, 111
Gregorian Calendar, 37
Group, 3

Half-life of uranium, 213
Herodotus, History of, 320
Heronic numbers, 344
Heronic triangles, 344
Hydrogen atom, mass of, 213

i, the imaginary unit, 217
Identifying the secret number, 415,
  416
Imaginary numbers, four rational
  operations on, 373, 374
  graphical representation of, 375
Impossible operations, 67, 68, 390
Improper fraction, 105
Incircle, 344
Indeterminate, 353, 451–454
Index of radical, 67
Indexing, as inverse of involution, 160,
  388
Infinite cardinal number, 24, 25, 112,
  113, 164, 281, 381–383
Infinite series of numbers, sum of, 383–
  387
Infinite set, 24, 25
Infinity, concept of, 450
Integer, 77, 157
  absolute value of, 80
  cyclical, 442–444
  as exponent, 182
  as pair of natural numbers, 89, 90
Interest, compound, 317, 318
  simple, 317
Interpolation of logarithms, for anti-
  logarithms, 361
  for mantissas, 361

Inverse operation, 42, 66, 87, 159–160, 180–181, 388
Involution, xii, 65, 245
  algebraic, 81
  of natural numbers, 48, 387
  is not commutative, 49
  of surds, 250
  use of zero in, 49
Irrational number, position on number line, 228
  surds, 247
Irving, Washington, 64
Isaiah, 14

Jack Dudley's problem, 214
John 8:32, xi
Johnston, C. L., slide rule text of, 365

Kepler's third law ($d^3 = P^2$), 285
Königsberg problem, 29
Kronecker, Leopold, vi, ix

Laplace, 352
Laws, of addition and multiplication, 39, 40, 47, 48, 65, 159, 162
  of exponents, 130, 353–357
Left-end multiplication, 326
Light year, 52, 105, 213, 371
Lindemann, Ferdinand, 277
Logarithm, 388
  change of base of, 369
  characteristic of, 359
  infinite number of, for any number, 387
  mantissa of, 359
  as symbol for indexing, 160
  tables of, 358
  Vega's tables of, 358
Long division, 100, 101
Long division curio, 389–398
Long multiplication, 46, 47

McGuffey's *Third Eclectic Reader*: Harry and the Guidepost, 304
Magic square, of order 3, 96, 401–406
  of order 4, 96, 97, 406–408
  pandiagonal of order 4, 406–409
  pandiagonal of order 5, 409–412
Magnitude of star, 285, 370
Mark 4:10–20, frontispiece
Mass of earth, 213
Measurement, approximate versus exact, 321
  of rectangular area, 51
Meter, definition by Federal statute, 334
Meterstick addition, 8, 25–29
Millimeter, 25
Milton, John, 224
Minuend, 66
Mixed decimal fraction, 204
Mixed number, 106
Mnemonic, 52, 339–342
Multiples, of a number, 125
  of single-digit numbers, 44
Multiplicand, 39
Multiplication, xii, 39
  algebraic, 81
  associative law, 40, 41, 65
  of common fractions, 131, 132, 144
  commutative curios, 57
  commutative law of, 39
  of decimal fractions, 226
  distributive law of, 42
  -division curios, 396
  long, 46, 47
  of natural numbers, 39, 40, 43, 387
  by prime factor forms, 131
  by power of 5, 121
  Russian peasant's method of, 416–418
  short, 45
  of surds, 249
  use of zero in, 44
Multiplication tables, 44
Multiplier, 39

Naperian logarithms, or natural logarithms, 385
Natural numbers, 54, 157
  addition of, 15, 16, 387
  associative law of, 40, 65
  basic operations on, 3
  as cardinal numbers, 7, 15
  commutative law of, 39, 65
  cube root of, 261–269
  division of, 388
  evolution of, 388
  indexing of, 388
  involution of, 48, 387
  kth powers of, 398–400
  multiples of, 44
  multiplication of, 39, 40, 43, 387
  names and symbols for, 4, 6
  number of exact divisors of, 439
  numbers smaller than and prime to, 441
  as ordinal numbers, 7, 15
  pointing off for reading, 6
  postulates of, 3
  properties of, 158, 159
  reading of, 6, 12
  reduction to prime factor form, 126
  subtraction of, 387
  successor and predecessor of, 4, 6, 15
  sum of divisors of, 440
Negative characteristic of logarithm, 359
Negative fraction, 389
Negative numbers, uses of, 83, 84
Negative signs, for operation and quality, 76
  for subtraction, 66, 75
NIM, game of, 13, 418, 419
Nonstandard magic squares, 403–406
Nonterminating decimal fractions, 208
Number line, 106, 139–142, 158
Number-pair, 159

Number system, of analysis, 105
  base of, 12
  binary, 12, 119, 413–415
  complex, 374, 376–379
  rational, 137
  real, 3, 73, 389
  septimal, 12
Numbers, algebraic, 275
  cardinal, 7, 11
  complex, 389
  even, 9
  Heronic, 344
  imaginary, 374
  oblong, 10
  odd, 9
  ordinal, 7
  perfect, 234, 418, 419
  Pythagorean, 424, 427
  square, 10
  surd, 275
  triangular, 9
Numerals, Arabic, 3
  Roman, 187–189

Oblong number, 10, 195
Observations on problem solving, 21
O. Henry, *The Four Million*, 372
One-to-one correspondence, 24
Ordinal number, 7, 15

π(pi, 3.141,592,6 . . .), approximations for, 232, 275
  to sixty-five digits, 231
  a transcendental number, 277
  various uses of, 278
Palindromic multiplication curios, 57
Pandiagonal magic squares, 406–412
Parallelogram, area of, 340
Parentheses, use of, 48
Parsec, 371
Partial fractions, 235
Partitioning, operation of, 233

Pascal's triangle, 318, 319

Patriarchs, first ten, 434

Pendulum, approximate period of, 370

Percent of error, 334

Percent relationships, 305–307

Perch of masonry, 337

Perfect numbers, 234, 235, 428, 429

Period of $1/p$, two remarkable properties of, 218, 444

Periodic decimal fractions, period of, 206, 238, 239

  reduction to common fraction, 229

Place value of digit, in decimal fraction, 211

  in natural number, 18

Plane of complex numbers, 373

Planets in the solar system, 22

Polaris (or North Star), distance of, 105

Postition of irrational number on number line, 228

Positive and negative signs, two uses of, 76

"Practice makes perfect," 59

Presidents of United States, first sixteen, 8

Prime factor forms, of natural numbers, 125

  reduction to, 126

  tables of, 126

  used in multiplication and division, 129, 130

Prime numbers, Euler's theorem on, 423, 424

  facts concerning, 420–422

  largest known, 429

  unproved properties of, 422

Priority of basic operations, 48

Progression, arithmetic, 33, 191

  geometric, 193–195

Proper fraction, 105

Proper subset, 26

Properties of period of $1/p$, 444–450

Pyramid, regular, 341

  slant height, 341

  volume of, 341

Pythagorean numbers, 424–428

Pythagorean relationship, 332

Quadratic residue, 303

Quotient, 36, 388

Radian, 365–367

Radicand, 67, 248

Rate in percentage relationships, 307, 313

Rational numbers, 137

  complete system of, 181

  graphical representation of, 181

  versus irrational numbers, 231

  operations on, 214

  properties of, 161

Real numbers, 373–389

Rectangle, area of, 52, 339

Rectangular solid, volume of, 341

Rectangular volume, 52

Regular polygon, constructibility of, 234

Relation of units of length, area, and volume, 52

Reliability of calculated results on inaccurate data, 322

Repeating decimal fraction, 206, 229–230, 238–239

Right circular cone, 242

Right-end long division, 300

Roman numbers, 187

Russian peasant's method of multiplying, 13, 120, 416

Scientific notation, 213

"St. Ives," nursery rhyme, 38

Seasons, length of, 37

Secant, 331, 332

Sector, area of, 366
Septimal system, 12
Series for *e*, 384, 385
Set, 3
    denumerable, 25
    equivalent, 25
    infinite, 25
    of numbers closed under opera-
        tion, 197
    subset of, 24
Seven indeterminates, 451–454
Shakespeare, vii, 191, 198
Short division, 101
Short multiplication, 45, 46
Sieve of Eratosthenes, 420, 421
Signs of quality and of operation, 76
sine, 331, 332
sin N, cos N, e^N for N a complex
    number, 386
Sirius B, mass of, 112
Slide rule, construction of, 363–364
    meter stick, 25
    scales on, 361–364
    text by C. L. Johnston, 365
Solutions of problems of arithmetic,
    observations on, 21
Space rocket, 157
Special units of length, 338
Sphere, area and volume, 232, 341,
    352
Square foot, definition of, 51
Square number, 10, 195
Square root, algorithms for, 252
    by successive approximations, 259
Standard form of natural number,
    126
Standard magic squares, 401–408
Star, absolute magnitude of, 370
    nearest, Proxima Centauri, 105
Subset, 24
Subtraction, of decimal fractions,
    226
    of integers, 79
    of natural numbers, 69–74, 378

Subtraction, of number-pairs, 89
    of surds, 248
    tables, 71
Subtrahend, 66
Sum, of arithmetic series, 191
    of consecutive Fibonacci numbers,
        93
    of cubes of natural numbers, 298
    of geometric series, 194
    of higher powers of natural num-
        bers, 298
    of squares of Fibonacci numbers,
        297
    of squares of natural numbers,
        297
Surd, 247, 275
    basic operations on, 248–251
    only ones geometrically con-
        structible, 278
System of rational numbers, dense,
    not discrete, 112
    as points on number line, 109

Tables, of logarithms, endpapers
    of weights and measures, 338
Tangent, trigonometric, 331, 332
Ternary number forms, 119
II Timothy 4:7–8, xiii
Triangle, area of, 340, 341, 343, 348,
    349
    semiperimeter of, 348
    solution of, 348–350
Triangular number, 9, 196
Trigonometry, formulas for solution
    of triangle, 349
    pretaste of, 315
    tables, endpaper
Twin primes, 423

Unicursal problem, 29, 31
Uniqueness of cardinal number of
    set, 10

Volume, and area of sphere, 232, 341, 352
  of circular cylinder, 242
  of cone, 342
  of pyramid, 341
  rectangular, 52
  of rectangular solid, 341

Weighing an elephant, 24, 33
Wordsworth: *We Are Seven*, 451

Zero, creation of, 389
  as exponent, 49
  as factor in multiplication, 44

This book was set in Monotype Baskerville and printed and bound by The Maple Press Company. The designer was Janet Bollow. Michael Ungersma supervised the editing and Charles Goehring was the production supervisor.

N	0	1	2	3	4	5	6	7	8	9
0	.0000	.0000	.3010	.4771	.6021	.6990	.7782	.8451	.9031	.9542
1	.0000	.0414	.0792	.1139	.1461	.1761	.2041	.2304	.2553	.2788
2	.3010	.3222	.3424	.3617	.3802	.3979	.4150	.4314	.4472	.4624
3	.4771	.4914	.5051	.5185	.5315	.5441	.5563	.5682	.5798	.5911
4	.6021	.6128	.6232	.6335	.6535	.6532	.6628	.6721	.6812	.6902
5	.6990	.7076	.7160	.7243	.7324	.7404	.7482	.7559	.7634	.7709
6	.7782	.7853	.7924	.7993	.8062	.8129	.8195	.8261	.8325	.8388
7	.8451	.8513	.8573	.8633	.8692	.8751	.8808	.8865	.8921	.8976
8	.9031	.9085	.9138	.9191	.9243	.9294	.9345	.9395	.9445	.9494
9	.9542	.9590	.9638	.9685	.9731	.9777	.9823	.9868	.9912	.9956
10	.0000	.0043	.0086	.0128	.0170	.0212	.0253	.0294	.0334	.0374
11	.0414	.0453	.0492	.0531	.0569	.0607	.0645	.0682	.0719	.0755
12	.0792	.0828	.0864	.0899	.0934	.0969	.1004	.1038	.1072	.1106
13	.1139	.1173	.1206	.1239	.1271	.1303	.1335	.1367	.1399	.1430
14	.1461	.1492	.1523	.1553	.1584	.1614	.1644	.1673	.1703	.1732
15	.1761	.1790	.1818	.1847	.1875	.1903	.1931	.1959	.1987	.2014
16	.2041	.2068	.2095	.2122	.2148	.2175	.2201	.2227	.2253	.2279
17	.2304	.2330	.2355	.2380	.2405	.2430	.2455	.2480	.2505	.2529
18	.2553	.2577	.2601	.2625	.2648	.2672	.2695	.2718	.2742	.2765
19	.2788	.2810	.2833	.2856	.2878	.2900	.2923	.2945	.2967	.2989
20	.3010	.3032	.3054	.3075	.3096	.3118	.3139	.3160	.3181	.3201
21	.3222	.3243	.3263	.3284	.3304	.3324	.3345	.3365	.3385	.3404
22	.3424	.3444	.3464	.3483	.3502	.3522	.3541	.3560	.3579	.3598
23	.3617	.3636	.3655	.3674	.3692	.3711	.3729	.3747	.3766	.3784
24	.3802	.3820	.3838	.3856	.3874	.3892	.3909	.3927	.3945	.3962
25	.3979	.3997	.4014	.4031	.4048	.4065	.4082	.4099	.4116	.4133
26	.4150	.4166	.4183	.4200	.4216	.4232	.4249	.4265	.4281	.4298
27	.4314	.4330	.4346	.4362	.4378	.4393	.4409	.4425	.4440	.4456
28	.4472	.4487	.4502	.4518	.4533	.4548	.4564	.4579	.4594	.4609
29	.4624	.4639	.4654	.4669	.4683	.4698	.4713	.4728	.4742	.4757
30	.4771	.4786	.4800	.4814	.4829	.4843	.4857	.4871	.4886	.4900
31	.4914	.4928	.4942	.4955	.4969	.4983	.4897	.5011	.5024	.5038
32	.5051	.5065	.5079	.5092	.5105	.5119	.5132	.5145	.5159	.5172
33	.5185	.5198	.5211	.5224	.5237	.5250	.5263	.5279	.5289	.5302
34	.5315	.5328	.5340	.5353	.5366	.5378	.5391	.5403	.5416	.5428
35	.5441	.5453	.5465	.5478	.5490	.5502	.5514	.5527	.5539	.5551
36	.5563	.5575	.5587	.5599	.5611	.5623	.5635	.5647	.5658	.5670
37	.5682	.5694	.5705	.5717	.5729	.5740	.5751	.5763	.5775	.5786
38	.5798	.5809	.5821	.5832	.5843	.5855	.5866	.5877	.5888	.5899
39	.5911	.5922	.5933	.5944	.5955	.5966	.5977	.5988	.5999	.6010
40	.6021	.6031	.6042	.6053	.6064	.6075	.6085	.6096	.6107	.6117
41	.6128	.6138	.6149	.6160	.6170	.6180	.6191	.6201	.6212	.6222
42	.6232	.6243	.6253	.6263	.6274	.6284	.6294	.6304	.6314	.6325
43	.6335	.6345	.6355	.6365	.6375	.6385	.6395	.6405	.6415	.6425
44	.6435	.6444	.6454	.6464	.6474	.6484	.6493	.6503	.6513	.6522
45	.6532	.6542	.6551	.6561	.6571	.6580	.6590	.6599	.6609	.6618
46	.6628	.6637	.6646	.6656	.6665	.6675	.6684	.6693	.6702	.6712
47	.6721	.6730	.6739	.6749	.6758	.6767	.6776	.6785	.6794	.6803
48	.6812	.6821	.6830	.6839	.6848	.6857	.6866	.6875	.6884	.6893
49	.6902	.6911	.6920	.6928	.6937	.6946	.6955	.6964	.6972	.6981
50	.6990	.6998	.7007	.7016	.7024	.7033	.7042	.7050	.7059	.7067